J. Willard Gibbs
1839-1903

Heike Kamerlingh Onnes
1853-1926

Max Planck
1858-1947

Walther Nernst
1864-1941

Constantin Carathéodory
1873-1950

Albert Einstein
1879-1955

Peter Debye
1884-1966

F. E. Simon
1893-1956

HEAT AND THERMODYNAMICS

HEAT AND THERMODYNAMICS

An Intermediate Textbook

Fifth Edition

MARK W. ZEMANSKY, Ph.D.

Professor of Physics, Emeritus
The City College of
The City University of New York

McGRAW-HILL BOOK COMPANY

New York   St. Louis   San Francisco
Toronto   London
Sydney

HEAT AND THERMODYNAMICS

Library of Congress Catalog Card Number 67-26891

07-072807-0

10 11 12 13   K P K P   7 9 8 7

dedicated to **ADELE C. ZEMANSKY**

PREFACE

When the first edition of "Heat and Thermodynamics" appeared thirty years ago, it was intended for students preparing for careers in physics, in chemistry, and in all branches of engineering. It was designed for sophomores, or at most juniors, and was meant to be a first introduction to the principles and subject matter of thermodynamics. To achieve this end, it started with the most elementary ideas of temperature and heat and developed the laws of thermodynamics from their experimental and engineering backgrounds, as well as presented applications of thermodynamics more or less equally divided among the disciplines of physics, chemistry, and engineering.

In subsequent editions, this original purpose was maintained, but more attention was paid to the needs of students interested in mathematics, physics, and physical chemistry, and only small changes were made in the engineering material. Owing to the fact that in 1966 a separate engineering version of this book, entitled "Basic Engineering Thermodynamics," became available and also that the conviction was expressed by many physics teachers that it was desirable to include some kinetic theory and statistical mechanics in courses on "heat," this latest edition, the fifth, is markedly different from the first four. Only the barest engineering principles involved in the operation of heat engines and refrigerators have been retained. Details concerning convective heat transfer and the analysis of heat exchangers have been removed. In their place, a chapter on the elementary principles of kinetic theory has been substituted; in addition, a separate chapter and several other articles have been devoted to the statistical mechanics of an ideal gas, an electron gas in a metal, a vibrating lattice, and a paramagnetic subsystem in a crystal.

The point of view is still preeminently thermodynamic. Thermodynamics is the fundamental discipline, and statistical methods are introduced only to supply details that are not included within the scope of thermodynamics, such as equations of state and temperature variation of heat capacities, and to provide greater insight with regard to processes such as the production of low temperatures by adiabatic demagnetization and the production of negative temperatures in a nuclear magnetic subsystem. The second law of thermodynamics is still regarded as a generalization from experience with heat engines and refrigerators. Through use of simple nonmathematical methods suggested in the writings of Turner, Pippard, and Landsberg, the existence of reversible adiabatic surfaces is shown to follow directly from the Kelvin-Planck statement of the second law. The existence of an absolute temperature and of an entropy function are then deduced, without invoking the advanced mathematical techniques of Caratheodory.

Low-temperature physics is not confined to one chapter. Most of the new data in tables and graphs are recent values in the temperature range from 0 to 300°K. As in the previous editions, the experimental aspects of the subject have been emphasized. The parallel between the superfluidity of liquid helium II and the superconductivity of conductors has been accented by devoting an entire chapter to these two phenomena alone. Some of the more recent developments in the experimental and theoretical aspects of these phenomena have been treated, in order to provide at least an inkling of what is going on in these rapidly advancing fields. As a result, this fifth edition is somewhat more sophisticated and more difficult; however, no further preparation than a year of college physics and a year of calculus is needed to understand the text.

In the ten-year period between the fourth and fifth editions, the author has received from teachers throughout the world many letters containing corrections and suggestions for changes. He is, of course, exceedingly grateful for this help and would like to thank these correspondents publicly and to apologize to those whose letters have gone astray and who are not included in this list: S. E. Babb, Jr., G. R. Beacon, L. S. Castlemen, D. E. Christie, E. U. Condon, H. H. Denman, J. H. Horlock, N. Kurti, the late D. K. C. MacDonald, N. Pearlman, M. Sanders, F. W. Sears, H. Sepehri, L. A. Turner, H. C. van Ness, J. H. Werntz, W. A. Woods, and H. D. Zeman.

Special mention must be made of the elaborate and penetrating analysis of the deficiencies of the fourth edition and the numerous suggestions, chapter by chapter, for improvements in the fifth edition supplied by Professor B. Kurrelmeyer of Brooklyn College. The author is tremendously grateful to him and to Professor H. A. Boorse, director of the Columbia University Low Temperature Laboratory, for the fruits of many years of firsthand association with all aspects of low-temperature physics. The final tribute goes to the author's wife for her diligence and patience in typing the entire manuscript.

Mark W. Zemansky

ACKNOWLEDGMENTS

The pictures of famous physicists who were pioneers in thermodynamics which adorn the end papers of this volume were provided by Professor P. T. Landsberg of University College, Cardiff, Wales, and by Mrs. Joan Warnow, Librarian of the Center for History and Philosophy of Physics of the American Institute of Physics. The author would like to express his sincerest thanks for their kindness.

CONTENTS

Chapter 3   Work

Chapter 4   Heat and the First Law

Chapter 5   Ideal Gases

Chapter 6   Kinetic Theory of an Ideal Gas

Chapter 7   Engines, Refrigerators, and the Second Law

Chapter 8   Reversibility and the Kelvin Temperature Scale

Chapter 9   Entropy

Chapter 10   Statistical Mechanics

Chapter 11   Pure Substances

Chapter 15   Superfluidity and Superconductivity

Chapter 16   Chemical Equilibrium

NOTATION

CAPITAL ITALIC (*continued*)

V	Volume
W	Work
X	Generalized displacement
Y	Generalized force; Young's modulus
Z	Electric charge; partition function; compressibility factor

SCRIPT CAPITALS

$\mathscr{B}$	Magnetic induction
$\mathscr{E}$	Electromotive force
$\mathscr{F}$	Tension; force
$\mathscr{H}$	Magnetic intensity
$\mathscr{M}$	Molecular weight
$\mathscr{N}$	Negciptemp
$\mathscr{R}$	Radiant emittance
$\mathscr{S}$	Surface tension

ROMAN SYMBOLS FOR UNITS

cm	centimeter
g	gram
s	second
deg	degree
atm	atmosphere
A	ampere
C	coulomb
Hz	hertz (cps)
J	joule
N	newton
Oe	oersted
V	volt
W	watt

SPECIAL SYMBOLS

N_A	Avogadro's number
đ	Inexact differential
N_F	Faraday's constant
T^*	Magnetic temperature

LOWERCASE ITALIC (*continued*)

v	Molar volume
w	Speed of a wave or a molecule
x	Space coordinate; mole fraction
y	Space coordinate; fraction
z	Space coordinate

GREEK LETTERS

α	Linear expansivity
β	Volume expansivity, $1/kT$
γ	Ratio of heat capacities; electronic term in heat capacity
Ω	Thermodynamic probability; solid angle
δ	Energy of a magnetic ion
Δ	Finite difference
ϵ	Degree of reaction; molecular energy
η	Efficiency
θ	Ideal-gas temperature; angle
Θ	Debye temperature
κ	Compressibility
λ	Wavelength; Lagrange multiplier; penetration depth
μ	Joule-Kelvin coefficient; molecular magnetic moment; chemical potential
ν	Molecular density; frequency; stoichiometric coefficient
π	Peltier coefficient
ρ	Density (mass per unit volume)
σ	Thomson coefficient; Stefan-Boltzmann constant
τ	Time; period
ϕ	Angle; function of temperature
φ	Number of phases
ω	Coefficient of performance; angular speed
χ	Magnetic susceptibility
ξ	Coherence length

1.

TEMPERATURE

1-1 Macroscopic Point of View

The study of any special branch of physics starts with a separation of a restricted region of space or a finite portion of matter from its surroundings. The portion which is set aside (in the imagination) and on which the attention is focused is called the *system*, and everything outside the system which has a direct bearing on its behavior is known as the *surroundings*. When a system has been chosen, the next step is to describe it in terms of quantities that will be helpful in discussing the behavior of the system or its interactions with the surroundings, or both. There are in general two points of view that may be adopted, the *macroscopic* point of view and the *microscopic* point of view.

Let us take as a system the contents of a cylinder of an automobile engine. A chemical analysis would show a mixture of hydrocarbons and air before explosion, and after the mixture has been ignited there would be combustion products describable in terms of certain chemical compounds. A statement of the relative amounts of these substances is a description of the *composition* of the system. At any moment, the system whose composition has just been described occupies a certain *volume*, depending on the position of the piston. The volume can be easily measured and, in the laboratory, is recorded automatically by means of an appliance coupled to the piston. Another quantity that is indispensable in the description of our system is the *pressure* of the gases in the cylinder. After explosion this pressure is large; after exhaust it is small. In the laboratory, a pressure gauge may be used to measure the changes of pressure and to make an automatic record as the engine operates. Finally, there is one more quantity without which we should have no adequate idea of the operation of the engine. This quantity is the *temperature;* as we shall see, in many instances, it can be measured just as simply as the other quantities.

We have described the materials in a cylinder of an automobile engine by specifying four quantities: composition, volume, pressure, and temperature. These quantities refer to the gross characteristics, or large-scale properties, of the system and provide a *macroscopic description*. They are therefore called *macroscopic coordinates*. The quantities that must be specified to provide a macroscopic description of other systems are, of course, different; but macroscopic coordinates in general have the following characteristics in common:

1   They involve no special assumptions concerning the structure of matter.
2   Only a few coordinates are needed for a macroscopic description.
3   They are suggested more or less directly by our sense perceptions.
4   They can in general be directly measured.

In short, a macroscopic description of a system involves the specification of a *few fundamental measurable properties* of a system.

1-2   Microscopic Point of View

From the viewpoint of *statistical mechanics*—or, as it is often called, *statistical thermodynamics*—a system is considered to consist of an enormous number N of molecules, each of which is capable of existing in a set of states whose energies are ϵ_1, ϵ_2, ... The molecules are assumed to interact with one another by means of collisions or by forces at a distance. The system of molecules may be imagined to be isolated or, in some cases, may be considered to be embedded in a set of similar systems, or *ensemble* of systems. Concepts of probability are applied, and the equilibrium state of the system is assumed to be the state of highest probability. The fundamental problem is to find the number of molecules in each of the molecular energy states (known as the *populations* of the states) when equilibrium is reached.

Since statistical thermodynamics will be treated at some length in Chap. 10, it is not necessary to pursue the matter further at this point. It is evident, however, that a microscopic description of a system involves the following characteristics:

1   Assumptions are made concerning the structure of matter; e.g., the existence of molecules is assumed.
2   Many quantities must be specified.
3   The quantities specified are not suggested by our sense perceptions.
4   These quantities cannot be measured.

1-3   Macroscopic vs. Microscopic

Although it might seem that the two points of view are hopelessly different and incompatible, there is nevertheless a relation between them; and when both points of view are applied to the same system, they must lead to the same conclusion. The relation between the two points of view lies in the fact that the few directly measurable properties whose specification constitutes the macroscopic description are really averages over a period of time of a large number of microscopic characteristics. For example, the macroscopic quantity, pressure, is the average rate of change of momentum due to all the molecular collisions made on a unit of area. Pressure, however, is a property that is perceived by our senses. We feel the effects of pressure. Pressure was experienced, measured, and used long before physicists had reason to believe in the existence of molecular impacts. If the molecular theory is changed or even discarded at some time in the future, the concept of pressure will still remain and will still mean the same thing to all normal human beings. Herein lies an important distinction between the macroscopic and microscopic points of view. The few measurable macroscopic properties are as sure as our senses. They will remain unchanged as long as our senses remain the same. The microscopic point of view, however, goes much further than our senses. It postulates the existence of molecules, their motion, their energy states, their interactions, etc. It is constantly being changed, and we can never be sure that the assumptions are justified until we have compared some deduction made on the basis of these assumptions with a similar deduction based on the macroscopic point of view.

1-4   Scope of Thermodynamics

It has been emphasized that a description of the gross characteristics of a system by means of a few of its measurable properties, suggested more or less directly by our sense perceptions, constitutes a macroscopic description. Such descriptions are the starting point of all investigations in all branches of physics. For example, in dealing with the mechanics of a rigid body, the macroscopic point of view is adopted in that only the external aspects of the rigid body are considered. The position of its center of mass is specified with reference to coordinate axes at a particular time. Position and time and a combination of both, such as velocity, constitute some of the macroscopic quantities used in mechanics and are called *mechanical coordinates*. The mechanical coordinates serve to determine the potential and the kinetic energy of the rigid body with reference to the coordinate axes, i.e., the kinetic and the potential energy of the body as a whole. These two types of energy constitute the *external*, or *mechanical*, *energy* of the rigid body. It is the purpose of mechanics to find such relations between the position coordinates and the time as are consistent with Newton's laws of motion.

In thermodynamics, however, the attention is directed to the *interior* of a system. A macroscopic point of view is adopted, but only those macroscopic quantities are considered which have a bearing on the internal state of a system. It is the function of experiment to determine the quantities that are necessary and sufficient for such a purpose. Macroscopic quantities having a bearing on the internal state of a system are called *thermodynamic coordinates.* Such coordinates serve to determine the *internal energy* of a system. It is the purpose of thermodynamics to find general relations among the thermodynamic coordinates that are consistent with the fundamental laws of thermodynamics.

A system that may be described in terms of thermodynamic coordinates is called a *thermodynamic system.* In engineering, the important thermodynamic systems are a gas, such as air; a vapor, such as steam; a mixture, such as gasoline vapor and air; and a vapor in contact with its liquid, such as liquid and vaporized ammonia. Chemical thermodynamics deals with the above systems and, in addition, with solids, surface films, and electric cells. Physical thermodynamics includes, in addition to the above, such systems as stretched wires, electric capacitors, thermocouples, and magnetic substances.

1-5   Thermal Equilibrium

We have seen that a macroscopic description of a gaseous mixture may be given by specifying such quantities as the composition, the mass, the pressure, and the volume. Experiment shows that, for a given composition and for a constant mass, many different values of pressure and volume are possible. If the pressure is kept constant, the volume may vary over a wide range of values, and vice versa. In other words, the pressure and the volume are independent coordinates. Similarly, experiment shows that, for a wire of constant mass, the tension and the length are independent coordinates, whereas, in the case of a surface film, the surface tension and the area may be varied independently. Some systems that, at first sight, seem quite complicated, such as an electric cell with two different electrodes and an electrolyte, may still be described with the aid of only two independent coordinates. On the other hand, some systems composed of a number of homogeneous parts require the specification of two independent coordinates for each homogeneous part. Details of various thermodynamic systems and their thermodynamic coordinates will be given in Chap. 2. For the present, to simplify our discussion, we shall deal only with systems of constant mass and composition, each requiring *only one pair* of independent coordinates for its description. This involves no essential loss of generality and results in a considerable saving of words. In referring to any nonspecified system, we shall use the symbols Y and X for the pair of independent coordinates.

Fig. 1-1   *Properties of adiabatic and diathermic walls.*

A state of a system in which Y and X have definite values that remain constant so long as the external conditions are unchanged is called an *equilibrium* state. Experiment shows that the existence of an equilibrium state in one system depends on the proximity of other systems and on the nature of the wall separating them. Walls are said to be either adiabatic or diathermic. If a wall is *adiabatic* (see Fig. 1-1a), a state Y, X for system A and Y', X' for system B may coexist as equilibrium states for *any* attainable values of the four quantities, provided only that the wall is able to withstand the stress associated with the difference between the two sets of coordinates. Thick layers of wood, concrete, asbestos, felt, etc., are good experimental approximations to adiabatic walls. If the two systems are separated by a *diathermic* wall (see Fig. 1-1b), the values of Y, X and Y', X' will change spontaneously until an equilibrium state of the combined system is attained. The two systems are then said to be in *thermal equilibrium* with each other. The most common diathermic wall is a thin metallic sheet. *Thermal equilibrium is the state achieved by two (or more) systems, characterized by restricted values of the coordinates of the systems, after they have been in communication with each other through a diathermic wall.*

Imagine two systems A and B separated from each other by an adiabatic wall but each in contact with a third system C through diathermic walls, the whole assembly being surrounded by an adiabatic wall as shown in Fig. 1-2a. Experiment shows that the two systems will come to thermal equilibrium with the third and that no further change will occur if the adiabatic wall separating A and B is then replaced by a diathermic wall (Fig. 1-2b). If, instead of allowing both systems A and B to come to equilibrium with C at the same time, we first have equilibrium between A and C and then equilibrium between B and C (the state of system C being the same in both cases), then, when A and B are brought into communication through a diathermic wall, they will be found to be in thermal equilibrium. We shall use the expression "two systems are in thermal equilibrium" to mean that the two systems

If A and B are each in
thermal equilibrium with C, then

(a)

A and B are in thermal
equilibrium with each other

(b)

Fig. 1-2   *The zeroth law of thermodynamics. (Adiabatic walls are designated by cross shading; diathermic walls, by heavy lines.)*

are in states such that, if the two *were* connected through a diathermic wall, the combined system *would be* in thermal equilibrium.

These experimental facts may then be stated concisely in the following form: *Two systems in thermal equilibrium with a third are in thermal equilibrium with each other.* Following R. H. Fowler, we shall call this postulate the *zeroth law of thermodynamics.*

1-6   Temperature Concept

Consider a system A in the state Y_1, X_1 in thermal equilibrium with a system B in the state Y'_1, X'_1. If system A is removed and its state changed, there will be found another state Y_2, X_2 in which it is in thermal equilibrium with the *original* state Y'_1, X'_1 of system B. Experiment shows that there exists a whole set of states Y_1, X_1; Y_2, X_2; Y_3, X_3; etc., every one of which is in thermal equilibrium with this *same* state Y'_1, X'_1 of system B and which, by the zeroth law, are in thermal equilibrium with one another. We shall suppose that *all* such states, when plotted on a YX diagram, lie on a curve such as I in Fig. 1-3, which we shall call an *isotherm*. *An isotherm is the locus of all points representing states at which a system is in thermal equilibrium with one state of another system.* We make no assumption as to the continuity of the isotherm, although experi-

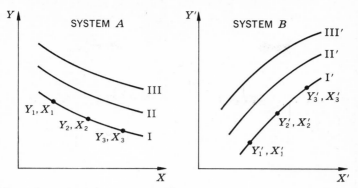

Fig. 1-3   *Isotherms of two different systems.*

ments on simple systems indicate usually that at least a portion of an isotherm is a continuous curve.

Similarly, with regard to system B, we find a set of states Y_1', X_1'; Y_2', X_2'; etc., all of which are in thermal equilibrium with one state (Y_1, X_1) of system A, and therefore in thermal equilibrium with one another. These states are plotted on the $Y'X'$ diagram of Fig. 1-3 and lie on the isotherm I′. From the zeroth law, it follows that all the states on isotherm I of system A are in thermal equilibrium with all the states on isotherm I′ of system B. We shall call curves I and I′ *corresponding isotherms* of the two systems.

If the experiments outlined above are repeated with different starting conditions, another set of states of system A lying on curve II may be found, every one of which is in thermal equilibrium with every state of system B lying on curve II′. In this way, a family of isotherms, I, II, III, etc., of system A and a corresponding family I′, II′, III′, etc., of system B may be found. Furthermore, by repeated applications of the zeroth law, corresponding isotherms of still other systems C, D, etc., may be obtained.

All states of corresponding isotherms of all systems have something in common, namely, that they are in thermal equilibrium with one another. The systems themselves, in these states, may be said to possess a property that ensures their being in thermal equilibrium with one another. We call this property *temperature. The temperature of a system is a property that determines whether or not a system is in thermal equilibrium with other systems.*

The concept of temperature may be arrived at in a more sophisticated manner. When a system A with coordinates Y, X is separated from a system C with coordinates Y'', X'', the approach to thermal equilibrium is indicated by changes in the four coordinates. The final state of thermal equilibrium is denoted by a relation among these coordinates which may be written in the general functional form

$$f_{AC}(Y, X; Y'', X'') = 0. \qquad (1\text{-}1)$$

For example, if A were a gas with coordinates P (pressure) and V (volume) and obeying Boyle's law, and if C were a similar gas with coordinates P'' and V'', Eq. (1-1) would be

$$PV - P''V'' = 0.$$

Thermal equilibrium between system B, with coordinates Y', X', and system C is similarly denoted by the relation

$$f_{BC}(Y',X'; Y'',X'') = 0, \tag{1-2}$$

where f_{BC} may be quite different from f_{AC} but is also assumed to be a well-behaved function.

Suppose Eqs. (1-1) and (1-2) are solved for Y''; then

$$Y'' = g_{AC}(Y,X,X''),$$

and
$$Y'' = g_{BC}(Y',X',X''),$$

or
$$g_{AC}(Y,X,X'') = g_{BC}(Y',X',X''). \tag{1-3}$$

Now, according to the zeroth law, thermal equilibrium between A and C and between B and C implies thermal equilibrium between A and B, which is denoted by a relation among *coordinates of systems A and B only;* thus,

$$f_{AB}(Y,X; Y',X') = 0. \tag{1-4}$$

Since Eq. (1-3) also expresses the same two equilibrium situations, it must agree with Eq. (1-4): that is, it must reduce to a relation among Y, X; Y', X' only. The extraneous coordinate X'' in Eq. (1-3) must therefore drop out, and the equation must reduce to

$$h_A(Y,X) = h_B(Y',X').$$

Applying the same argument a second time with systems A and C in equilibrium with B, we get finally, when the three systems are in thermal equilibrium,

$$h_A(Y,X) = h_B(Y',X') = h_C(Y'',X''). \tag{1-5}$$

In other words, *a function of each set of coordinates exists, and these functions are all equal when the systems are in thermal equilibrium with one another.* The common value t of these functions is the *empirical temperature* common to all the systems.

$$t = h_A(Y,X) = h_B(Y',X') = h_C(Y'',X''). \tag{1-6}$$

The relation $t = h_A(Y,X)$ is merely *the equation of an isotherm of system A*, such as curve I of Fig. 1-3. If t is given a different numerical value, a different curve is obtained, such as II in Fig. 1-3.

The temperature of all systems in thermal equilibrium may be represented by a number. The establishment of a temperature scale is merely the adoption of a set of rules for assigning one number to one set of corresponding isotherms and a different number to a different set of corresponding isotherms.

1-7   Measurement of Temperature

To establish an empirical temperature scale, we select some system with coordinates Y and X as a standard, which we call a *thermometer*, and adopt a set of rules for assigning a numerical value to the temperature associated with each of its isotherms. To every other system in thermal equilibrium with the thermometer, we assign the same number for the temperature. The simplest procedure is to choose any convenient path in the YX plane, such as that shown in Fig. 1-4 by the dashed line $Y = Y_1$ which intersects the isotherms at points each of which has the same Y coordinate but a different X coordinate. The temperature associated with each isotherm is then taken to be a convenient function of the X at this intersection point. The coordinate X is called the *thermometric property*, and the form of the *thermometric function $\theta(X)$* determines the temperature scale. There are six important kinds of thermometer, each with its own thermometric property, as shown in Table 1-1.

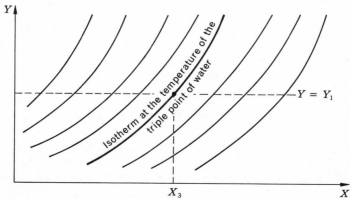

Fig. 1-4   *Setting up a temperature scale involves assignment of numerical values to the isotherms of an arbitrarily chosen standard system, or thermometer.*

Table 1-1   **Thermometers and Thermometric Properties**

Thermometer	Thermometric property	Symbol
Gas (const. volume)	Pressure	P
Electric resistor (const. tension)	Electric resistance	R'
Thermocouple (const. tension)	Thermal emf	$\mathcal{E}$
Helium vapor (saturated)	Pressure	P
Paramagnetic salt	Magnetic susceptibility	χ
Blackbody radiation	Radiant emittance	$\mathcal{R}_{B,\lambda}$

Let X stand for any one of the thermometric properties listed in Table 1-1, and let us *arbitrarily choose* for the temperature common to the thermometer *and to all systems in thermal equilibrium with it* the following linear function of X:

$$\theta(X) = aX \qquad \text{(const. } Y\text{)},$$

where a is an arbitrary constant. It follows that two temperatures on this "linear X scale" are to each other as the ratio of the corresponding X's, or

$$\frac{\theta(X_1)}{\theta(X_2)} = \frac{X_1}{X_2}. \tag{1-7}$$

To determine the temperature $\theta(X)$ of a system, either of two procedures may be adopted:

1   *Method in use before 1954.*   Apply Eq. (1-7) to a thermometer placed first in contact with the system whose temperature $\theta(X)$ is to be measured, and then in contact with an arbitrarily chosen standard system in an easily reproducible state where the temperature is $\theta(X_1)$. Thus

$$\frac{\theta(X_1)}{\theta(X)} = \frac{X_1}{X}. \tag{1-8}$$

Apply Eq. (1-7) to the thermometer at the temperature $\theta(X)$, and then at the temperature of another arbitrarily chosen standard system in another easily reproducible state where the temperature is $\theta(X_2)$. Thus

$$\frac{\theta(X_2)}{\theta(X)} = \frac{X_2}{X}. \tag{1-9}$$

Subtracting Eq. (1-9) from Eq. (1-8),

$$\frac{\theta(X_1) - \theta(X_2)}{\theta(X)} = \frac{X_1 - X_2}{X};$$

and solving for $\theta(X)$, we get

$$\theta(X) = \frac{\theta(X_1) - \theta(X_2)}{X_1 - X_2} X \qquad (\text{const. } Y).$$

Now assign an arbitrary number of "degrees" to the temperature interval $\theta(X_1) - \theta(X_2)$. Then $\theta(X)$ can be calculated from the three measurements X, X_1, X_2.

An easily reproducible state of an arbitrarily chosen standard system is called a fixed point. Before 1954 there were two fixed points: (1) the temperature at which pure ice coexisted in equilibrium with air-saturated water at one atmosphere pressure (the ice point); and (2) the temperature of equilibrium between pure water and pure steam at one atmosphere pressure (the steam point). The temperature interval between these two fixed points was chosen to be 100 deg.

2   *Method after 1954.*   With this method, only one fixed point is chosen, namely, the temperature and pressure at which ice, liquid water, and water vapor coexist in equilibrium, a state known as the *triple point of water.* We choose arbitrarily for the temperature at this fixed point 273.16 degrees Kelvin, abbreviated 273.16°K. (The reason for the use of Kelvin's name will be made clear later.) Thus, designating the triple point of water by the subscript 3, we have, from Eq. (1-7),

$$\frac{\theta(X)}{\theta(X_3)} = \frac{X}{X_3},$$

with

$$\boxed{\theta(X_3) = 273.16°\text{K.}}$$

Hence,

$$\boxed{\theta(X) = 273.16° \frac{X}{X_3} \qquad (\text{const. } Y).} \qquad (1\text{-}10)$$

The temperature of the triple point of water is the *standard fixed point* of thermometry. To achieve the triple point, water of the highest purity is distilled into a vessel depicted schematically in Fig. 1-5. When all air has been removed, the vessel is sealed off. With the aid

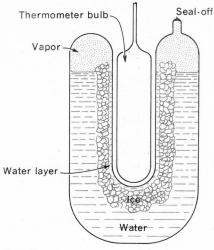

Thermometer bulb

Seal-off

Vapor

Water layer

Ice

Water

Fig. 1-5   *Triple-point cell.*

of a freezing mixture in the inner well, a layer of ice is formed around the well. When the freezing mixture is replaced by a thermometer bulb, a thin layer of ice is melted nearby. So long as the solid, liquid, and vapor phases coexist in equilibrium, the system is at the triple point. The actual shape of the apparatus used by the U.S. National Bureau of Standards is shown in Fig. 1-6.

1-8   Comparison of Thermometers

Applying the principles outlined in the preceding paragraphs to the first three thermometers listed in Table 1-1, we have three different ways of measuring temperature. Thus, for a gas at constant volume,

$$\theta(P) = 273.16° \frac{P}{P_3} \quad \text{(const. } V\text{)};$$

for an electric resistor,

$$\theta(R') = 273.16° \frac{R'}{R'_3};$$

and for a thermocouple,

$$\theta(\mathcal{E}) = 273.16° \frac{\mathcal{E}}{\mathcal{E}_3}.$$

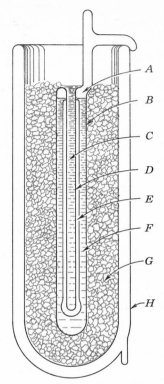

Fig. 1-6 *Diagram of the NBS triple-point cell (B, D) in use in an ice bath (G) within a Dewar flask (H). A, water vapor; C, thermometer well; E, ice mantle; F, liquid water.*

Now imagine a series of tests in which the temperature of a given system is measured simultaneously with each of the three thermometers. Such a comparison is shown in Table 1-2. The initials NBP stand for the *normal boiling point*, which is the temperature at which a liquid boils at atmospheric pressure; the letters NMP stand for *normal melting point*, NSP for the *normal sublimation point*, and TP for the *triple point*. The numerical values are not meant to be exact, and 273.16 has been written simply 273. If one compares the θ columns, it may be seen that at any fixed point, except the triple point of water, the thermometers disagree. Even the two hydrogen thermometers disagree slightly, but the variation among gas thermometers may be greatly reduced by using low pressures, so that a gas thermometer has been chosen as the standard thermometer in terms of which the empiric temperature scale is defined.

Table 1-2   Comparison of Thermometers

Fixed point	Copper-constantan thermocouple		Platinum resistance thermometer		Constant-volume H_2 thermometer		Constant-volume H_2 thermometer	
	$\mathcal{E}$, mV	$\theta(\mathcal{E})$	R', ohms	$\theta(R')$	P, atm	$\theta(P)$	P, atm	$\theta(P)$
N_2 (NBP)	0.73	32.0	1.96	54.5	1.82	73	0.29	79
O_2 (NBP)	0.95	41.5	2.50	69.5	2.13	86	0.33	90
CO_2 (NSP)	3.52	154	6.65	185	4.80	193	0.72	196
H_2O (TP)	$\mathcal{E}_3 = 6.26$	273	$R_3 = 9.83$	273	$P_3 = 6.80$	273	$P_3 = 1.00$	273
H_2O (NBP)	10.05	440	13.65	380	9.30	374	1.37	374
Sn (NMP)	17.50	762	18.56	516	12.70	510	1.85	505

1-9   Gas Thermometer

A schematic diagram of a constant-volume gas thermometer is shown in Fig. 1-7. The materials, construction, and dimensions differ in the various bureaus and institutes throughout the world where these instruments are used and depend on the nature of the gas and the temperature range for which the thermometer is intended. The gas is contained in the bulb B (usually made of platinum or a platinum alloy), which communicates with the mercury column M through a capillary. The volume of the gas is kept constant by adjusting the height of the mercury column M until the mercury level just touches the tip of a small pointer in the space above M, known as the *dead space* or *nuisance volume*. The mercury column M is adjusted by raising or lowering the reservoir. The difference in height h between the two mercury columns M and M' is measured when the bulb is surrounded by the system whose temperature is to be measured, and when it is surrounded by water at the triple point.

The various values of the pressure must be corrected to take account of the following sources of error:

1   The gas present in the dead space (and in any other nuisance volumes) is at a temperature different from that in the bulb.
2   The gas in the capillary connecting the bulb with the manometer has a temperature gradient; i.e., it is not at a uniform temperature.

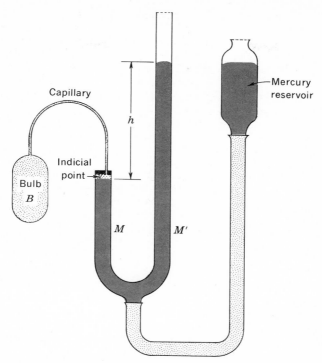

Fig. 1-7   *Simplified constant-volume gas thermometer. Mercury reservoir is raised or lowered so that meniscus at left always touches indicial point. Bulb pressure equals h plus atmospheric pressure.*

3   The bulb, capillary, and nuisance volumes undergo changes of volume when the temperature and pressure change.

4   If the diameter of the capillary is comparable with the mean free path of the molecules of the gas, a pressure gradient exists in the capillary (Knudsen effect).

5   Some gas is adsorbed on the walls of the bulb and capillary, the lower the temperature, the greater the adsorption.

6   There are effects due to temperature and compressibility of the mercury in the manometer.

Many great improvements in the design of gas thermometers have been made in recent years. Two of these are depicted schematically in Fig. 1-8. Instead of the thermometric gas in the bulb communicating directly with the mercury in the manometer, there are two separate volumes of gas: the thermometric gas, which goes as far as a diaphragm and exerts a pressure

Fig. 1-8   *Schematic diagram of two improvements in a gas thermometer in use at the U.S.
National Bureau of Standards.*

on one side of it, and a manometric gas on the other side of the diaphragm
leading to the manometer. The diaphragm itself is one plate of a capacitor,
with the other plate fixed nearby. A difference of pressure across the diaphragm causes a slight motion of the diaphragm, resulting in a change of
capacitance that is observed with the aid of an ac bridge. At about 1 atm, a
pressure differential of 1 part per million is detectable. When the diaphragm
shows no deflection, the manometric gas pressure is the same as that of the
thermometric gas, and a reading of the manometer gives the gas pressure
in the bulb.

Another improvement depicted in Fig. 1-8 is an equalizing gas space
surrounding the bulb. The manometric gas is allowed to fill this space. At
the moment when a manometer reading is made, there is no net force tending
to alter the dimensions of the bulb, and therefore no correction need be made
for a variation of bulb volume with pressure.

The greatest improvements have been made in the mercury manometer.
The mercury meniscus in each tube is made very flat by widening the tubes,
since the dead space does not depend on this width as it did in the older
instrument depicted in Fig. 1-7. The position of a mercury meniscus is
obtained by using it as one plate of a capacitor, with the other being fixed
nearby, and measuring the capacitance with an ac bridge. Gauge blocks
are used to measure the difference in height of the two mercury columns.
Pressures can be measured exact to a few ten-thousandths of a millimeter of
mercury.

One gas thermometer has been built with a differential pressure diaphragm
in the thermometer bulb itself, thereby eliminating the dead space entirely.

1-10   Ideal-gas Temperature

Suppose that an amount of gas is introduced into the bulb of a constant-volume gas thermometer so that the pressure P_3, when the bulb is surrounded by water at its triple point, is equal to 1000 mm Hg. Keeping the volume V constant, suppose the following procedures are carried out:

1   Surrounding the bulb with steam condensing at 1 atm pressure, determine the gas pressure P_s and calculate

$$\theta(P_s) = 273.16° \frac{P_s}{1000}.$$

2   Remove some of the gas so that P_3 has a smaller value, say, 500 mm Hg. Determine the new value of P_s and calculate a new value

$$\theta(P_s) = 273.16° \frac{P_s}{500}.$$

3   Continue reducing the amount of gas in the bulb so that P_3 and P_s have smaller and smaller values, P_3 having values of, say, 250 mm Hg, 100 mm Hg, etc. At *each* value of P_3, calculate the corresponding $\theta(P_s)$.

4   Plot $\theta(P_s)$ against P_3 and extrapolate the resulting curve to the axis where $P_3 = 0$. Read from the graph

$$\lim_{P_3 \to 0} \theta(P_s).$$

The results of a series of tests of this sort are plotted in Fig. 1-9 for four different gases in order to measure $\theta(P)$ not only of condensing steam but also of condensing sulfur. The graph conveys the information that, although the readings of a constant-volume gas thermometer depend upon the nature of the gas at ordinary values of P_3, *all gases indicate the same temperature as P_3 is lowered and made to approach zero.*

We therefore define the *ideal-gas temperature* θ by the equation

$$\boxed{\theta = 273.16° \lim_{P_3 \to 0} \left(\frac{P}{P_3}\right) \qquad (\text{const. } V).} \qquad (1\text{-}11)$$

Although the ideal-gas temperature scale is independent of the properties of any one particular gas, it still depends on the properties of gases in general.

Fig. 1-9   *Readings of a constant-volume gas thermometer for the temperature of condensing steam and for that of condensing sulfur, when different gases are used at various values of P_3.*

Helium is the most useful gas for thermometric purposes for two reasons. At high temperatures helium does not diffuse through platinum, whereas hydrogen does. Furthermore, helium becomes a liquid at a temperature lower than any other gas, and therefore a helium thermometer may be used to measure temperatures lower than those which can be measured with any other gas thermometer.

The lowest ideal-gas temperature that can be measured with a gas thermometer is about 0.5°K, provided that low-pressure He³ is used. *The temperature $\theta = 0$ remains as yet undefined.* In Chap. 7 the Kelvin temperature scale, which is independent of the properties of any particular substance, will be developed. It will be shown that, in the temperature region in which a gas thermometer may be used, the ideal-gas scale and the Kelvin scale are identical. In anticipation of this result, we write °K after an ideal-gas temperature. It will also be shown in Chap. 7 how the absolute zero of temperature is defined on the Kelvin scale. Until then, the phrase "absolute zero" will have no meaning. It should be remarked that the statement, found in so many textbooks of elementary physics, that, at the temperature $T = 0$, all molecular activity ceases is entirely erroneous. First, such a statement involves an assumption connecting the purely macroscopic concept of temperature and the microscopic concept of molecular motion. If we want our theory to be general, this is precisely the sort of assumption that must be avoided. Second, when it is necessary in statistical mechanics to correlate temperature to molecular activity, it is found that classical statistical mechanics must be modified with the aid of quantum mechanics and that, when this modification is carried out, the molecules of a substance at absolute zero have a *finite* amount of kinetic energy, known as the *zero-point energy*.

1-11   Celsius Temperature Scale

The Celsius temperature scale employs a degree of the same magnitude as that of the ideal-gas scale, but its zero point is shifted so that *the Celsius temperature of the triple point of water is* 0.01 *degree Celsius*, abbreviated 0.01°C. Thus, if t denotes the Celsius temperature,

$$t = \theta - 273.15°.$$ (1-12)

Thus, the Celsius temperature t_s at which steam condenses at 1 atm pressure is

$$t_s = \theta_s - 273.15°,$$

and reading θ_s from Fig. 1-9,

$$t_s = 373.15° - 273.15°$$

$$= 100.00°C.$$

The accurate measurement of temperature with a gas thermometer requires months of painstaking laboratory work and mathematical computation and when completed becomes an international event. Such work is published in a physical journal and eventually is listed in tables of physical constants. The temperatures of the normal boiling points (NBP) and normal melting points (NMP) of a number of materials have been measured, and the results are tabulated in Table 1-3. The fixed points designated in the table as basic are used to calibrate other thermometers in a manner that will be described in Art. 1-14.

Table 1-3   Temperatures of Fixed Points

Fixed points		Temp., °C	Temp., °K
Standard	Triple point of water	**0.01**	**273.16**
Basic	NBP of hydrogen (hydrogen point)	−252.88	20.26
	NBP of oxygen (oxygen point)	−182.97	90.17
	Equilibrium of ice and air-saturated water (ice point)	0.00	273.15
	NBP of water (steam point)	100.00	373.15
	NMP of zinc (zinc point)	419.51	692.66
	NMP of antimony (antimony point)	630.50	903.65
	NMP of silver (silver point)	961.90	1235.05
	NMP of gold (gold point)	1064.5	1337.65
Secondary	NBP of helium	−268.93	4.22
	NBP of neon	−246.09	27.09
	NBP of nitrogen	−195.81	77.35
	NMP of mercury	−38.86	234.29
	Transition point of sodium sulfate	32.38	305.53
	NBP of naphthalene	217.96	491.11
	NMP of tin	231.913	505.00
	NBP of benzophenone	305.90	579.05
	NMP of cadmium	320.90	594.05
	NMP of lead	327.30	600.45

Notice that among the basic fixed points there are two normal boiling points, those of oxygen and of water. The normal boiling point is the temperature at which a liquid and its vapor remain in equilibrium when the vapor exerts a pressure of exactly 1 atm. Should the pressure depart from 1 atm by only 1 cm of mercury, the temperature change would be several tenths of a degree. It is necessary therefore to have elaborate controls on the vapor pressure to keep it constant to within a fraction of a millimeter of mercury. Such controls are available at the major bureaus of standards, but not in the average laboratory.

A normal melting (or freezing) point is defined also at 1 atm pressure. A change of pressure of 1 cm of mercury on a solid, however, produces a change in melting point of only about 0.00001 deg, and therefore no precautions need be taken. As a result, there is a growing tendency to eliminate all boiling points as fixed points and to retain only melting points and triple points.

1-12   Electric Resistance Thermometry

When the resistance thermometer is in the form of a long, fine wire, it is usually wound around a thin frame constructed so as to avoid excessive strains when the wire contracts upon cooling. In special circumstances the wire may be wound on or embedded in the material whose temperature is to be measured. In the very-low-temperature range, resistance thermometers often consist of small carbon-composition radio resistors or a germanium crystal doped with arsenic and sealed in a helium-filled capsule. These may be bonded to the surface of the substance whose temperature is to be measured or placed in a hole drilled for that purpose.

It is customary to measure the resistance by maintaining a known constant current in the thermometer and measuring the potential difference across it with the aid of a very sensitive potentiometer. A typical circuit is shown in Fig. 1-10. The current is held constant by adjusting a rheostat so that the potential difference across a standard resistor in series with the thermometer, as observed with a monitoring potentiometer, remains constant.

The platinum resistance thermometer may be used for very accurate work within the range of -253 to $1200°C$. The calibration of the instrument involves the measurement of R'_{Pt} at various known temperatures and the representation of the results by an empiric formula. In a restricted range, the following quadratic equation is often used:

$$R'_{Pt} = R'_0(1 + At + Bt^2),$$

Fig. 1-10   *Circuit for measuring the resistance of a resistance thermometer through which a constant current is maintained.*

Fig. 1-11   *Thermocouple of wires A and B with a reference junction consisting of two junctions with copper, connected to a potentiometer.*

where R_0' is the resistance of the platinum wire when it is surrounded by water at the triple point and A and B are constants.

1-13   Thermocouple

The correct use of a thermocouple is shown in Fig. 1-11. The thermal electromotive force (emf) is measured with a potentiometer, which, as a rule, must be placed at some distance from the system whose temperature is to be measured. The reference junction, therefore, is placed near the test junction and consists of two connections with copper wire, maintained at the temperature of melting ice. This arrangement allows the use of copper wires for connection to the potentiometer. The binding posts of the potentiometer are usually made of brass, and therefore at the potentiometer there are two copper-brass thermocouples. If the two binding posts are at the same temperature, these two copper-brass thermocouples introduce no error.

A thermocouple is calibrated by measuring the thermal emf at various known temperatures, the reference junction being kept at 0°C. The results of such measurements on most thermocouples can usually be represented by a cubic equation as follows:

$$\mathcal{E} = a + bt + ct^2 + dt^3,$$

where $\mathcal{E}$ is the thermal emf and the constants a, b, c, and d are different for each thermocouple. Within a restricted range of temperature, a quadratic equation is often sufficient. The range of a thermocouple depends upon the materials of which it is composed. A platinum-platinum-rhodium couple has a range of 0 to 1600°C. The advantage of a thermocouple is that it comes to thermal equilibrium quite rapidly with the system whose temperature is to be measured, because its mass is small. It therefore follows temperature changes easily, but it is not so accurate as a platinum resistance thermometer.

1-14   International Practical Temperature Scale

At the meeting of the Seventh General Conference of Weights and Measures in 1927, at which 31 nations were represented, an international practical temperature scale was adopted, not to replace the Celsius or ideal-gas scales, but to provide a scale that could be easily and rapidly used to calibrate scientific and industrial instruments. Slight refinements were incorporated into the scale in revisions adopted in 1948 and in 1960. The international practical scale agrees with the Celsius scale at the basic fixed points listed in Table 1-3. At temperatures between these fixed points, the departure from the Celsius scale is small enough to be neglected in most practical work. The temperature interval from the oxygen point to the gold point is divided into three main parts, as follows:

1   *From the oxygen point to the triple point of water.*   A platinum resistance thermometer with a platinum wire whose diameter must lie between the limits 0.05 and 0.20 mm is used, and the temperature is determined from the following relation between R' and t containing four constants:

$$R' = R_0'[1 + At + Bt^2 + C(t - 100)t^3].$$

The constants are determined by measurements at the oxygen point, the triple point of water, the steam point, and the zinc point.

2   *From the triple point of water to the antimony point.*   The same platinum resistance thermometer is used, and the temperature is determined from a relation between R' and t containing three constants:

$$R' = R_0'(1 + At + Bt^2).$$

The constants are determined by measurements at the triple point, the steam point, and the zinc point.

3   *From the antimony point to the gold point.*   The Celsius temperature t is defined by the formula

$$\mathcal{E} = a + bt + ct^2,$$

where $\mathcal{E}$ is the emf of a standard thermocouple of platinum and of an alloy of 90 percent platinum and 10 percent rhodium, when one of the junctions is at the triple point of water. The constants are determined by measurements at the antimony point, the silver point, and the gold point.

The international practical temperature scale is not defined below the oxygen point. Temperature measurements in the liquid hydrogen and liquid helium ranges, as well as in the range above the gold point, will be discussed fully in later chapters.

PROBLEMS

1-1   Systems A, B, and C are gases with coordinates P, V; P', V'; P'', V''. When A and C are in thermal equilibrium, the equation

$$PV - nbP - P''V'' = 0$$

is found to be satisfied. When B and C are in thermal equilibrium, the relation

$$P'V' - P''V'' + \frac{nB'P''V''}{V'} = 0$$

holds. The symbols n, b, and B' are constants.

(a)   What are the three functions which are equal to one another at thermal equilibrium and each of which is equal to t, where t is the empiric temperature?

(b)   What is the relation expressing thermal equilibrium between A and B?

1-2   Systems A and B are paramagnetic salts with coordinates $\mathcal{H}$, M and $\mathcal{H}'$, M', respectively. System C is a gas with coordinates P, V. When A and C are in thermal equilibrium, the equation

$$nRC\mathcal{H} - MPV = 0$$

$$\quad -PV = \frac{tnRCH}{M}$$

is found to hold. When B and C are in thermal equilibrium, we get

$$nR\Theta M' + nRC'\mathscr{H}' - M'PV = 0,$$

$$PV = \frac{nR\Theta M' + nRC'\mathscr{H}'}{M'}$$

where n, R, C, C', and Θ are constants.

(a)   What are the three functions that are equal to one another at thermal equilibrium?

(b)   Set each of these functions equal to the ideal-gas temperature θ, and see whether any of these equations are equations of state as discussed in Chap. 2.

1-3   In the table below, a number in the top row represents the pressure of a gas in the bulb of a constant-volume gas thermometer (corrected for dead space, thermal expansion of bulb, etc.) when the bulb is immersed in a water triple-point cell. The bottom row represents the corresponding readings of pressure when the bulb is surrounded by a material at a constant unknown temperature. Calculate the ideal-gas temperature θ of this material. (Use five significant figures.)

P_3, mm Hg	1000.0	750.00	500.00	250.00
P, mm Hg	1535.3	1151.6	767.82	383.95

1-4   The resistance R' of a particular Allen-Bradley carbon resistor obeys Clement's equation, namely,

$$\sqrt{\frac{\log R'}{\theta}} = a + b \log R',$$

with $a = -1.16$ and $b = 0.675$.

(a)   In a liquid helium cryostat, the resistance is found to be exactly 1000 Ω. What is the temperature?

(b)   Make a log-log graph of R' against θ in the resistance range from 1000 to 30,000 Ω.

1-5   The resistance of a doped germanium crystal obeys the equation

$$\log R' = 4.697 - 3.917 \log \theta.$$

(a)   In a liquid helium cryostat the resistance is measured to be 218 Ω. What is the temperature?

(b)   Make a log-log graph of R' against θ in the resistance range from 200 to 30,000 Ω.

2.

SIMPLE THERMODYNAMIC SYSTEMS

2-1   Thermodynamic Equilibrium

Suppose that experiments have been performed on a thermodynamic system and that the coordinates necessary and sufficient for a macroscopic description have been determined. When these coordinates change in any way whatsoever, either spontaneously or by virtue of outside influence, the system is said to undergo a *change of state*.† When a system is not influenced in any way by its surroundings, it is said to be isolated. In practical applications of thermodynamics, isolated systems are of little importance. We usually have to deal with a system that is influenced in some way by its surroundings. In general, the surroundings may exert forces on the system or provide contact between the system and a body at some definite temperature. When the state of a system changes, interactions usually take place between the system and its surroundings.

When there is no unbalanced force in the interior of a system and also none between a system and its surroundings, the system is said to be in a state of *mechanical equilibrium*. When these conditions are not satisfied, either the system alone or both the system and its surroundings will undergo a change of state, which will cease only when mechanical equilibrium is restored.

When a system in mechanical equilibrium does not tend to undergo a spontaneous change of internal structure, such as a chemical reaction, or a transfer of matter from one part of the system to another, such as diffusion or solution, however slow, then it is said to be in a state of *chemical equilibrium*. A system not in chemical equilibrium undergoes a change of state that, in

---

† This must not be confused with the terminology of elementary physics, where the expression "change of state" is often used to signify a transition from solid to liquid or liquid to gas, etc. Such a change in the language of thermodynamics is called a *change of phase*.

some cases, is exceedingly slow. The change ceases when chemical equilibrium is reached.

Thermal equilibrium exists when there is no spontaneous change in the coordinates of a system in mechanical and chemical equilibrium when it is separated from its surroundings by a diathermic wall. In thermal equilibrium, all parts of a system are at the same temperature, and this temperature is the same as that of the surroundings. When these conditions are not satisfied, a change of state will take place until thermal equilibrium is reached.

When the conditions for all three types of equilibrium are satisfied, the system is said to be in a state of *thermodynamic equilibrium;* in this condition, it is apparent that there will be no tendency whatever for any change of state, either of the system or of the surroundings, to occur. *States of thermodynamic equilibrium can be described in terms of macroscopic coordinates that do not involve the time, i.e., in terms of thermodynamic coordinates.* Classical thermodynamics does not attempt to deal with any problem involving the rate at which a process takes place. The investigation of such problems is carried out in other branches of science, as in the kinetic theory of gases, hydrodynamics, and chemical kinetics.

When the conditions for any one of the three types of equilibrium that constitute thermodynamic equilibrium are not satisfied, the system is said to be in a *nonequilibrium state.* Thus, when there is an unbalanced force in the interior of a system or between a system and its surroundings, the following phenomena may take place: acceleration, turbulence, eddies, waves, etc. While such phenomena are in progress, a system passes through nonequilibrium states. If an attempt is made to give a macroscopic description of any one of these nonequilibrium states, it is found that the pressure varies from one part of a system to another. There is no single pressure that refers to the system as a whole. Similarly, in the case of a system at a different temperature from its surroundings a nonuniform temperature distribution is set up and there is no single temperature that refers to the system as a whole. We therefore conclude that, *when the conditions for mechanical and thermal equilibrium are not satisfied, the states traversed by a system cannot be described in terms of thermodynamic coordinates referring to the system as a whole.*

It must not be concluded, however, that we are entirely helpless in dealing with such nonequilibrium states. If we divide the system into a large number of small mass elements, then thermodynamic coordinates may be found in terms of which a macroscopic description of each mass element may be approximated. There are also special methods for dealing with systems in mechanical and thermal equilibrium but not in chemical equilibrium. All these special methods will be considered later. At present we shall deal exclusively with systems in thermodynamic equilibrium.

Imagine, for the sake of simplicity, a constant mass of gas in a vessel so equipped that the pressure, volume, and temperature may be easily measured. If we fix the volume at some arbitrary value and cause the temperature to assume an arbitrarily chosen value, then we shall not be able to vary the pressure at all. Once V and θ are chosen by us, the value of P at equilibrium is determined by nature. Similarly, if P and θ are chosen arbitrarily, then the value of V at equilibrium is fixed. That is, of the three thermodynamic coordinates P, V, and θ, only two are independent variables. This implies that there exists an equation of equilibrium which connects the thermodynamic coordinates and which robs one of them of its independence. Such an equation is called an *equation of state*. Every thermodynamic system has its own equation of state, although in some cases the relation may be so complicated that it cannot be expressed in terms of simple mathematical functions.

An equation of state expresses the individual peculiarities of one system in contradistinction to another and must therefore be determined either by experiment or by molecular theory. A general theory like thermodynamics, based on general laws of nature, is incapable of expressing the behavior of one material as opposed to another. An equation of state therefore is not a theoretical deduction from thermodynamics but is usually an experimental addition to thermodynamics. It expresses the results of experiments in which the thermodynamic coordinates of a system were measured as accurately as possible, within a limited range of values. An equation of state is therefore only as accurate as the experiments that led to its formulation and holds only within the range of values measured. As soon as this range is exceeded, a different form of equation of state may be valid.

No equation of state exists for the states traversed by a system that is not in mechanical and thermal equilibrium, since such states cannot be described in terms of thermodynamic coordinates referring to the system as a whole. For example, if a gas in a cylinder were to expand and to impart to a piston an accelerated motion, the gas might have, at any moment, a definite volume and temperature, but the corresponding pressure could not be calculated from an equation of state. The pressure would not be a thermodynamic coordinate because it would not only depend on the velocity and the acceleration of the piston but would also perhaps vary from point to point.

Any system of constant mass that exerts on the surroundings a uniform hydrostatic pressure, in the absence of surface, gravitational, electric, and magnetic effects, we shall call a *hydrostatic system*. Hydrostatic systems are divided into the following categories:

1   A *pure substance*, which is one chemical constituent in the form of a solid, a liquid, a gas, a mixture of any two, or a mixture of all three.

2   A *homogeneous mixture of different constituents*, such as a mixture of inert

gases, a mixture of chemically active gases, a mixture of liquids, or a solution.

3 A *heterogeneous mixture*, such as a mixture of different gases in contact with a mixture of different liquids.

Experiment shows that the states of equilibrium† of a hydrostatic system can be described with the aid of three coordinates, namely, the pressure P exerted by the system on the surroundings, the volume V, and the absolute temperature θ. The pressure is measured in dynes per square centimeter and the volume in cubic centimeters; the most convenient scale of temperature is the ideal-gas scale. Other units of pressure, such as pounds per square inch, atmospheres, millimeters of mercury, and kilograms per square centimeter, are used in various applications of thermodynamics and will be used occasionally in this book. In the absence of any special remarks about units, however, it will be understood that cgs units are to be employed.

2-2   *PV* **Diagram for a Pure Substance**

If 1 g of water at about 94°C is introduced into a vessel about 2 liters in volume from which all the air has been exhausted, the water will evaporate completely and the system will be in the condition known as *unsaturated vapor*, the pressure of the vapor being less than 1 atm. On the *PV* diagram shown in Fig. 2-1, this state is represented by the point A. If the vapor is then compressed slowly and isothermally, the pressure will rise until there is *saturated vapor* at the point B. If the compression is continued, condensation takes place, with the pressure remaining constant (*isobaric* process) as long as the temperature remains constant. The straight line BC represents the isothermal isobaric condensation of water vapor, the constant pressure being called the *vapor pressure*. At any point between B and C, water and steam are in equilibrium; at the point C, there is only liquid water, or *saturated liquid*. Since a very large increase of pressure is needed to compress liquid water, the line CD is almost vertical. At any point on the line CD, the water is said to be in the *liquid phase;* at any point on AB, in the *vapor phase;* and at any point on BC, there is equilibrium between the liquid and the vapor phases. $ABCD$ is a typical isotherm of a pure substance on a *PV* diagram.

At other temperatures the isotherms are of similar character, as shown in Fig. 2-1. It is seen that the lines representing equilibrium between liquid and vapor phases, or *vaporization lines*, get shorter as the temperature rises until a certain temperature is reached—the *critical temperature*—above which there is no longer any distinction between a liquid and a vapor. The isotherm at the critical temperature is called the *critical isotherm*, and the point

† In the remainder of this book the word "equilibrium," unmodified by any adjective, will refer to thermodynamic equilibrium.

Fig. 2-1   *Isotherms of a pure substance.*

that represents the limit of the vaporization lines is called the *critical point*. It is seen that the critical point is a point of inflection on the critical isotherm. The pressure and volume at the critical point are known as the *critical pressure* and the *critical volume*, respectively. All points at which the liquid is saturated lie on the *liquid saturation curve*, and all points representing saturated vapor lie on the *vapor saturation curve*. The two saturation curves denoted by dotted lines meet at the critical point. Above the critical point the isotherms are continuous curves that at large volumes and low pressures approach the isotherms of an ideal gas.

In the *PV* diagram shown in Fig. 2-1, the low-temperature region representing the solid phase has not been shown. The solid region and the region of equilibrium between solid and vapor are indicated by isotherms of the same general character as those in Fig. 2-1. The horizontal portion of one of these isotherms represents the transition from saturated solid to saturated vapor, or *sublimation*. There is obviously one such line that is the boundary between the liquid-vapor region and the solid-vapor region. This *line* is associated with the *triple point*. In the case of ordinary water, the triple point is at a pressure of 4.58 mm and a temperature of 0.01°C, and the line extends from a volume of 1.00 cm³/g (saturated liquid) to a volume of 206,000 cm³/g (saturated vapor).

2-3   *Pθ* **Diagram for a Pure Substance**

If the vapor pressure of a solid is measured at various temperatures until the triple point is reached and then that of the liquid is measured until the critical point is reached, the results when plotted on a *Pθ* diagram appear as in Fig. 2-2. If the substance at the triple point is compressed until there is no vapor left and the pressure on the resulting mixture of liquid and solid is increased, the temperature will have to be changed for equilibrium to exist between the solid and the liquid. Measurements of these pressures and temperatures give rise to a third curve on the *Pθ* diagram, starting at the triple point and continuing indefinitely. The points representing the coexistence of (1) solid and vapor lie on the *sublimation curve;* (2) liquid and vapor lie on the *vaporization curve;* (3) liquid and solid lie on the *fusion curve.* In the particular case of water, the sublimation curve is called the *frost line,*

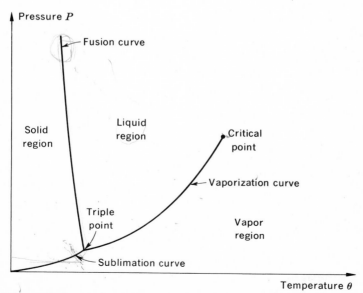

Fig. 2-2   *Pθ diagram for a substance such as water.*

the vaporization curve is called the *steam line*, and the fusion curve is called the *ice line*.

The slopes of the sublimation and the vaporization curves for all substances are positive. The slope of the fusion curve, however, may be positive or negative. The fusion curve of most substances has a positive slope. Water is one of the important exceptions. When an equation known as the Clapeyron equation is derived in Chap. 12, it will be seen that any substance, such as water, which contracts upon melting has a fusion curve with a negative slope, whereas the opposite is true for a substance which expands upon melting.

The triple point is the point of intersection of the sublimation and vaporization curves. It must be understood that only on a $P\theta$ diagram is the triple point represented by a point. On a PV diagram it is a line. Triple-point data for some interesting substances are given in Table 2-1.

In investigating the ice line of water at very high pressures, Bridgman and Tammann discovered five new modifications of ice, designated as ice II, III, V, VI, and VII—ordinary ice being denoted by ice I. Two other

Table 2-1   Triple-point Data

Substance	Temp., °K	Pressure, mm Hg
Helium (4) (λ point)	2.172	37.80
Hydrogen (normal)	13.84	52.8
Deuterium (normal)	18.63	128
Neon	24.57	324
Nitrogen	63.18	94
Oxygen	54.36	1.14
Ammonia	195.40	45.57
Carbon dioxide	216.55	3880
Sulfur dioxide	197.68	1.256
Water	273.16	4.58

Table 2-2   Triple Points of Water

Phases in equilibrium	Pressure	Temp., °C
Ice I, liquid, vapor	4.579 mm Hg	+ 0.01
Ice I, liquid, ice III	2,115 kg/cm²	−22.0
Ice I, ice II, ice III	2,170 kg/cm²	−34.7
Ice II, ice III, ice V	3,510 kg/cm²	−24.3
Ice III, liquid, ice V	3,530 kg/cm²	−17.0
Ice V, liquid, ice VI	6,380 kg/cm²	+ 0.16
Ice VI, liquid, ice VII	22,400 kg/cm²	+81.6

modifications of ice, IV and VIII, were found to be unstable. Equilibrium conditions among these forms of ice and liquid give rise to six other triple points, which, along with the low-pressure triple point, are listed in Table 2-2.

2-4 $PV\theta$ **Surface**

All the information that is represented on both the PV and the $P\theta$ diagrams can be shown on one diagram if the three coordinates P, V, and θ are plotted along rectangular axes. The result is called the $PV\theta$ *surface*. Two such surfaces are shown in Figs. 2-3 and 2-4: the first for a substance like H_2O that contracts upon melting, and the second for a substance like CO_2 that expands upon melting. These diagrams are not drawn to scale, the volume axis being considerably foreshortened. If the student imagines a $PV\theta$ surface projected on the PV plane, he will see the usual PV diagram. Upon projecting the surface on the $P\theta$ plane, the whole solid-vapor region projects into the sublimation curve, the whole liquid-vapor region projects into the vaporization curve, the whole solid-liquid region projects into the fusion curve, and finally the *triple-point line* projects into the triple point. The critical point is denoted by the letters Cr, and the triple point by Tr. The critical isotherm is marked θ_c. A substance with no free surface and with a volume determined by that of the container is called a *gas* when its temperature is above the critical temperature; otherwise it is called a *vapor*.

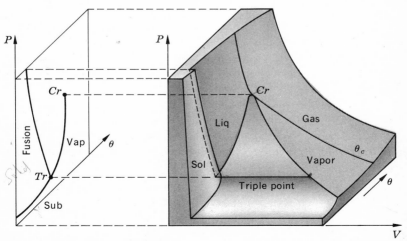

Fig. 2-3   *Surface for a substance that contracts on melting.*

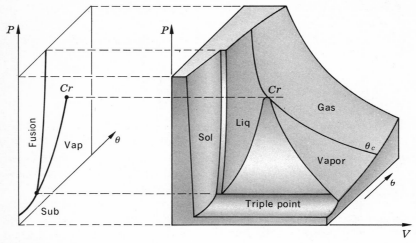

Fig. 2-4   *Surface for a substance that expands on melting.*

All the triple points of water are shown on the *PVt* surface shown in Fig. 2-5, which was constructed by Verwiebe on the basis of measurements by Bridgman.

2-5   Equations of State

It is impossible to express the complete behavior of a substance over the whole range of measured values of *P*, *V*, and θ by means of one simple equation. There have been over sixty equations of state suggested to represent only the liquid, vapor, and liquid-vapor regions, ranging from the ideal gas equation

$$Pv = R\theta, \qquad (2\text{-}1)$$

which holds only at low pressures in the vapor and gas regions, to the Beattie-Bridgman equation:

$$P = \frac{R\theta(1 - \epsilon)}{v^2}(v + B) - \frac{A}{v^2}, \qquad (2\text{-}2)$$

where $A = A_0\left(1 - \dfrac{a}{v}\right), \qquad B = B_0\left(1 - \dfrac{b}{v}\right), \qquad \epsilon = \dfrac{c}{v\theta^3},$

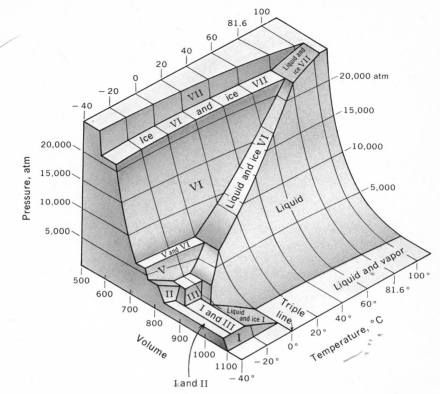

Fig. 2-5   *Surface for water, showing all the triple points. (Constructed by Verwiebe on the basis of measurements by Bridgman.)*

which, because of its five adjustable constants, represents with some accuracy the whole range above the triple point.

Some of these equations are frankly empirical, designed to represent as closely as possible the measured values of P, V, and θ, while others are theoretical, having been calculated on the basis of the kinetic theory of gases. One of the most famous of the theoretical equations of state, based on assumptions concerning molecular behavior that are still of use today, is the van der Waals equation of state:

$$\left(P + \frac{a}{v^2}\right)(v - b) = R\theta. \tag{2-3}$$

This equation holds fairly well in the liquid region, the vapor region, and near and above the critical point.

In all these equations, v is the gram-molar volume where

$$1 \text{ g mole} = \mathcal{M} \text{ grams}$$

and $\mathcal{M}$ is the molecular weight; R is a constant called the *universal gas constant*.

2-6   Differential Changes of State

If a system undergoes a small change of state whereby it passes from an initial state of equilibrium to another state of equilibrium very near the initial one, then all three coordinates, in general, undergo slight changes. If the change of, say, V is very small in comparison with V and very large in comparison with the space occupied by a few molecules, then this change of V may be written as a differential dV. If V were a geometrical quantity referring to the volume of *space*, then dV could be used to denote a portion of that space arbitrarily small. Since, however, V is a macroscopic coordinate denoting the volume of *matter*, then, for dV to have a meaning, it must be large enough to include enough molecules to warrant the use of the macroscopic point of view.

Similarly, if the change of P is very small in comparison with P and very large in comparison with molecular fluctuations, then it also may be represented by the differential dP. *Every infinitesimal in thermodynamics must satisfy the requirement that it represents a change in a quantity which is small with respect to the quantity itself and large in comparison with the effect produced by the behavior of a few molecules.* The reason for this is that thermodynamic coordinates such as volume, pressure, and temperature have no meaning when applied to a few molecules. This is another way of saying that thermodynamic coordinates are macroscopic coordinates.

We may imagine the equation of state solved for any coordinate in terms of the other two. Thus,

$$V = \text{function of } (\theta, P).$$

An infinitesimal change from one state of equilibrium to another state of equilibrium involves a dV, a $d\theta$, and a dP, all of which we shall assume satisfy the condition laid down in the previous paragraph. A fundamental theorem in partial differential calculus enables us to write

$$dV = \left(\frac{\partial V}{\partial \theta}\right)_P d\theta + \left(\frac{\partial V}{\partial P}\right)_\theta dP,$$

where each partial derivative is itself a function of θ and P. Both the above partial derivatives have an important physical meaning. The student will remember from elementary physics a quantity called the *average coefficient of volume expansion*, or volume expansivity. This was defined as

$$\text{Av. vol. exp.} = \frac{\text{change of vol. per unit vol.}}{\text{change of temp.}}$$

and referred to conditions under which the pressure was constant. If the change of temperature is made infinitesimal, then the change in volume also becomes infinitesimal and we have what is known as the instantaneous volume expansivity, or just *volume expansivity*, which is denoted by β. Thus,

$$\beta = \frac{1}{V}\left(\frac{\partial V}{\partial \theta}\right)_P. \qquad (2\text{-}4)$$

Strictly speaking, β is a function of θ and P, but experiments to be described later show that there are many substances for which β is quite insensitive to a change in P and varies only slightly with θ. Consequently, within a small temperature range β may, as a rule, be regarded as a constant. β is expressed in reciprocal degrees.

The effect of a change of pressure on the volume of a hydrostatic system when the temperature is kept constant is expressed by a quantity called *isothermal compressibility* and is represented by the symbol κ (Greek kappa). Thus,

$$\kappa = -\frac{1}{V}\left(\frac{\partial V}{\partial P}\right)_\theta. \qquad (2\text{-}5)$$

The unit of compressibility is 1 atm^{-1}, where 1 atm $= 1.01 \times 10^6$ dyn/cm^2. The value of κ for solids and liquids varies but little with temperature and pressure, so that κ may often be regarded as constant.

If the equation of state is solved for P, then

$$P = \text{function of } (\theta, V)$$

and
$$dP = \left(\frac{\partial P}{\partial \theta}\right)_V d\theta + \left(\frac{\partial P}{\partial V}\right)_\theta dV.$$

Finally, if θ is imagined as a function of P and V,

$$d\theta = \left(\frac{\partial \theta}{\partial P}\right)_V dP + \left(\frac{\partial \theta}{\partial V}\right)_P dV.$$

In all the above equations the system was assumed to undergo an infinitesimal process from an initial state of equilibrium to another. This enabled us to use an equation of equilibrium (equation of state) and to solve it for any coordinate in terms of the other two. The differentials dP, dV, and $d\theta$ therefore are differentials of actual functions and are called *exact differentials*. If dz is an exact differential of a function of, say, x and y, then dz may be written

$$dz = \left(\frac{\partial z}{\partial x}\right)_y dx + \left(\frac{\partial z}{\partial y}\right)_x dy.$$

An infinitesimal that is not the differential of an actual function is called an *inexact differential* and cannot be expressed by an equation of the above type. Other distinctions between exact and inexact differentials will be made clear later.

2-7   Mathematical Theorems

There are two simple theorems in partial differential calculus that are used very often in this subject. The proofs are as follows: Suppose there exists a relation among the three coordinates x, y, and z; thus,

$$f(x,y,z) = 0.$$

Then x can be imagined as a function of y and z, and

$$dx = \left(\frac{\partial x}{\partial y}\right)_z dy + \left(\frac{\partial x}{\partial z}\right)_y dz.$$

Also, y can be imagined as a function of x and z, and

$$dy = \left(\frac{\partial y}{\partial x}\right)_z dx + \left(\frac{\partial y}{\partial z}\right)_x dz.$$

Substituting the second equation into the first, we have

$$dx = \left(\frac{\partial x}{\partial y}\right)_z \left[\left(\frac{\partial y}{\partial x}\right)_z dx + \left(\frac{\partial y}{\partial z}\right)_x dz\right] + \left(\frac{\partial x}{\partial z}\right)_y dz,$$

or
$$dx = \left(\frac{\partial x}{\partial y}\right)_z \left(\frac{\partial y}{\partial x}\right)_z dx + \left[\left(\frac{\partial x}{\partial y}\right)_z \left(\frac{\partial y}{\partial z}\right)_x + \left(\frac{\partial x}{\partial z}\right)_y\right] dz.$$

Now, of the three coordinates, only two are independent. Choosing x and z as the independent coordinates, the above equation must be true for all sets of values of dx and dz. Thus, if $dz = 0$ and $dx \neq 0$, it follows that

$$\left(\frac{\partial x}{\partial y}\right)_z \left(\frac{\partial y}{\partial x}\right)_z = 1,$$

or

$$\left(\frac{\partial x}{\partial y}\right)_z = \frac{1}{(\partial y/\partial x)_z}. \tag{2-6}$$

If $dx = 0$ and $dz \neq 0$, it follows that

$$\left(\frac{\partial x}{\partial y}\right)_z \left(\frac{\partial y}{\partial z}\right)_x + \left(\frac{\partial x}{\partial z}\right)_y = 0,$$

$$\left(\frac{\partial x}{\partial y}\right)_z \left(\frac{\partial y}{\partial z}\right)_x = - \left(\frac{\partial x}{\partial z}\right)_y$$

and

$$\left(\frac{\partial x}{\partial y}\right)_z \left(\frac{\partial y}{\partial z}\right)_x \left(\frac{\partial z}{\partial x}\right)_y = -1. \tag{2-7}$$

In the case of a hydrostatic system, the second theorem yields the result

$$\left(\frac{\partial P}{\partial V}\right)_\theta \left(\frac{\partial V}{\partial \theta}\right)_P = - \left(\frac{\partial P}{\partial \theta}\right)_V.$$

The volume expansivity β and the isothermal compressibility κ were defined as

$$\beta = \frac{1}{V} \left(\frac{\partial V}{\partial \theta}\right)_P$$

and

$$\kappa = - \frac{1}{V} \left(\frac{\partial V}{\partial P}\right)_\theta.$$

Therefore,

$$\left(\frac{\partial P}{\partial \theta}\right)_V = \frac{\beta}{\kappa}.$$

An infinitesimal change in pressure may now be expressed in terms of these physical quantities. Thus,

$$dP = \left(\frac{\partial P}{\partial \theta}\right)_V d\theta + \left(\frac{\partial P}{\partial V}\right)_\theta dV,$$

or

$$dP = \frac{\beta}{\kappa} d\theta - \frac{1}{\kappa V} dV. \tag{2-8}$$

At constant volume,

$$dP = \frac{\beta}{\kappa} \, d\theta.$$

If we cause the temperature to change a finite amount from θ_i to θ_f at constant volume, the pressure will change from P_i to P_f, where the subscripts i and f denote the initial and final states, respectively. Upon integrating between these two states, we get

$$P_f - P_i = \int_{\theta_i}^{\theta_f} \frac{\beta}{\kappa} \, d\theta.$$

The right-hand member can be integrated if we know the way in which β and κ vary with θ at constant volume. If the temperature range $\theta_f - \theta_i$ is small, very little error is introduced by assuming that both are constant. With these assumptions we get

$$P_f - P_i = \frac{\beta}{\kappa} (\theta_f - \theta_i),$$

from which the final pressure may be calculated. For example, consider the following problem: A mass of mercury at a pressure of 1 atm and a temperature of 0°C is kept at constant volume. If the temperature is raised to 10°C, what will be the final pressure? From tables of physical constants, β and κ of mercury remain practically constant within the temperature range of 0 to 10°C and have the values

$$\beta = 181 \times 10^{-6} \text{ deg}^{-1}$$

and

$$\kappa = 3.87 \times 10^{-6} \text{ atm}^{-1};$$

whence

$$P_f - P_i = \frac{181 \times 10^{-6} \text{ deg}^{-1} \times 10 \text{ deg}}{3.87 \times 10^{-6} \text{ atm}^{-1}}$$

$$= 468 \text{ atm},$$

and

$$P_f = 468 + 1 = 469 \text{ atm}.$$

2-8   Stretched Wire

Experiments on stretched wires are usually performed under conditions in which the pressure remains constant at 1 atm and changes in volume are negligible. For most practical purposes, it is found unnecessary to include the pressure and the volume among the thermodynamic coordinates. A sufficiently complete thermodynamic description of a wire is given in terms of only three coordinates:

1 The tension in the wire $\mathscr{F}$, measured in newtons (N).
2 The length of the wire L, measured in meters (m).
3 The ideal-gas temperature θ.

The states of thermodynamic equilibrium are connected by an equation of state that as a rule cannot be expressed by a simple equation. For a wire at constant temperature within the limit of elasticity, Hooke's law holds; namely,

$$\mathscr{F} = \text{const.}\ (L - L_0),$$

where L_0 is the length at zero tension.

If a wire undergoes an infinitesimal change from one state of equilibrium to another, then the infinitesimal change of length is an exact differential and can be written

$$dL = \left(\frac{\partial L}{\partial \theta}\right)_{\mathscr{F}} d\theta + \left(\frac{\partial L}{\partial \mathscr{F}}\right)_{\theta} d\mathscr{F},$$

where both partial derivatives are functions of θ and $\mathscr{F}$. These derivatives are connected with important physical quantities. We define the *linear expansivity* α as

$$\boxed{\alpha = \frac{1}{L}\left(\frac{\partial L}{\partial \theta}\right)_{\mathscr{F}}.} \qquad (2\text{-}9)$$

The experimental measurement of α will be considered later. Measurements of α show that it depends only slightly on $\mathscr{F}$ and varies mostly with θ. In a small temperature range, however, it may be regarded as practically constant. α is expressed in reciprocal degrees.

By definition, the *isothermal Young's modulus*, denoted by Y, is

$$\boxed{Y = \frac{L}{A}\left(\frac{\partial \mathscr{F}}{\partial L}\right)_{\theta},} \qquad (2\text{-}10)$$

where A denotes the area of the wire. The isothermal Young's modulus is found experimentally to depend but little on $\mathscr{F}$ and mostly on θ. For a small temperature range, it may be regarded as practically constant. The unit of Y is 1 dyn/cm^2.

2-9   Surface Film

The study of surface films is an interesting branch of physical chemistry. There are three important examples of such films:

1   The upper surface of a liquid in equilibrium with its vapor.
2   A soap bubble, or soap film, stretched across a wire framework, consisting of two surface films with a small amount of liquid between.
3   A thin (sometimes monomolecular) oil film on the surface of water.

A surface film is somewhat like a stretched membrane. The surface on one side of any imaginary line pulls perpendicular to this line with a force equal and opposite to that exerted by the surface on the other side of the line. The force acting perpendicularly to a line of unit length is called the *surface tension*. An adequate thermodynamic description of a surface film is given by the specifying three coordinates:

1   The surface tension $\mathscr{S}$, measured in dyn/cm.
2   The area of the film A, measured in cm^2.
3   The ideal-gas temperature θ.

In dealing with a surface film, the accompanying liquid must always be considered as part of the system. This may be done, however, without introducing the pressure and volume of the composite system because, as a rule, the pressure remains constant and volume changes are negligible. The surface of a pure liquid in equilibrium with its vapor has a particularly simple equation of state. Experiment shows that the surface tension of such a film does not depend on the area but is a function of the temperature only. For most pure liquids, the equation of state can be written

$$\mathscr{S} = \mathscr{S}_0 \left(1 - \frac{t}{t'}\right)^n,$$

where $\mathscr{S}_0$ is the surface tension at 0°C, t' is a temperature within a few degrees of the critical temperature, and n is a constant that lies between 1 and 2. It is clear from this equation that the surface tension decreases as t increases, becoming zero when $t = t'$.

The equation of state of a monomolecular oil film on water is particularly interesting. If $\mathscr{S}_W$ denotes the surface tension of a clean water surface and $\mathscr{S}$ the surface tension of the water covered by the monolayer, then, within a restricted range of values of A,

$$(\mathscr{S} - \mathscr{S}_W)A = \text{const. } \theta.$$

The difference $\mathscr{S} - \mathscr{S}_W$ is sometimes called the *surface pressure*. Such films can be compressed and expanded and, when deposited on glass, have interesting optical properties.

2-10   Reversible Cell

A reversible cell consists of two electrodes each immersed in a different electrolyte. The emf depends on the nature of the materials, the concentrations of the electrolytes, and the temperature. In Fig. 2-6 a schematic diagram of a reversible cell, the Daniell cell, is shown. A copper electrode immersed in a saturated $CuSO_4$ solution is separated by a porous wall from a zinc electrode immersed in a saturated solution of $ZnSO_4$. Experiment shows that the copper electrode is positive with respect to the zinc.

Suppose that the cell is connected to a potentiometer whose potential difference is slightly smaller than the emf of the cell. Under these conditions, the current that exists may be described conventionally as a transfer of positive electricity externally from the copper electrode to the zinc electrode. When this is the case, zinc goes into solution, zinc sulfate is formed, copper is deposited, and copper sulfate is used up. These changes are expressed by the chemical reaction

$$Zn + CuSO_4 \rightarrow Cu + ZnSO_4.$$

When positive electricity is transferred in the opposite direction, i.e.,

Fig. 2-6   *The Daniell cell.*

externally from zinc to copper, the reaction proceeds in the reverse direction (hence the name reversible cell); thus,

$$Cu + ZnSO_4 \rightarrow Zn + CuSO_4.$$

The important feature of a reversible cell is that the chemical changes accompanying the transfer of electricity in one direction take place to the same extent in the reverse direction when the same quantity of electricity is transferred in the reverse direction. Furthermore, according to one of Faraday's laws of electrolysis, the simultaneous disappearance of 1 mole of zinc and deposit of 1 mole of copper are accompanied by the transfer of exactly jN_F coulombs of electricity, where j is the valence and N_F is Faraday's constant, or 96,500 C. We may therefore define a quantity Z, called the *charge* of the cell, as a number whose absolute magnitude is of no consequence but whose change is numerically equal to the quantity of electricity that is transferred during the chemical reaction, the change being negative when positive electricity is transferred externally from the positive to the negative electrode. Thus, if Δn moles of zinc disappear and Δn moles of copper are deposited, the charge of the cell changes from Z_i to Z_f, where

$$Z_f - Z_i = -\Delta n j N_F. \tag{2-11}$$

Now, if we limit ourselves to reversible cells in which no gases are liberated and which operate at constant atmospheric pressure, we may ignore the pressure and the volume and describe the cell with the aid of three coordinates only:

1   The emf $\mathcal{E}$, measured in V.
2   The charge Z, measured in C.
3   The ideal-gas temperature θ.

When the cell is on open circuit, there is a tendency for diffusion to take place slowly and the cell is not in equilibrium. If the cell is connected to a potentiometer, however, and the circuit is adjusted until there is no current, then the emf of the cell is balanced and the cell is in mechanical and chemical equilibrium. When thermal equilibrium is also satisfied, the cell is then in thermodynamic equilibrium. The states of thermodynamic equilibrium of a reversible cell are connected by an equation of state among the coordinates $\mathcal{E}$, Z, and θ. If the electrolytes are saturated solutions, a transfer of electricity accompanying the performance of the chemical reaction at constant temperature and pressure will not alter the concentrations of the electrolytes. The emf will therefore remain constant. Experiment shows that the emf of a saturated reversible cell at constant pressure is a function of the temperature only. The equation of state is usually written

$$\mathcal{E} = \mathcal{E}_{20} + \alpha(t - 20°) + \beta(t - 20°)^2 + \gamma(t - 20°)^3,$$

where t is the Celsius temperature, $\mathcal{E}_{20}$ is the emf at 20°C, and α, β, and γ are constants depending on the materials. We shall see later that, once the equation of state of a reversible cell is known, all the quantities of interest to a chemist which refer to the chemical reaction going on in the cell can be determined.

2-11   Paramagnetic Solid

A paramagnetic substance in the absence of an external magnetic field is not a magnet. Upon being introduced into a magnetic field it becomes slightly magnetized in the direction of the field. Its permeability, however, is still very nearly unity, in contradistinction to a ferromagnetic substance like iron, whose permeability may be very large. The magnetized state of a paramagnetic substance may be described macroscopically by specifying the total magnetic moment of the substance, which we shall call the *magnetization.* This quantity should not be confused with the intensity of magnetization, which is the magnetic moment per unit volume. In thermodynamics it is not convenient to refer to the properties of a unit volume of material. The magnetization of any substance may be measured in pole centimeters.

If a unit pole, placed in a magnetic field, is acted on by a force of 1 dyn, the *magnetic intensity* is said to be 1 Oe. Most experiments on magnetic solids are performed at constant atmospheric pressure and involve only minute volume changes. Consequently, we may ignore the pressure and the volume and describe a paramagnetic solid with the aid of only three thermodynamic coordinates:

1   The magnetic intensity $\mathcal{H}$, measured in oersteds (1 Oe = 1 dyn/pole).
2   The magnetization M, measured in pole centimeters.
3   The ideal-gas temperature θ.

The states of thermodynamic equilibrium of a paramagnetic solid can be represented by an equation of state among these coordinates. Experiment shows that the magnetization of many paramagnetic solids is a function of the ratio of the magnetic intensity to the temperature. For small values of this ratio the function reduces to a very simple form, namely,

$$M = C_C \frac{\mathcal{H}}{\theta},$$

which is known as *Curie's equation*—C_C being called the *Curie constant*. The Curie constant may be written

$$C_C = \frac{M}{\mathcal{H}} \theta = \frac{\mathcal{H}M}{\mathcal{H}^2} \theta.$$

It will be shown in the next chapter that, when $\mathcal{H}$ is measured in oersteds and M in pole centimeters, $\mathcal{H}M$ is measured in ergs and $\mathcal{H}^2$ in ergs per cubic centimeter. The unit in which the Curie constant is expressed is, therefore,

$$\text{Unit of } C_C = \frac{\text{erg}}{\text{erg/cm}^3} \text{ deg} = \text{cm}^3 \cdot \text{deg}.$$

Since the Curie constant depends upon the amount of material, its unit may be taken to be any one of the four listed in the accompanying table:

Units of the Curie Constant

Total	Per mole	Per g	Per cm³
$\text{cm}^3 \cdot \text{deg}$	$\dfrac{\text{cm}^3 \cdot \text{deg}}{\text{mole}}$	$\dfrac{\text{cm}^3 \cdot \text{deg}}{\text{g}}$	deg

Paramagnetic solids are of particular interest in thermodynamics. It will be seen later how these are used to obtain extremely low temperatures.

2-12   Intensive and Extensive Quantities

Imagine a system in equilibrium to be divided into two equal parts, each with equal mass. Those properties of each half of the system which remain the same are said to be *intensive;* those which are halved are called *extensive.* The intensive coordinates of a system, such as temperature and pressure, are independent of the mass; the extensive coordinates are proportional to the mass. The thermodynamic coordinates that have been introduced in this chapter are listed in Table 2-3. The student should notice that four of the five intensive quantities listed in the table are denoted by script capital letters, whereas all the extensive quantities are represented by italic capital letters.

Table 2-3   Intensive and Extensive Quantities

Simple systems	Intensive coordinate		Extensive coordinate	
Hydrostatic system	Pressure	P	Volume	V
Stretched wire	Tension	$\mathcal{F}$	Length	L
Surface film	Surface tension	$\mathcal{S}$	Area	A
Electric cell	Emf	$\mathcal{E}$	Charge	Z
Paramagnetic solid	Magnetic intensity	$\mathcal{H}$	Magnetization	M

PROBLEMS

Bulk modulus

2-1   The equation of state of an ideal gas is $Pv = R\theta$. Show that (a) $\beta = 1/\theta$, and (b) $\kappa = 1/P$.

2-2   An approximate equation of state of a real gas at moderate pressures, devised to take into account the finite size of the molecules, is $P(v - b) = R\theta$, where R and b are constants. Show that

(a)
$$\beta = \frac{1/\theta}{1 + bP/R\theta},$$

(b)
$$\kappa = \frac{1/P}{1 + bP/R\theta}.$$

2-3   An approximate equation of state of a real gas at moderate pressures is given by $Pv = R\theta(1 + B/v)$, where R is a constant and B is a function of θ only. Show that

(a)
$$\beta = \frac{1}{\theta} \cdot \frac{v + B + \theta(dB/d\theta)}{v + 2B},$$

(b)
$$\kappa = \frac{1}{P} \cdot \frac{1}{1 + BR\theta/Pv^2}.$$

2-4   A metal whose volume expansivity is 5.0×10^{-5} deg^{-1} and isothermal compressibility is 1.2×10^{-6} atm^{-1} is at a pressure of 1 atm and a temperature of 20°C. A thick surrounding cover of invar, of negligible expansivity and compressibility, fits it very snugly.

(a)   What will be the final pressure if the temperature is raised to 32°C?

(b)   If the surrounding cover can withstand a maximum pressure of

1200 atm, what is the highest temperature to which the system may be raised?

2-5   A block of the same metal as in Prob. 2-4 at a pressure of 1 atm, a volume of 5 liters, and a temperature of 20°C undergoes a temperature rise of 12 deg and an increase in volume of 0.5 cm³. Calculate the final pressure.

2-6

(a)   Express the volume expansivity and the isothermal compressibility in terms of the density ρ and its partial derivatives.

(b)   Derive the equation

$$\frac{dV}{V} = \beta \, d\theta - \kappa \, dP.$$

2-7   The thermal expansivity and the compressibility of liquid oxygen are given in the accompanying table. Draw a graph showing how $(\partial P/\partial \theta)_V$ depends on the temperature.

θ, °K	60	65	70	75	80	85	90
β, 10^{-3} deg^{-1}	3.48	3.60	3.75	3.90	4.07	4.33	4.60
κ, 10^{-4} atm^{-1}	0.95	1.06	1.20	1.35	1.54	1.78	2.06

2-8   The thermal expansivity and the compressibility of water are given in the accompanying table. Draw a graph showing how $(\partial P/\partial \theta)_V$ depends on the temperature. If water were kept at constant volume and the temperature were continually raised, would the pressure increase indefinitely?

t, °C	0	50	100	150	200	250	300
β, 10^{-3} deg^{-1}	0	0.45	0.74	1.02	1.35	1.80	2.90
κ, 10^{-4} atm^{-1}	0.45	0.45	0.50	0.62	0.85	1.50	3.05

2-9   At the critical point $(\partial P/\partial V)_T = 0$. Show that, at the critical point, both the volume expansivity and the isothermal compressibility are infinite.

2-10   If a wire undergoes an infinitesimal change from an initial equilibrium state to a final equilibrium state, show that the change of tension is equal to

$$d\mathcal{F} = -\alpha A Y \, d\theta + \frac{AY}{L} \, dL.$$

2-11   A metal wire of cross-sectional area 0.0085 cm² under a tension of 2×10^6 dyn and at a temperature of 20°C is stretched between two rigid supports 1.2 m apart. If the temperature is reduced to 8°C, what is the final tension? (Assume that α and Y remain constant at the values 1.5×10^{-5} deg⁻¹ and 2.0×10^{12} dyn/cm², respectively.)

2-12   The fundamental frequency of vibration of a wire of length L, mass m, and tension $\mathcal{F}$ is given by

$$f_1 = \frac{1}{2L} \sqrt{\frac{\mathcal{F}L}{m}}.$$

With what frequency will the wire in Prob. 2-11 vibrate at 20°C; at 8°C? (The density of the wire is 9.0 g/cm³.)

2-13   If, in addition to the conditions mentioned in Prob. 2-11, the supports approach each other by 0.012 cm, what will be the final tension?

2-14   The equation of state of an ideal elastic substance is

$$\mathcal{F} = K\theta \left(\frac{L}{L_0} - \frac{L_0^2}{L^2} \right),$$

where K is a constant and L_0 (the value of L at zero tension) is a function of the temperature only.

(a)   Show that the isothermal Young's modulus is given by

$$Y = \frac{K\theta}{A} \left(\frac{L}{L_0} + \frac{2L_0^2}{L^2} \right).$$

(b)   Show that the isothermal Young's modulus at zero tension is given by

$$Y_0 = \frac{3K\theta}{A}.$$

(c)   Show that the linear expansivity is given by

$$\alpha = \alpha_0 - \frac{\mathcal{F}}{AY\theta} = \alpha_0 - \frac{1}{\theta} \cdot \frac{L^3/L_0^3 - 1}{L^3/L_0^3 + 2},$$

where α_0 is the value of the linear expansivity at zero tension, or

$$\alpha_0 = \frac{1}{L_0} \frac{dL_0}{d\theta}.$$

(d) Assume the following values for a certain sample of rubber: $\theta = 300°\text{K}$, $K = 1.33 \times 10^3$ dyn/deg, $A = 1$ mm^2, $\alpha_0 = 5 \times 10^{-4}$ deg^{-1}. Calculate $\mathcal{F}$, Y, and α for the following values of L/L_0: 0.5, 1.0, 1.5, 2.0. Show graphically how $\mathcal{F}$, Y, and α depend on the ratio L/L_0.

2-15   The equation of state of an ideal paramagnetic material valid for all values of the ratio $\mathcal{H}/\theta$ is given by Brillouin's equation, as follows:

$$M = Ng\mu_B \left[(J + \tfrac{1}{2}) \coth (J + \tfrac{1}{2}) \frac{g\mu_B \mathcal{H}}{k\theta} - \tfrac{1}{2} \coth \tfrac{1}{2} \frac{g\mu_B \mathcal{H}}{k\theta} \right]$$

where N, g, μ_B, J, and k are atomic constants.

(a) Find out how the hyperbolic cotangent of x behaves as x approaches zero.

(b) Show that Brillouin's equation reduces to Curie's equation when $\mathcal{H}/\theta$ approaches zero.

(c) Show that the Curie constant is given by

$$C_C = \frac{Ng^2 J(J + 1)\mu_B^2}{3k}.$$

3.

WORK

3-1 Work

If a system undergoes a displacement under the action of a force, *work* is said to be done, the amount of work being equal to the product of the force and the component of the displacement parallel to the force. If a system as a *whole* exerts a force on its surroundings and a displacement takes place, the work that is done either by or on the system is called *external work*. Thus, a gas, confined in a cylinder and at uniform pressure, while expanding and imparting motion to a piston does external work on its surroundings. The work done, however, by part of a system on another part is called *internal work*. The interactions of molecules or electrons on one another constitute internal work.

Internal work has no place in thermodynamics. Only the work that involves an interaction between a system and its surroundings is significant. When a system does external work, the changes that take place can be described by means of macroscopic quantities referring to the system as a whole, in which case the changes may be imagined to accompany the raising or lowering of a suspended body, the winding or unwinding of a spring, or, in general, the alteration of the position or configuration of some external mechanical device. This may be regarded as the ultimate criterion as to whether external work is done or not. It will often be found convenient throughout the remainder of this book to describe the performance of external work in terms of or in conjunction with the operation of a mechanical device such as a system of suspended weights. *Unless otherwise indicated, the word work, unmodified by any adjective, will mean external work.*

A few examples will be found helpful. If an electric cell is on open circuit, changes that take place in the cell (such as diffusion) are not accompanied by the performance of work. If, however, the cell is connected to an external circuit through which electricity is transferred, the current may be imagined to produce rotation of the armature of a motor, thereby lifting a weight or winding a spring. Therefore, *for an electric cell to do work it must be connected to an external circuit.* As another example, consider a magnet far removed from any external electric conductor. A change of magnetization within the magnet is not accompanied by the performance of work. If, however, the magnet undergoes a change of magnetization while it is surrounded by an electric conductor, eddy currents are set up in the conductor, constituting an external transfer of electricity. Hence, *for a magnetic system to do work it must interact with an electric conductor or with other magnets.*

In mechanics, we are concerned with the behavior of systems acted on by external forces. When the resultant force exerted *on* a mechanical system is in the same direction as the displacement of the system, the work of the force is positive, work is said to be done on the system, and the energy of the system increases.

In thermodynamics, however, we focus our attention on the resultant force exerted *by the system on its surroundings.* When this force is in the *same* direction as the displacement, work is done *by* the system, and the convention is to call this work *positive.* Conversely, when the force exerted by a system on its surroundings is *opposite* to the displacement, work is done *on* the system, and this work is called *negative.*

3-2   Quasi-static Process

A system in thermodynamic equilibrium satisfies the following stringent requirements:

1   *Mechanical equilibrium.*   There are no unbalanced forces acting on any part of the system or on the system as a whole.
2   *Thermal equilibrium.*   There are no temperature differences between parts of the system or between the system and its surroundings.
3   *Chemical equilibrium.*   There are no chemical reactions within the system and no motion of any chemical constituent from one part of a system to another part.

Once a system is in thermodynamic equilibrium and the surroundings are kept unchanged, no motion will take place and no work will be done. If, however, the sum of the external forces is changed so that there is a finite unbalanced force acting on the system, then the condition for mechanical equilibrium is no longer satisfied and the following situations may arise:

1   Unbalanced forces may be created within the system; as a result, turbulence, waves, etc., may be set up. Also, the system as a whole may execute some sort of accelerated motion.

2   As a result of this turbulence, acceleration, etc., a nonuniform temperature distribution may be brought about, as well as a finite difference of temperature between the system and its surroundings.

3   The sudden change in the forces and in the temperature may produce a chemical reaction or the motion of a chemical constituent.

It follows that a finite unbalanced force may cause the system to pass through nonequilibrium states. If it is desired during a process to describe every state of a system by means of thermodynamic coordinates referring to the system as a whole, the process must *not* be brought about by a finite unbalanced force. We are led, therefore, to conceive of an ideal situation in which the external forces acting on a system are varied only slightly so that the unbalanced force is infinitesimal. A process performed in this ideal way is said to be *quasi-static*. *During a quasi-static process, the system is at all times infinitesimally near a state of thermodynamic equilibrium*, and all the states through which the system passes can be described by means of thermodynamic coordinates referring to the system as a whole. An equation of state is valid, therefore, for all these states. A quasi-static process is an idealization that is applicable to all thermodynamic systems, including electric and magnetic systems. The conditions for such a process can never be rigorously satisfied in the laboratory, but they can be approached with almost any degree of accuracy. In the next few articles it will be seen how approximately quasi-static processes may be performed by all the systems treated in Chap. 2.

3-3   Work of a Hydrostatic System

Imagine any hydrostatic system contained in a cylinder equipped with a movable piston on which the system and the surroundings may act. Suppose that the cylinder has a cross-sectional area A, that the pressure exerted *by the system* at the piston face is P, and that the force is PA. The surroundings also exert an opposing force on the piston. The origin of this opposing force is irrelevant; it might be due to friction or a combination of friction and the push of a spring. The system within the cylinder does not have to know how the opposing force originated. The important condition that must be satisfied is that the opposing force must differ only slightly from the force PA. If, under these conditions, the piston moves a distance dx, the system performs an infinitesimal amount of work dW (the differential symbol with the line drawn through it will be explained later), where

$$dW = PA\,dx.$$

But

$$A\,dx = dV,$$

and hence

$$\boxed{dW = P\,dV.} \qquad (3\text{-}1)$$

During this process, we might have a chemical reaction or a transport of a component from one point to another taking place slowly enough to keep the system near mechanical equilibrium; or we might have some dissipative process such as friction taking place—or even all these processes. The lack of chemical equilibrium (and therefore of complete thermodynamic equilibrium) and the presence of dissipation *do not preclude* writing $dW = P\,dV$. A lack of mechanical equilibrium, however, such as exists when there is no opposing force, definitely precludes expressing dW as $P\,dV$.

The expansion or contraction of a hydrostatic system need not necessarily take place in a cylinder. In Fig. 3-1, the system has any arbitrary boundary and expands quasi-statically to another boundary, as represented by the dashed curve. Any small element of area ΔA is acted on by a force $P\,\Delta A$ and undergoes a displacement ds in a direction normal to ΔA. The work of $P\,\Delta A$ is therefore $P\,\Delta A\,ds$, and thus the total work done by the system is

$$dW = P\Sigma\,\Delta A\,ds = P\,dV.$$

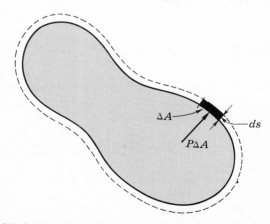

Fig. 3-1   *Work of the infinitesimal hydrostatic force $P\,\Delta A$ is $P\,\Delta A\,ds$. Work over the entire surface is $P\Sigma\,\Delta A\,ds = P\,dV$.*

In a *finite* quasi-static process in which the volume changes from V_i to V_f, the work is

$$W = \int_{V_i}^{V_f} P\,dV. \tag{3-2}$$

Since the change in volume is performed quasi-statically, P is at all times a thermodynamic coordinate and can be expressed as a function of θ and V by means of an equation of state. The evaluation of the integral can be accomplished once the behavior of θ is specified, because then P can be expressed as a function of V only. If P is expressed as a function of V, the *path* of integration is defined. Along a particular quasi-static path, the work done by a system in going from a volume V_i to a larger volume V_f is expressed as

$$W_{if} = \int_{V_i}^{V_f} P\,dV;$$

whereas from f to i, along the same path but in the opposite direction, the work absorbed by the system is

$$W_{fi} = \int_{V_f}^{V_i} P\,dV.$$

When the path is quasi-static,

$$W_{if} = -W_{fi}.$$

Sufficient approximation to a quasi-static process may be achieved in practice by having the external pressure differ from that exerted by the system by only a small finite amount.

The mks unit of P is 1 N/m² and that of V is 1 m³. The mks unit of work is therefore 1 J. It is often convenient to take 1 atm as a unit of P and 1 liter as a unit of V. The unit of work is then 1 liter · atm, which is equal to 101 J.

3-4   *PV* **Diagram**

As the volume of a chemical system changes by virtue of the motion of a piston in a cylinder, the position of the piston at any moment is proportional to the volume. A pen whose motion along the X axis of a diagram follows exactly the motion of the piston will trace out a line every point of which represents an instantaneous value of the volume. If, at the same time, this pen is given a motion along the Y axis such that the Y coordinate is proportional to the pressure, then the pressure and volume changes of the system during expansion or compression are indicated simultaneously on the same diagram. Such a device is called an *indicator*. The diagram in which pressure is plotted along the Y axis and volume along the X axis is called an *indicator diagram* or *PV diagram*.

In Fig. 3-2a, the pressure and volume changes of a gas during expansion are indicated by curve I. The $\int P\, dV$ for this process is evidently the shaded area under curve I. Similarly, for a compression, the work absorbed by the gas is represented by the shaded area under curve II in Fig. 3-2b. In conformity with the sign convention for work, the area under I is regarded as positive, and that under II as negative. In Fig. 3-2c, curves I and II are drawn together so that they constitute a series of processes whereby the gas is brought back to its initial state. Such a series of processes, represented by a closed figure, is called a *cycle*. The area within the closed figure is obviously the difference between the areas under curves I and II and therefore represents the *net* work done in the cycle. It should be noticed that the cycle is traversed in a direction such that the net work is positive. If the direction were reversed, the net work would be negative.

3-5   Work Depends on the Path

On the *PV* diagram depicted in Fig. 3-3, an initial equilibrium state and a final equilibrium state of a chemical system are represented by the two points i and f, respectively. There are many ways in which the system may be taken from i to f. For example, the pressure may be kept constant from i to a (*isobaric process*) and then the volume kept constant from a to f (*isochoric process*), in which case the work done is equal to the area under the line ia, which is equal to $2P_0V_0$. Another possibility is the path ibf, in which case

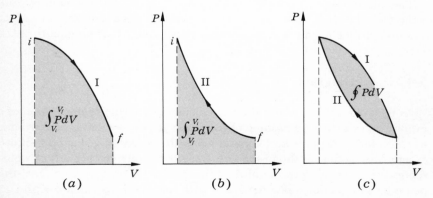

Fig. 3-2   *PV diagram. (a) Curve I, expansion; (b) curve II, compression; (c) curves I and II together constitute a cycle.*

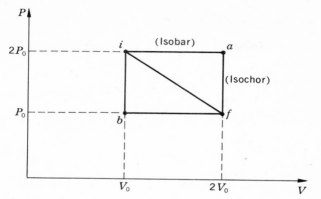

Fig. 3-3 *Work depends on the path.*

the work is the area under the line *bf*, or P_0V_0. The straight line from *i* to *f* represents another path, where the work is $\frac{3}{2}P_0V_0$. We can see, therefore, that the *work done by a system depends not only on the initial and final states but also on the intermediate states, i.e., on the path.* This is merely another way of saying that, for a quasi-static process, the expression

$$W = \int_{V_i}^{V_f} P \, dV$$

cannot be integrated until P is specified as a function of V.

The expression $P \, dV$ is an infinitesimal amount of work and has been represented by the symbol dW. There is, however, an important distinction between an infinitesimal amount of work and the other infinitesimals we have considered up to now. An infinitesimal amount of work is an *inexact differential;* i.e., it is *not* the differential of an actual function of the thermo-dynamic coordinates. There is no function of the thermodynamic coordinates representing the work in a body. The phrase "work in a body" has no meaning. To indicate that an infinitesimal amount of work is *not* a mathe-matical differential of a function W and to emphasize at all times that it is an inexact differential, a line is drawn through the differential sign thus: dW.

3-6 Work in Quasi-static Processes

The preceding ideas will be clarified by the following examples:

Quasi-static isothermal expansion or compression of an ideal gas

$$W = \int_{V_i}^{V_f} P \, dV,$$

but an ideal gas is one whose equation of state is

$$PV = nR\theta$$

where n and R are constants. Substituting for P, we get

$$W = \int_{V_i}^{V_f} \frac{nR\theta}{V} \, dV$$

and, since θ is also constant,

$$W = nR\theta \int_{V_i}^{V_f} \frac{dV}{V}$$

$$= nR\theta \ln \frac{V_f}{V_i},$$

where the symbol ln denotes the natural, or napierian, logarithm. In terms of the common logarithm, denoted by log,

$$W = 2.30nR\theta \log \frac{V_f}{V_i}.$$

If there are 2 g moles of gas kept at a constant temperature of 0°C and if this gas is compressed from a volume of 4 liters to 1 liter, then $n = 2$ moles, $R = 8.31$ J/g mole · deg, $\theta = 273$ deg (using three significant figures), $V_i = 4$ liters, $V_f = 1$ liter, and

$$W = 2.30 \times 2 \text{ moles} \times 8.31 \frac{\text{J}}{\text{mole} \cdot \text{deg}} \times 273 \text{ deg} \times \log \frac{1}{4}$$

$$= -6300 \text{ J}$$

(the minus sign indicating that work was done *on* the gas).

Quasi-static isothermal increase of pressure on a solid   Suppose the pressure on 10^{-2} kg of solid copper is increased quasi-statically and isothermally at 0°C from 0 to 1000 atm. The work is calculated as follows:

$$W = \int P \, dV,$$

$$dV = \left(\frac{\partial V}{\partial P} \right)_\theta dP + \left(\frac{\partial V}{\partial \theta} \right)_P d\theta.$$

Since the isothermal compressibility is

$$\kappa = -\frac{1}{V}\left(\frac{\partial V}{\partial P}\right)_\theta,$$

we have, at constant temperature,

$$dV = -\kappa V \, dP.$$

Substituting for dV,

$$W = -\int_{P_i}^{P_f} \kappa V P \, dP.$$

Now the changes in V and κ at constant temperature are so small that they may be neglected. Hence,

$$W \approx -\frac{\kappa V}{2}(P_f^2 - P_i^2).$$

Since the volume is equal to the mass m divided by the density ρ,

$$W \approx -\frac{m\kappa}{2\rho}(P_f^2 - P_i^2).$$

For copper at 0°C, $\rho = 8.93$ g/cm², $\kappa = 0.725 \times 10^{-6}$ atm⁻¹, $m = 10$ g, $P_i = 0$, and $P_f = 1000$ atm $= 1.01 \times 10^9$ dyn/cm². Hence,

$$W = -\frac{10 \text{ g} \times 0.725 \times 10^{-6} \text{ atm}^{-1} \times 10^6 \text{ atm}^2}{2 \times 8.93 \text{ g/cm}^3}$$

$$= -\frac{7.25}{17.8} \text{ cm}^3 \cdot \text{atm} = -0.407 \times 10^{-3} \text{ liter} \cdot \text{atm}.$$

Since 1 liter · atm = 101 J,

$$W = -0.0411 \text{ J},$$

where the minus sign indicates that work was done on the copper. This result, together with that of the first example, indicates that when a gas is compressed we can usually neglect the work done on the material of the container.

3-7   Work of a Wire, a Surface Film, and a Reversible Cell

If the length of a wire in which there is a tension $\mathcal{F}$ is changed from L to $(L + dL)$, the infinitesimal amount of work that is done is equal to

$$dW = -\mathcal{F}\,dL. \qquad (3\text{-}3)$$

The minus sign is used because a positive value of dL means an extension of the wire, for which work must be done *on* the wire, i.e., negative work. For a finite change of length from L_i to L_f,

$$W = -\int_{L_i}^{L_f} \mathcal{F}\,dL,$$

where $\mathcal{F}$ indicates the instantaneous value of the tension at any moment during the process. If the wire is undergoing a motion involving large unbalanced forces, the integral cannot be evaluated in terms of thermodynamic coordinates referring to the wire as a whole. If, however, the external force is maintained at all times only slightly different from the tension, the process is sufficiently quasi-static to warrant the use of an equation of state, in which case the integration can be carried out once $\mathcal{F}$ is known as a function of L. When $\mathcal{F}$ is measured in newtons and L in meters, W will be in joules.

Consider a double surface film with liquid in between, stretched across a wire framework, one side of which is movable, as shown in Fig. 3-4. If the movable wire has a length L and the surface tension is $\mathcal{S}$, the force exerted by both films is $2\mathcal{S}L$. For an infinitesimal displacement dx, the work is

$$dW = -2\mathcal{S}L\,dx;$$

but

$$2L\,dx = dA.$$

Hence

$$dW = -\mathcal{S}\,dA. \qquad (3\text{-}4)$$

(Why the minus sign?) For a finite change from A_i to A_f,

$$W = -\int_{A_i}^{A_f} \mathcal{S}\,dA.$$

A quasi-static process may be approximated by maintaining the external force at all times only slightly different from that exerted by the film.

The conventional description of an electric current is that it is the motion of positive electricity from a region of higher to a region of lower potential. Although this is opposite to the direction of electron drift, the convention is still used, and it is convenient to adopt it in thermodynamics. Imagine a

$$L \qquad \mathscr{S}L\{$$

$$dx$$

Fig. 3-4   *Surface film stretched across a wire framework.*

reversible cell of emf $\mathscr{E}$ to be connected to a potentiometer so that an almost continuous variation of potential difference may be obtained with a sliding contactor. The circuit is shown in Fig. 3-5. The external potential difference may be made equal to, slightly less, or slightly more than $\mathscr{E}$ by sliding the contactor.

If the external potential difference is made infinitesimally smaller than $\mathscr{E}$, then, during the short time this difference exists, there is a transfer of a quantity of electricity dZ through the external circuit in a direction from the positive to the negative electrode. In this case, work is done by the cell on the outside. If the external potential difference is made slightly larger than $\mathscr{E}$, electricity is transferred in the opposite direction and work is done on the cell. In either case, the amount of work is

$$\boxed{dW = -\mathscr{E}\, dZ.} \tag{3-5}$$

$$\mathcal{O} = \frac{W}{A}$$

$$A\,\mathcal{O} = F \times \Delta x$$

$$\frac{2\ell\,\Delta x\,\mathcal{O}}{A\,x} = F$$

$$2\ell\mathcal{O} = F$$

Potentiometer

G

$\mathscr{E}$

Cu   Zn

$CuSO_4$ $ZnSO_4$

Fig. 3-5   *Approximately quasi-static transfer of electricity in a reversible cell.*

When the cell is discharging through the external circuit, dZ is negative; i.e., there is a quantity Z connected with the *state of charge* of the cell which decreases by an amount dZ, where dZ is the actual quantity of electricity transferred. Charging the cell involves an increase in Z or a positive dZ.

If Z changes by a finite amount,

$$W = - \int_{Z_i}^{Z_f} \mathcal{E} \, dZ.$$

If the current is i, then in time $d\tau$ the quantity $dZ = i \, d\tau$, and

$$W = - \int_{i}^{f} \mathcal{E} i \, d\tau.$$

With $\mathcal{E}$ in volts and the charge in coulombs, the work will be expressed in joules.

3-8   Work in Changing the Magnetization of a Magnetic Solid

Consider a sample of magnetic material in the form of a ring of cross-sectional area A and of mean circumference L. Suppose an insulated wire is wound on top of the sample, forming a toroidal winding of N closely spaced turns, as shown in Fig. 3-6. A current may be maintained in the winding by a battery, and by moving the sliding contactor of a rheostat this current may be changed.

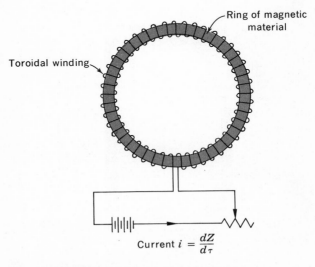

Current $i = \dfrac{dZ}{d\tau}$

Fig. 3-6   *Changing the magnetization of a magnetic solid.*

The effect of a current in the winding is to set up a magnetic field with magnetic induction $\mathcal{B}$. If the dimensions are as shown in the figure, $\mathcal{B}$ will be nearly uniform over the cross-section of the toroid. Suppose that the current is changed and that in time $d\tau$ the magnetic induction changes by an amount $d\mathcal{B}$. Then, by Faraday's principle of electromagnetic induction, there is induced in the winding a back emf $\mathcal{E}$, where

$$\mathcal{E} = -NA\frac{d\mathcal{B}}{d\tau}.$$

During the time interval $d\tau$, a quantity of electricity dZ is transferred in the circuit, and the work done by the system to maintain the current is calculated as

$$dW = \mathcal{E}\,dZ$$

$$= -NA\frac{d\mathcal{B}}{d\tau}\,dZ$$

$$= -NA\frac{dZ}{d\tau}\,d\mathcal{B}$$

$$= -NAi\,d\mathcal{B},$$

where i, equal to $dZ/d\tau$, is the momentary value of the current.

The magnetic intensity $\mathcal{H}$ due to a current i in a toroidal winding is given by

$$\mathcal{H} = \frac{4\pi Ni}{L} = \frac{4\pi NAi}{AL} = \frac{4\pi NAi}{V},$$

where V is the volume of magnetic material. Therefore,

$$NAi = \frac{V}{4\pi}\mathcal{H},$$

and

$$dW = -\frac{V}{4\pi}\mathcal{H}\,d\mathcal{B}. \tag{3-6}$$

If M is the *total magnetic moment* of the material (assumed to be isotropic), or *total magnetization*, we have the relation

$$\mathcal{B} = \mathcal{H} + 4\pi\frac{M}{V}. \tag{3-7}$$

Therefore,

$$dW = -\frac{V}{4\pi}\mathcal{H}\,d\mathcal{H} - \mathcal{H}\,dM.$$

If no material were present within the toroidal winding, M would be zero, $\mathscr{B}$ would equal $\mathscr{H}$, and

$$dW = -\frac{V}{4\pi}\mathscr{H}\, d\mathscr{H} \qquad \text{(vacuum only)}.$$

This is the work necessary to increase the magnetic field in a volume V *of empty space* by an amount $d\mathscr{H}$. The second term, $-\mathscr{H}\, dM$, is the work done in increasing the magnetization of the material by an amount dM. We shall be concerned in this book with changes of temperature, energy, etc., of the material only, brought about by work done on or by the material. Consequently, for the purpose of this book,

$$\boxed{dW = -\mathscr{H}\, dM.} \qquad (3\text{-}8)$$

The minus sign merely provides that an increase of magnetization (positive dM) involves negative work. If $\mathscr{H}$ is measured in oersteds (dynes per unit pole) and I in pole centimeters, then the work will be expressed in ergs. If the magnetization is caused to change a finite amount from M_i to M_f, the work will be

$$W = -\int_{M_i}^{M_f} \mathscr{H}\, dM.$$

Modern experiments on paramagnetic materials are usually performed on samples in the form of cylinders or ellipsoids, not toroids. In these cases, the $\mathscr{H}$ field inside the material is somewhat smaller than the $\mathscr{H}$ field generated by the electric current in the surrounding winding because of the reverse field (demagnetizing field) set up by magnetic poles which form on the surfaces of the samples. In longitudinal magnetic fields, the demagnetizing effect either may be rendered negligible by using cylinders whose length is much larger than the diameter or may be corrected for in a simple way. In transverse magnetic fields, a correction factor must be applied. We shall limit ourselves to toroids or to long thin cylinders in longitudinal fields where the internal and external $\mathscr{H}$ fields are the same.

In any actual case, a change of magnetization is accomplished very nearly quasi-statically, and therefore an equation of state may be used in the integration of the expression denoting the work.

3-9   Summary

The work values of the various simple systems are summarized in Table 3-1. It should be noted that each expression for work is the product of an intensive and an extensive quantity; consequently, *work is an extensive quantity.*

Table 3-1   Work of Simple Systems

Simple system	Intensive quantity (generalized force)	Extensive quantity (generalized displacement)	Work
Hydrostatic system	P, in atm	V, in liters	$P\,dV$, in liter · atm (1 liter · atm = 101 J)
Wire	$\mathscr{F}$, in N	L, in m	$-\mathscr{F}\,dL$, in J
Surface film	$\mathscr{S}$, in dyn/cm	A, in cm²	$-\mathscr{S}\,dA$, in ergs (10^7 ergs = 1 J)
Reversible cell	$\mathscr{E}$, in V	Z, in C	$-\mathscr{E}\,dZ$, in J
Magnetic solid	$\mathscr{H}$, in Oe	M, in pole · cm	$-\mathscr{H}\,dM$, in ergs

We have seen that a work diagram is obtained if any one of the intensive coordinates is plotted against its corresponding extensive coordinate. There are therefore as many work diagrams as there are systems. It is desirable at times, for the sake of argument, to formulate a work diagram which does not refer to one system in particular but which represents the behavior of any system. If we designate the intensive quantities P, $\mathscr{F}$, $\mathscr{S}$, $\mathscr{E}$, and $\mathscr{H}$ as *generalized forces* and their corresponding extensive quantities V, L, A, Z, and M as *generalized displacements*, we may represent the work done by any simple system on a *generalized work diagram* by plotting the generalized force Y against the generalized displacement X. Conclusions based on such a diagram will hold for any simple system.

3-10   Compound Systems

Up to this point we have dealt exclusively with simple systems, whose equilibrium states are described with the aid of three thermodynamic coordinates, one of which is always the temperature. A single equation of

Fig. 3-7   (a) *A composite system whose coordinates are P, V, P', V', and θ. (b) A graph of the independent coordinates θ, V, and V'.*

state was found to exist in each case, so that only two of the coordinates are independent. The laws of thermodynamics, however, which are to be developed in the next few chapters, must apply to any system no matter how complicated—i.e., to systems having more than three coordinates and more than one equation of state.

Consider the composite system depicted schematically in Fig. 3-7a with two different simple hydrostatic systems separated by a diathermic wall, which ensures that both parts have the same temperature. There are five thermodynamic coordinates (P, V, P', V', and $θ$) and two equations of state, one for each of the simple systems. Consequently, only three of the five coordinates are independent. In any small displacement of each piston, the work is

$$dW = P\, dV + P'\, dV'.$$

The most convenient diagram to use in demonstrating the features of this system is a three-dimensional diagram with $θ$, V, and V' plotted along rectangular axes, as shown in Fig. 3-7b. A typical isothermal process would be a curve on a plane such as the one marked $θ =$ const. A curve on a plane such as that marked $V =$ const. would represent a process in which no work is done by the left-hand part. The points a and b lie on a vertical line every point of which refers to a constant V and V'. The straight line ab therefore represents a process in which no work is done by the composite system.

Two simple systems do not have to be separated spatially by a diathermic wall in order to have two equations of state and a common temperature.

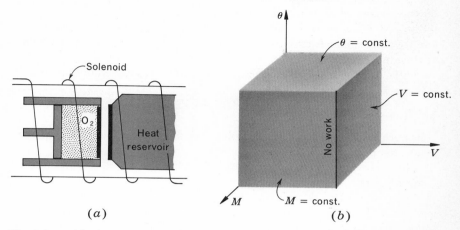

Fig. 3-8   (a) *A composite system whose coordinates are P, V, $\mathscr{H}$, M, and θ. (b) A graph of the independent coordinates θ, V, and M.*

Consider an ideal paramagnetic gas, such as oxygen at low pressures, as depicted schematically in Fig. 3-8a. The oxygen may have its pressure P and volume V varied with the aid of a piston-cylinder combination, and it is immersed in a magnetic field whose intensity $\mathscr{H}$ may be varied by varying the current in the surrounding solenoid. The gas is kept at a uniform temperature θ. The coordinates are P, V, $\mathscr{H}$, M, and θ, only three of which are independent because of the two equations of state: the ideal-gas equation $PV = nR\theta$ and Curie's equation $M/\mathscr{H} = C/\theta$. Since the work done in any infinitesimal process is

$$dW = P\,dV - \mathscr{H}\,dM,$$

the most convenient independent coordinates are θ, V, and M, which are plotted along rectangular axes in Fig. 3-8b. Any vertical line would represent a process in which no work is done.

Later on, we shall have occasion to refer to a general five-coordinate system whose coordinates are Y, X, Y', X', and θ and whose work is

$$dW = Y\,dX + Y'\,dX'.$$

The most convenient independent coordinates of this system are θ, X, and X'.

PROBLEMS

3-1   A thin-walled metal bomb of volume V_B contains a gas at high pressure. Connected to the bomb is a capillary tube and stopcock. When the stopcock is opened slightly, the gas leaks slowly into a cylinder equipped with a nonleaking, frictionless piston where the pressure remains constant at the atmospheric value P_0.

(a)   Show that, after as much gas as possible has leaked out, an amount of work

$$W = P_0(V_0 - V_B)$$

has been done, where V_0 is the volume of the gas at atmospheric pressure and temperature.

(b)   How much work would be done if the gas leaked directly into the atmosphere?

3-2   Calculate the work done by 1 mole of gas during a quasi-static, isothermal expansion from an initial volume v_i to a final volume v_f when the equation of state is:

(a) $P(v - b) = R\theta$ $(R, b = \text{const.})$.

(b) $Pv = R\theta \left(1 - \dfrac{B}{v}\right)$ $[R = \text{const.}; B = f(\theta)]$.

3-3   During a quasi-static adiabatic expansion of an ideal gas, the pressure at any moment is given by the equation

$$PV^\gamma = K,$$

where γ and K are constants. Show that the work done in expanding from a state (P_i, V_i) to a state (P_f, V_f) is

$$W = \frac{P_i V_i - P_f V_f}{\gamma - 1}.$$

If the initial pressure and volume are 10 atm and 1 liter, respectively, and the final values are 2 atm and 3.16 liters, how many joules of work are done by a gas whose $\gamma = 1.4$? (1 liter · atm of work = 101 J.)

3-4   A vertical cylinder, closed at the bottom, is placed on a spring scale. The cylinder contains a gas whose volume may be changed with the aid of a frictionless, nonleaking piston. The piston is pushed down.

(a)   How much work is done by an outside agent in compressing the gas an amount dV while the spring scale goes down a distance dy?

(*b*)   If this device is used only to produce effects in the gas—or, in other words, if the gas is the system—what expression for work is appropriate?

3-5   A stationary vertical cylinder, closed at the top, contains a gas whose volume may be changed with the aid of a heavy, frictionless, non-leaking piston of weight w.

(*a*)   How much work is done by an outside agent in compressing the gas an amount dV by raising the piston a distance dy?

(*b*)   If this device is used only to produce temperature changes of the gas, what expression for work would be appropriate?

(*c*)   Compare this situation with that of Prob. 3-4, and also with that involved in increasing the magnetic induction of a ring of magnetic material.

3-6   The pressure on 100 g of metal is increased quasi-statically and isothermally from 0 to 1000 atm. Assuming the density and the isothermal compressibility to remain constant at the values 10 g/cm³ and 0.675 × 10^{-6} atm⁻¹, respectively, calculate the work in joules.

3-7

(*a*)   The tension in a wire is increased quasi-statically and isothermally from $\mathcal{F}_i$ to $\mathcal{F}_f$. If the length, cross-sectional area, and isothermal Young's modulus of the wire remain practically constant, show that the work done is

$$W = - \frac{L}{2AY} (\mathcal{F}_f^2 - \mathcal{F}_i^2).$$

(*b*)   The tension in a metal wire 1 m long and 1.0 × 10^{-7} m² in area is increased quasi-statically and isothermally at 0°C from 10 to 100 N. How many joules of work are done? (Isothermal Young's modulus at 0°C is 2.5 × 10^{11} N/m².)

3-8   The equation of state of an ideal elastic substance is

$$\mathcal{F} = K\theta \left(\frac{L}{L_0} - \frac{L_0^2}{L^2} \right),$$

where K is a constant and L_0 (the value of L at zero tension) is a function of temperature only. Calculate the work necessary to compress the substance from $L = L_0$ to $L = L_0/2$ quasi-statically and isothermally.

3-9   Prove that the work done during a quasi-static isothermal change of state of a paramagnetic substance obeying Curie's equation is given by

$$W = \frac{\theta}{2C} (M_i^2 - M_f^2)$$

$$= \frac{C}{2\theta} (\mathcal{H}_i^2 - \mathcal{H}_f^2).$$

3-10   Show that the magnetic energy per unit volume in empty space is $\mathcal{H}^2/8\pi$.

3-11   A volume of 200 cm³ of a paramagnetic substance is maintained at constant temperature. A magnetic field is increased quasi-statically and isothermally from 0 to 15,000 Oe. Assuming Curie's equation to hold and the Curie constant per unit volume to be 0.15 deg:

(a)   How much work would have to be done if no material were present?

(b)   How much work is done to change the magnetization of the material when the temperature is 300°K and when it is 1°K?

(c)   How much work is done at both temperatures by the agent supplying the magnetic field?

3-12   A chamber with rigid walls consists of two compartments, one containing a gas and the other evacuated; the partition between the two compartments is destroyed suddenly. Is the work done during any infinitesimal portion of this process (called a *free expansion*) equal to $P\,dV$? Explain.

3-13   A reversible cell consists of an electrolyte, one solid electrode, and one electrode involving gaseous hydrogen.

(a)   What coordinates are needed to describe the equilibrium states of this system?

(b)   How many equations of state are there? What are typical examples of these equations?

(c)   What is the expression for dW?

(d)   Choose convenient independent coordinates.

3-14   A framework such as that shown in Fig. 3-4 is placed in a vessel where the air pressure may be varied at will. Consider the two surface films *and* the liquid between the films as the system.

(a)   What coordinates are needed?

(b)   How many equations of state are there?

(c)   What is the expression for dW?

(d)   Choose convenient independent coordinates.

3-15   Devise a system consisting of an ideal nonmagnetic gas, a paramagnetic solid, and a reversible cell, all separated by diathermic walls. Draw a diagram.

(a)   What are the coordinates?

(b)   How many equations of state are there?

(c)   What is the expression for dW?

(d)   Choose convenient independent coordinates.

4.

HEAT AND THE FIRST LAW

4-1 Work and Heat

It was shown in Chap. 3 how a system could be transferred from an initial to a final state by means of a quasi-static process and how the work done during the process could be calculated. There are, however, other means of changing the state of a system that do not necessarily involve the performance of work. Consider for example the three processes depicted schematically in Fig. 4-1. In (*a*) a fluid undergoes an adiabatic expansion in a cylinder-piston combination that is coupled to the surroundings with a suspended body so that, as the expansion takes place, the body is lifted while the fluid remains always close to equilibrium.† In (*b*), a liquid in equilibrium with its vapor is in contact through a diathermic wall with the hot combustion products of a bunsen burner and undergoes vaporization, accompanied by a rise of temperature and of pressure, without the performance of work. In (*c*) a fluid is expanded while in contact with the flame of a bunsen burner.

What happens when two systems at different temperatures are placed together is one of the most familiar experiences of mankind. It is well known that the final temperature reached by both systems is intermediate between the two starting temperatures. Up to the beginning of the nineteenth century, such phenomena, which comprise the subject of *calorimetry*, were explained by postulating the existence of a substance or form of matter termed *caloric*, or heat, in every body. It was believed that a body at a high temperature contained much caloric and that one at a low temperature had only a little. When the two bodies were put together, the body rich in caloric lost some to the other, and thus the final temperature was intermediate. Although we now know that heat is not a substance whose total amount remains

† The author is indebted to Professor Ernst Schmidt for the clever coupling device consisting of rack, pinion, and cam.

Fig. 4-1   *Distinction between work and heat. (a) Adiabatic work; (b) heat flow without work; (c) work and heat.*

Fig. 4-2   *Whether a process is designated as a work or a heat interaction depends on the choice of system.*

constant, nevertheless we ascribe the changes that take place in Fig. 4-2*b* and *c* to the transfer of "something" from the body at the higher temperature to the one at the lower, and this something we call *heat*. We therefore adopt as a *calorimetric* definition of heat *that which is transferred between a system and its surroundings by virtue of a temperature difference only.* It is obvious that an adiabatic wall is one which is impervious to heat, or a *heat insulator*, and that a diathermic wall is a *heat conductor*.

It is important to observe that the decision as to whether a particular change of state involves the performance of work or the transfer of heat requires first an unequivocal answer to these questions: What is the system, and what are the surroundings? For example, in Fig. 4-2, a resistor immersed in water carries a current provided by an electric generator that is rotated with the aid of a descending body. If we assume the absence of friction in the shafts of the pulleys and the absence of electrical resistance in the generator and the connecting wires, we have a device whereby the thermodynamic state of a system composed of *water and the resistor* is changed by purely mechanical means, i.e., by the performance of work. If, however, the resistor is regarded as the system and the water as the surroundings, then there is a *transfer of heat from the resistor* by virtue of the temperature difference between the resistor and the water. Also, if a small part of the water is regarded as the system, with the rest of the water being considered the surroundings, then again there is a transfer of heat. Regarding the composite system comprising both the water and the resistor, however, the surroundings do not contain any object whose temperature differs from that of the system, and hence no heat is transferred between *this composite system* and its surroundings.

Electric cell

Fig. 4-3   *Adiabatic work.*

4-2   Adiabatic Work

Figures 4-1*a* and 4-2 show that a system completely surrounded by an adiabatic envelope may still be coupled to the surroundings so that work may be done. Three other simple examples of adiabatic work are shown in Fig. 4-3. It is an important fact of experience that the state of a system may be caused to change from a given initial state to a final state by the performance of adiabatic work *only*.

Consider the composite system shown in Fig. 4-4*a*, consisting of a hydrostatic fluid *and* an immersed resistor on each side of a diathermic wall. This system can undergo an adiabatic work interaction with its surroundings in two ways. It may be done by moving one or both of the pistons in or out, either slowly (a quasi-static process) so that $W = \int P\,dV$, with P being equal to the equilibrium value, or very rapidly (a non-quasi-static process) so that the pressure at the piston face is less than the equilibrium value. If the piston is pulled out at a faster rate than the velocity of the molecules of the fluid, the fluid will do no work on the piston at all. Such a process is called a *free expansion*, and it will be discussed in some detail in the next chapter. To repeat, one way of doing work is by slow or rapid motion, in or out, of either or both of the pistons. Another way in which work may be done on the system is by dissipation of electrical energy in the resistors, in which currents are maintained by generators actuated by the descending bodies. (Exactly the same effects could be produced by the dissipation of mechanical energy in the fluids by irregular churning of the fluids with paddle wheels actuated by the descending bodies.)

As in Chap. 3, the most convenient independent coordinates of this system are θ, the common temperature, and the two volumes V and V'. States i and f of the system, shown on a $\theta V V'$ diagram in Fig. 4-4*b*, are arbitrarily chosen, and it is purely a coincidence that f corresponds to a higher temperature than i. In the path *iaf*, the dashed curve *ia* represents a frictionless, quasi-static adiabatic compression accomplished with one of the pistons. It is

(a)

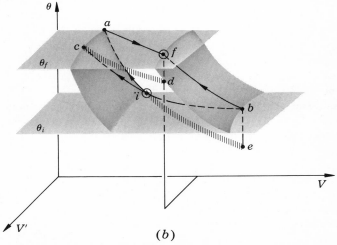

(b)

Fig. 4-4   (a) *A composite system on which adiabatic work may be done in two ways.* (b) *Joining two states i and f by several different adiabatic paths.*

drawn on a surface cutting the two isothermal planes. The existence of such a surface will be proved in a later chapter, but it should be noted at this point that, since *ia* is accomplished only through a frictionless slow motion of the piston, it may be performed in *either* the direction *ia* or *ai*. The curve *af* represents the adiabatic dissipation of electrical energy in conjunction with piston movements that keep the system at constant temperature. In other words, the line *af* represents a process that is *both* adiabatic and iso-thermal! There is, however, an important distinction between this process and the previous one: the process *af* can go in *only one* direction. You can add energy with a current in a resistor, but you cannot extract it.

The path *ibf* represents another adiabatic way of changing the system from *i* to *f*. The curve *ib* represents the dissipation process accomplished with the resistors, and the curve *bf* stands for the quasi-static process achieved with frictionless pistons only. As before, *bf* could go in either direction, but *ib* in only one.

There are, of course, many other adiabatic paths joining *if*, such as *icdf*, in which the process *cd* is a non-quasi-static expansion accomplished by a rapid outward motion of one or both of the pistons, and the process *df* is performed by keeping both pistons motionless and by dissipating electrical energy in either or both of the resistors. Another possible adiabatic path consists of rapid outward motion of the pistons, producing a non-quasi-static expansion *ie*, followed by isochoric dissipation of electric energy *eb*, followed by a quasi-static compression *bf*. Although accurate measurements of adiabatic work along different paths between the same two states have never been made, indirect experiments indicate that the adiabatic work is the same along all such paths. The generalization of this result is known as the *first law of thermodynamics:*

If a system is caused to change from an initial state to a final state by adiabatic means only, the work done is the same for all adiabatic paths connecting the two states.

Whenever a quantity is found to depend only on the initial and final states, and not on the path connecting them, an important conclusion can be drawn. The student will recall from mechanics that, in moving an object from a point in a gravitational field to another point, in the absence of friction the work done depends only on the positions of the two points and not on the path through which the body was moved. It was concluded from this that there exists a function of the space coordinates of the body whose final value minus its initial value is equal to the work done. This function was called the *potential-energy function*. Similarly, the work done in moving an electric charge from one point in an electric field to another is also independent of the path and therefore is also expressible as the value of a function (the electric potential function) at the final state minus its value at the initial state. It therefore follows from the first law of thermodynamics that there exists a function of the coordinates of a thermodynamic system whose value at the final state minus its value at the initial state is equal to the adiabatic work in going from one state to the other. This function is known as the *internal-energy function*.

Denoting the internal-energy function by U, we have

$$\boxed{-W_{i \to f} \text{ (adiabatic)} = U_f - U_i,}$$ (4-1)

where the signs are such that, if the system does work, its energy decreases.

4-3   Internal-energy Function

The physical interpretation of the difference $U_f - U_i$ is the change in energy of the system. The equality, therefore, of the change of energy and the adiabatic work expresses the principle of the conservation of energy. It should be emphasized, however, that the equation expresses more than the principle of the conservation of energy. It states that *there exists an energy function*, the difference between two values of which is the energy change of the system.

The internal energy is a function of as many thermodynamic coordinates as are necessary to specify the state of a system. The equilibrium states of a hydrostatic system, for example, describable by means of three thermo-dynamic coordinates P, V, and θ are completely determined by only two, since the third is fixed by the equation of state. Therefore, the internal energy may be thought of as a function of only two (any two) of the thermodynamic coordinates. This is true for each of the simple systems described in Chap. 2. It is not always possible to write this function in simple mathematical form. Very often the exact form of the function is unknown. It must be understood, however, that it is not necessary to know actually what the internal-energy function is, so long as we can be sure that such a function exists.

If the coordinates characterizing the two states differ from each other only infinitesimally, the change of internal energy is dU, where dU is an exact differential, since it is the differential of an actual function. In the case of a hydrostatic system, if U is regarded as a function of θ and V, then

$$dU = \left(\frac{\partial U}{\partial \theta}\right)_V d\theta + \left(\frac{\partial U}{\partial V}\right)_\theta dV,$$

or, regarding U as a function of θ and P,

$$dU = \left(\frac{\partial U}{\partial \theta}\right)_P d\theta + \left(\frac{\partial U}{\partial P}\right)_\theta dP.$$

The student should realize that the two partial derivatives $(\partial U/\partial \theta)_V$ and $(\partial U/\partial \theta)_P$ are not equal. The first is a function of θ and V, and the second a function of θ and P. They are different mathematically and also have a different physical meaning.

4-4 Mathematical Formulation of the First Law

We have been considering, up to now, processes wherein a system under-goes a change of state through the performance of adiabatic work only. Such experiments must be performed in order to measure the change in the energy function of a system, but they are not the usual processes that are carried out in the laboratory. In Fig. 4-5 there are depicted two examples of processes involving changes of state that take place nonadiabatically. In (a) a gas is in contact with a bunsen flame whose temperature is higher than that of the gas and at the same time is allowed to expand. In (b) the magnetization of a

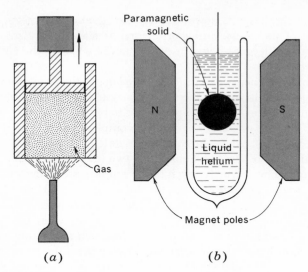

Fig. 4-5   *Nonadiabatic processes.*

paramagnetic solid is increased while it is in contact with liquid helium, the temperature of which is lower than that of the solid. As a matter of fact, some of the helium boils away during the magnetization.

Let us now imagine two different experiments performed on the same system. In one we measure the adiabatic work necessary to change the state of the system from i to f. This is $U_f - U_i$. In the other we cause the system to undergo the *same* change of state, but nonadiabatically, and measure the work done. The result of all such experiments is that *the nonadiabatic work is* not *equal to* $U_f - U_i$. In order that this result shall be consistent with the principle of the conservation of energy, we are forced to conclude that energy has been transferred by means *other than* the performance of work. This energy, whose transfer between the system and its surroundings is required by the principle of the conservation of energy and which has taken place only by virtue of the temperature difference between the system and its surroundings, is what we have previously called heat. We therefore give the following as our *thermodynamic* definition of heat: *When a system whose surroundings are at a different temperature and on which work may be done undergoes a process, the energy transferred by nonmechanical means, equal to the difference between the internal-energy change and the work done, is called heat.* Denoting this difference by Q, we have

$$Q = U_f - U_i - (-W),$$

or

$$Q = U_f - U_i + W, \qquad (4\text{-}2)$$

where the convention has been adopted that Q is positive when it enters a system and negative when it leaves (just the opposite of the sign convention for W). The preceding equation is known as the *mathematical formulation of the first law*.

It seems a pity that the sign convention for work is opposite that for heat. Positive work ought to be work that goes into a system and raises its energy, as it is in the subject of mechanics. The conventions in thermodynamics, however, were devised to fit the behavior of heat engines whose normal operation involves the inflow of heat and the output of work. There are so many textbooks, handbooks, articles, and tables in which these standard conventions are adopted that a change would be feasible only if agreed to by engineers, chemists, and physicists. At the present time, such an accord seems out of the question. A convenient way to remember the sign convention is to write the first law in the form

$$U_f - U_i = Q - W,$$

and to think of a system as an energy "bank," in which positive heat is regarded as a *deposit* and positive work as a *withdrawal*.

It should be emphasized that the mathematical formulation of the first law contains three related ideas: (1) the existence of an internal-energy function; (2) the principle of the conservation of energy; (3) the definition of heat as *energy* in transit by virtue of a temperature difference.

It was many years before it was understood that heat is energy. The first really conclusive evidence that heat could not be a substance was given by Benjamin Thompson, an American from Woburn, Massachusetts, who later became Count Rumford of Bavaria. In 1798, Rumford observed the temperature rise in brass chips produced during the boring of cannon and concluded that the work of boring was responsible for the flow of heat. One year later, Sir Humphry Davy tried to show that two pieces of ice could be melted by rubbing them together. His idea was to show that heat is a manifestation of energy, but his experiment was highly inconclusive.

The idea that heat is a form of energy was put forward in 1839 by Séguin, a French engineer, and in 1842 by Mayer, a German physician, but no conclusive experiments were performed by either. It remained for Joule, an independent investigator with a private laboratory, in the period from 1840 to 1849, to convince the world by performing a series of admirable experiments on the relation between heat and work and to establish once and for all the equivalence of these two quantities. Von Helmholtz recognized the epoch-making importance of Joule's work and wrote a brilliant paper in 1847, in which he applied Joule's ideas to the sciences of physical chemistry and physiology.

4-5   Concept of Heat

Heat is energy in transit. It flows from one part of a system to another, or from one system to another, by virtue of only a temperature difference. When this flow has ceased, there is no longer any occasion to use the word "heat." It would be just as incorrect to refer to the "heat in a body" as it would be to speak of the "work in a body." The performance of work and the flow of heat are methods whereby the internal energy of a system is changed. It is impossible to separate or divide the internal energy into a mechanical and a thermal part.

We have seen that, in general, the work done on or by a system is not a function of the coordinates of the system but depends on the path by which the system was brought from the initial to the final state. Exactly the same is true of the heat transferred to or from a system. Q is not a function of the thermodynamic coordinates but depends on the path. An infinitesimal amount of heat, therefore, is an inexact differential and is represented by the symbol dQ.

To quote from Slater's "Introduction to Chemical Physics":

⚓ At first sight, it seems too bad that ∫ dQ is not independent of the path, for some such quantity would be useful. It would be pleasant to be able to say, in a given state of the system, that the system had so and so much heat energy. Starting from the absolute zero of temperature, where we could say that the heat energy was zero, we could heat the body up to the state we were interested in, find ∫ dQ from absolute zero up to this state, and call that the heat energy. But the stubborn fact remains that we should get different answers if we heated it up in different ways. For instance, we might heat it at an arbitrary constant pressure until we reached the desired temperature, then adjust the pressure at constant temperature to the desired value; or we might raise it first to the desired pressure, then heat it at that pressure to the final temperature; or many other equally simple processes. Each would give a different answer, as we can easily verify. There is nothing to do about it.

Imagine a system A in thermal contact with a system B, the two systems being surrounded by adiabatic walls. For system A alone,

$$Q = U_f - U_i + W;$$

and for system B alone,

$$Q' = U'_f - U'_i + W'.$$

Adding, we get

$$Q + Q' = (U_f + U'_f) - (U_i + U'_i) + W + W'.$$

Since $(U_f + U'_f) - (U_i + U'_i)$ is the change in energy of the composite system and $W + W'$ is the work done by the composite system, it follows that $Q + Q'$ is the heat transferred by the composite system. Since the composite system is surrounded by adiabatic walls,

$$Q + Q' = 0,$$

and

$$Q = -Q'. \tag{4-3}$$

In other words, *under adiabatic conditions, the heat lost (or gained) by system A is equal to the heat gained (or lost) by system B.*

4-6 Differential Form of the First Law

A process involving only infinitesimal changes in the thermodynamic coordinates of a system is known as an *infinitesimal process*. For such a process the first law becomes

$$\boxed{dQ = dU + dW.} \tag{4-4}$$

If the infinitesimal process is quasi-static, then dU and dW can be expressed in terms of thermodynamic coordinates only. An infinitesimal quasi-static process is one in which the system passes from an initial equilibrium state to a neighboring equilibrium state.

For an infinitesimal quasi-static process of a hydrostatic system, the first law becomes

$$dQ = dU + P \, dV, \tag{4-5}$$

where U is a function of any two of the three thermodynamic coordinates and P is, of course, a function of V and θ. A similar equation may be written for each of the other simple systems as shown in Table 4-1.

Table 4-1 The First Law for Simple Systems

System	First law	U is a function of *any two* of
Hydrostatic system	$dQ = dU + P \, dV$	P, V, θ
Wire	$dQ = dU - \mathcal{F} \, dL$	$\mathcal{F}, L, \theta$
Surface film	$dQ = dU - \mathcal{S} \, dA$	$\mathcal{S}, A, \theta$
Electric cell	$dQ = dU - \mathcal{E} \, dZ$	$\mathcal{E}, Z, \theta$
Paramagnetic solid	$dQ = dU - \mathcal{H} \, dM$	$\mathcal{H}, M, \theta$

To deal with more complicated systems, it is merely necessary to replace dW in the first law by two or more expressions. For example, in the case of a composite system consisting of two hydrostatic parts separated by a diathermic wall, we may express dQ as follows:

$$dQ = dU + P\,dV + P'\,dV', \tag{4-6}$$

whereas for a paramagnetic gas

$$dQ = dU + P\,dV - \mathcal{H}\,dM. \tag{4-7}$$

The right-hand members of Eqs. (4-5), (4-6), and (4-7) are known as *Pfaffian differential forms*, and the question of their integrability is an interesting and important one that will be studied later. At this point, however, it is worth while to state a fundamental difference between Eq. (4-5) and Eq. (4-6), in order to justify the seemingly undue emphasis on systems of more than two independent coordinates. Since the left-hand expression in Eqs. (4-5) and (4-6) represents an infinitesimal amount of heat dQ, and since the heat transferred depends on the path, dQ is an inexact differential and the Pfaffian differential forms are inexact differentials. An inexact differential, however, may often be made exact by multiplying it by a function, known as an *integrating factor*. The Pfaffian differential form representing dQ of a simple system with two independent coordinates has the mathematical property that *an integrating factor can always be found*. This is not the result of a law of nature; it is a purely mathematical result of the fact that there are only two independent coordinates.

When there are three or more independent coordinates, however, the situation is entirely different. In general, a Pfaffian differential form containing three differentials does *not* admit of an integrating factor! But, because of the existence of a new law of nature (the second law of thermodynamics), the Pfaffian differential form representing dQ *does* have an integrating factor. It is a most remarkable circumstance that the integrating factor for dQ which is found for systems with *any* number of independent variables is *a function of the empiric temperature only, which is the same function for all systems*. This result enables us to define an absolute thermodynamic (or Kelvin) temperature, as we shall see in Chap. 8.

4-7   Heat Capacity and Its Measurement

When heat is absorbed by a system, a change of temperature may or may not take place, depending on the process. If a system undergoes a change of temperature from θ_i to θ_f during the transfer of Q units of heat, the average *heat capacity* of the system is defined as the ratio

$$\text{Average heat capacity} = \frac{Q}{\theta_f - \theta_i}.$$

As both Q and $(\theta_f - \theta_i)$ get smaller, this ratio approaches the instantaneous value of the *heat capacity* C thus:

$$C = \lim_{\theta_f \to \theta_i} \frac{Q}{\theta_f - \theta_i}$$

$$\boxed{C = \frac{dQ}{d\theta}.} \tag{4-8}$$

The heat capacity of a system per unit mass is called the specific heat capacity, or *specific heat*, and is measured in joules per gram-degree. The gram, however, is not a convenient unit of mass to use in most calorimetric work. Most physicists and chemists prefer the gram-mole (rather than the kilogram-mole)—that is, the number of grams equal to the molecular weight. The heat capacity per mole, or *molar heat capacity*, is designated with a lower-case letter thus:

$$c = \frac{C}{n} = \frac{1}{n}\frac{dQ}{d\theta}.$$

This quantity is measured in joules per mole-degree.

The heat capacity may be negative, zero, positive, or infinite, depending on the process the system undergoes during the heat transfer. It has a definite value only for a definite process. In the case of a hydrostatic system, the ratio $dQ/d\theta$ has a unique value when the pressure is kept constant. Under these conditions, C is called the *heat capacity at constant pressure* and is denoted by the symbol C_P, where

$$C_P = \left(\frac{dQ}{d\theta}\right)_P. \tag{4-9}$$

In general, C_P is a function of P and θ. Similarly, the heat capacity *at constant volume* is

$$C_V = \left(\frac{dQ}{d\theta}\right)_V. \tag{4-10}$$

and depends on both V and θ. In general, C_P and C_V are different. Both will be thoroughly discussed throughout the book. Each simple system has its own heat capacities as shown in Table 4-2.

Table 4-2   Heat Capacities of Simple Systems

System	Heat capacities	Symbol
Hydrostatic	At constant pressure At constant volume	C_P C_V
Linear	At constant tension At constant length	$C_{\mathcal{F}}$ C_L
Surface	At constant surface tension At constant area	$C_{\mathcal{S}}$ C_A
Electric	At constant emf At constant charge	$C_{\mathcal{E}}$ C_Z
Magnetic	At constant field At constant magnetization	$C_{\mathcal{H}}$ C_M

Each heat capacity is a function of two variables. Within a small range of variation of these coordinates, however, the heat capacity may be regarded as practically constant. Very often, one heat capacity can be set equal to another without much error. Thus, the $C_{\mathcal{H}}$ of a paramagnetic solid is at times very nearly equal to C_P.

The measurement of the heat capacity of solids is one of the most important experimental projects of modern physics, because numerical values of heat capacity provide one of the most direct means of verifying the calculations of theoretical physicists and of deciding on the validity of the assumptions constituting some of the modern theories. An electrical method of measurement is used almost invariably. If a resistance wire is wound around a cylindrical sample of material and if both the wire and the sample are regarded as the system, then the electrical energy dissipated in the wire is interpreted as work. When the wire is not included as part of the system, however, the energy which is dissipated within the wire and which flows into the sample by virtue of the temperature difference between the wire and the sample (however small) is designated as heat. The wire is often called a *heating coil*. If the current in the wire is I and the potential difference across it is $\mathcal{E}$, then the heat dQ that leaves the heating coil over a time $d\tau$ is calculated as

$$dQ = \mathcal{E}I \, d\tau.$$

If $\mathcal{E}$ is measured in volts, I in amperes, and τ in seconds, the heat will be expressed in joules. The shape, size, and construction of the calorimeter, heating coils, thermometers, etc., depend on the nature of the material to be studied and the temperature range desired. It is impossible to describe one calorimeter that suffices for all purposes. In general, the measurement of any heat capacity is a research problem requiring all the ability of a trained physicist or physical chemist, the facilities of a good workshop, and the skill of an expert glass blower.

In modern calorimetry, particularly in the case of solids at low temperatures, the sample is suspended in a highly evacuated space by means of fine threads of nylon or some other poorly conducting material. A heating coil is wound around the sample, and a thermocouple or a resistance thermometer (platinum, carbon, or germanium, depending on the temperature range) is placed in a small hole drilled for that purpose. The connecting wires for the heater, for the current in the thermometer, and for the potential difference across the thermometer are made very thin so as not to allow much heat to be transferred between the sample and its surroundings. The temperature of the sample is measured as a function of the time; when plotted as in Fig. 4-6, this gives the line AB, marked "foreperiod." At the time corresponding to point B, a switch is closed and a current is established in the heater at the same moment that an electric stop clock is started. After a short interval of time $\Delta\tau$, the switch is opened and the stop clock is stopped. Then the temperature is again measured as a function of time and is plotted as the line DE, marked "afterperiod" in Fig. 4-6.

As a rule, no reading of temperature or time is attempted while the stop

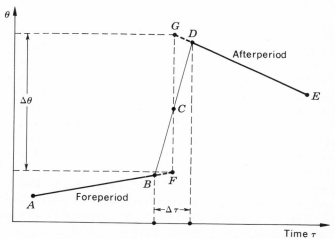

Fig. 4-6   *Temperature-vs.-time graph in the measurement of heat capacity.*

clock is on, that is, from B to D. A vertical line is drawn through the center C of the line BD, and both the foreperiod and the afterperiod lines are extrapolated to this vertical line, giving the points F and G, as shown. The molar heat capacity c at the temperature corresponding to point C is then given by

$$c = \frac{\mathcal{E}I \, \Delta\tau}{n \, \Delta\theta}.$$

Sometimes $\Delta\theta$ is made as small as 0.01 deg. Strictly speaking, the graph shown in Fig. 4-6 is not a graph of θ versus τ but of the resistance R' versus τ, and it is possible to have the entire $R'\tau$ curve drawn automatically with the aid of a recording potentiometer. When many values of R' and $\Delta R'$ are read from recorder graphs, the corresponding θ's, $\Delta\theta$'s, and c's are obtained with the aid of a computer.

4-8   Heat Capacity of Water; The Calorie

When the subject of calorimetry was first presented in the middle of the eighteenth century, measurements were confined to the temperature range between the freezing and boiling points of water. The unit of heat found most convenient was called the *calorie* and was defined as the amount of heat required to raise the temperature of 1 g of water one Celsius degree. To measure the amount of heat transferred between a system and some water, it was necessary merely to make two measurements: of the mass of water and of its temperature change. Later on, as measurements became more precise and more elaborate corrections were made, it was discovered that the heat necessary to change 1 g of water from 0 to 1 °C was different from the heat necessary to go from, say, 30 to 31 °C. The calorie was then defined to be the heat necessary to go from 14.5 to 15.5 °C (the 15-deg calorie).

The amount of work that had to be dissipated in water—either by maintaining a current in a resistor immersed in water or by churning the water in an irregular manner—per unit mass of water in going from 14.5 to 15.5 °C was called the *mechanical equivalent of heat*, which was measured to be 4.1860 J/cal. In the 1920s it was recognized that the measurement of this mechanical equivalent of heat was really a measurement of the specific heat of water, with the joule as the unit of heat. Since heat is a form of energy and the joule is a universal unit of energy, the calorie seemed superfluous. Therefore, in a large and important collection of tables of physical constants published at that time, which were called the International Critical Tables, all thermal quantities such as specific and molar heat capacities were expressed in terms of joules. This move proved to be somewhat premature. Physicists and chemists preferred to think in terms of calories, and even when the electrical method of calorimetry was used and thermal quantities were actually measured in joules, the measurements were then converted to calories.

Mechanical and chemical engineers also preferred to keep the calorie as a unit of heat, but they were not inclined to accept the conversion factor of 4.1860 J for the 15-deg calorie. They therefore defined their own calories in terms of the joule. For purposes of mechanical engineering, the *International Table calorie* (or IT calorie) was defined as

$$1 \; \text{IT cal} = \frac{1}{860} \; \text{watt} \cdot \text{hr} = 4.1860 \; \text{J.}$$

The *thermochemical calorie*, on the other hand, was given the following value:

$$1 \; \text{thermochemical cal} = 4.1840 \; \text{J.}$$

Among physicists and chemists today, the calorie is being dropped, and all thermal quantities—at least at very low and very high temperatures, where water is not used but electrical methods are employed exclusively—are expressed in joules. There is no mechanical equivalent of heat, but instead there is the specific heat of water, expressed in J/g · deg, whose temperature variation in the range from 0 to 100°C is shown in Fig. 4-7.

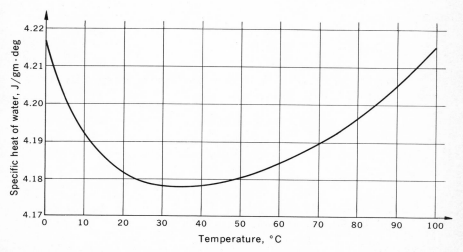

Fig. 4-7   *Most probable values of specific heat of water. (Compiled by W. J. de Haas, 1950.)*

4-9   Equations for a Hydrostatic System

The mathematical formulation of the first law for a hydrostatic system is

$$dQ = dU + P\,dV,$$

where U is a function of any two of P, V, and θ. Choosing θ and V, we have

$$dU = \left(\frac{\partial U}{\partial \theta}\right)_V d\theta + \left(\frac{\partial U}{\partial V}\right)_\theta dV.$$

Therefore the first law becomes

$$dQ = \left(\frac{\partial U}{\partial \theta}\right)_V d\theta + \left[\left(\frac{\partial U}{\partial V}\right)_\theta + P\right] dV. \qquad (4\text{-}11)$$

Dividing by $d\theta$, we get

$$\frac{dQ}{d\theta} = \left(\frac{\partial U}{\partial \theta}\right)_V + \left[\left(\frac{\partial U}{\partial V}\right)_\theta + P\right]_\theta \frac{dV}{d\theta}. \qquad (4\text{-}12)$$

This equation is true for *any* process involving any temperature change $d\theta$ and any volume change dV.

(*a*)   If V is constant, $dV = 0$, and

$$\left(\frac{dQ}{d\theta}\right)_V = \left(\frac{\partial U}{\partial \theta}\right)_V.$$

But the ratio on the left, by definition, is the heat capacity at constant volume C_V; therefore,

$$\boxed{C_V = \left(\frac{\partial U}{\partial \theta}\right)_V.} \qquad (4\text{-}13)$$

If U is calculated mathematically by making special assumptions about the atoms of a particular material, one of the first methods of checking these assumptions is to differentiate U with respect to θ at constant V and to compare the resulting quantity with the experimentally measured value of C_V.

(b)   If P is constant, Eq. (4-12) becomes

$$\left(\frac{dQ}{d\theta}\right)_P = \left(\frac{\partial U}{\partial \theta}\right)_V + \left[\left(\frac{\partial U}{\partial V}\right)_\theta + P\right]\left(\frac{\partial V}{\partial \theta}\right)_P.$$

But, by definition, $(dQ/d\theta)_P = C_P$ and also $(\partial V/\partial \theta)_P = V\beta$. Hence,

$$C_P = C_V + \left[\left(\frac{\partial U}{\partial V}\right)_\theta + P\right]V\beta$$

or $$\left(\frac{\partial U}{\partial V}\right)_\theta = \frac{C_P - C_V}{V\beta} - P. \qquad (4\text{-}14)$$

Although this equation is not important in its present form, it is a good example of an equation that relates a quantity $(\partial U/\partial V)_\theta$, which is ordinarily not measured, with quantities such as C_P, C_V, and β, which may be measured.

4-10   Quasi-static Flow of Heat; Heat Reservoir

It was shown in Chap. 3 that a process caused by a finite unbalanced force is attended by phenomena such as turbulence and acceleration which cannot be handled by means of thermodynamic coordinates that refer to the system as a whole. A similar situation exists when there is a finite difference between the temperature of a system and that of its surroundings. A nonuniform temperature distribution is set up in the system, and the calculation of this distribution and its variation with time is in most cases an elaborate mathematical problem. During a quasi-static process, however, the difference between the temperature of a system and that of its surroundings is infinitesimal. As a result, the temperature of the system is at any moment uniform throughout, and its changes are infinitely slow. The flow of heat is also infinitely slow and may be calculated in a simple manner in terms of thermodynamic coordinates referring to the system as a whole.

Suppose that a system is in good thermal contact with a body of extremely large mass and that a quasi-static process is performed. A finite amount of heat flow during this process will not bring about an appreciable change in the temperature of the surrounding body if the mass is large enough. For example, a cake of ice of ordinary size, if thrown into the ocean, will not produce a drop in temperature of the ocean. No ordinary flow of heat into the outside air will produce a rise of temperature of the air. The ocean and the outside air are approximate examples of an ideal body called a *heat reservoir*.

A heat reservoir is a body of such a large mass that it may absorb or reject an unlimited quantity of heat without suffering an appreciable change in temperature or in any other thermodynamic coordinate. It is not to be understood that there is no change in the thermodynamic coordinates of a heat reservoir when a finite amount of heat flows in or out. There is a change, but an extremely small one, too small to be measured. In other words: in any small unit of mass, a change in a physical property is infinitesimal, but there is an infinite number of such units of mass in the heat reservoir.

Any quasi-static process of a system in contact with a heat reservoir is bound to be isothermal. To describe a quasi-static flow of heat involving a change of temperature, one could conceive of a system placed in contact successively with a series of reservoirs. Thus, if we imagine a series of reservoirs ranging in temperature from θ_i to θ_f placed successively in contact with a system at constant pressure of heat capacity C_P, in such a way that the difference in temperature between the system and the reservoir with which it is in contact is infinitesimal, the flow of heat will be quasi-static and can be calculated as follows: by definition,

$$C_P = \left(\frac{dQ}{d\theta}\right)_P,$$

and therefore

$$Q_P = \int_{\theta_i}^{\theta_f} C_P \, d\theta.$$

For example, the heat absorbed by m g of water from a series of reservoirs varying in temperature from θ_i to θ_f during a quasi-static isobaric process is

$$Q_P = \int_{\theta_i}^{\theta_f} C_P \, d\theta$$

$$= m \int_{\theta_i}^{\theta_f} c_P \, d\theta.$$

If the specific heat c_P is assumed to remain practically constant,

$$Q_P = m c_P (\theta_f - \theta_i).$$

For a quasi-static isochoric process

$$Q_V = \int_{\theta_i}^{\theta_f} C_V \, d\theta.$$

Similar considerations hold for other systems and other quasi-static processes.

4-11   Heat Conduction

When two parts of a material substance are maintained at different temperatures and the temperature of each small volume element of the intervening substance is measured, experiment shows a continuous distribution of temperature. The transport of energy between neighboring volume elements by virtue of the temperature difference between them is known as *heat conduction*. The fundamental law of heat conduction is a generalization of the results of experiments on the linear flow of heat through a slab perpendicular to the faces. A piece of material is made in the form of a slab of thickness Δx and of area A. One face is maintained at the temperature θ and the other at $\theta + \Delta\theta$. The heat Q that flows perpendicular to the faces for a time τ is measured. The experiment is repeated with other slabs of the same material but with different values of Δx and A. The results of such experiments show that, for a given value of $\Delta\theta$, Q is proportional to the time and to the area. Also, for a given time and area, Q is proportional to the ratio $\Delta\theta/\Delta x$, provided that both $\Delta\theta$ and Δx are small. These results may be written

$$\frac{Q}{\tau} \propto A \frac{\Delta\theta}{\Delta x},$$

which is only approximately true when $\Delta\theta$ and Δx are finite but which is rigorously true in the limit as $\Delta\theta$ and Δx approach zero. If we generalize this result for an infinitesimal slab of thickness dx, across which there is a temperature difference $d\theta$, and introduce a constant of proportionality K, the fundamental law of heat conduction becomes

$$\dot{Q} = \frac{dQ}{d\tau} = -KA\frac{d\theta}{dx}. \qquad (4\text{-}15)$$

The derivative $d\theta/dx$ is called the *temperature gradient*. The minus sign is introduced in order that the positive direction of the flow of heat should coincide with the positive direction of x. For heat to flow in the positive direction of x, this must be the direction in which θ decreases. K is called the *thermal conductivity*. A substance with a large thermal conductivity is known as a *thermal conductor*, and one with a small value of K as a *thermal insulator*. It will be shown in the next article that the numerical value of K depends upon a number of factors, one of which is the temperature. Volume elements of a conducting material may therefore differ in thermal conductivity. If the temperature difference between parts of a substance is small, however, K can be considered practically constant throughout the substance. This simplification is usually made in practical problems.

To handle general problems in the conduction of heat, it is necessary to transform the general equation into the form of a second-order partial differential equation. The solution of this equation subject to given boundary conditions involves, as a rule, the use of functions and series beyond the scope of collegiate mathematics. There are three simple cases, however, that can be handled in an elementary way. In all cases, we shall assume that K is constant throughout the conducting substance.

1   *Linear flow of heat perpendicular to the faces of a slab.*   If the temperature difference $\theta_1 - \theta_2$ and the thickness x are small, it is obvious that

$$\dot{Q} = KA \frac{\theta_1 - \theta_2}{x}.$$

2   *Radial flow of heat between two coaxial cylinders.*   Suppose the conducting material lies between an inner cylinder of radius r_1 and an outer cylinder of radius r_2, both of length L. If the inner cylinder is maintained at the constant temperature θ_1 and the outer at θ_2, there will be a steady radial flow of heat at the *constant* rate of $\dot{Q}$. Consider the flow of this amount of heat across a cylindrical shell of material bounded by the cylinders at r and $r + dr$ (see Fig. 4-8). Let θ be the temperature at r, and $\theta + d\theta$ be the temperature at $r + dr$. The area of the shell is

$$A = 2\pi r L,$$

and the temperature gradient is $d\theta/dr$. Hence,

$$\dot{Q} = -K 2\pi r L \frac{d\theta}{dr},$$

and $$d\theta = -\frac{\dot{Q}}{2\pi LK} \frac{dr}{r}.$$

Integrating between r_1 and r_2, we get

$$\theta_1 - \theta_2 = \frac{\dot{Q}}{2\pi LK} \ln \frac{r_2}{r_1}. \tag{4-16}$$

3   *Radial flow of heat between two concentric spheres.*   If the conducting material lies between an inner sphere of radius r_1 held at constant

Fig. 4-8   *Radial flow of heat in a cylinder.*

temperature θ_1 and an outer sphere of radius r_2 held at constant temperature θ_2, there will be a steady radial flow of heat at the *constant* rate of $\dot{Q}$. Considering this flow across the spherical shell bounded by the spheres at r and $r + dr$, we have

$$\dot{Q} = -KA \frac{d\theta}{dr}$$

$$= -K4\pi r^2 \frac{d\theta}{dr},$$

and

$$d\theta = -\frac{\dot{Q}}{4\pi K} \frac{dr}{r^2}.$$

Integrating between r_1 and r_2, we get

$$\theta_1 - \theta_2 = \frac{\dot{Q}}{4\pi K} \left(\frac{1}{r_1} - \frac{1}{r_2} \right). \tag{4-17}$$

4-12   Thermal Conductivity

When the substance to be investigated is a metal, it is made into the form of a bar, and one end is heated electrically while the other end is cooled with a stream of water. The surface of the bar is thermally insulated, and the heat lost through the insulation is calculated by subtracting the rate at which heat enters the water from the rate at which electrical energy is supplied. In the case of most metals, the heat lost from the surface is very small in comparison with that which flows through the bar. The temperature is measured with suitable thermocouples at two places L cm apart, and the equation

$$K = \frac{L}{A(\theta_1 - \theta_2)} \dot{Q}$$

is used to determine the average thermal conductivity within the given temperature range. If $\theta_1 - \theta_2$ is small, K is practically equal to the thermal conductivity at the mean temperature.

When the substance to be investigated is a nonmetal, it is made into the form of a thin disk or plate, and the same general method is used. The substance is contained between two copper blocks, one of which is heated electrically and the other cooled by running water. The thermal contact between the copper blocks and the substance is improved by smearing them with glycerin. In most cases, the rate at which heat is supplied is almost equal to the rate at which heat enters the water, showing that there is little loss of heat through the edges.

Since the thermal conductivity is equal to $\dot{Q}/A(d\theta/dx)$, it has the unit

$$K = 1 \; \frac{\text{J/sec}}{\text{m}^2 \cdot \text{deg/m}} = 1 \; \frac{\text{W}}{\text{m} \cdot \text{deg}}.$$

Lengths are usually expressed in centimeters, however, so that it has become the custom to express thermal conductivity in the hybrid unit 1 W/cm · deg.

Experiments show that the thermal conductivity of a metal is extraordinarily sensitive to impurities. The slightest trace of arsenic in copper reduces the thermal conductivity by a factor of 3. A change in internal structure brought about by continued heating or a large increase in pressure also affects the value of K. No appreciable change in the K of solids and liquids takes place, however, under moderate changes of pressure. Liquefaction always produces a decrease in the thermal conductivity, and the thermal conductivity of a liquid usually increases as the temperature is raised. Nonmetallic solids behave in a manner similar to that of liquids. At ordinary temperatures these are poor conductors of heat; in general, the thermal conductivity increases as the temperature is raised. In the low-temperature range, however, the behavior is quite different, as shown in Fig. 4-9, where it may be seen that the thermal conductivity of sapphire rises to a maximum of over 50 W/cm · deg at 30°K (four times the conductivity of silver at room temperature). The thermal conductivity of some metals remains quite constant over a wide temperature range. Thus, silver, copper, and gold have thermal conductivities that remain practically constant at the values 4.2, 3.8, and 2.9 W/cm · deg, respectively, in the temperature range from 100 to 1000°K. As a general rule, the thermal conductivity of metals increases as the temperature is lowered, until a maximum is reached. Further reduction of temperature causes a decrease toward zero, as shown in the case of copper in Fig. 4-9.

Thermal and electric conductivity of metals go together. This important fact was first stated by Wiedemann and Franz, who showed that the ratio of

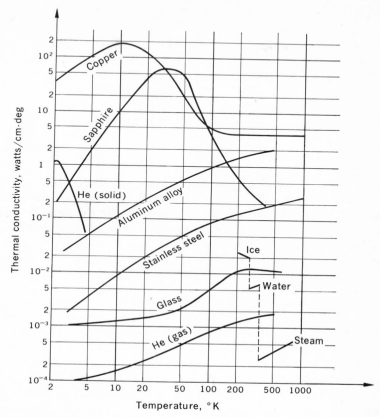

Fig. 4-9   *Typical curves showing temperature dependence of thermal conductivity. (R. L. Powell, AIP Handbook, McGraw-Hill, 1963.)*

the thermal to the electric conductivity was approximately the same for most metals at the same temperature. Lorentz later showed that this ratio was not only the same for all metals at the same temperature but varied directly with the absolute temperature. If σ denotes the electric conductivity in Ω^{-1} cm^{-1} (reciprocal of resistivity), Lorentz's law can be written

$$\frac{K}{\sigma \theta} = \text{const.} = 2.23 \times 10^{-8} \frac{\text{V}^2}{\text{deg}^2}. \tag{4-18}$$

The approximate validity of this law in the temperature range from -170 to $100°$C is shown in Table 4-3.

Table 4-3   **Values of $K/\sigma\theta$ in 10^{-8} V^2/deg^2**

Metal	$-170°C$	$-100°C$	$0°C$	$18°C$	$100°C$
Copper	1.85	2.17	2.30	2.32	2.32
Silver	2.04	2.29	2.33	2.33	2.37
Zinc	2.20	2.39	2.45	2.43	2.33
Cadmium	2.39	2.43	2.40	2.39	2.44
Tin	2.48	2.51	2.49	2.47	2.49
Lead	2.55	2.54	2.53	2.51	2.51

Gases are by far the poorest heat conductors. At pressures above a certain value, depending on the nature of the gas and the dimensions of the containing vessel, the thermal conductivity is independent of the pressure. Under the usual laboratory conditions, this limiting pressure is considerably below 1 atm. The thermal conductivity of a gas always increases as the temperature is raised, as is evident in Fig. 4-9.

4-13   Heat Convection

A current of liquid or gas that absorbs heat at one place and then moves to another place, where it mixes with a cooler portion of the fluid and rejects heat, is called a *convection current*. If the motion of the fluid is caused by a difference in density that accompanies a temperature difference, the phenomenon is called *natural convection*. If the fluid is made to move by the action of a pump or a fan, it is called *forced convection*.

Consider a fluid in contact with a flat or curved wall whose temperature is higher than that of the main body of the fluid. Although the fluid may be in motion, there is a relatively thin film of stagnant fluid next to the wall, the thickness of the film depending upon the character of the motion of the main body of fluid. The more turbulent the motion, the thinner the film. Heat is transferred from the wall to the fluid by a combination of conduction through the film and convection in the fluid. Neglecting the transfer of heat by radiation (which must be taken into account separately), we may define a convection coefficient h that includes the combined effect of conduction through the film and convection in the fluid. Thus,

$$\dot{Q} = hA\,\Delta\theta, \qquad (4\text{-}19)$$

where $\dot{Q}$ is the rate of heat transfer by convection, A is the area of the wall, and $\Delta\theta$ or Δt is the temperature difference between the surface of the wall and the main body of the fluid. The fundamental problem of heat convection is to find the value of h that is appropriate to a particular piece of equipment.

Experiment shows that the convection coefficient depends on the following factors:

1   Whether the wall is flat or curved.
2   Whether the wall is horizontal or vertical.
3   Whether the fluid in contact with the wall is a gas or a liquid.
4   The density, viscosity, specific heat, and thermal conductivity of the fluid.
5   Whether the velocity of the fluid is small enough to give rise to laminar flow or large enough to cause turbulent flow.
6   Whether evaporation, condensation, or formation of scale takes place.

Since the physical properties of the fluid depend upon temperature and pressure, it is clear that the rigorous calculation of a convection coefficient appropriate to a given wall and fluid is an enormously complicated problem. It is only in recent years that solutions of the problem good enough for practical purposes have been achieved with the aid of dimensional analysis. Such analysis yields an expression for h containing the physical properties and velocity of the fluid and unknown constants and exponents. The constants and exponents are then evaluated by experiment.

4-14   Thermal Radiation; Blackbody

A substance may be stimulated to emit electromagnetic radiation in a number of ways:

1   An electric conductor carrying a high-frequency alternating current emits radio waves.
2   A hot solid or liquid emits thermal radiation.
3   A gas carrying an electric discharge may emit visible or ultraviolet radiation.
4   A metal plate bombarded by high-speed electrons emits X rays.
5   A substance whose atoms are radioactive may emit γ rays.
6   A substance exposed to radiation from an external source may emit fluorescent radiation.

All these radiations are electromagnetic waves, differing only in wavelength. We shall be concerned in this article only with thermal radiation, i.e., the radiation emitted by a solid, liquid, or gas by virtue of its temperature. When thermal radiation is dispersed by a suitable prism, a continuous spectrum is obtained. The distribution of energy among the various wavelengths is such that, at temperatures below about 500°C, most of the energy is associated with infrared waves, whereas at higher temperatures some visible radiation is emitted. In general, the higher the temperature of a body, the greater the total energy emitted.

The loss of energy due to the emission of thermal radiation may be compensated in a variety of ways. The emitting body may be a source of energy itself, such as the sun; or there may be a constant supply of electrical energy from the outside, as in the case of the filament of an electric light. Energy may be supplied also by heat conduction or by the performance of work on the emitting body. In the absence of these sources of supply, the only other way in which a body may receive energy is by the absorption of radiation from surrounding bodies. In the case of a body that is surrounded by other bodies, the internal energy of the body will remain constant when the rate at which radiant energy is emitted is equal to that at which it is absorbed.

Experiment shows that the rate at which a body emits thermal radiation depends on the temperature and on the nature of the surface. The total radiant power emitted per unit area is called the *radiant emittance* of the body. For example, the radiant emittance of tungsten at 2177°C is 50 W/cm². When thermal radiation is incident upon a body equally from all directions, the radiation is said to be *isotropic*. Some of the radiation may be absorbed, some reflected, and some transmitted. In general, the fraction of the incident isotropic radiation of all wavelengths that is absorbed depends on the temperature and the nature of the surface of the absorbing body. This fraction is called the *absorptivity*. At 2477°C the absorptivity of tungsten is approximately 0.25. To summarize:

Radiant emittance $= \mathcal{R} =$ total radiant power emitted per unit area.

Absorptivity $= \alpha =$ fraction of the total energy of isotropic radiation that is absorbed.

There are some substances, such as lampblack, whose absorptivity is very nearly unity. For theoretical purposes it is useful to conceive of an ideal substance capable of absorbing all the thermal radiation falling on it. Such a substance is called a *blackbody*. If a blackbody is indicated by the subscript B, we have

$$\alpha_B = 1.$$

A very good experimental approximation to a blackbody is provided by a cavity for which the interior walls are maintained at a uniform temperature and which communicates with the outside by means of a hole having a diameter small in comparison with the dimensions of the cavity. Any radiation entering the hole is partly absorbed and partly diffusely reflected a large number of times at the interior walls, with only a negligible fraction eventually finding its way out of the hole. *This is true regardless of the materials of which the interior walls are composed.*

The radiation emitted by the interior walls is similarly absorbed and diffusely reflected a large number of times, so that the cavity is filled with isotropic radiation. Let us define as the *irradiance* within the cavity the radiant energy falling in unit time upon unit area of any surface within the cavity. Suppose a blackbody whose temperature is the same as that of the walls is introduced into the cavity. Then, denoting the irradiance by H,

$$\text{Radiant power absorbed per unit area} = \alpha_B H = H,$$

and $\qquad$ Radiant power emitted per unit area $= \mathcal{R}_B.$

Since the temperature of the blackbody remains constant, the rate at which the energy is absorbed must equal the rate at which it is emitted; whence

$$\boxed{H = \mathcal{R}_B,} \tag{4-20}$$

or *the irradiance within a cavity whose walls are at the temperature θ is equal to the radiant emittance of a blackbody at the same temperature.* For this reason, the radiation within a cavity is called *blackbody radiation.* Such radiation is studied by allowing a small amount to escape from a small hole leading to the cavity. Since H is independent of the materials of which the interior walls are composed, it follows that *the radiant emittance of a blackbody is a function of the temperature only.*

4-15   Kirchhoff's Law; Radiated Heat

The radiant emittance of a non-blackbody depends as much on the nature of the surface as on the temperature, according to a simple law that we may derive as follows: Suppose that a non-blackbody at the temperature θ, with radiant emittance $\mathcal{R}$ and absorptivity α, is introduced into a cavity whose interior walls are at the same temperature and where the irradiance is H. Then,

$$\text{Radiant power absorbed per unit area} = \alpha H,$$

and $\qquad$ Radiant power emitted per unit area $= \mathcal{R}.$

Since the non-blackbody is in equilibrium, *no change in temperature*

$$\mathcal{R} = \alpha H.$$

But, from Eq. (4-20), $H = \mathcal{R}_B$; hence,

$$\boxed{\mathcal{R} = \alpha \mathcal{R}_B,} \tag{4-21}$$

or *the radiant emittance of any body at any temperature is equal to a fraction of the radiant emittance of a blackbody at that temperature, this fraction being the absorptivity at that temperature.*

This equation, known as *Kirchhoff's law*, shows that the absorptivity of a body may be determined experimentally by measuring the radiant emittance of the body and dividing it by that of a blackbody at the same temperature. Values of the absorptivity of various surfaces, measured in this way, are given in Table 4-4. It should be emphasized that the tabulated values of absorptivity refer to the thermal radiation appropriate to the temperature listed in

Table 4-4   Approximate Absorptivities of Various Surfaces, as Compiled by Hottel

(Values at intermediate temperatures may be obtained by linear interpolation.)

Material	Temperature range, °C	Absorptivity
Polished metals:		
Aluminum	250– 600	0.039–0.057
Brass	250– 400	0.033–0.037
Chromium	50– 550	0.08 –0.26
Copper	100	0.018
Iron	150–1000	0.05 –0.37
Nickel	20– 350	0.045–0.087
Zinc	250– 350	0.045–0.053
Filaments:		
Molybdenum	750–2600	0.096–0.29
Platinum	30–1200	0.036–0.19
Tantalum	1300–3000	0.19 –0.31
Tungsten	30–3300	0.032–0.35
Other materials:		
Asbestos	40– 350	0.93 –0.95
Ice (wet)	0	0.97
Lampblack	20– 350	0.95
Rubber (gray)	25	0.86

column 1. Thus, the absorptivity of ice is 0.97 not for visible radiation but for the long infrared waves associated with matter at 0°C.

It should be noticed that the word "heat" has not appeared as yet. If there is a temperature difference between a body and its surroundings, then in a given interval of time the body loses an amount of internal energy equal to the energy radiated minus the energy absorbed, whereas the surroundings gain an amount of internal energy equal to the energy absorbed minus the energy radiated. The gain of one equals the loss of the other. *The gain or loss of internal energy, equal to the difference between the energy of the thermal radiation which is absorbed and that which is radiated, is called heat.* This statement is in agreement with the original definition of heat, since a gain or loss of energy by radiation and absorption will take place *only if there is a difference in temperature* between a body and its surroundings. If the two temperatures are the same, there is no net gain or loss of internal energy of either the body or its surroundings, and there is therefore no transfer of heat.

Imagine a cavity whose interior walls are maintained at a constant temperature θ_W. Suppose that a non-blackbody at a temperature θ different from that of the walls is placed in the cavity. If the body is small compared with the size of the cavity, then the character of the radiation in the cavity will not be appreciably affected by its introduction. Let H, as before, denote the irradiance within the cavity, and $\mathcal{R}$ and α the radiant emittance and absorptivity, respectively, of the body. Then, as before,

$$\text{Radiant power absorbed per unit area} = \alpha H,$$

and
$$\text{Radiant power emitted per unit area} = \mathcal{R};$$

but now *these two rates are not equal.* The difference between them is the heat transferred by radiation per second per unit area. If dQ is the heat transferred in time $d\tau$ to the whole body whose area is A, then

$$\dot{Q} = \frac{dQ}{d\tau} = A(\alpha H - \mathcal{R}), \qquad (4\text{-}22)$$

where, it must be remembered, α and $\mathcal{R}$ refer to the temperature θ and H to the temperature θ_W. Now,

$$H = \mathcal{R}_B(\theta_W),$$

and
$$\mathcal{R} = \alpha \mathcal{R}_B(\theta).$$

Hence,
$$\dot{Q} = A\alpha[\mathcal{R}_B(\theta_W) - \mathcal{R}_B(\theta)], \qquad (4\text{-}23)$$

or the rate at which heat is transferred by radiation is proportional to the difference between the radiant emittances of a blackbody at the two temperatures in question.

4-16   Stefan-Boltzmann Law (very important)

The first measurements of the heat transferred by radiation between a body and its surroundings were made by Tyndall. On the basis of these experiments, it was concluded by Stefan in 1879 that the heat radiated was proportional to the difference of the fourth powers of the absolute temperatures. This purely experimental result was later derived thermodynamically by Boltzmann, who showed that the radiant emittance of a blackbody at any temperature θ is equal to

$$\mathcal{R}_B(\theta) = \sigma\theta^4. \tag{4-24}$$

This law is now known as the *Stefan-Boltzmann law*, and σ is called the Stefan-Boltzmann constant.

Referring to Eq. (4-23), we have for the heat transferred by radiation between a body at the temperature θ and walls at θ_W,

$$\dot{Q} = A\alpha\sigma(\theta_W^4 - \theta^4), \tag{4-25}$$

where α refers to the temperature θ.

Two simple methods may be employed for the determination of the Stefan-Boltzmann constant:

1   *Nonequilibrium method.*   A blackened silver disk is placed in the center of a large blackened copper hemisphere. The silver disk is covered and shielded from radiation until the copper hemisphere achieves the temperature of condensing steam; this temperature is measured with a thermocouple. Then the disk is uncovered, and its temperature is measured as a function of the time. From the resulting heating curve, the slope $d\theta/d\tau$ is obtained. Assuming the silver disk to be a blackbody and putting $dQ = C_P\,d\theta$, where C_P is the heat capacity at constant pressure, we have

$$\frac{C_P\,d\theta}{d\tau} = A\sigma(\theta_W^4 - \theta^4),$$

whence
$$\sigma = \frac{C_P}{A(\theta_W^4 - \theta^4)}\frac{d\theta}{d\tau}.$$

2   *Equilibrium method.*   A hollow blackened copper sphere is provided with an electric heater and a thermocouple and is suspended inside a vessel whose walls are maintained at a constant temperature θ_W. Electrical energy is supplied at a constant rate $\mathcal{E}i$ until the sphere achieves an equilibrium temperature θ at which the rate of supply of energy is equal to the rate of emission of radiation. Assuming the sphere to be a blackbody, we have at equilibrium

$$\mathcal{E}i = A\sigma(\theta^4 - \theta_W^4);$$

whence

$$\sigma = \frac{\mathcal{E}i}{4\pi r^2(\theta^4 - \theta_W^4)},$$

where r is the radius of the sphere. The best measurements, to date, have yielded the value

$$\boxed{\sigma = 56.697 \frac{\text{nW}}{\text{m}^2 \cdot \text{deg}^4}.}$$

(4-26)

PROBLEMS

4-1   A gas contained in a cylinder surrounded by a thick layer of felt is quickly compressed, the temperature rising several hundred degrees. Has there been a transfer of heat? Has the "heat of the gas" been increased?

4-2   A combustion experiment is performed by burning a mixture of fuel and oxygen in a constant-volume "bomb" surrounded by a water bath. During the experiment the temperature of the water is observed to rise. If we regard the mixture of fuel and oxygen as the system:

(*a*)   Has heat been transferred?

(*b*)   Has work been done?

(*c*)   What is the sign of ΔU?

4-3   A liquid is irregularly stirred in a well-insulated container and thereby undergoes a rise in temperature. If we regard the liquid as the system:

(*a*)   Has heat been transferred?

(*b*)   Has work been done?

(*c*)   What is the sign of ΔU?

4-4   The amount of water in a lake may be increased by action of underground springs, by inflow from a river, and by rain. It may be decreased by various outflows and by evaporation.

(*a*) Is it correct to ask: How much rain is there in the lake?

(*b*) Would it be preferable or sensible to ask: How much water in the lake is due to rain?

(*c*) What concept is analogous to "rain in the lake"?

4-5 A vessel with rigid walls and covered with asbestos is divided into two parts by a partition. One part contains a gas, and the other is evacuated. If the partition is suddenly broken, show that the initial and final internal energies of the gas are equal.

4-6 A gas is enclosed within a cylinder-piston combination. Embedded in the gas is a junction of two dissimilar metals (a *thermojunction*) whose connecting wires pass through the walls of the cylinder and lead to a reversing switch and an electric generator rotated by means of a descending weight. As the weight descends, the current generated may be caused to exist in the thermojunction in either direction. Owing to the *Peltier effect*, the thermojunction undergoes a rise of temperature when the current is in one direction and a drop when in the opposite direction. The entire system is adiabatically shielded so that *all work interactions are adiabatic.* Assume that θ and U refer to the entire system, composed of gas plus thermojunction.

(*a*) Draw a schematic diagram of the apparatus.

(*b*) What is the result of allowing the piston to go out, with no current in the thermojunction? What is the sign of ΔU?

(*c*) Keeping the piston stationary, how could one produce a rise of temperature? What is the sign of ΔU?

(*d*) If the piston is kept stationary, is it possible to produce a drop in temperature? If so, what is the sign of ΔU?

(*e*) How could one produce an adiabatic, isothermal process?

4-7 When an electric current is maintained in an electrolytic cell of acidulated water and 1 mole of water is electrolyzed into hydrogen and oxygen, 2 faradays of electricity are transferred through a seat of emf $\mathcal{E}$ (1 faraday = 96,500 C). The energy change of the system is $+286,500$ J, and 50,000 J of heat are absorbed. What is $\mathcal{E}$?

4-8 A cylindrical tube with rigid walls and covered with asbestos is divided into two parts by a rigid insulating wall with a small hole in it. A frictionless insulating piston is held against the perforated partition, thus preventing the gas that is on the other side from seeping through the hole. The gas is maintained at a pressure P_i by another frictionless insulating piston. Imagine both pistons to move simultaneously in such a way that, as the gas streams through the hole, the pressure remains at the constant value P_i on one side of the dividing wall and at a constant lower value P_f on the other side, until all the gas is forced through the hole. Prove that

$$U_i + P_i V_i = U_f + P_f V_f.$$

4-9   An exhausted chamber with nonconducting walls is connected through a valve to the atmosphere, where the pressure is P_0. The valve is opened, and air flows into the chamber until the pressure within the chamber is P_0. Prove that $u_0 + P_0 v_0 = u_f$, where u_0 and v_0 are the molar energy and molar volume of the air at the temperature and pressure of the atmosphere and u_f is the molar energy of the air in the chamber. (*Hint:* Connect to the chamber a cylinder equipped with a frictionless nonleaking piston. Suppose the cylinder to contain exactly the amount of atmospheric air that will enter the chamber when the valve is opened. As soon as the first small quantity of air enters the chamber, the pressure in the cylinder is reduced a small amount below atmospheric pressure, and the outside air forces the piston in.)

4-10   A bomb of volume V_B contains n moles of gas at high pressure. Connected to the bomb is a capillary tube through which the gas may slowly leak out into the atmosphere, where the pressure is P_0. Surrounding the bomb and capillary is a water bath, in which is immersed an electrical resistor. The gas is allowed to leak slowly through the capillary into the atmosphere while, at the same time, electrical energy is dissipated in the resistor at such a rate that the temperature of the gas, the bomb, the capillary, and the water is kept equal to that of the outside air. Show that, after as much gas as possible has leaked out during time τ, the change of internal energy is

$$\Delta U = \mathscr{E} i \tau - P_0(n v_0 - V_B),$$

where v_0 is the molar volume of the gas at atmospheric pressure, $\mathscr{E}$ is the pd across the resistor, and i is the current in the resistor.

4-11   A thick-walled insulated metal chamber contains n_i moles of helium at high pressure P_i. It is connected through a valve with a large almost empty gasholder in which the pressure is maintained at a constant value P', very nearly atmospheric. The valve is opened slightly, and the helium flows slowly and adiabatically into the gasholder until the pressure on the two sides of the valve is equalized. Prove that

$$\frac{n_f}{n_i} = \frac{h' - u_i}{h' - u_f},$$

where n_f = number of moles of helium left in the chamber,
u_i = initial molar energy of helium in the chamber,
u_f = final molar energy of helium in the chamber, and
$h' = u' + P'v'$ (where u' = molar energy of helium in the gasholder;
v' = molar volume of helium in the gasholder).

4-12   The molar heat capacity at constant pressure of a gas varies with the temperature according to the equation

$$c_P = a + b\theta - \frac{c}{\theta^2},$$

where a, b, and c are constants. How much heat is transferred during an isobaric process in which n moles of gas undergo a temperature rise from θ_i to θ_f?

4-13   The molar heat capacity of a metal at low temperature varies with the temperature according to the equation

$$c = \frac{a}{\Theta^3} \theta^3 + b\theta,$$

where a, Θ, and b are constants. How much heat per mole is transferred during a process in which the temperature changes from 0.01 to 0.02 Θ?

4-14   Regarding the internal energy of a hydrostatic system to be a function of θ and P, derive the equations:

(a) $$dQ = \left[\left(\frac{\partial U}{\partial \theta}\right)_P + P \left(\frac{\partial V}{\partial \theta}\right)_P \right] d\theta + \left[\left(\frac{\partial U}{\partial P}\right)_\theta + P \left(\frac{\partial V}{\partial P}\right)_\theta \right] dP.$$

(b) $$\left(\frac{\partial U}{\partial \theta}\right)_P = C_P - PV\beta.$$

(c) $$\left(\frac{\partial U}{\partial P}\right)_\theta = PV\kappa - (C_P - C_V)\frac{\kappa}{\beta}.$$

4-15   Taking U to be a function of P and V, derive the following equations:

(a) $$dQ = \left(\frac{\partial U}{\partial P}\right)_V dP + \left[\left(\frac{\partial U}{\partial V}\right)_P + P \right] dV.$$

(b) $$\left(\frac{\partial U}{\partial P}\right)_V = \frac{C_V \kappa}{\beta}.$$

(c) $$\left(\frac{\partial U}{\partial V}\right)_P = \frac{C_P}{V\beta} - P.$$

4-16   Derive the equations listed in the accompanying table.

System	Heat capacity at constant extensive variable	Heat capacity at constant intensive variable
Stretched wire	$C_L = \left(\dfrac{\partial U}{\partial \theta}\right)_L$	$C_{\mathcal{F}} = \left(\dfrac{\partial U}{\partial \theta}\right)_{\mathcal{F}} - \mathcal{F}L\alpha$
Paramagnetic solid obeying Curie's equation	$C_M = \left(\dfrac{\partial U}{\partial \theta}\right)_M$	$C_{\mathcal{H}} = \left(\dfrac{\partial U}{\partial \theta}\right)_{\mathcal{H}} + \dfrac{M^2}{C}$

4-17   One mole of a gas obeys the equation of state

$$\left(P + \frac{a}{v^2}\right)(v - b) = R\theta,$$

where v is the molar volume, and its molar internal energy is given by

$$u = c\theta - \frac{a}{v},$$

where a, b, c, R are constants. Calculate molar heat capacities c_V and c_P.

4-18   The equation of state of a monatomic solid is

$$Pv + f(V) = \Gamma(u - u_0),$$

where v is the molar volume, and Γ and u_0 are constants. Prove that

$$\Gamma = \frac{\beta v}{c_V \kappa},$$

where κ is the isothermal compressibility. This relation, first derived by Grüneisen, plays a role in the theory of the solid state.

4-19   In the case of a paramagnetic gas:

(a)   Derive the equation

$$dQ = \left(\frac{\partial U}{\partial \theta}\right)_{V,M} d\theta + \left[\left(\frac{\partial U}{\partial V}\right)_{M,\theta} + P\right] dV + \left[\left(\frac{\partial U}{\partial M}\right)_{\theta,V} - \mathcal{H}\right] dM.$$

(b)   Derive expressions for $C_{V,M}$, $C_{V,\mathcal{H}}$, $C_{P,M}$, and $C_{P,\mathcal{H}}$.

4-20   Heat flows radially outward through a cylindrical insulator of outside radius r_2 surrounding a steam pipe of outside radius r_1. The temperature of the inner surface of the insulator is θ_1, and that of the outer surface is θ_2. At what radial distance from the center of the pipe is the temperature exactly halfway between θ_1 and θ_2?

4-21   Two thin concentric spherical shells of radius 5 and 15 cm, respectively, have their annular cavity filled with charcoal. When energy is supplied at the steady rate of 10.8 W to a heater at the center, a temperature difference of 50.0°C is set up between the spheres. Find the thermal conductivity of charcoal.

4-22   A wall, maintained at a constant temperature t_W, is coated with a layer of insulating material of thickness x and of thermal conductivity K. The outside of the insulation is in contact with the air at temperature t_A. Heat is transferred by conduction through the insulation and by natural convection through the air.

(*a*)   Show that, in the steady state,

$$\frac{\dot{Q}}{A} = \bar{U}(t_W - t_A),$$

where $\bar{U}$, the *overall coefficient of heat transfer*, is given by

$$\frac{1}{\bar{U}} = \frac{x}{K} + \frac{1}{h}.$$

(*b*)   How do you determine t, the temperature of the outer surface of the insulation?

4-23   Show that the unit of $K/\sigma\theta$ is 1 V²/deg².

4-24   The air above the surface of a freshwater lake is at a temperature θ_A, while the water is at its freezing point θ_i (with $\theta_A < \theta_i$). After a time τ has elapsed, ice of thickness y has formed. Assuming that the heat which is liberated when the water freezes flows up through the ice by conduction and thence into the air by natural convection, prove that

$$\frac{y}{h} + \frac{y^2}{2K} = \frac{\theta_i - \theta_A}{\rho l}\tau,$$

where h is the convection coefficient per unit area and is assumed constant while the ice forms; K is the thermal conductivity of ice; l is the heat of fusion of ice; and ρ is the density of ice. (*Hint:* The temperature θ of the upper surface of the ice is variable. Assume the ice to have a thickness y, and imagine an infinitesimal thickness dy to form in time $d\tau$.)

4-25   A solid cylindrical copper rod 10 cm long has one end maintained at a temperature of 20.00°K. The other end is blackened and exposed to thermal radiation from a body at 300°K, with no energy lost or gained elsewhere. When equilibrium is reached, what is the temperature difference between the two ends? (*Note:* Refer to Fig. 4-9.)

4-26   A cylindrical metal can blackened on the outside, 10 cm high and 5 cm in diameter, contains liquid helium at its normal boiling point of 4.2°K, at which its heat of vaporization is 21 J/g. Completely surrounding the helium can are walls maintained at the temperature of liquid nitrogen (78°K), and the intervening space is evacuated. How much helium is lost per hour?

4-27   The operating temperature of a tungsten filament in an incandescent lamp is 2460°K, and its absorptivity is 0.35. Find the surface area of the filament of a 100-W lamp.

4-28   A copper wire of length 130.2 cm and diameter 0.0326 cm is blackened and placed along the axis of an evacuated glass tube. The wire is connected to a battery, a rheostat, an ammeter, and a voltmeter, and the current is increased until, at the moment the wire is about to melt, the ammeter reads 12.8 A and the voltmeter 20.2 V. Assuming that all the energy supplied was radiated and that the radiation of the glass tube is negligible, calculate the melting temperature of copper.

4-29   The *solar constant* is the energy falling per unit of time on a unit area of a surface placed at right angles to a sunbeam just outside the earth's atmosphere. Measurements by Abbot have yielded the value 1.35 kW/m². The area of a sphere with a radius of 93,000,000 miles is 2.806×10^{23} m², and the surface area of the sun is 6.07×10^{18} m². Assuming the sun to be a blackbody, calculate its surface temperature.

4-30

(*a*)   A small body with temperature θ and absorptivity α is placed in a large evacuated cavity whose interior walls are at a temperature θ_W. When $\theta_W - \theta$ is small, show that the rate of heat transfer by radiation is

$$\dot{Q} = 4\theta_W^3 A\alpha\sigma(\theta_W - \theta).$$

(*b*)   If the body remains at constant pressure, show that the time for the temperature of the body to change from θ_1 to θ_2 is given by

$$\tau = \frac{C_P}{4\theta_W^3 A\alpha\sigma} \ln \frac{\theta_W - \theta_1}{\theta_W - \theta_2}.$$

(*c*)   Two small blackened spheres of identical size, one of copper, the other of aluminum, are suspended by silk threads within a large hole in a block of melting ice. It is found that it takes 10 min for the temperature of the aluminum to drop from 3 to 1°C, and 14.2 min for the copper to undergo the same temperature change. What is the ratio of specific heats of aluminum and copper? (Densities of Al and Cu are 2.7 and 8.9 g/cm³, respectively.)

4-31   A blackened solid copper sphere with a radius of 2 cm is placed in an evacuated enclosure whose walls are kept at 100°C. In what time does its temperature change from 103 to 102°C? (c_P = 3.81 J/g · deg; ρ = 8.93 g/cm³.)

5.

IDEAL GASES

5-1   Equation of State of a Gas

It was emphasized in Chap. 1 that a gas is the best-behaved thermometric substance because of the fact that the ratio of the pressure P of a gas at any temperature to the pressure P_3 of the same gas at the triple point, as both P and P_3 approach zero, approaches a value independent of the nature of the gas. The limiting value of this ratio, multiplied by 273.16 deg, was defined to be the ideal-gas temperature θ of the system at whose temperature the gas exerts the pressure P. The reason for this regular behavior may be found by investigating the way in which the product PV of a gas depends on the density or, if the mass is constant, on the reciprocal of the volume.

Suppose that the pressure P and the volume V of n moles of gas held at any constant temperature are measured over a wide range of values of the pressure, and the product Pv, where $v = V/n$, is plotted as a function of $1/v$. Experiments of this sort were first performed by Amagat in France in 1870 and later by Holborn and Otto in Berlin and by Kamerlingh-Onnes and Keesom in Leiden. Nowadays, such measurements are made at many bureaus of standards and universities. The relation between Pv and $1/v$ may be expressed by means of a power series (or *virial expansion*) of the form

$$Pv = A\left(1 + \frac{B}{v} + \frac{C}{v^2} + \frac{D}{v^3} + \cdots\right), \tag{5-1}$$

where A, B, C, etc., are called *virial coefficients* (A being the first virial coefficient, B the second, etc.) and depend on the temperature and on the nature of the gas. In the pressure range from 0 to about 40 atm, the relation between Pv and $1/v$ is practically linear, so that only the first two terms in the expansion are significant. In general, the greater the pressure range, the larger the number of terms in the virial expansion.

The virial coefficients play an important role not only in practical thermodynamics but also in theoretical physics, where they are related to molecular properties. Except at very low temperatures, the virial coefficients are quite small, as shown in Table 5-1, where the virial coefficients are given for nitrogen in the temperature range 80 to 273°K and in the pressure range from 0 to 200 atm. These data, obtained by Friedman, White, and Johnston of the Ohio State Cryogenic Laboratory, are listed in the "American Institute of Physics Handbook" (McGraw-Hill Book Company, New York, 1963)—hereafter referred to simply as "AIP Handbook."

Table 5-1   Virial Coefficients for Nitrogen

T, °K	B, cm³/mole	C, 10^2 cm⁶/mole²	D, 10^4 cm⁹/mole³	E, 10^5 cm¹²/mole⁴	F, 10^7 cm¹⁵/mole⁵
80	−250.80	210	−2000		
90	−200.50	135	−1000		
100	−162.10	85	− 600		
110	−131.80	65	− 200		
120	−114.62	48	− 27		
150	− 71.16	22	13	−123	41
200	− 34.33	12	14	−118	36
273	− 9.50	8.2	16	− 75	−16

The remarkable property of gases that makes them so valuable in thermometry is displayed in Fig. 5-1, where the product Pv is plotted against P for four different gases, all at the temperature of boiling water in the top graph, all at the triple point of water in the next lower graph, and all at the temperature of solid CO_2 in the lowest. In each case, it is seen that as the pressure approaches zero the product Pv approaches the same value for all gases at the same temperature. As the pressure of a constant mass of gas approaches zero, the volume approaches infinity, and according to the virial expansion [Eq. (5-1)], the product Pv approaches the first virial coefficient A. Thus,

$$\lim_{P \to 0} (Pv) = A = \begin{cases} \text{function of temperature only,} \\ \text{independent of gas.} \end{cases} \qquad (5\text{-}2)$$

The ideal-gas temperature θ is defined as

$$\theta = 273.16° \lim \frac{P}{P_3} \qquad \text{(const. } V \text{ and } n \text{)},$$

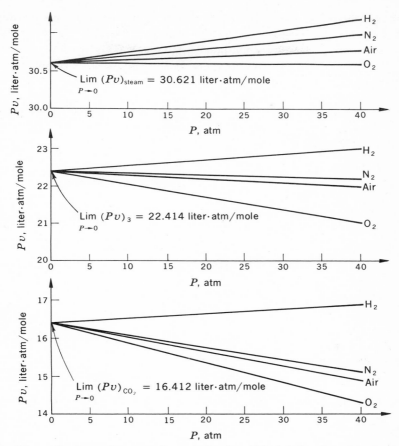

Fig. 5-1   *Fundamental property of gases is that* $\lim\limits_{P\to 0}(Pv)_\theta$ *is independent of the nature of the gas and depends only on* θ.

so that
$$\theta = 273.16° \lim \frac{PV/n}{P_3V/n} = 273.16° \frac{\lim (Pv)}{\lim (Pv)_3},$$

and
$$\lim (Pv) = \left[\frac{\lim (Pv)_3}{273.16°} \right] \theta$$

The bracketed term is called the *universal gas constant* and is denoted by R. Thus,

$$R = \frac{\lim (Pv)_3}{273.16°}. \tag{5-3}$$

The accepted value (1968) of $\lim (Pv)_3$ is 22.4144 liter · atm/g mole (where

1 liter is *exactly* equal to 10^3 cm³). Hence,

$$R = \begin{cases} 0.08206 \text{ liter} \cdot \text{atm/mole} \cdot \text{deg} \\ 8.3143 \text{ J/mole} \cdot \text{deg}. \end{cases}$$

Finally, substituting for v its value V/n, we may write the equation of state of a gas in the limit of low pressures in the form

$$\boxed{\lim (PV) = nR\theta.} \tag{5-4}$$

Fig. 5-2   *Graphical representation of the virial equation for nitrogen. (U.S. National Bureau of Standards, Circular 564.)*

Since $\lim (Pv) = A = R\theta$, the virial expansion may therefore be written

$$\frac{Pv}{R\theta} = 1 + \frac{B}{v} + \frac{C}{v^2} + \cdots$$

The ratio $Pv/R\theta$ is called the *compressibility factor* and is denoted by Z. It is tabulated for many values of temperature and pressure in several reports and circulars published by the National Bureau of Standards. A condensed set of tables of Z values for the important gases is given in the "AIP Handbook."

The general behavior of the compressibility factor may be displayed graphically by plotting $v(Pv/R\theta - 1)$ against $1/v$, since

$$v\left(\frac{Pv}{R\theta} - 1\right) = B + \frac{C}{v} + \cdots$$

In the region of small values of $1/v$, the left-hand member should be linear in $1/v$, with B equal to the y intercept and C equal to the slope. A few typical curves for nitrogen are shown in Fig. 5-2, where it may be seen that the graphs are linear in the low-density region and cut the y axis at values in agreement with the B values in Table 5-1.

5-2   Internal Energy of a Gas

Imagine a thermally insulated vessel with rigid walls, divided into two compartments by a partition. Suppose that there is a gas in one compartment and that the other is empty. If the partition is removed, the gas will undergo what is known as a *free expansion* in which no work is done and no heat is transferred. From the first law, since both Q and W are zero, it follows that *the internal energy remains unchanged during a free expansion*. The question of whether or not the temperature of a gas changes during a free expansion and, if it does, of the magnitude of the temperature change has engaged the attention of physicists for over a hundred years. Starting with Joule in 1843, many attempts have been made to measure either the quantity $(\partial\theta/\partial V)_U$, which may be called the *Joule coefficient*, or related quantities that are all a measure, in one way or another, of the effect of a free expansion—or, as it is often called, the *Joule effect*.

In general, the energy of a gas is a function of any two of the coordinates P, V, and θ. Considering U as a function of θ and V, we have

$$dU = \left(\frac{\partial U}{\partial \theta}\right)_V d\theta + \left(\frac{\partial U}{\partial V}\right)_\theta dV.$$

If no temperature change ($d\theta = 0$) takes place in a free expansion ($dU = 0$), then it follows that

$$\left(\frac{\partial U}{\partial V}\right)_\theta = 0;$$

or, in other words, U does not depend on V. Considering U to be a function of θ and P, we have

$$dU = \left(\frac{\partial U}{\partial \theta}\right)_P d\theta + \left(\frac{\partial U}{\partial P}\right)_\theta dP.$$

If no temperature change ($d\theta = 0$) takes place in a free expansion ($dU = 0$), then it follows that

$$\left(\frac{\partial U}{\partial P}\right)_\theta = 0;$$

or, in other words, U does not depend on P. It is apparent then that, if no temperature change takes place in a free expansion, U is independent of V and of P, and therefore U *is a function of θ only*.

Two methods of studying the Joule effect have been employed. In the original method of Joule, two vessels connected by a short tube and stopcock were immersed in a water bath. One vessel contained air at high pressure, and the other was evacuated. The temperature of the water was measured before and after the expansion, the idea being to infer the temperature change of the gas from the temperature change of the water. Since the heat capacity of the vessels and the water was approximately one thousand times as large as the heat capacity of the air, Joule was unable to detect any temperature change of the water, although, in the light of our present knowledge, the air must have undergone a temperature change of several degrees.

The second method of studying the Joule coefficient consists of an attempt to measure the temperature of the gas almost immediately after the free expansion, before the gas has had a chance to exchange heat with its surroundings, by using the gas itself as its own thermometer. In the experiments of Hirn in 1865, a vessel was divided into two equal compartments by a thin partition, which could be broken with the aid of a metal ball. Originally, both compartments contained air at atmospheric pressure. The air from one compartment was then pumped into the other compartment, and the temperature of the compressed gas was allowed to come to its original value. The partition was then broken, and soon afterward the pressure was measured with the aid of a U-tube manometer containing a light liquid and found to be the value that existed when the gas originally occupied the whole vessel.

It was therefore concluded that no temperature change took place. Cazin repeated this experiment in 1870 with similar apparatus.

The results of this method are doubtful because of the oscillations of the liquid in the manometer tube. If sufficient time elapses in order to allow the oscillations of the manometric liquid to subside, then, during this time, there is a transfer of heat between the gas and the walls of the vessel, which vitiates the results. Further complications arise from the conduction of heat through metal valve connections due to a temperature difference created by the rapidly streaming gas. In the experiments of Keyes and Sears in 1924, the gas was not used as its own thermometer; instead, a platinum resistance thermometer was employed to measure the temperature immediately after expansion. Temperature changes of approximately the right order were measured, but only a few rough measurements were made.

A direct measurement of the temperature change associated with a free expansion is so difficult that it seems necessary to give up the idea of a precise measurement of the Joule coefficient. Modern methods of attacking the problem of the internal energy of a gas involve the measurement of the quantity $(\partial u/\partial P)_\theta$ by having the gas undergo an isothermal expansion in which heat is transferred and work is done. The most extensive series of measurements of this kind was performed by Rossini and Frandsen in 1932 at the National Bureau of Standards with a method elaborated by Washburn. The apparatus is shown in Fig. 5-3. A bomb B contains n moles of gas at a pressure P and

Fig. 5-3   *Apparatus of Rossini and Frandsen for measuring $(\partial u/\partial P)_\theta$ of a gas.*

communicates with the atmosphere through a long coil wrapped around the bomb. The whole apparatus is immersed in a water bath whose temperature can be maintained constant at exactly the same value as that of the surrounding atmosphere.

The experiment is performed as follows: When the stopcock is opened slightly, the gas flows slowly through the long coil and out into the air. At the same time, the temperature of the gas, the bomb, the coils, and the water is maintained constant by an electric heating coil immersed in the water. The electrical energy supplied to the water is therefore the heat Q absorbed by the gas during the expansion. The work done by the gas is evidently

$$W = P_0(nv_0 - V_B),$$

where P_0 is atmospheric pressure, v_0 is the molar volume at atmospheric temperature and pressure, and V_B is the volume of the bomb.

If $u(P,\theta)$ is the molar energy at pressure P and temperature θ and if $u(P_0,\theta)$ is the molar energy at atmospheric pressure and the same temperature, then, from the first law,

$$u(P,\theta) - u(P_0,\theta) = \frac{W - Q}{n},$$

provided that corrections have been made to take account of the energy changes due to the contraction of the walls of the bomb. In this way, the energy change was measured for various values of the initial pressure and was plotted against the pressure, as shown in Fig. 5-4. Since $u(P_0,\theta)$ is con-

Fig. 5-4   *Dependence of internal energy of a gas on pressure.*

stant, it follows that the slope of the resulting curve at any value of P is equal to $(\partial u/\partial P)_\theta$. Within the pressure range of 1 to 40 atm, it is seen that $(\partial u/\partial P)_\theta$ *is independent of the pressure*, depending only on the temperature. Thus,

$$\left(\frac{\partial u}{\partial P}\right)_\theta = f(\theta),$$

and

$$u = f(\theta)P + F(\theta),$$

where $F(\theta)$ is another function of the temperature only.

Rossini and Frandsen's experiments with air, oxygen, and mixtures of oxygen and carbon dioxide lead to the conclusion that the internal energy of a gas is a function of both temperature and pressure. They found no pressure or temperature range in which the quantity $(\partial u/\partial P)_\theta$ was equal to zero.

Washburn's method has somewhat the same disadvantage as Joule's original method, in that the heat capacity of the gas is much smaller than that of the calorimeter and water bath. To keep the temperature of the gas constant within reasonable limits, the temperature of the water must be kept constant to within less than a thousandth of a degree. In Rossini and Frandsen's measurements, the final precision was estimated to be $2\frac{1}{2}$ percent.

Another determination of the average value of $(\partial u/\partial P)_\theta$ of air in a pressure range of over 50 atm was made by Baker in 1938 with a somewhat different method, capable of an accuracy of 0.1 percent. In Baker's experiment, the air expanded from a thin spherical metal bomb into the space between it and a thin outer concentric spherical shell. The temperature of the outer shell was measured at small time intervals, starting from the moment after the expansion until the temperature returned to its original value; during this time, heat flowed into the gas at a rate that was a known function of the temperature difference between the outer shell and its surroundings, which were held at a constant temperature. By making the two shells very thin, the ratio of the heat capacity of the shells to that of the gas was very much smaller than in any previous work. The heat transferred to the gas could be calculated with great accuracy, and many corrections were applied with extreme care. The few measurements that have been made with this apparatus up to the present time have substantiated the results of Rossini and Frandsen.

5-3 Ideal Gas

We have seen that, in the case of a real gas, only in the limit as the pressure approaches zero does the equation of state assume the simple form $PV = nR\theta$. Furthermore, the internal energy of a real gas is a function of pressure as well as of temperature. It is convenient at this point to define an *ideal gas* whose properties, while not corresponding to those of any existing gas, are approximately those of a real gas at low pressures. By definition, an ideal gas satisfies the equations

$$\begin{array}{|c|} \hline PV = nR\theta \\ \left(\dfrac{\partial U}{\partial P}\right)_\theta = 0 \\ \hline \end{array} \qquad \text{(ideal gas).} \qquad (5\text{-}5)$$

The requirement that $(\partial U/\partial P)_\theta = 0$ may be written in other ways. Thus,

$$\left(\frac{\partial U}{\partial V}\right)_\theta = \left(\frac{\partial U}{\partial P}\right)_\theta \left(\frac{\partial P}{\partial V}\right)_\theta,$$

and since $(\partial P/\partial V)_\theta = -nR\theta/V^2 = -P/V$, and therefore is not zero, whereas $(\partial U/\partial P)_\theta$ is zero, it follows that for an ideal gas

$$\boxed{\left(\frac{\partial U}{\partial V}\right)_\theta = 0} \qquad \text{(ideal gas).} \qquad (5\text{-}6)$$

Finally, since both $(\partial U/\partial P)_\theta$ and $(\partial U/\partial V)_\theta$ are zero,

$$\boxed{U = f(\theta) \text{ only}} \qquad \text{(ideal gas).} \qquad (5\text{-}7)$$

Whether an actual gas may be treated as an ideal gas depends upon the error that may be tolerated in a given calculation. An actual gas at pressures below about 2 atm may be treated as an ideal gas without introducing an error greater than a few percent. Even in the case of a saturated vapor in equilibrium with its liquid, the ideal-gas equation of state may be used with only a small error if the vapor pressure is low.

For an infinitesimal quasi-static process of a hydrostatic system, the first law is

$$dQ = dU + P\,dV,$$

and the heat capacity at constant volume is given by

$$C_V = \left(\frac{\partial U}{\partial \theta}\right)_V.$$

In the special case of an ideal gas, U is a function of θ only; therefore the partial derivative with respect to θ is the same as the total derivative. Consequently,

$$C_V = \frac{dU}{d\theta},$$

and

$$\boxed{dQ = C_V \, d\theta + P \, dV.}$$ (5-8)

Now, all equilibrium states are represented by the ideal-gas equation

$$PV = nR\theta,$$

and, for an infinitesimal quasi-static process,

$$P \, dV + V \, dP = nR \, d\theta.$$

Substituting the above in Eq. (5-8), we get

$$dQ = (C_V + nR) \, d\theta - V \, dP,$$

and, dividing by $d\theta$,

$$\frac{dQ}{d\theta} = C_V + nR - V\frac{dP}{d\theta}.$$

At constant pressure, the left-hand member becomes C_P; whence

$$\boxed{C_P = C_V + nR.}$$ (5-9)

We have the result, therefore, that the heat capacity at constant pressure of an ideal gas is always larger than that at constant volume, the difference remaining constant and equal to nR.

Since U is a function of θ only, it follows that

$$C_V = \frac{dU}{d\theta} = \text{a function of } \theta \text{ only,}$$

and

$$C_P = C_V + nR = \text{a function of } \theta \text{ only.}$$

One more useful equation can be obtained. Since

$$dQ = (C_V + nR) \, d\theta - V \, dP,$$

we get

$$\boxed{dQ = C_P \, d\theta - V \, dP.}$$ (5-10)

5-4   Experimental Determination of Heat Capacities

The heat capacities of gases are measured by the electrical method. To measure C_V, the gas is contained in a thin-walled steel flask with a heating wire wound around it. By maintaining an electric current in the wire, an equivalent amount of heat is supplied to the gas, and the specific heat at constant volume is obtained by measuring the temperature rise of the gas. The same method is used to measure C_P except that, instead of confining the gas to a constant volume, the gas is allowed to flow at constant pressure through a calorimeter, where it receives electrically a known equivalent heat per unit of time. From the initial (inlet) and final (outlet) temperatures, the rate of supply of heat, and the rate of flow of gas, the value of C_P is calculated. The results of such measurements on gases at *low pressures* (approximately ideal gases) can be stated in a simple manner in terms of molar heat capacities.

1   *All gases:*
   (*a*) c_V is a function of θ only.
   (*b*) c_P is a function of θ only, and $> c_V$.
   (*c*) $c_P - c_V = $ const. $= R$.
   (*d*) $\gamma = c_P/c_V = $ a function of θ only, and > 1.

2   *Monatomic gases,* such as He, Ne, and A, and most metallic vapors, such as the vapors of Na, Cd, and Hg:
   (*a*) c_V is constant over a wide temperature range and is very nearly equal to $\frac{3}{2}R$.
   (*b*) c_P is constant over a wide temperature range and is very nearly equal to $\frac{5}{2}R$.
   (*c*) γ is constant over a wide temperature range and is very nearly equal to $\frac{5}{3}$.

3   *So-called permanent diatomic gases,* namely, H_2, D_2, O_2, N_2, NO, and CO:
   (*a*) c_V is constant at ordinary temperatures, being equal to about $\frac{5}{2}R$, and increases as the temperature is raised.
   (*b*) c_P is constant at ordinary temperatures, being equal to about $\frac{7}{2}R$, and increases as the temperature is raised.
   (*c*) γ is constant at ordinary temperatures, being equal to about $\frac{7}{5}$, and decreases as the temperature is raised.

4   *Polyatomic gases and gases that are chemically active,* such as CO_2, NH_3, CH_4, Cl_2, and Br_2:
   c_P, c_V, and c_P/c_V vary with the temperature, the variation being different for each gas.

These experimental results indicate that the universal gas constant R (8.31 J/mole · deg) is a natural unit with which to express the molar heat capacity

Fig. 5-5   *Experimental values of c_P/R for hydrogen as a function of temperature, plotted on a logarithmic scale.*

of a gas. It is a very interesting consequence of theory that this is also true for solids. In the remainder of this book we shall specify not the heat capacities themselves but the ratios c_V/R and c_P/R.

The behavior of hydrogen is quite exceptional, as shown in Fig. 5-5. At very low temperatures, c_P/R drops to a value of $\frac{5}{2}$, appropriate to a *monatomic* gas. For all other diatomic gases, c_P/R may always be written

$$\frac{c_P}{R} = \tfrac{7}{2} + f(\theta),$$

where $f(\theta)$ is often one or more functions of the type

$$\left(\frac{b}{\theta}\right)^2 \frac{e^{b/\theta}}{(e^{b/\theta} - 1)^2}.$$

Exact equations of the above type are difficult to handle and are not suitable for the practical calculations of the laboratory scientist; consequently, approximate empiric equations are used. Empiric equations for c_P/R of some of the most important gases, compiled by H. M. Spencer, are given in Table 5-2, within the temperature range of 300 to 1500°K. In recent years, other and more accurate empiric equations have been suggested, some of these being valid up to 3000°K. The simple quadratic equations of Table 5-2, however, will serve the purposes of this book.

Table 5-2 c_P/R **of Important Gases**

$c_P/R = a + b\theta + c\theta^2$ (from 300 to 1500°K)

Gas	a	b, 10^{-3} deg^{-1}	c, 10^{-6} deg^{-2}
H_2	3.495	−0.101	0.243
O_2	3.068	1.638	−0.512
Cl_2	3.813	1.220	−0.486
Br_2	4.240	0.490	−0.179
N_2	3.247	0.712	−0.041
CO	3.192	0.924	−0.141
HCl	3.389	0.218	0.186
HBr	3.311	0.481	0.079
CO_2	3.206	5.082	−1.714
H_2O	3.634	1.195	0.135
NH_3	3.116	3.970	−0.366
H_2S	3.214	2.871	−0.608
CH_4	1.702	9.083	−2.164

5-5   Quasi-static Adiabatic Process

When an ideal gas undergoes a quasi-static adiabatic process, the pressure, volume, and temperature change in a manner that is described by a relation between P and V, θ and V, or P and θ. In order to derive the relation between P and V, we start with Eqs. (5-8) and (5-10) of Art. 5-4. Thus,

$$dQ = C_V \, d\theta + P \, dV,$$

and

$$dQ = C_P \, d\theta - V \, dP.$$

Since, in an adiabatic process, $dQ = 0$,

$$V \, dP = C_P \, d\theta,$$

and

$$P \, dV = -C_V \, d\theta.$$

Dividing the first by the second,

$$\frac{dP}{P} = -\frac{C_P}{C_V} \frac{dV}{V},$$

and denoting the ratio of the heat capacities by the symbol γ, we have

$$\frac{dP}{P} = -\gamma \frac{dV}{V}.$$

This equation cannot be integrated until we know something about the behavior of γ. We have seen that for monatomic gases γ is constant, whereas for diatomic and polyatomic gases it may vary with the temperature. It requires, however, a very large change of temperature to produce an appreciable change in γ. For example, in the case of carbon monoxide, a temperature rise from 0 to 2000°C produces a decrease in γ from 1.4 to 1.3. Most adiabatic processes that we deal with do not involve such a large temperature change. We are therefore entitled, in an adiabatic process that involves only a moderate temperature change, to neglect the small accompanying change in γ. Regarding γ, therefore, as constant and integrating, we obtain

$$\ln P = -\gamma \ln V + \ln \text{const.},$$

or

$$\boxed{PV^\gamma = \text{const.}} \tag{5-11}$$

The above equation holds at all equilibrium states through which an ideal gas passes during a quasi-static adiabatic process. It is important to understand that a free expansion is an adiabatic process but is not quasi-static. It is therefore entirely fallacious to attempt to apply Eq. (5-11) to the states traversed by an ideal gas during a free expansion.

A family of curves representing quasi-static adiabatic processes may be plotted on a PV diagram by assigning different values to the constant in Eq. (5-11). The slope of any adiabatic curve is

$$\left(\frac{\partial P}{\partial V}\right)_s = -\gamma \text{ const. } V^{-\gamma-1}$$

$$= -\gamma \frac{P}{V},$$

where the subscript s is used to denote an adiabatic process.

Quasi-static isothermal processes are represented by a family of equilateral hyperbolas obtained by assigning different values to θ in the equation $PV = nR\theta$. Since

$$\left(\frac{\partial P}{\partial V}\right)_\theta = -\frac{P}{V},$$

it follows that an adiabatic curve has a steeper negative slope than does an isothermal curve at the same point.

The isothermal curves and adiabatic curves of an ideal gas may be shown in a revealing way on a $PV\theta$ surface. If P, V, and θ are plotted along rectangular axes, the resulting surface is shown in Fig. 5-6, where it may be seen that the adiabatic curves cut across the isotherms.

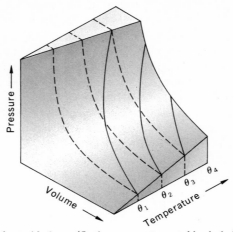

Fig. 5-6   *Surface for an ideal gas. (Isotherms are represented by dashed curves, and adiabatics by full curves.)*

5-6   Clément and Désormes Method of Measuring γ

The earliest and simplest method of measuring the γ of an ideal gas is that of Clément and Désormes. The gas is contained in a vessel at room temperature and at a pressure P_i slightly above atmospheric pressure (see Fig. 5-7). Suppose that the volume of *any small constant mass* of the gas is V_i. By rapidly opening and closing a stopcock (flipping a poppet valve), the small amount of gas under consideration is caused to expand adiabatically until its volume is V_f and its pressure is that of the atmosphere P_0, with the temperature dropping slightly below room temperature. Assuming this adiabatic expansion to be approximately quasi-static, we may write

$$P_i V_i^\gamma = P_0 V_f^\gamma.$$

The gas is allowed to stand for a few minutes at constant volume until its

Fig. 5-7   *Schematic representation of the method of Clément and Désormes.*

temperature comes back to its initial value, thus causing the pressure to rise to the final value P_f. Since the initial and final temperatures are equal, we have

$$P_i V_i = P_f V_f.$$

Eliminating V_i and V_f from the two equations, we get

$$\frac{P_i}{P_0} = \left(\frac{P_i}{P_f}\right)^{\gamma}.$$

Taking the natural logarithm of both sides and solving for γ, we obtain

$$\gamma = \frac{\ln (P_i/P_0)}{\ln (P_i/P_f)}.$$

The pressures are usually measured with an open U-tube manometer containing a convenient light liquid. Denoting the height of the barometric column of this liquid by h_0, we may write

$$P_i = h_0 + h_i = h_0(1 + h_i/h_0),$$
$$P_0 = h_0,$$

and
$$P_f = h_0 + h_f = h_0(1 + h_f/h_0),$$

where h_i and h_f are very small compared with h_0. Upon substituting,

$$\gamma = \frac{\ln (1 + h_i/h_0)}{\ln (1 + h_i/h_0) - \ln (1 + h_f/h_0)}.$$

Now it is easy to show that, if x is small compared with unity,

$$\ln (1 + x) = x.$$

Since the ratios h_i/h_0 and h_f/h_0 are small compared with unity, we obtain finally

$$\gamma = \frac{h_i}{h_i - h_f}.$$

5-7   Rüchhardt's Method of Measuring γ

An ingenious method of measuring γ developed by Rüchhardt in 1929, although no more accurate than the preceding method, makes use of elementary mechanics. The gas is contained in a large jar of volume V. Fitted to the jar (see Fig. 5-8) is a glass tube with an accurate bore of cross-sectional area A, into which a metal ball of mass m fits snugly like a piston. Since the gas is slightly compressed by the steel ball in its equilibrium position, its pressure P is slightly larger than atmospheric pressure P_0. Thus, neglecting friction,

$$P = P_0 + \frac{mg}{A}.$$

If the ball is given a slight downward displacement and then let go, it will oscillate with a period τ. Friction will cause the ball to come to rest eventually. Let the displacement of the ball from its equilibrium position at any moment be denoted by y, where y is positive when the ball is above the equilibrium position and negative below. A small positive displacement causes an increase in volume which is very small compared with the equilibrium volume V and which therefore can be denoted by dV, where

$$dV = yA.$$

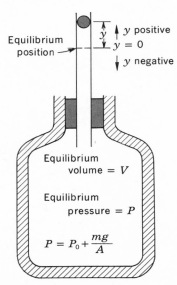

Fig. 5-8   *Rüchhardt's apparatus for measurement of γ.*

Similarly, a small positive displacement causes a decrease in pressure which is very small compared with the equilibrium pressure P and which therefore can be denoted by dP, where dP is a negative quantity. The resultant force $\mathcal{F}$ acting on the ball is equal to $A\,dP$ if we neglect friction, or

$$dP = \frac{\mathcal{F}}{A}.$$

Notice that, when y is positive, dP is negative and therefore $\mathcal{F}$ is negative; that is, $\mathcal{F}$ is a restoring force.

Now, as the ball oscillates fairly rapidly, the variations of P and V are adiabatic. Since the variations are also quite small, the states through which the gas passes can be considered to be approximately states of equilibrium. We may therefore assume that the changes of P and V represent an approximately quasi-static adiabatic process, and we may write

$$PV^{\gamma} = \text{const.}$$

and
$$P\gamma V^{\gamma-1}\,dV + V^{\gamma}\,dP = 0.$$

Substituting for dV and dP, we get

$$\mathcal{F} = -\frac{\gamma P A^2}{V}\,y.$$

The above equation expresses the fact that the restoring force is directly proportional to the displacement and is in the opposite direction. This is precisely the condition for *simple harmonic motion*, for which the period τ is

$$\tau = 2\pi\sqrt{\frac{m}{-\mathcal{F}/y}}.$$

Consequently,
$$\tau = 2\pi\sqrt{\frac{mV}{\gamma P A^2}},$$

and
$$\gamma = \frac{4\pi^2 mV}{A^2 P \tau^2}.$$

The mass of the ball, the cross-sectional area of the tube, the pressure, and the volume are all known beforehand, and only the period has to be measured to obtain γ. The values obtained by Rüchhardt for air and for CO_2 were in good agreement with those obtained from calorimetric measurements.

5-8   Modifications of Rüchhardt's Method

A variation of Rüchhardt's method was suggested by Rinkel in 1929. This method consists of holding the ball in the position where the gas pressure is exactly atmospheric and then letting it drop, measuring the distance L that the ball falls before starting to go up again. Measuring y from this initial position, the gravitational potential energy liberated is mgL, and the work done in compressing the gas is

$$\int_0^L \mathcal{F} \, dy = \frac{\gamma P_0 A^2}{V_0} \int_0^L y \, dy = \frac{\gamma P_0 A^2 L^2}{2V_0} \; ;$$

whence

$$\frac{\gamma P_0 A^2 L^2}{2V_0} = mgL,$$

or

$$\gamma = \frac{2mgV_0}{P_0 A^2 L}.$$

Rinkel's method has the advantage over Rüchhardt's that L may be measured with greater accuracy than τ. Moreover, an error in the measurement of L produces an error in γ determined by only the first power of L, whereas an error in τ produces an error involving the second power.

Both Rüchhardt's and Rinkel's methods involve errors due to three simplifying assumptions: (1) that the gas is ideal, (2) that there is no friction, and (3) that volume changes are strictly adiabatic. Rinkel estimated that the second assumption is responsible for the largest error, amounting to about 3 percent.

The large frictional damping in the usual Rüchhardt method may be avoided by using a glass tube with a slight taper, with the wider diameter at the top. A slow flow of gas maintains a steady oscillation of a ball about an equilibrium position. The flow is controlled by a throttle valve between the experimental apparatus and a high-pressure gas tank. With this method, Hafner and Duthie found γ to be 1.664 for argon, 1.406 for nitrogen, and 1.313 for carbon dioxide. If a small rod is attached to the underside of the oscillating ball, the total mass of the oscillating system may be varied by attaching metal washers to the rod, and the variation of period with mass may be measured. The results of H. C. Jensen are shown in Fig. 5-9, where it is seen that the line passes almost through the origin, indicating that one has here the equivalent of a nearly massless spring.

A modification of Rüchhardt's experiment in which accurate account is taken of the real equation of state of the gas, the friction present, and the departure from strict adiabatic conditions was achieved by Clark and Katz in 1940. The method was improved by Katz, Woods, and Leverton in 1949.

Fig. 5-9   *The square of the period against the mass for the oscillating ball in Rüchhardt's experiment.* (*H. C. Jensen, 1963.*)

A steel piston at the center of a cylindrical tube divides the gas into two equal parts, as shown in Fig. 5-10. It is set in vibration at any desired frequency by external coils in which an alternating current of suitable frequency is maintained. The cylinder is kept in a horizontal position, and friction between the piston and the cylinder is reduced by balancing the weight of the piston by the attraction of an electromagnet.

The amplitude of vibration of the piston is measured with a microscope equipped with a micrometer eyepiece, at a number of values of the frequency of the impressed alternating current, and the resonance curve is plotted.

Fig. 5-10   *Apparatus of Clark and Katz for measuring* γ *of a real gas as a function of pressure.*

From the resonance frequency and very elaborate calculations not involving the assumptions made by Rüchhardt and Rinkel, γ is calculated. Since friction was reduced to a great extent by the lift magnet, the corrections amounted to only about 1 percent. The authors measured γ at various pressures from 1 to 25 atm and expressed the results in the form of empiric equations, as shown in Table 5-3.

Table 5-3   Pressure Variation of γ ($\gamma = a + bP + cP^2$)

Gas	Temp., °C	a	b, atm^{-1}	c, atm^{-2}	γ extrapolated to zero pressure (ideal gas)
He	23.1	1.6669	−0.0002	0	1.667
A	24.2	1.6667	0.00353	0	1.667
H_2	24.4	1.4045	0.00025	0	1.405
N_2	23.0	1.4006	0.00221	0	1.401
CO_2	29.9	1.2857	0.00629	0	1.286
N_2O	25.3	1.2744	0.00225	0.000973	1.274
CH:	25.1	1.3029	−0.00105	0.000484	1.303

5-9   Speed of a Longitudinal Wave

If a compression is produced at one place in a substance, it will travel with a constant speed w, depending on certain properties of the substance that we shall now proceed to determine. Directing our attention to a column of material of cross section A, let us suppose that a piston, on the left in Fig. 5-11, actuated by an agent exerting a force $A(P + \Delta P)$ moves to the right with a constant velocity w_0. This sets up a compression traveling with a constant velocity w, so that in time τ the compression has traveled a distance $w\tau$ while the piston has traveled a distance $w_0\tau$.

Consider as a "free body" the compressed column whose length, if uncompressed, would be $w\tau$ and whose uncompressed volume $V = Aw\tau$. If ρ is the density of the normal or uncompressed material, the mass of the free body is $\rho Aw\tau$. At time τ, the

$$\left.\begin{array}{l}\text{Rate of increase of mass of} \\ \text{the compressed column}\end{array}\right\} = \frac{\rho Aw\tau}{\tau} = \rho Aw.$$

The entire compressed column has a velocity w_0 equal to that of the piston. Therefore,

$$\left.\begin{array}{l}\text{Rate of increase of momentum} \\ \text{of the compressed column}\end{array}\right\} = \rho Aww_0.$$

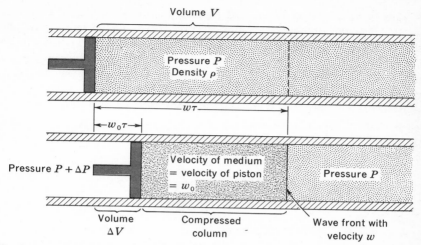

Fig. 5-11   *Propagation of a compression with constant velocity w by motion of a piston with constant velocity w_0. Upper diagram at the start; lower diagram after time τ.*

The free body is acted on by a force $A(P + \Delta P)$ to the right and a force AP to the left. Therefore,

$$\left. \begin{array}{r} \text{Unbalanced force on the} \\ \text{compressed column} \end{array} \right\} = A\,\Delta P.$$

Since the unbalanced force is equal to the rate of change of momentum,

$$A\,\Delta P = \rho Aww_0,$$

or

$$\Delta P = \rho w^2 \frac{w_0}{w}.$$

The "uncompressed free body" of volume $V = Aw\tau$ has undergone a compression $\Delta V = Aw_0\tau$. That is,

$$\frac{\Delta V}{V} = \frac{Aw_0\tau}{Aw\tau} = \frac{w_0}{w}.$$

Therefore,

$$\Delta P = \rho w^2 \frac{\Delta V}{V},$$

which may be written

$$w = \sqrt{\frac{1}{\rho\,\Delta V/V\,\Delta P}}.$$

This formula was first obtained by Newton, who regarded the quantity $\Delta V/V\,\Delta P$ as the isothermal compressibility. It was shown later by Laplace that the expression is really the adiabatic compressibility. To see why this is so, let us consider a column of material of cross section A, bounded by two planes, one at the center of a compression and the other at the center of a rarefaction, a distance $\lambda/2$ apart, where λ is the wavelength. Let us suppose that the temperature at the center of the compression exceeds the temperature at the center of the rarefaction by an amount $\Delta\theta$. Then the heat conducted a distance $\lambda/2$ in the time $\lambda/2w$ (time for the wave to travel the distance $\lambda/2$) is given by

$$\left.\begin{array}{c}\text{Heat conducted in the time for the}\\ \text{wave to travel a distance } \lambda/2\end{array}\right\} = KA\,\frac{\Delta\theta}{\lambda/2}\,\frac{\lambda}{2w} = KA\,\frac{\Delta\theta}{w}\,,$$

where K is the thermal conductivity of the medium. The mass of material between the compression and rarefaction is $\rho A\lambda/2$, and the heat necessary to raise the temperature of this mass by the amount $\Delta\theta$ is

$$\left.\begin{array}{c}\text{Heat necessary to raise temperature}\\ \text{of mass } \rho A\lambda/2 \text{ by } \Delta\theta\end{array}\right\} = \rho A\,\frac{\lambda}{2}\,c_V\,\Delta\theta,$$

where c_V is the specific heat at constant volume.

The propagation of the wave would be adiabatic if the conducted heat were much too small to raise the temperature of the mass $\rho A\lambda/2$ by the amount $\Delta\theta$, or

$$\frac{KA\,\Delta\theta}{w} \ll \rho A\,\frac{\lambda}{2}\,c_V\,\Delta\theta \qquad \text{(adiabatic condition)}.$$

This may be written

$$\frac{2K}{w\rho c_V} \ll \lambda \qquad \text{(adiabatic condition)}.$$

The usual range of wavelengths of compressional waves is from a few centimeters to a few hundred centimeters. Let us compare these values with $2K/w\rho c_V$. Taking a gas like air as a typical case, we have, roughly,

$$K = 2 \times 10^{-4}\ \text{J/s} \cdot \text{cm} \cdot \text{deg,}$$
$$w = 3 \times 10^{4}\ \text{cm/s,}$$
$$\rho = 10^{-3}\ \text{g/cm}^3,$$
$$c_V = 0.4\ \text{J/g} \cdot \text{deg,}$$

and
$$\frac{2K}{w\rho c_V} = \frac{2 \times 2 \times (10^{-4}\,\text{J/s} \cdot \text{cm} \cdot \text{deg})}{3 \times (10^4\,\text{cm/s})(10^{-3}\,\text{g/cm}^3)(0.4\,\text{J/g} \cdot \text{deg})}$$
$$= 3.3 \times 10^{-5}\,\text{cm}.$$

In the case of a metal, K would be much larger, but this would be compensated by the much larger values of w and ρ, and the quantity $2K/w\rho c_V$ would be still smaller than 3.3×10^{-5} cm. This quantity is therefore seen to be so much smaller than the usual value of a wavelength of a compressional wave (3.3×10^{-5} cm is the wavelength of ultraviolet light) that the adiabatic condition is well fulfilled. We therefore conclude that, in view of the properties of ordinary matter, *the volume changes which take place under the influence of a longitudinal wave at ordinary frequencies are adiabatic*, not isothermal.

Returning now to the expression for the velocity of a longitudinal wave and identifying $\Delta V / V\,\Delta P$ as the *adiabatic* compressibility κ_S, we have finally

$$w = \sqrt{\frac{1}{\rho \kappa_S}}.$$

From Art. 5-5 we have, for an ideal gas,

$$\kappa_S = -\frac{1}{V}\left(\frac{\partial V}{\partial P}\right)_S = \frac{1}{\gamma P},$$

and
$$\rho = \frac{m}{v},$$

where m is the molecular weight and v is the molar volume. Hence,

$$w = \sqrt{\frac{\gamma P v}{m}},$$

or
$$\boxed{w = \sqrt{\frac{\gamma R\theta}{m}}.}$$

(5-12)

Equation (5-12) enables us to calculate γ from experimental measurements of w and θ. For example, the speed of sound in air at 0°C is about 1100 ft/s, or about 332 m/s. Therefore, using the values

$w = 332$ m/s,
$\theta = 273°$K,
$R = 8.31$ J/mole · deg,
$m = \frac{4}{5} \times 28 + \frac{1}{5} \times 32 = 28.8$ g/mole,

we get

$$\gamma = \frac{mw^2}{R\theta}$$

$$= \frac{(28.8 \text{ g/mole})(3.32)^2(10^4 m^2/s^2)}{(8.31 \text{ J/mole} \cdot \text{deg})(273 \text{ deg})} \frac{10^{-3} \text{ kg}}{1 \text{ g}}$$

$$= \tfrac{317}{227} = 1.40.$$

The speed of a sound wave in a gas can be measured roughly by means of Kundt's tube. The gas is admitted to a cylinder tube closed at one end and supplied at the other end with a movable piston capable of being set in vibration parallel to the axis of the tube. In the tube is a small amount of light powder. For a given frequency, a position of the piston can be found at which standing waves are set up. Under these conditions small heaps of powder pile up at the nodes. The distance between any two adjacent nodes is one-half a wavelength, and the speed of the waves is the product of the frequency and the wavelength.

Much greater accuracy is achieved with an acoustic interferometer, at one end of which is a source of waves such as a piezoelectric crystal and at the other a receiver. When the distance between the two is kept constant and the frequency is varied, the various resonances corresponding to different numbers of antinodes are noted. Using a frequency range of 50 to 3000 Hz, and applying corrections for errors due to viscosity and heat conduction that are present when a gas is confined within a tube, Cronin measured the temperature variation of γ of He, N_2, air, and CO_2; his results are shown in Fig. 5-12. (These are correct to within about 1 percent.)

Between the triple point of hydrogen and the liquid helium region (roughly, from 14 to 4°K), there are no fixed points with which to calibrate carbon or

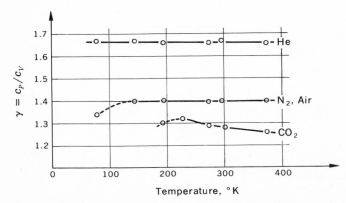

Fig. 5-12   *Dependence of γ on temperature from measurements of the speed of sound.* (*D. J. Cronin, 1963.*)

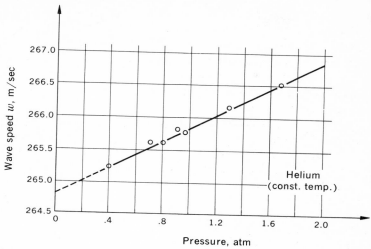

Fig. 5-13   *Speed of an ultrasonic wave in helium as a function of pressure.* (*H. H. Plumb,*
NBS, 1965.)

germanium resistance thermometers. Low-temperature physicists have felt
the lack of an absolute standardizing instrument in this range for many
years. Accordingly, an acoustic interferometer was developed by Plumb at
the National Bureau of Standards, and this is now capable of a reproducibility of 0.002 deg at 2°K and of 0.007 deg at 20°K. The resonance tube has a
fixed frequency of about 1 MHz, but a variable path length. A movable
piston forms the upper reflecting surface, and when resonance occurs, it is
detected by monitoring a small voltage applied across the crystal, with peaks
appearing on a chart whenever resonance occurs. The displacement of the
piston, divided by the number of peaks, is one-half the wavelength. The
pressure of the helium is varied from 2 to 0.4 atm, and the speed of sound is
plotted as a function of pressure as seen in Fig. 5-13. Extrapolation to zero
pressure gives the wave speed under ideal-gas conditions, so that

$$\theta = \frac{w^2 \mathcal{M}_{He}}{\gamma R}.$$

PROBLEMS

$$[R = 0.0821 \text{ liter} \cdot \text{atm/mole} \cdot \text{deg} = 8.31 \text{ J/mole} \cdot \text{deg};$$
1 liter · atm = 101 J.]

5-1   A thermally insulated horizontal cylinder closed at both ends is
fitted with a *frictionless heat-conducting* piston that divides the volume into two

unequal parts. The piston is initially clamped so that the volume to the left of it is V_0 and that to the right is $3V_0$. The left-hand volume contains an ideal monatomic gas at temperature θ_0 and pressure $2P_0$. The right-hand volume contains the same gas at temperature θ_0 and pressure P_0. The piston is now released.

(a)   What are the final temperature and pressure on each side?

(b)   What are the final volumes?

(c)   Describe the processes that bring the piston to rest. Are these processes quasi-static?

5-2   A vertical cylindrical tank of length greater than 76 cm has its top end closed by a tightly fitting frictionless piston of negligible weight. The air inside the cylinder is at an absolute pressure of 1 atm. The piston is depressed by pouring mercury on it slowly, so that the temperature of the air is maintained constant. What is the length of the air column when mercury starts to spill over the top of the cylinder?

5-3   Mercury is poured into the open end of a J-shaped glass tube which is closed at the short end, trapping the air in that end. Assuming air to act like an ideal gas, how much mercury can be poured in before it overflows? The long and short ends are 1 m and 50 cm long, respectively, and effects due to the curvature of the bottom may be neglected. Take atmospheric pressure to be 75 cm of Hg.

5-4   A cylindrical highball glass 15 cm high and 35 cm² in cross section contains water up to the 10-cm mark. A card is placed over the top and held there while the glass is inverted. When the support is removed, what mass of water must leave the glass in order that the rest of the water should remain in the glass, if one neglects the weight of the card? (*Caution:* Try this over a sink.)

5-5   Two bulbs containing air, one of which has a volume three times the other, are connected by a capillary of negligible volume and are initially at the same temperature. To what temperature must the air in the larger bulb be raised in order that the pressure be doubled? Neglect heat conduction through the air in the capillary.

5-6

(a)   Prove that the volume expansivity β of a real gas and the compressibility factor Z are connected by the following relation:

$$\beta = \frac{1}{\theta} + \frac{1}{Z}\left(\frac{\partial Z}{\partial \theta}\right)_p.$$

(b)   Prove that the isothermal compressibility κ of a real gas is given by the relation

$$\kappa = \frac{1}{P} - \frac{1}{Z}\left(\frac{\partial Z}{\partial P}\right)_\theta.$$

5-7   Expand the following equations in the form

$$Pv = R\theta \left(1 + \frac{B}{v} + \frac{C}{v^2} + \frac{D}{v^3} + \cdots \right),$$

and determine the second virial coefficient in each case:

(a) $\left(P + \dfrac{a}{v^2}\right)(v - b) = R\theta$ (van der Waals).

(b) $P = \dfrac{R\theta(1 - c/v\theta^3)}{v^2}\left[v + B_0\left(1 - \dfrac{b}{v}\right)\right] - \dfrac{A_0(1 - a/v)}{v^2}$
       (Beattie-Bridgeman).

(c) $Pv = R\theta + B'P + C'P^2 + D'P^3 + \cdots$
       (Another type of virial expansion).

(d) $P = \dfrac{R\theta}{v - b}\, e^{-a/R\theta v}$ (Dieterici).

5-8   An ideal gas is contained in a cylinder equipped with a frictionless, nonleaking piston of area A. When the pressure is atmospheric P_0, the piston face is at a distance l from the closed end. The gas is compressed by moving the piston a distance x. Calculate the spring constant, or force constant, $\mathcal{F}/x$, under (a) isothermal conditions and (b) under adiabatic conditions. (c) In what respect is a gas cushion superior to a steel spring? (d) Using Eq. (4-14), show that $C_P - C_V = nR$ for an ideal gas.

5-9   The temperature of an ideal gas in a capillary of constant cross-sectional area varies linearly from one end ($x = 0$) to the other ($x = L$), according to the equation

$$\theta = \theta_0 + \frac{\theta_L - \theta_0}{L}\, x.$$

If the volume of the capillary is V and the pressure P is uniform throughout, show that the number of moles of gas n is given by

$$PV = nR\,\frac{\theta_L - \theta_0}{\ln\,(\theta_L/\theta_0)}.$$

Show that, when $\theta_L = \theta_0 = \theta$, the above equation reduces to the obvious one $PV = nR\theta$.

5-10   Prove that the work done by an ideal gas with constant heat capacities during a quasi-static adiabatic expansion is equal to

(a) $$W = C_V(\theta_i - \theta_f).$$

(b) $$W = \frac{P_iV_i - P_fV_f}{\gamma - 1}.$$

(c) $$W = \frac{P_iV_i}{\gamma - 1}\left[1 - \left(\frac{P_f}{P_i}\right)^{(\gamma-1)/\gamma}\right].$$

5-11

(a)   Show that the heat transferred during an infinitesimal quasi-static process of an ideal gas can be written

$$dQ = \frac{C_V}{nR} V\, dP + \frac{C_P}{nR} P\, dV.$$

Applying this equation to an adiabatic process, show that $PV^\gamma = $ const.

(b)   An ideal gas of volume 0.05 ft³ and pressure 120 lb/in.² undergoes a quasi-static adiabatic expansion until the pressure drops to 15 lb/in.² Assuming γ to remain constant at the value 1.4, what is the final volume? How much work is done?

5-12

(a)   Derive the following formula for a quasi-static adiabatic process of an ideal gas, assuming γ to be constant:

$$\theta V^{\gamma-1} = \text{const}.$$

(b)   At about 100 ms after detonation of a uranium fission bomb, the "ball of fire" consists of a sphere of gas with a radius of about 50 ft and a temperature of 300,000°K. Making very rough assumptions, estimate at what radius its temperature would be 3000°K.

5-13

(a)   Derive the following formula for a quasi-static adiabatic process of an ideal gas, assuming γ to be constant:

$$\frac{\theta}{P^{(\gamma-1)/\gamma}} = \text{const}.$$

(b)   Helium ($\gamma = \frac{5}{3}$) at 300°K and 1 atm pressure is compressed quasi-statically and adiabatically to a pressure of 5 atm. Assuming that the helium behaves like an ideal gas, what is the final temperature?

5-14   A horizontal insulated cylinder contains a frictionless noncon-ducting piston. On each side of the piston are 54 liters of an inert monatomic ideal gas at 1 atm and 273°K. Heat is slowly supplied to the gas on the left side until the piston has compressed the gas on the right side to 7.59 atm.

(a)   How much work is done on the gas on the right side?

(b)   What is the final temperature of the gas on the right side?

(c)   What is the final temperature of the gas on the left side?

(d)   How much heat is added to the gas on the left side?

5-15   An evacuated bottle with nonconducting walls is connected through a valve to a gasholder, where the pressure is P_0 and the tempera-ture θ_0. The valve is opened slightly, and helium flows into the bottle until the pressure within the bottle is P_0. Assuming the helium to behave like an ideal gas with constant heat capacities, show that the final temperature of the helium in the bottle is $\gamma\theta_0$.

5-16   A thick-walled insulated chamber contains n_i moles of helium at high pressure P_i. It is connected through a valve with a large almost empty gasholder in which the pressure is maintained at a constant value P_0, very nearly atmospheric. The valve is opened slightly, and the helium flows slowly and adiabatically into the gasholder until the pressures on the two sides of the valve are equalized. Assuming the helium to behave like an ideal gas with constant heat capacities, show that:

(a)   The final temperature of the gas in the chamber is

$$\theta_f = \theta_i \left(\frac{P_f}{P_i}\right)^{(\gamma-1)/\gamma},$$

(b)   The number of moles of gas left in the chamber is

$$n_f = n_i \left(\frac{P_f}{P_i}\right)^{1/\gamma},$$

(c)   The final temperature of the gas in the gasholder is

$$\theta' = \frac{\theta_i}{\gamma} \frac{1 - P_f/P_i}{1 - (P_f/P_i)^{1/\gamma}}.$$

(*Hint:* See Prob. 4-11.)

5-17

(a)   If y is the height above sea level, show that the decrease of atmos-phere pressure due to a rise dy is given by

$$\frac{dP}{P} = -\frac{Mg}{R\theta}\, dy,$$

where M is the molecular weight of the air, g the acceleration of gravity, and θ the absolute temperature at the height y.

(b) If the decrease of pressure in (a) is due to an adiabatic expansion, show that

$$\frac{dP}{P} = \frac{\gamma}{\gamma - 1} \frac{d\theta}{\theta}.$$

(c) From (a) and (b), using some of the numerical data of Art. 5-9, calculate $d\theta/dy$ in degrees per kilometer.

5-18 In the Clément and Désormes method, gas is admitted into a container until a manometer containing a light liquid indicates a pressure of 12 cm in excess of atmospheric pressure. The adiabatic expansion is then performed. When the gas has finally come back to its initial temperature, the pressure is 3.5 cm in excess of atmospheric pressure. What is the value of γ?

5-19 A steel ball of mass 10 g is placed in a tube of cross-sectional area 1 cm². The tube is connected to an air tank of 5 liters capacity, the pressure of the air being 76 cm mercury.

(a) With what period will the ball vibrate?

(b) If the ball is held originally at a position where the gas pressure is exactly atmospheric and is then allowed to drop, how far will it go before it starts to come up?

5-20 A steel ball of mass 8 g is placed in a tube of cross-sectional area 1.2 cm². The tube is connected to an air tank of 6 liters capacity, the pressure of the air being 76 cm Hg.

(a) With what period will the ball vibrate?

(b) If the ball is held originally at a position where the gas pressure is exactly atmospheric and is then allowed to drop, how far will it go before it starts to come up?

5-21 Carbon dioxide is contained in a vessel whose volume is 5270 cm³. A ball of mass 16.65 g, placed in a tube of cross-sectional area 2.01 cm², vibrates with a period of 0.834 s. What is γ when the barometer reads 72.3 cm?

5-22 Mercury is poured into a U tube open at both ends until the total length of the mercury is h.

(a) If the level of mercury on one side of the tube is depressed and then the mercury is allowed to oscillate with small amplitude, show that, neglecting friction, the period τ_1 is given by

$$\tau_1 = 2\pi \sqrt{\frac{h}{2g}}.$$

(b) One end of the U tube is now closed so that the length of the entrapped air column is L, and again the mercury is caused to oscillate.

Assuming friction to be negligible, the air to be ideal, and the changes of volume to be adiabatic, show that the period τ_2 is now

$$\tau_2 = 2\pi \sqrt{\frac{h}{2g + \gamma h_0 g/L}} \, ,$$

where h_0 is the height of the barometric column.

(c)   Show that

$$\gamma = \frac{2L}{h_0} \left(\frac{\tau_1^2}{\tau_2^2} - 1 \right).$$

5-23   Prove that the expression for the speed of a longitudinal wave in an ideal gas may be transformed to

$$w = \sqrt{\left(\frac{\partial P}{\partial \rho} \right)_s}.$$

5-24   What is the speed of a longitudinal wave in argon at 20°C?

5-25   A standing wave of frequency 1100 vibrations per second in a column of methane at 20°C produces nodes that are 20 cm apart. What is γ?

5-26   The speed of a longitudinal wave in a mixture of helium and neon at 300°K was found to be 758 m/s. What is the composition of the mixture?

5-27   The atomic weight of iodine is 127. A standing wave in iodine vapor at 400°K produces nodes that are 6.77 cm apart when the frequency is 1000 vibrations per second. Is iodine vapor monatomic or diatomic?

5-28   Determine the temperature of the helium gas in the acoustical interferometer from which the data of Fig. 5-13 were obtained.

5-29   An open glass tube of uniform bore is bent into the shape of an L. One arm is immersed in a liquid of density ρ', and the other arm, of length L, remains in the air in a horizontal position. The tube is rotated with constant angular speed ω about the axis of the vertical arm. Prove that the height y to which the liquid rises in the vertical arm is equal to

$$y = \frac{P_0(1 - e^{-\omega^2 L^2 \mathcal{M}/2R\theta})}{g\rho'}$$

where P_0 is atmospheric pressure, $\mathcal{M}$ is the molecular weight of air, and g is the acceleration of gravity.

5-30   One mole of an ideal paramagnetic gas obeys Curie's law, with a Curie constant C_C. Assume that the internal energy U is a function of θ only, so that $dU = C_{V,M}\, d\theta$ where $c_{V,M}$ is a constant.

(a)   Show that the equation of the family of adiabatic surfaces is

$$\frac{c_{V,M}}{R} \ln \theta + \ln V = \frac{M^2}{2RC_C} + \ln A,$$

where A is a constant for one surface.

(b)   Sketch one of these surfaces on a θVM diagram.

6.

KINETIC THEORY OF
AN IDEAL GAS

6-1   The Microscopic Point of View

We have emphasized that the point of view of classical thermodynamics is entirely macroscopic. Systems are described with the aid of their gross, or large-scale, properties. The first law of thermodynamics is a relation among the fundamental physical quantities of work, internal energy, and heat. When the first law is applied to a class of systems, a general relation is obtained which holds for *any* member of the class but which contains no quantities or properties of a particular system that would distinguish it from another. Equation (4-13), for example,

$$C_V = \left(\frac{\partial U}{\partial \theta}\right)_V,$$

is true for all hydrostatic systems whether solid, liquid, or gas. It enables one to calculate C_V of a hydrostatic system, *provided that one knows the internal energy* as a function of θ and V. The heat transferred during an isochoric process (Art. 4-10), which is

$$Q_V = \int_{\theta_i}^{\theta_f} C_V \, d\theta,$$

may be calculated once the C_V of the particular system under consideration is known as a function of θ. But there is nothing in classical thermodynamics that provides detailed information concerning U or C_V.

Another example of the limitation of classical thermodynamics is its failure to provide the equation of state of any desired system. To make use of any thermodynamic equation involving P, V, θ, and the derivatives $(\partial P/\partial V)_\theta$, $(\partial V/\partial \theta)_P$, and $(\partial \theta/\partial P)_V$, one must have an equation of state. Experimental values are very often useful, but there are occasions when it is not feasible to perform the necessary experiments. If an experiment is performed on, let us say, oxygen, the numerical constants in the equation of state of oxygen only are obtained, and no clue is at hand concerning the values of the constants for any other gas.

To obtain detailed information concerning the thermodynamic coordinates and thermal properties of systems without having to resort to experimental measurements, we require calculations based on the properties and behavior of the molecules of the system. There are two such microscopic theories; one is called *kinetic theory*, and the other is *statistical mechanics*. Both theories deal with molecules, their internal and external motion, their collisions with one another and with any existing walls, and their forces of interaction. Making use of the laws of mechanics and the theory of probability, kinetic theory concerns itself with the details of molecular motion and impact and is capable of dealing with the following *nonequilibrium* situations:

1   Molecules escaping from a hole in a container, a process known as *effusion*.
2   Molecules moving through a pipe under the action of a pressure difference, a motion called *laminar flow*.
3   Molecules with momentum moving across a plane and mixing with molecules of lesser momentum—a molecular process responsible for *viscosity*.
4   Molecules with kinetic energy moving across a plane and mixing with molecules of lesser energy—a process responsible for *heat conduction*.
5   Molecules of one sort moving across a plane and mixing with molecules of another sort, a process known as *diffusion*.
6   Chemical combination between two or more kinds of molecules, which takes place at a finite rate and is known as *chemical kinetics*.
7   Inequality of molecular impacts made on various sides of a very small object suspended in a fluid, a difference that give rise to a haphazard zigzag motion of the suspended particle that is known as *Brownian motion*.

Statistical mechanics avoids the mechanical details concerning molecular motions and deals only with the energy aspects of the molecules. It relies heavily on the theory of probability but is mathematically simpler than kinetic theory, although more subtle conceptually. Only equilibrium states can be handled—but in a uniform, straightforward manner, so that once the energy levels of the molecules or of systems of molecules are understood a program of calculations may be carried out through which the equation of state, the energy, and other thermodynamic functions may be obtained.

In this chapter we shall limit ourselves to a small part of the kinetic theory of an ideal gas. A simplified treatment of statistical mechanics will be reserved for Chap. 10.

6-2   Equation of State of an Ideal Gas

The fundamental hypotheses of the kinetic theory of an ideal gas are as follows:

1   Any small sample of gas consists of an enormous number of molecules N. For any one chemical species, all molecules are identical. If m is the mass of each molecule, then the total mass is mN. If $\mathcal{M}$ denotes the molar mass in grams (more commonly called the *molecular weight*), then the number of gram-moles n is given by

$$n = \frac{mN}{\mathcal{M}}.$$

The number of molecules per mole of gas is called *Avogadro's number* N_A, where

$$N_A = \frac{N}{n} = \frac{\mathcal{M}}{m} = 6.0225 \times 10^{23} \frac{\text{molecules}}{\text{g mole}}.$$

Since a mole of ideal gas at 273°K and at 1 atm pressure occupies a volume of 2.24×10^4 cm^3, there are approximately 3×10^{19} molecules in a volume of only 1 cm^3 and 3×10^{16} molecules per mm^3, and even a volume as small as a cubic micron contains as many as 3×10^7 molecules.

2   The molecules of an ideal gas are supposed to resemble small hard spheres that are in perpetual random motion. Within the temperature and pressure range of an ideal gas, the average distance between neighboring molecules is large compared with the size of a molecule. The diameter of a molecule is of the order of 2 or 3×10^{-8} cm. Under standard conditions, the average distance between molecules is about 50 times their diameter.

3   The molecules of an ideal gas are assumed to exert no forces of attraction or repulsion on other molecules except when they collide with one another and with a wall. Between collisions, they therefore move with uniform rectilinear motion.

4   The portion of a wall with which a molecule collides is considered to be smooth, and the collision is assumed to be perfectly elastic.

If w is the speed of a molecule approaching a wall, only the perpendicular component of velocity $w_\perp$ is changed upon collision with the wall, from $w_\perp$ to $-w_\perp$, or a total change of $-2w_\perp$.

5   When there is no external field of force, the molecules are distributed uniformly throughout a container. The *molecular density* N/V is assumed constant, so that in any small element of volume dV there are dN molecules, where

$$dN = \frac{N}{V} dV.$$

The infinitesimal dV must satisfy the same conditions in kinetic theory as in thermodynamics, namely, that it is small compared with V but large enough to make dN a large number. If, for example, a volume of 1 cm³ contains 10^{19} molecules, then one-millionth of a cubic centimeter would still contain 10^{13} molecules and would qualify as a differential volume element.

6   There is no preferred direction for the velocity of any molecule, so that at any moment there are as many molecules moving in one direction as in another.

7   Not all molecules have the same speed. A few molecules at any moment move slowly and a few move very rapidly, so that speeds may be considered to cover the range from zero to the speed of light. Since most molecular speeds are so far below the speed of light, no error is introduced in integrating the speed from 0 to ∞. If dN_w represents the number of molecules with speeds between w and $w + dw$, it is assumed that dN_w remains constant at equilibrium, even though the molecules are perpetually colliding and changing their speeds.

Since the velocity vectors of the molecules of gas have no preferred direction, consider an arbitrary velocity vector $\boldsymbol{w}$ directed from the point O in Fig. 6-1 to the elementary area dA'. It is important to know how many molecules have velocity vectors in the neighborhood of $\boldsymbol{w}$. The calculation of this quantity involves the concept of a *solid angle*. Taking O as the origin of polar coordinates r, θ, and ϕ, we construct a sphere of radius r. The area dA' on the surface of this sphere, formed by two circles of latitude differing by $d\theta$ and two circles of longitude differing by $d\phi$, has the magnitude

$$dA' = (r\, d\theta)(r \sin\theta\, d\phi).$$

The solid angle $d\Omega$, formed by lines radiating from O and touching the edge of

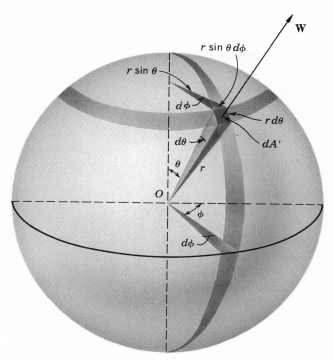

Fig. 6-1   *The solid angle $d\Omega = \sin \theta \, d\theta \, d\phi$.*

dA', is by definition

$$d\Omega = \frac{dA'}{r^2} = \frac{(r \, d\theta)(r \sin \theta \, d\phi)}{r^2},$$

or

$$d\Omega = \sin \theta \, d\theta \, d\phi. \tag{6-1}$$

Since the largest area on the surface of the sphere is that of the entire sphere $4\pi r^2$, the maximum solid angle is 4π sr (*steradians*).

The fraction of molecules with velocity vectors in the neighborhood of **w** will have speeds between w and $w + dw$ and directions within the solid angle $d\Omega$ about **w**. If dN_w is the number of molecules with speeds between w and $w + dw$, then the fraction of *these* molecules whose directions lie within the solid angle $d\Omega$ is $d\Omega/4\pi$, so that the number of molecules within the speed range dw, in the θ range of $d\theta$ and the ϕ range of $d\phi$, is given by

$$d^3N_{w,\theta,\phi} = dN_w \frac{d\Omega}{4\pi}, \tag{6-2}$$

an equation expressing the fact that *molecular velocities have no preferred direction.*

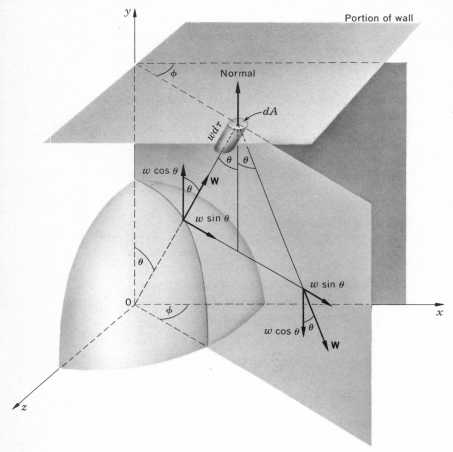

Fig. 6-2   *All the molecules in the cylinder of length w dτ strike the area dA at the angle θ to the normal. The perpendicular component of velocity w cos θ is reversed, but the parallel component w sin θ is unchanged.*

Now consider this group of molecules approaching a small area dA of the wall of the containing vessel. Many of these molecules will undergo collisions along the way, but if we consider only those members of the group that lie within the cylinder (Fig. 6-2) whose side is of length $w \, d\tau$, where $d\tau$ is such a short time interval that no collisions are made, then *all* the $d^3N_{w,\theta,\phi}$ molecules *within this cylinder* will collide with dA. The volume of the cylinder dV is

$$dV = w \, d\tau \cos \theta \, dA, \qquad (6\text{-}3)$$

and if V is the total volume of the container, only the fraction dV/V of the molecules will be contained within the cylinder. Therefore the number of molecules (speed range, dw; θ range, $d\theta$; ϕ range, $d\phi$) striking dA in time $d\tau$ is expressed as

$$\text{No. of } w,\theta,\phi \text{ molecules striking } dA \text{ in time } d\tau = d^3N_{w,\theta,\phi}\frac{dV}{V}, \quad (6\text{-}4)$$

which expresses the fact that *molecules have no preferred location*.

According to our fundamental assumptions, a molecular collision is perfectly elastic. It follows, therefore, that a molecule moving with speed w in a direction making an angle θ with the normal to a wall will undergo a change only in its perpendicular component of velocity, as shown in Fig. 6-2. Furthermore, it follows that the total change in momentum per collision is

$$\text{Change of momentum per collision} = -2mv\cos\theta. \quad (6\text{-}5)$$

Now,

$$
\begin{bmatrix}\text{Total change}\\\text{of momentum}\end{bmatrix} =
\begin{bmatrix}\text{No. of molecules}\\\text{of speed } w \text{ in}\\\text{solid angle } d\Omega\end{bmatrix}
\begin{bmatrix}\text{Fraction of}\\\text{these molecules}\\\text{striking } dA\\\text{in time } d\tau\end{bmatrix}
\begin{bmatrix}\text{Change in}\\\text{momentum}\\\text{per collision}\end{bmatrix}
$$

$$= \left(dN_w\frac{d\Omega}{4\pi}\right) \qquad \left(\frac{dV}{V}\right) \qquad (-2mw\cos\theta)$$

$$= \left(\frac{dN_w}{4\pi}\sin\theta\,d\theta\,d\phi\right)\left(\frac{1}{V}w\,d\tau\cos\theta\,dA\right)(-2mw\cos\theta).$$

$$\text{[Eq. (6-1)]} \qquad\qquad \text{[Eq. (6-3)]} \qquad \text{[Eq. (6-5)]}$$

The change in momentum per unit time and per unit area due to collisions from all directions is the pressure dP_w exerted by the wall on the dN_w gas molecules. Reversing the sign of the momentum change, we get the pressure dP_w exerted by the dN_w molecules *on the wall*:

$$dP_w = mw^2\frac{dN_w}{V}\left(\frac{1}{2\pi}\int_0^{2\pi}d\phi\int_0^{\pi/2}\cos^2\theta\sin\theta\,d\theta\right). \quad (6\text{-}6)$$

The quantity in parentheses may be integrated at sight and is found to be $\frac{1}{3}$, so that the total pressure due to molecules of all speeds is given by

$$PV = \tfrac{1}{3}m\int_0^\infty w^2\,dN_w.$$

The average of the square of the molecular speeds $\langle w^2 \rangle$ is defined to be

$$\langle w^2 \rangle = \frac{1}{N} \int_0^\infty w^2 \, dN_w, \tag{6-7}$$

so that we have

$$PV = \tfrac{1}{3} Nm\langle w^2 \rangle,$$

or

$$PV = \tfrac{2}{3} N(\tfrac{1}{2} m\langle w^2 \rangle). \tag{6-8}$$

The quantity $\tfrac{1}{2} m\langle w^2 \rangle$ is the average kinetic energy per molecule. Comparing our theoretical equation of state with the experimental one, we see that an association must be made between the average kinetic energy per molecule and the ideal gas temperature. Thus,

$$\tfrac{2}{3} N(\tfrac{1}{2} m\langle w^2 \rangle) = nR\theta.$$

But N/n is the number of molecules per mole, or Avogadro's N_A, so that

$$\frac{1}{2} m\langle w^2 \rangle = \frac{3}{2} \frac{R}{N_A} \theta = \frac{3}{2} k\theta, \tag{6-9}$$

where k is *Boltzmann's constant*, given by

$$k = \frac{R}{N_A} = \frac{8.3143 \times 10^7 \text{ ergs/mole} \cdot \text{deg}}{6.0225 \times 10^{23} \text{ molecules/mole}} = 1.3805 \times 10^{-16} \frac{\text{erg}}{\text{deg}}.$$

In this derivation, the average energy per molecule, $\tfrac{1}{2} m\langle w^2 \rangle$, is wholly kinetic energy of translation. This is the only kind of energy that a hard spherical molecule, uninfluenced by its neighbors, can possess. We have therefore limited ourselves to monatomic molecules only. Diatomic and polyatomic molecules can also rotate and vibrate and may therefore be expected to possess kinetic energy of rotation and vibration as well as potential energy of vibration, even though there are no forces among neighbors.

It is worth while at this point to compare the symbolism used in our treatment of kinetic theory with that used in thermodynamics. This is shown in Table 6-1. The molecular form of the ideal-gas equation has another simple form. Since $PV = \tfrac{2}{3} N(\tfrac{1}{2} m\langle w^2 \rangle)$ and $\tfrac{1}{2} m\langle w^2 \rangle = \tfrac{3}{2} k\theta$, we get

$$PV = (\tfrac{2}{3}N)(\tfrac{3}{2}k\theta) = Nk\theta$$

and

$$P = \frac{N}{V} k\theta. \tag{6-10}$$

Table 6-1   Comparison of Symbols

Thermodynamics	Kinetic theory
M' = Mass of system	N = No. of molecules
n = No. of g moles	m = Mass of a molecule
$\mathcal{M}$ = Mass per mole = M'/n (molecular weight)	N_A = Molecules per mole = N/n (Avogadro's number)
R = Universal gas constant	k = Boltzmann's constant = R/N_A
V = Volume	V = Volume
ρ = Mass density = M'/V	Molecular density = N/V

6-3   Distribution of Molecular Velocities

In the preceding derivation, the average square of the molecular speed was defined by the equation

$$\langle w^2 \rangle = \frac{1}{N} \int_0^\infty w^2 \, dN_w,$$

where dN_w was the number of molecules with speeds between w and $w + dw$. It is often necessary to know the expression for dN_w in terms of w—a relation known as the *Maxwellian law of distribution of velocities*, since it was first derived by James Clerk Maxwell. To derive this law is merely a mathematical exercise, for it is not necessary to use any physical laws governing the behavior of molecules when colliding with one another or with the wall. These physical laws are hidden within the fundamental assumptions of chaos: that, at (or near) equilibrium, the molecules have no preferred direction of velocity and no preferred location within the container.

If altogether there are N molecules, a fraction of these, or dN_{w_x}/N, will have x components of velocity lying within the range w_x and $w_x + dw_x$. The assumption of chaos allows us to say that this fraction is a function of w_x only and is proportional to dw_x, or $dN_{w_x}/N = f(w_x) \, dw_x$. Therefore,

$$dN_{w_x} = N f(w_x) \, dw_x. \tag{6-11}$$

There are similar equations for the y and z directions:

$$dN_{w_y} = N f(w_y) \, dw_y, \tag{6-12}$$

and
$$dN_{w_z} = N f(w_z) \, dw_z. \tag{6-13}$$

Now N is enormously large and dw_x is small compared with the range of w_x.

Nevertheless, in the range dw_x there are very many molecules—so many in fact that the fraction of the dN_{w_x} molecules whose y components of velocity lie in the range between w_y and $w_y + dw_y$ ($d^2N_{w_x,w_y}$) is given by the same expression as the fraction dN_{w_y}/N. Thus, using Eq. (6-12),

$$\frac{d^2N_{w_x,w_y}}{dN_{w_x}} = \frac{dN_{w_y}}{N} = f(w_y)\,dw_y;$$

and from Eq. (6-11),

$$d^2N_{w_x,w_y} = Nf(w_x)f(w_y)\,dw_x\,dw_y.$$

The number of molecules represented by the symbol $d^2N_{w_x,w_y}$ is still large, and again we assume that the fraction of these molecules $d^3N_{w_x,w_y,w_z}$ whose z components of velocity lie between w_z and $w_z + dw_z$ is the same as the fraction dN_{w_z}/N given by Eq. (6-13). Hence,

$$d^3N_{w_x,w_y,w_z} = Nf(w_x)f(w_y)f(w_z)\,dw_x\,dw_y\,dw_z. \tag{6-14}$$

If we consider a velocity space (Fig. 6-3) in which w_x, w_y, and w_z are plotted along rectangular axes, the *density of velocity points*, or the number of molecules

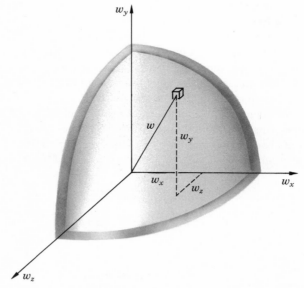

Fig. 6-3   *Velocity space of the molecules. All molecules whose speeds lie in the range from w to $w + dw$ have components within the spherical shell.*

associated with points within the cubical volume element, divided by that volume is given by

$$\rho = \frac{d^3 N_{w_x, w_y, w_z}}{dw_x \, dw_y \, dw_z} = N f(w_x) f(w_y) f(w_z). \tag{6-15}$$

Since there is no preferred direction for the velocities (the velocity space is said to be isotropic), the density should be constant at all points on the sphere

$$w_x^2 + w_y^2 + w_z^2 = w^2,$$

whose radius is the speed w. Therefore,

$$N f(w_x) f(w_y) f(w_z) = \text{const.} \tag{6-16}$$

when

$$w_x^2 + w_y^2 + w_z^2 = \text{const.} \tag{6-17}$$

Both of these equations must be satisfied at the same time. If Eq. (6-16) were alone, we could consider the three variables w_x, w_y, and w_z to be independent. The presence of Eq. (6-17), however, limits or constrains the values of the variables and essentially reduces the number of independent variables to two. This is therefore called an *equation of constraint*.

Taking the differential of Eqs. (6-16) and (6-17), we get

$$f(w_y)f(w_z) \frac{\partial f(w_x)}{\partial w_x} dw_x + f(w_z)f(w_x) \frac{\partial f(w_y)}{\partial w_y} dw_y + f(w_x)f(w_y) \frac{\partial f(w_z)}{\partial w_z} dw_z = 0,$$

and

$$2w_x \, dw_x + \qquad\qquad 2w_y \, dw_y + \qquad\qquad 2w_z \, dw_z = 0.$$

or

$$\frac{1}{f(w_x)} \frac{\partial f(w_x)}{\partial w_x} dw_x + \frac{1}{f(w_y)} \frac{\partial f(w_y)}{\partial w_y} dw_y + \frac{1}{f(w_z)} \frac{\partial f(w_z)}{\partial w_z} dw_z = 0,$$

and

$$w_x \, dw_x + \qquad\qquad w_y \, dw_y + \qquad\qquad w_z \, dw_z = 0.$$

Since there are only two independent variables, we cannot give arbitrary values to all three differentials, but only to two of them, say, dw_y and dw_z. Therefore, let us multiply the second equation by the quantity $m\beta$, where m is the mass of a molecule and β is an arbitrary, unknown function. The product $m\beta$ is called a *Lagrange undetermined multiplier*. Adding the two equations, we then get

$$\left[\frac{1}{f(w_x)} \frac{\partial f(w_x)}{\partial w_x} + m\beta w_x \right] dw_x + \left[\frac{1}{f(w_y)} \frac{\partial f(w_y)}{\partial w_y} + m\beta w_y \right] dw_y$$

$$+ \left[\frac{1}{f(w_z)} \frac{\partial f(w_z)}{\partial w_z} + m\beta w_z \right] dw_z = 0.$$

Since the two variables w_y and w_z have been taken to be independent, their differentials are arbitrary, and we may assign them the values $dw_y = 0$ and $dw_z = 0$. Then the multiplier $m\beta$ may be *chosen* to make

$$\frac{1}{f(w_x)} \frac{\partial f(w_x)}{\partial w_x} + m\beta w_x = 0.$$

Choosing $dw_z = 0$ and $dw_y \neq 0$, we get

$$\frac{1}{f(w_y)} \frac{\partial f(w_y)}{\partial w_y} + m\beta w_y = 0;$$

and choosing $dw_y = 0$ and $dw_z \neq 0$, we get

$$\frac{1}{f(w_z)} \frac{\partial f(w_z)}{\partial w_z} + m\beta w_z = 0.$$

To satisfy any one of the preceding equations, β would have to be either a constant or a function of the variable in that equation. A constant is the only value of β that satisfies all the equations. It is also seen that the function f satisfies the same differential equation (as indeed it must) regardless of the component. Taking the x component,

$$\frac{d}{dw_x} \ln f(w_x) = -m\beta w_x,$$

$$\int d \ln f(w_x) = -m\beta \int w_x \, dw_x,$$

and
$$\ln f(w_x) = -\beta(\tfrac{1}{2}mw_x^2) + \ln A,$$

where $\ln A$ is a constant of integration. Therefore,

$$f(w_x) = Ae^{-\beta(\frac{1}{2}mw_x{}^2)},$$

$$f(w_y) = Ae^{-\beta(\frac{1}{2}mw_y{}^2)},$$
(6-18)

and
$$f(w_z) = Ae^{-\beta(\frac{1}{2}mw_z{}^2)}.$$

Using Eq. (6-15),

$$\boxed{\rho = NA^3 e^{-\beta\frac{1}{2}m(w_x{}^2 + w_y{}^2 + w_z{}^2)},}$$
(6-19)

and also

$$\boxed{\rho = NA^3 e^{-\beta(\frac{1}{2}mw^2)}.}$$
(6-20)

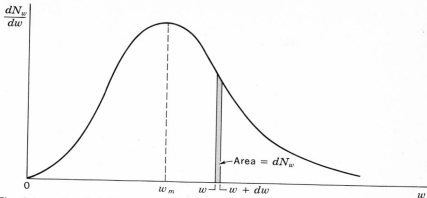

Fig. 6-4   *Graph of Maxwell speed-distribution function.*

Let us go back for a moment to the definition of ρ; namely,

$$\rho = \frac{d^3 N_{w_x, w_y, w_z}}{dw_x \, dw_y \, dw_z},$$

or the number of molecules whose components of velocity lie in the small cubical volume element shown in Fig. 6-3, divided by that volume element. But ρ is constant at all points within the infinitesimal spherical shell lying between the radii w and $w + dw$, whose volume is $4\pi w^2 \, dw$ and which contains the velocity points of dN_w molecules. The density ρ may therefore be expressed also as

$$\rho = \frac{dN_w}{4\pi w^2 \, dw}.$$

It follows from Eq. (6-20) that

$$\boxed{\frac{dN_w}{dw} = 4\pi N A^3 w^2 e^{-\beta(\frac{1}{2}mw^2)},}$$

(6-21)

which is the equation for the *Maxwellian distribution of speeds*, plotted in Fig. 6-4.

6-4   Maxwellian Speeds and Temperature

We have seen that the number of molecules dN_w with speeds between w and $w + dw$ is equal to

$$dN_w = 4\pi N A^3 w^2 e^{-\beta(\frac{1}{2}mw^2)} \, dw,$$

where β is an undetermined multiplier and A is an integration constant. To determine the value of A, it is merely necessary to integrate this equation from zero to infinity. The integral of the left-hand member is N, so that

$$\frac{1}{4\pi A^3} = \int_0^\infty w^2 e^{-\beta(\frac{1}{2}mw^2)} \, dw.$$

The integral on the right is commonly encountered in mathematical physics. It is listed along with others in Table 6-2. Its value is $\frac{1}{4}\pi^{\frac{1}{2}}/(\frac{1}{2}m\beta)^{\frac{3}{2}}$; therefore,

$$4\pi A^3 = \frac{4(\frac{1}{2}m\beta)^{\frac{3}{2}}}{\pi^{\frac{1}{2}}}, \tag{6-22}$$

or

$$A = \left(\frac{\frac{1}{2}m\beta}{\pi}\right)^{\frac{1}{2}}.$$

To find the physical meaning of the multiplier β, we recall the definition of the average of the square of the molecular speeds:

$$\langle w^2 \rangle = \frac{1}{N} \int_0^\infty w^2 \, dN_w. \tag{6-7}$$

Substituting for dN_w, we get

$$\langle w^2 \rangle = 4\pi A^3 \int_0^\infty w^4 e^{-\beta(\frac{1}{2}mw^2)} \, dw.$$

From Table 6-2, the right-hand integral has the value $\frac{3}{8}\pi^{\frac{1}{2}}/(\frac{1}{2}m\beta)^{\frac{5}{2}}$. Therefore,

$$\langle w^2 \rangle = \frac{4(\frac{1}{2}m\beta)^{\frac{3}{2}}}{\pi^{\frac{1}{2}}} \frac{3\pi^{\frac{1}{2}}}{8(\frac{1}{2}m\beta)^{\frac{5}{2}}} = \frac{3}{m\beta}. \tag{6-23}$$

The comparison, however, of the theoretical equation of state of an ideal gas with the empirical one led to the relation

$$\tfrac{1}{2}m\langle w^2 \rangle = \tfrac{3}{2}k\theta. \tag{6-9}$$

Therefore,

$$\tfrac{1}{2}m \frac{3}{m\beta} = \tfrac{3}{2}k\theta,$$

and

$$\boxed{\beta = \frac{1}{k\theta}.} \tag{6-24}$$

Table 6-2   **Values of** $I_n = \int_0^\infty x^n e^{-ax^2}\, dx$

n	I_n	n	I_n
0	$\dfrac{1}{2}\sqrt{\dfrac{\pi}{a}}$	1	$\dfrac{1}{2a}$
2	$\dfrac{1}{4}\sqrt{\dfrac{\pi}{a^3}}$	3	$\dfrac{1}{2a^2}$
4	$\dfrac{3}{8}\sqrt{\dfrac{\pi}{a^5}}$	5	$\dfrac{1}{a^3}$
6	$\dfrac{15}{16}\sqrt{\dfrac{\pi}{a^7}}$	7	$\dfrac{3}{a^4}$

If n is even,   If n is odd,

$$\int_{-\infty}^{+\infty} x^n e^{-ax^2}\, dx = 2I_n. \qquad \int_{-\infty}^{+\infty} x^n e^{-ax^2}\, dx = 0.$$

Substituting the values of $4\pi A^3$ and of β in our previous equation for dN_w, Eq. (6-21), the Maxwellian equation for the distribution of molecular speeds becomes

$$\frac{dN_w}{dw} = \frac{4N}{\sqrt{\pi}}\left(\frac{m}{2k\theta}\right)^{\frac{3}{2}} w^2 e^{-\frac{1}{2}mw^2/k\theta}. \tag{6-25}$$

This is plotted for three different temperatures in Fig. 6-5. The larger the temperature, the wider is the spread of values of the speed.

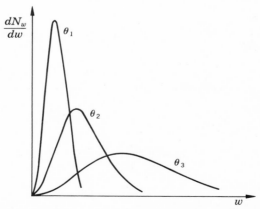

Fig. 6-5   *Maxwellian speed distribution at various temperatures,* $\theta_3 > \theta_2 > \theta_1.$

Fig. 6-6   *Apparatus of Estermann, Simpson, and Stern for the deflection of a molecular beam by gravity. O, oven; F and C, slits; D, detector.*

Maxwell's equation for the distribution of molecular speeds has been experimentally verified directly as well as indirectly. One of the most convincing experiments was performed by Estermann, Simpson, and Stern in 1947, making use of the apparatus depicted schematically in Fig. 6-6, in which atoms are deflected *by gravity only*. Cesium atoms issue from a minute slit in an oven *O* at the left of a long, highly evacuated chamber. Most of these atoms are stopped by the diaphragm *F*, and those which go through the slit constitute a narrow, almost horizontal beam. The slit *C*, called the *collimating slit*, is halfway between *F* and the detector *D*. The atoms are detected by the method of surface ionization, in which nearly every cesium atom striking a hot tungsten wire leaves the wire as a positive ion and is collected by a negatively charged plate. The plate current is then a measure of the number of cesium atoms striking the detector wire per unit of time.

Fig. 6-7   *Distribution of speeds of cesium atoms in atomic beam deflected by gravity. (Estermann, Simpson, and Stern.)*

A simple analysis of the parabolic paths of the atoms that pass through F and C provides a relation between the deflection s and the speed w. The departure angle θ is practically zero. The experimental results are shown in Fig. 6-7, where the smooth curve is a plot of Maxwell's equation and the dots are experimental points.

6-5   Equipartition of Energy

One of the most important results of elementary kinetic theory, and one that has been used throughout this chapter, is the relation obtained by comparing the theoretical ideal-gas equation with the empirical one,

$$\tfrac{1}{2}m\langle w^2\rangle = \tfrac{3}{2}k\theta. \tag{6-9}$$

Since

$$w^2 = w_x^2 + w_y^2 + w_z^2,$$

$$\tfrac{1}{2}m\langle w^2\rangle = \tfrac{1}{2}m\langle w_x^2\rangle + \tfrac{1}{2}m\langle w_y^2\rangle + \tfrac{1}{2}m\langle w_z^2\rangle.$$

Since the x, y, and z directions are all equivalent,

$$\langle w_x^2\rangle = \langle w_y^2\rangle = \langle w_z^2\rangle$$

and
$$\tfrac{1}{2}m\langle w^2\rangle = 3(\tfrac{1}{2}m\langle w_x^2\rangle) = \tfrac{3}{2}k\theta.$$

It follows that
$$\tfrac{1}{2}m\langle w_x^2\rangle = \tfrac{1}{2}k\theta,$$

$$\tfrac{1}{2}m\langle w_y^2\rangle = \tfrac{1}{2}k\theta,$$

and
$$\tfrac{1}{2}m\langle w_z^2\rangle = \tfrac{1}{2}k\theta,$$

or, in words, that *the average kinetic energy associated with each translational degree of freedom is $\tfrac{1}{2}k\theta$.*

The molecules we have considered up to this point have been spherically symmetrical, rigid structures capable of undergoing translational motion only. Actual molecules, however, are neither spherical nor rigid and have been found, mostly by spectroscopic methods, to rotate about two or, in some cases, three axes and to vibrate with many different frequencies. A molecule such as, let us say, CO has three translational degrees of freedom, two rotational degrees of freedom (since it is dumbbell-shaped), and, at moderate temperatures, one frequency of vibration. Its energy ϵ may be written

$$\epsilon = \tfrac{1}{2}mw_x^2 + \tfrac{1}{2}mw_y^2 + \tfrac{1}{2}mw_z^2 + \tfrac{1}{2}I_A\omega_A^2 + \tfrac{1}{2}I_B\omega_B^2 + \tfrac{1}{2}mw_\xi^2 + \tfrac{1}{2}k\xi^2,$$

where I_A and I_B are moments of inertia with reference to axes A and B, about which the molecule rotates with angular speeds ω_A and ω_B, respectively; ξ is the displacement of the C and O atoms from their equilibrium separation; and w_ξ is the derivative of this displacement with respect to the time. The last two terms represent the contribution to the energy of *one* frequency of vibration. Notice that the expression for ϵ contains only squares of independently varying quantities. There are no first-power terms, and there are no "cross-product" terms, which would be present if interaction existed between neighboring molecules.

We have seen that, at equilibrium, the average energy associated with *each* of the three translational terms is $\frac{1}{2}k\theta$. By the methods of classical statistical mechanics, a beautiful theorem known as the *principle of the equipartition of energy* may be proved which asserts that *the average energy associated with any squared term in the energy of a molecule is $\frac{1}{2}k\theta$.* It follows that, for each degree of freedom of translation and of rotation, the molecule has the average energy $\frac{1}{2}k\theta$; but for each frequency of vibration the average energy is $k\theta$, since each vibration is represented by two squared terms.

A monatomic ideal gas has only three translational degrees of freedom; therefore N_A atoms (1 mole) will have an energy u equal to

$$u = N_A(\tfrac{3}{2}k\theta) = \tfrac{3}{2}R\theta,$$

and

$$c_V = \frac{du}{d\theta} = \tfrac{3}{2}R.$$

Since $c_P = c_V + R$, $c_P = \frac{5}{2}R$ and $\gamma = \frac{5}{3}$. These calculations are in agreement with the experimental results listed in Art. 5-4.

The diatomic gases H_2, D_2, O_2, N_2, NO, and CO, in the neighborhood of room temperature—where rotation takes place, but not vibration—are dumbbell-shaped with two rotational degrees of freedom. Hence the molar energy is

$$u = \tfrac{5}{2}R\theta,$$

and

$$c_V = \tfrac{5}{2}R, \qquad c_P = \tfrac{7}{2}R, \qquad \text{and} \qquad \gamma = \tfrac{7}{5},$$

in agreement with the results of Art. 5-4.

When polyatomic molecules are "soft" and vibrate easily with many frequencies, say, q, the principle of the equipartition of energy would require that

$$u = (3 + q)R\theta,$$

and

$$c_V = (3 + q)R, \qquad c_P = (4 + q)R, \qquad \text{and} \qquad \gamma = \frac{4 + q}{3 + q}.$$

If q is large, γ is nearly 1. This result is *in complete disagreement* with experiment. The heat capacities of such molecules are not constant but vary markedly with the temperature even around room temperature, and γ is not in the neighborhood of unity.

When the principle of the equipartition of energy is applied to solids and liquids, the disagreement is still worse, and this principle must be abandoned in favor of quantum ideas.

PROBLEMS

6-1   Prove that the number of molecules striking unit area of the container wall per unit time is equal to $N\langle w \rangle/4V$, where, by definition,

$$\langle w \rangle = \frac{1}{N} \int_0^\infty w \, dN_w.$$

6-2   Plot

$$\frac{d^3 N_{w_x, w_y, w_z}}{dw_x \, dw_y \, dw_z}$$

against w and compare with Fig. 6-4. Why are the two curves different?

6-3

(a)   In Fig. 6-4, let w_m be the value of w at which dN_w/dw is a maximum. Calculate w_m.

(b)   Choose a new variable $x = w/w_m$, and calculate $dN_x/N \, dx$. What is the maximum value of $dN_x/N \, dx$?

6-4   Show that the number of molecules dN_ϵ with translational kinetic energy between ϵ and $\epsilon + d\epsilon$ is given by

$$dN_\epsilon = \frac{2N}{(k\theta)^{\frac{3}{2}}} \left(\frac{\epsilon}{\pi}\right)^{\frac{1}{2}} e^{-\epsilon/k\theta} \, d\epsilon.$$

6-5   The root-mean-square speed w_{rms} is defined as $\sqrt{\langle w^2 \rangle}$.

(a)   Show that

$$w_{\text{rms}} = \sqrt{\frac{3k\theta}{m}}.$$

(b)   Show that $w_{\text{rms}} = \sqrt{3/\gamma}$ times the speed of sound.

(c)   Show that $\langle w \rangle$, defined in Prob. 6-1, is equal to

$$\langle w \rangle = \sqrt{\frac{8k\theta}{\pi m}}.$$

(d)   Calculate $\langle 1/w \rangle$ and compare this with $1/\langle w \rangle$.

(e)   Show that the number of molecules striking unit area of a wall per unit time is equal to

$$\frac{P}{\sqrt{2\pi m k \theta}}.$$

6-6   The Doppler broadening of a spectral line increases with the rms speed of the atoms in the source of light. Which should give narrower spectral lines: a mercury 198 lamp at 300°K or a krypton 86 lamp at 77°K?

6-7   At what temperature is the mean translational kinetic energy of a molecule equal to that of a singly charged ion of the same mass which has been accelerated from rest through a potential difference of (a) 1 V? (b) 1000 V? (c) 1,000,000 V? (Neglect relativistic effects.)

6-8   An oven contains cadmium vapor at a pressure of 1.71×10^{-2} mm of mercury and at a temperature of 550°K. In one wall of the oven there is a slit with a length of 1 cm and a width of 10^{-3} cm. On the other side of the wall is a very high vacuum. If one assumes that all the atoms arriving at the slit pass through, what is the atomic beam current?

6-9   A vessel of volume V contains a gas that is kept at constant temperature. The gas slowly leaks out of a small hole of area A. The outside pressure is so low that no molecules leak back. Prove that the pressure P at any time τ is given by

$$P = P_0 e^{-k'\tau},$$

where P_0 is the initial pressure; and calculate k' in terms of V, A, and $\langle w \rangle$. (Assume that all the molecules arriving at the hole pass through.)

Fig. P6-1

6-10   A spherical glass bulb 10 cm in radius is maintained at 300°K, except for an appendix with a cross-sectional area of 1 cm² immersed in liquid nitrogen, as shown in Fig. P6-1. The bulb contains water vapor originally at a pressure of 0.1 mm of mercury. Assuming that every water molecule which enters the appendix condenses on the wall and stays there, find the time required for the pressure to decrease to 10^{-6} mm of mercury.

6-11   A vessel partially filled with mercury and closed except for a hole of area 10^{-3} cm² above the liquid level is kept at 0°C in a continuously evacuated enclosure. After 30 days it is found that 0.024 g of mercury has been lost. What is the vapor pressure of mercury at 0°C?

7.

ENGINES, REFRIGERATORS, AND THE SECOND LAW

7-1   Conversion of Work into Heat, and Vice Versa

When two stones are rubbed together under water, the work done against friction is transformed into internal energy tending to produce a rise of temperature of the stones. As soon as the temperature of the stones rises above that of the surrounding water, however, there is a flow of heat into the water. If the mass of water is large enough or if the water is continually flowing, there will be no appreciable rise of temperature, and the water can be regarded as a heat reservoir. Since the state of the stones is the same at the end of the process as at the beginning, the net result of the process is merely the conversion of mechanical work into heat. Similarly, when an electric current is maintained in a resistor immersed either in running water or in a very large mass of water, there is also a conversion of electrical work into heat, without any change in the thermodynamic coordinates of the wire. In general, work of any kind W may be done upon a system in contact with a reservoir, giving rise to a flow of heat Q without altering the state of the system. The system acts merely as an intermediary. It is apparent from the first law that the work W is equal to the heat Q; or in other words, the transformation of work into heat is accomplished with 100 percent efficiency. Moreover, this transformation can be continued indefinitely.

To study the converse process, namely, the conversion of heat into work, we must also have at hand a process or series of processes by means of which such a conversion may continue indefinitely without involving any resultant changes in the state of any system. At first thought, it might appear that the isothermal expansion of an ideal gas might be a suitable process to consider in discussing the conversion of heat into work. In this case there is no internal-energy change since the temperature remains constant, and therefore $W = Q$, or heat has been converted completely into work. This process, however, involves a change of state of the gas. The volume increases and the pressure decreases until atmospheric pressure is reached, at which point the process stops. It therefore cannot be used indefinitely.

What is needed is a series of processes in which a system is brought back to its initial state, i.e., a *cycle*. Each of the processes that constitute a cycle may involve a flow of heat to or from the system and the performance of work by or on the system. For one complete cycle, let

Q_H = amount of heat absorbed by the system,
Q_C = amount of heat rejected by the system,
W = net amount of work done by the system.

Both Q_H and Q_C have been defined as positive numbers. If Q_H is larger than Q_C and if W is done by the system, the mechanical device by whose agency the system is caused to undergo the cycle is called a *heat engine*. The purpose of a heat engine is to deliver work continuously to the outside by performing the same cycle over and over again. The net work in the cycle is the output, and the heat absorbed by the working substance is the input. The *thermal efficiency* of the engine η is defined as

$$\text{Thermal efficiency} = \frac{\text{work output, in any energy units}}{\text{heat input, in the same energy units}},$$

or

$$\eta = \frac{W}{Q_H}. \tag{7-1}$$

Applying the first law to one complete cycle and remembering that there is no net change of internal energy, we get

$$Q_H - Q_C = W,$$

and therefore

$$\eta = \frac{Q_H - Q_C}{Q_H},$$

or

$$\boxed{\eta = 1 - \frac{Q_C}{Q_H}.} \tag{7-2}$$

It is seen from this equation that η will be unity (efficiency of 100 percent) when Q_C is zero. In other words, if an engine can be built to operate in a cycle in which there is no outflow of heat from the system, there will be 100 percent conversion of the absorbed heat into work. We shall see later under what conditions this is possible in principle and why it is not possible in practice.

The transformation of heat into work is usually accomplished in practice by two general types of engine: the *external combustion engine*, such as the Stirling engine and the steam engine, and the *internal-combustion engine*, such as the gasoline engine and the diesel engine. In both types, a gas or a mixture of gases contained in a cylinder undergoes a cycle, thereby causing a piston to impart to a shaft a motion of rotation against an opposing force. It is necessary in both engines that, at some time in the cycle, the gas in the cylinder be raised to a high temperature and pressure. In the Stirling and steam engines this is accomplished by an outside furnace. The high temperature and pressure achieved in the internal-combustion engine, however, are produced by a chemical reaction between a fuel and air that takes place in the cylinder itself. In the gasoline engine, the combustion of the gasoline and air takes place explosively through the agency of an electric spark. The diesel engine, however, uses oil as a fuel, the combustion of which is accomplished more slowly by spraying the oil into the cylinder at a convenient rate.

7-2   The Stirling Engine

In 1816, before the science of thermodynamics had even been begun, a minister of the Church of Scotland named Robert Stirling designed and patented a hot-air engine that could convert some of the energy liberated by a burning fuel into work. The Stirling engine remained useful and popular for many years but, with the development of steam engines and internal-combustion engines, finally became obsolete. In the 1940s the Stirling engine was revived by the engineers of the Philips company in Eindhoven, Holland, and has once again become the subject of a great amount of interest and research.

The steps in the operation of a somewhat idealized Stirling engine are shown schematically in Fig. 7-1a. Two pistons, an expansion piston on the left and a compression piston on the right, are connected to the same shaft. As the shaft rotates, these pistons move in different phase, with the aid of suitable connecting linkages. The space between the two pistons is filled with gas, and the left-hand portion of the space is kept in contact with a hot reservoir (burning fuel), while the right-hand portion is in contact with a cold reservoir. Between the two portions of gas is a device R, called a *regenerator*, consisting of a packing of steel wool or a series of metal baffles, whose thermal conductivity is low enough to support the temperature difference between the hot and cold ends without appreciable heat conduction. The Stirling cycle consists of four processes depicted schematically in Fig. 7-1a and involving pressure and volume changes plotted (as though ideal conditions existed) on the PV diagram of Fig. 7-1b.

Fig. 7-1   (a) Schematic diagram of steps in the operation of an idealized Stirling engine.
(*The numbers under each diagram refer to the processes shown on PV diagram in Fig. 7-1b.*)
(b) Idealized Stirling engine cycle on PV diagram.

1 → 2   While the left piston remains at the top, the right piston moves halfway up, compressing cold gas while in contact with the cold reservoir and therefore causing heat Q_C to leave. This is an approximately isothermal compression and is depicted as a rigorously isothermal process at the temperature θ_C in Fig. 7-1b.

2 → 3   The left piston moves down and the right piston up, so that there is no change in volume, but gas is forced through the regenerator from the cold side to the hot side and enters the left-hand side at the higher temperature θ_H. To accomplish this, the regenerator supplied heat Q_R to the gas. Note that the process 2 → 3 in Fig. 7-1b is at constant volume.

3 → 4   The right piston now remains stationary as the left piston continues moving down while in contact with the hot reservoir, causing the gas to undergo an approximately isothermal expansion, during which heat Q_H is absorbed at the temperature θ_H, as shown in Fig. 7-1b.

4 → 1   Both pistons move in opposite directions, thereby forcing gas through the regenerator from the hot to the cold side and giving up approximately the same amount of heat Q_R to the regenerator that it absorbed in the process 2 → 3. This process takes place at practically constant volume.

The net result of the cycle is the absorption of heat Q_H at the high temperature θ_H, the rejection of heat Q_C at the low temperature θ_C, and the delivery of work $W = Q_H - Q_C$ to the surroundings, with no net heat transfer resulting from the two constant-volume processes. It must be emphasized that Fig. 7-1b is based on the assumptions that (1) the gas is ideal, (2) no leakage of gas takes place, (3) no heat is lost or gained through cylinder walls, (4) no heat is conducted through the regenerator, and (5) there is no friction. An

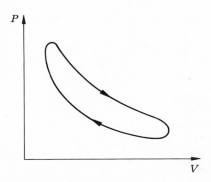

Fig. 7-2   *Indicator diagram of an actual Stirling engine.*

indicator diagram of an actual Stirling cycle would look much more like the diagram in Fig. 7-2. Even if these idealizations could be realized in practice, there would still be some heat Q_C rejected at the lower temperature, and therefore all the input Q_H could not be converted into work.

7-3 The Steam Engine

A schematic diagram of an elementary steam power plant is shown in Fig. 7-3a. The operation of such a plant can be understood by following the pressure and volume changes of a small constant mass of water as it is conveyed from the condenser, through the boiler, into the expansion chamber, and back to the condenser. The water in the condenser is at a pressure less than atmospheric and at a temperature less than the normal boiling point. By means of a pump it is introduced into the boiler, which is at a much higher pressure and temperature. In the boiler the water is first heated to its boiling point and then vaporized, both processes taking place approximately at constant pressure. The steam is then superheated at the same pressure. It is then allowed to flow into a cylinder, where it expands approximately adiabatically against a piston or a set of turbine blades, until its pressure and temperature drop to that of the condenser. In the condenser, finally, the steam condenses into water at the same temperature and pressure as at the beginning, and the cycle is complete.

In the actual operation of the steam plant there are several processes that render an exact analysis difficult. These are: (1) acceleration and turbulence caused by the pressure difference required to cause the flow of the steam from one part of the apparatus to another, (2) friction, (3) conduction of heat through the walls during expansion of the steam, (4) irreversible heat transfers due to a finite temperature difference between the furnace and the boiler.

A first approximation to the solution of the problem of the steam plant may be made by introducing some simplifying assumptions which, although in no way realizable in practice, provide at least an upper limit to the efficiency of such a plant and which define a cycle called the *Rankine cycle*, in terms of which the actual behavior of a steam plant may be discussed.

In Fig. 7-3b three isotherms of water are shown on a PV diagram: one at θ_C corresponding to the temperature of the condenser, another at θ_B for the temperature of the boiler, and a third at a still higher temperature θ_H. The dashed curves are the liquid and the vapor saturation curves, respectively. In the Rankine cycle all processes are assumed to be well-behaved; complications that arise from acceleration, turbulence, friction, and heat losses are thus eliminated. Starting at the point 1, representing the state of 1 lb of

Fig. 7-3   (a) *Elementary steam power plant.* (b) *PV diagram of Rankine cycle.*

saturated liquid water at the temperature and pressure of the condenser, the Rankine cycle comprises the following six processes:

$1 \rightarrow 2$ Adiabatic compression of water to the pressure of the boiler (only a very small change of temperature takes place during this process).

$2 \rightarrow 3$ Isobaric heating of water to the boiling point.

$3 \rightarrow 4$ Isobaric, isothermal vaporization of water into saturated steam.

$4 \rightarrow 5$ Isobaric superheating of steam into superheated steam at temperature θ_H.

$5 \rightarrow 6$ Adiabatic expansion of steam into wet steam.

$6 \rightarrow 1$ Isobaric, isothermal condensation of steam into saturated water at the temperature θ_C.

During the processes $2 \rightarrow 3$, $3 \rightarrow 4$, and $4 \rightarrow 5$, heat Q_H enters the system from a hot reservoir; whereas during the condensation process $6 \rightarrow 1$, heat Q_C is rejected by the system to a reservoir at θ_C. This condensation process *must* exist in order to bring the system back to its initial state 1. Since heat is always rejected during the condensation of water, Q_C cannot be made equal to zero, and therefore the input Q_H cannot be converted completely into work.

7-4   Internal Combustion Engines

In the gasoline engine, the cycle involves the performance of six processes, four of which require motion of the piston and are called *strokes:*

1   *Intake stroke.*   A mixture of gasoline vapor and air is drawn into the cylinder by the suction stroke of the piston. The pressure of the outside is greater than that of the mixture by an amount sufficient to cause acceleration and to overcome friction.
2   *Compression stroke.*   The mixture of gasoline vapor and air is compressed until its pressure and temperature rise considerably. This is accomplished by the compression stroke of the piston, in which friction, acceleration, and heat loss by conduction are present.
3   *Explosion.*   Combustion of the hot mixture is caused to take place very rapidly by an electric spark. The resulting combustion products attain a very high pressure and temperature, but the volume remains unchanged. The piston does not move during this process.
4   *Power stroke.*   The hot combustion products expand and push the piston out, thus suffering a drop in pressure and temperature. This is the power stroke of the piston and is also accompanied by friction, acceleration, and heat conduction.
5   *Valve exhaust.*   The combustion products at the end of the power stroke are still at a higher pressure and temperature than the outside. An exhaust valve allows some gas to escape until the pressure drops to that of the atmosphere. The piston does not move during this process.
6   *Exhaust stroke.*   The piston pushes almost all the remaining combustion products out of the cylinder by exerting a pressure sufficiently larger than that of the outside to cause acceleration and overcome friction. This is the exhaust stroke.

In the above processes there are several phenomena that render an exact mathematical analysis almost impossible. Among these are friction, acceleration, loss of heat by conduction, and the chemical reaction between gasoline vapor and air. A drastic but useful simplification is provided by eliminating these troublesome effects. When this is done, we have a sort of idealized gasoline engine that performs a cycle known as an *Otto cycle.*

The behavior of a gasoline engine can be approximated by assuming a set

Fig. 7-4   (*a*) *Air-standard Otto cycle.* (*b*) *Air-standard Diesel cycle.*

of ideal conditions as follows: (1) The working substance is at all times air, which behaves like an ideal gas with constant heat capacities. (2) All processes are quasi-static. (3) There is no friction. On the basis of these assumptions the air-standard Otto cycle is composed of six simple processes of an ideal gas, which are plotted on a *PV* diagram in Fig. 7-4*a*.

$5 \rightarrow 1$ represents a quasi-static isobaric intake at atmospheric pressure. There is no friction and no acceleration. The volume varies from zero to V_1 as the number of moles varies from zero to n_1 according to the equation

$$P_0 V = nR\theta_1,$$

where P_0 is atmospheric pressure and θ_1 is the temperature of the outside air.

$1 \rightarrow 2$ represents a quasi-static, adiabatic compression of n_1 moles of air. There is no friction and no loss of heat through the cylinder wall. The temperature rises from θ_1 to θ_2 according to the equation

$$\theta_1 V_1^{\gamma-1} = \theta_2 V_2^{\gamma-1}.$$

$2 \rightarrow 3$ represents a quasi-static isochoric increase of temperature and pressure of n_1 moles of air, brought about by an absorption of heat Q_H from a series of external reservoirs whose temperatures range from θ_2 to θ_3. If there were only one reservoir at temperature θ_3, the flow of heat would not be quasi-static. This process is meant to approximate the effect of the explosion in a gasoline engine.

$3 \rightarrow 4$ represents a quasi-static adiabatic expansion of n_1 moles of air, involving a drop in temperature from θ_3 to θ_4 according to the equation

$$\theta_3 V_2^{\gamma-1} = \theta_4 V_1^{\gamma-1}.$$

$4 \rightarrow 1$ represents a quasi-static isochoric drop in temperature and pressure of n_1 moles of air, brought about by a rejection of heat Q_C to a series of external reservoirs ranging in temperature from θ_4 to θ_1. This process is meant to approximate the drop to atmospheric pressure upon opening the exhaust valve.

$1 \rightarrow 5$ represents a quasi-static isobaric exhaust at atmospheric pressure. The volume varies from V_1 to zero as the number of moles varies from n_1 to zero, with the temperature remaining constant at the value θ_1.

The two isobaric processes $5 \rightarrow 1$ and $1 \rightarrow 5$ obviously cancel each other and need not be considered further. Of the four remaining processes, only two involve a flow of heat. There occur an absorption of Q_H units of heat at high temperatures from $2 \rightarrow 3$ and a rejection of Q_C units of heat at lower temperatures from $4 \rightarrow 1$, as indicated in Fig. 7-4a.

Assuming C_V to be constant along the line $2 \rightarrow 3$, we get

$$Q_H = \int_{\theta_2}^{\theta_3} C_V \, d\theta = C_V(\theta_3 - \theta_2).$$

Similarly, for process $4 \rightarrow 1$, regarding Q_C as a positive number,

$$Q_C = \int_{\theta_4}^{\theta_1} C_V \, d\theta = C_V(\theta_4 - \theta_1).$$

The thermal efficiency is therefore

$$\eta = 1 - \frac{Q_C}{Q_H} = 1 - \frac{\theta_4 - \theta_1}{\theta_3 - \theta_2}.$$

The two adiabatic processes provide the equations

$$\theta_4 V_1^{\gamma-1} = \theta_3 V_2^{\gamma-1}$$

and

$$\theta_1 V_1^{\gamma-1} = \theta_2 V_2^{\gamma-1},$$

which, after subtraction, yield

$$(\theta_4 - \theta_1) V_1^{\gamma-1} = (\theta_3 - \theta_2) V_2^{\gamma-1},$$

or

$$\frac{\theta_4 - \theta_1}{\theta_3 - \theta_2} = \left(\frac{V_2}{V_1}\right)^{\gamma-1}.$$

Denoting the ratio V_1/V_2 by r, where r is called the *compression ratio* or the *expansion ratio*, we have finally

$$\eta = 1 - \frac{1}{(V_1/V_2)^{\gamma-1}} = 1 - \frac{1}{r^{\gamma-1}}. \tag{7-3}$$

In an actual gasoline engine, r cannot be made greater than about 10 because, if r is larger, the rise of temperature upon compression of the mixture of gasoline and air is great enough to cause an explosion before the advent of the spark. This is called *preignition*. Taking r equal to 9 and γ equal to 1.5 (for air, γ is more nearly 1.4),

$$\eta = 1 - \frac{1}{\sqrt{9}}$$

$$= 0.67 = 67 \text{ percent.}$$

All the troublesome effects present in an actual gasoline engine, such as acceleration, turbulence, and heat conduction by virtue of a finite temperature difference, are such as to make the efficiency much lower than that of the air-standard Otto cycle.

In the Diesel engine, only air is admitted on the intake. The air is compressed adiabatically until the temperature is high enough to ignite oil that is sprayed into the cylinder after the compression. The rate of supply of oil is adjusted so that combustion takes place approximately isobarically, the piston moving out during combustion. The rest of the cycle—namely, power stroke, valve exhaust, and exhaust stroke—is exactly the same as in the gasoline engine. The usual troublesome effects, such as chemical combination, friction, acceleration, and heat losses, take place in the Diesel engine as in the gasoline engine. Eliminating these effects by making the same assumptions as before, we are left with a sort of idealized Diesel engine that performs a cycle known as the *air-standard Diesel cycle*. If the line $2 \rightarrow 3$ in Fig. 7-4a is imagined horizontal instead of vertical, the resulting cycle will be the air-standard Diesel cycle. This is shown in Fig. 7-4b.

It is a simple matter to show that the efficiency of an engine operating in an idealized Diesel cycle is given by

$$\eta = 1 - \frac{1}{\gamma} \frac{(1/r_E)^{\gamma} - (1/r_C)^{\gamma}}{(1/r_E) - (1/r_C)}, \tag{7-4}$$

where
$$r_E = \frac{V_1}{V_3} = \text{expansion ratio}$$

and
$$r_C = \frac{V_1}{V_2} = \text{compression ratio.}$$

In practice, the compression ratio of a Diesel engine can be made much larger than that of a gasoline engine, because there is no fear of preignition since only air is compressed. Taking, for example, $r_C = 15$, $r_E = 5$, and $\gamma = 1.5$,

$$\eta = 1 - \frac{2}{3} \frac{1/5^{\frac{3}{2}} - 1/15^{\frac{3}{2}}}{\frac{1}{5} - \frac{1}{15}}$$

$$= 1 - 5(0.0895 - 0.0172)$$

$$= 64 \text{ percent.}$$

The efficiencies of actual Diesel engines are still lower, of course, for the reasons mentioned in connection with the gasoline engine.

In the Diesel engine just considered, four strokes of the piston are needed for the execution of a cycle, and only one of the four is a power stroke. Since only air is compressed in the Diesel engine, it is possible to do away with the exhaust and intake strokes and thus complete the cycle in two strokes. In the two-stroke-cycle Diesel engine, every other stroke is a power stroke, and thus the power is doubled. The principle is very simple: At the conclusion of the power stroke, when the cylinder is full of combustion products, the valve opens, exhaust takes place until the combustion products are at atmospheric pressure, and then, instead of using the piston itself to exhaust the remaining gases, fresh air is blown into the cylinder, replacing the combustion products. A blower, operated by the engine itself, is used for this purpose, and thus it accomplishes in one simple operation what formerly required two separate piston strokes.

7-5 Kelvin-Planck Statement of the Second Law

In the preceding pages, four different heat engines have been briefly and somewhat superficially described. There are, of course, more types of engines and a tremendous number of structural details, methods of increasing thermal efficiency, mathematical analyses, etc., which constitute the subject matter of engineering thermodynamics. Thermodynamics owes its origin to the attempt to convert heat into work and to develop the theory of operation of devices for this purpose. It is therefore fitting that one of the fundamental laws of thermodynamics is based upon the operation of heat engines. Reduced to their simplest terms, the important characteristics of heat-engine cycles may be summed up as follows:

1   There is some process or series of processes during which there is an absorption of heat from an external reservoir at a high temperature (called simply the *hot reservoir*).

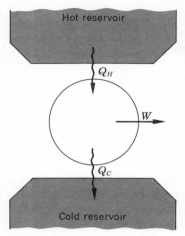

Fig. 7-5   *Symbolic representation of heat engine.*

2   There is some process or series of processes during which heat is rejected to an external reservoir at a lower temperature (called simply the *cold reservoir*).

This is represented schematically in Fig. 7-5. No engine has ever been developed that converts the heat extracted from one reservoir into work without rejecting some heat to a reservoir at a lower temperature. This negative statement, which is the result of engineering experience, constitutes the *second law of thermodynamics* and has been formulated in several ways. The original statement of Kelvin is: "It is impossible by means of inanimate material agency to derive mechanical effect from any portion of matter by cooling it below the temperature of the coldest of the surrounding objects." In the words of Planck, "It is impossible to construct an engine which, working in a complete cycle, will produce no effect other than the raising of a weight and the cooling of a heat reservoir." We may combine these statements into one equivalent statement, to which we shall refer hereafter as the *Kelvin-Planck statement of the second law*, thus:

No process is possible whose sole *result is the absorption of heat from a reservoir and the conversion of this heat into work.*

If the second law were not true, it would be possible to drive a steamship across the ocean by extracting heat from the ocean or to run a power plant by extracting heat from the surrounding air. The student should notice that neither of these "impossibilities" violates the first law of thermodynamics. After all, both the ocean and the surrounding air contain an enormous store of internal energy, which, in principle, may be extracted in the form of a flow of heat. There is nothing in the first law to preclude the possibility of converting this heat completely into work. The second law, therefore, is not a deduction from the first but stands by itself as a separate law of nature, referring to an aspect of nature different from that contemplated by the first law. The first law denies the possibility of creating or destroying energy; the second denies the possibility of utilizing energy in a particular way. The continual operation of a machine that creates its own energy and thus violates the first law is called *perpetual motion of the first kind*. The operation of a machine that utilizes the internal energy of only one heat reservoir, thus violating the second law, is called *perpetual motion of the second kind*.

7-6   The Refrigerator

We have seen that a heat engine is a device by which a system is taken through a cycle in such a direction that some heat is absorbed while the temperature is high, a smaller amount is rejected at a lower temperature, and a net amount of work is done on the outside. If we imagine a cycle performed in a direction opposite to that of an engine, the net result would be the absorption of some heat at a low temperature, the rejection of a *larger* amount at a higher temperature, and a net amount of work done *on* the system. A device that performs a cycle in this direction is called a *refrigerator*, and the system undergoing the cycle is called a *refrigerant*.

The Stirling cycle is capable of being reversed and, when reversed, it gives rise to one of the most useful types of refrigerator. The operation of an ideal Stirling refrigerator may best be understood with the aid of the schematic diagrams shown in Fig. 7-6a, and the accompanying PV diagram of Fig. 7-6b.

$1 \rightarrow 2$ While the right piston remains stationary, the left piston moves up, compressing the gas isothermally at the temperature θ_H and rejecting heat Q_H to the hot reservoir.

$2 \rightarrow 3$ Both pistons move the same amount simultaneously, forcing gas through the regenerator, giving up some heat Q_R to the regenerator, and emerging cold in the right-hand space. This takes place at constant volume.

$3 \rightarrow 4$ While the left piston remains stationary, the right piston moves down and causes an isothermal expansion at the low temperature θ_C, during which heat Q_C is absorbed by the gas from the cold reservoir.

$4 \rightarrow 1$ Both pistons move and force gas at constant volume from the cold to the hot end through the regenerator, thereby taking up approximately the same heat Q_R that was supplied to the regenerator in process $2 \rightarrow 3$.

Fig. 7-6   (a) *Schematic diagram of steps in the operation of idealized Stirling refrigerator.* (b) *Idealized Stirling refrigeration cycle on PV diagram.*

Fig. 7-7   (a) *Elementary refrigeration plant.* (b) *PV diagram of commercial refrigerator cycle.*

The Stirling refrigeration cycle has been utilized in recent years by a number of engineering firms in the construction of practical refrigerators for the production of low temperatures, from 90 down to 12°K. As in the case of the Stirling engine, the Philips Company in Holland has been in the forefront in the design and construction of large industrial installations. (Miniature units suitable for academic laboratories are available from North American Philips, A. D. Little, Hughes Aircraft, and Malaker Laboratories.)

In order to gain a little more insight into the working of a refrigerator, let us consider some of the details of a commercial refrigeration plant that are reflected in most electric home refrigerators. The schematic diagram in Fig. 7-7a shows the path of a constant mass of refrigerant as it is conveyed from the liquid storage, where it is at the temperature and pressure of the condenser, through the throttling valve, through the evaporator, into the compressor, and finally back to the condenser.

In the condenser the refrigerant is at a high pressure and at as low a temperature as can be obtained with air or water cooling. The refrigerant is always of such a nature that, at this pressure and temperature, it is a saturated liquid. When a fluid passes through a narrow opening (a needle valve) from a region of constant high pressure to a region of constant lower pressure adiabatically, it is said to undergo a *throttling process* (see Prob. 4-8), or a *Joule-Thomson* or *Joule-Kelvin expansion*. This process will be considered in some detail in Chap. 11. It is a property of saturated liquids (not of gases) that a throttling process always produces cooling and partial vaporization. In the evaporator the fluid is completely vaporized, with the heat of vaporization being supplied by the materials to be cooled. The vapor is then compressed adiabatically, thereby increasing in temperature. In the condenser, the vapor is cooled until it condenses and becomes completely liquefied.

The ideal refrigeration cycle depicted on a *PV* diagram in Fig. 7-7b is the result of ignoring the usual difficulties due to turbulence, friction, heat losses, etc. In Fig. 7-7b, two isotherms of a fluid such as ammonia or freon are shown on a *PV* diagram—one at θ_H, the temperature of the condenser, and the other at θ_C, the temperature of the evaporator. Starting at the point 1, representing the state of 1 lb of saturated liquid at the temperature and pressure of the condenser, the commercial refrigeration cycle comprises the following processes:

1 → 2   Throttling process involving a drop of pressure and temperature. The states between the initial and final states of a fluid during a throttling process cannot be described with the aid of thermodynamic coordinates referring to the system as a whole and, therefore, cannot be represented by points on a *PV* diagram. Hence the series of dashes between 1 and 2.

2 → 3   Isothermal, isobaric vaporization in which heat Q_C is absorbed by the refrigerant at the low temperature θ_C, thereby cooling the materials of the cold reservoir.

3 → 4   Adiabatic compression of the vapor to a temperature higher than that of the condenser θ_H.

4 → 1   Isobaric cooling and condensation at θ_H.

The purpose of any refrigerator is to extract as much heat as possible from a cold reservoir with the expenditure of as little work as possible. The "output," so to speak, is the heat extracted from the cold reservoir, and the "input" is work. A convenient measure, therefore, of the performance of a refrigerator is expressed by the *coefficient of performance* ω (also called the *cooling energy ratio*), where

$$\omega = \frac{\text{heat extracted from cold reservoir}}{\text{work done on refrigerant}}.$$

If, in one cycle, heat Q_C is absorbed by the refrigerant from the cold reservoir and work W is done by the electric motor that operates the refrigerator, then

$$\omega = \frac{Q_C}{W} = \frac{Q_C}{Q_H - Q_C}.$$

The coefficient of performance of a refrigerator may be considerably larger than unity. If, for the sake of argument, one assumes the value 5,

$$\omega = \frac{Q_C}{W} = 5.$$

But

$$Q_C = Q_H - W;$$

hence

$$\frac{Q_H - W}{W} = 5,$$

$$\frac{Q_H}{W} = 6,$$

and therefore the *heat liberated at the higher temperature is equal to six times the work done.* If the work is supplied by an electric motor, for every joule of electrical energy supplied, 6 J of heat will be liberated; whereas if 1 J of electrical energy were dissipated in a resistor, one could obtain at most 1 J of heat. Consequently, it would seem to be highly advantageous to heat a house by refrigerating the outdoors.

This was first pointed out in 1852 by Lord Kelvin, who designed a machine for the purpose. The device was never built, however, and it remained for Haldane, about 75 years later, to utilize the principle and heat his house in Scotland by refrigerating the outdoor air, supplemented by city water. Since about 1938, many devices known as "heat pumps" have appeared on the market for warming the house in winter by refrigerating either the ground, the outside air, or the water supplied in the mains. By turning a valve and reversing the flow of refrigerant, the heat pump may also be used to cool the house in summer, as shown in Fig. 7-8. Various commercial units have coefficients of performance ranging from about 2 to 7. The design, installation, and operation of such units are now an important branch of engineering.

The operation of a refrigerator may be symbolized by the schematic diagram shown in Fig. 7-9, which should be compared with the corresponding engine diagram of Fig. 7-5. Work is always necessary to transfer heat from a cold to a hot reservoir. In household refrigerators, this work is usually done by an electric motor, whose cost of operation appears regularly on the monthly bill. It would be a boon to mankind if no external supply of energy were needed, but it must certainly be admitted that experience indicates the

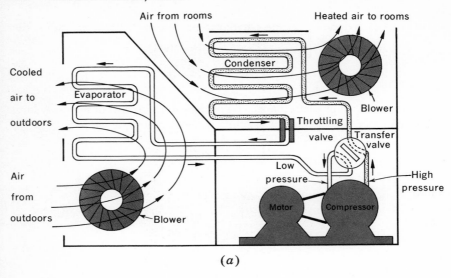

Air from rooms

Heated air to rooms

Cooled

air to

outdoors

Condenser

Evaporator

Blower

Throttling

valve

Transfer

valve

Low

pressure

High

pressure

Air

from

outdoors

Blower

Motor

Compressor

(*a*)

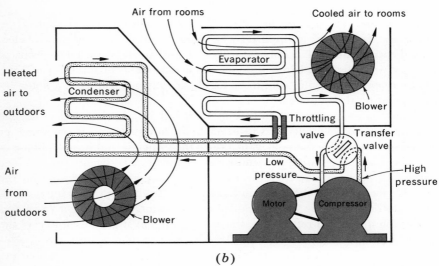

Air from rooms

Cooled air to rooms

Heated

air to

outdoors

Evaporator

Condenser

Blower

Throttling

valve

Transfer

valve

Low

pressure

High

pressure

Air

from

outdoors

Blower

Motor

Compressor

(*b*)

Fig. 7-8   (*a*) *Heating the house by refrigerating the outside air.* (*b*) *Cooling the house by heating the outside air.* (*J. Partington, Jr., G.E. Educational Service News, December, 1951.*)

contrary. This negative statement leads us to the *Clausius*† *statement of the second law:*

   No process is possible whose sole *result is the transfer of heat from a cooler to a hotter body.*

   † R. J. Clausius (pronounced *Klow'-zee-oos*).

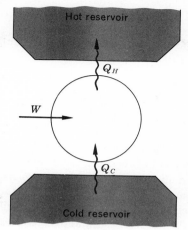

Fig. 7-9   *Symbolic representation of refrigerator.*

At first sight, the Kelvin-Planck and the Clausius statements appear to be quite unconnected, but we shall see immediately that they are in all respects equivalent.

7-7   Equivalence of Kelvin-Planck and Clausius Statements

Let us adopt the following notation:

K = truth of the Kelvin-Planck statement,
$-K$ = falsity of the Kelvin-Planck statement,
C = truth of the Clausius statement,
$-C$ = falsity of the Clausius statement.

Two propositions or statements are said to be equivalent when the truth of one implies the truth of the second and the truth of the second implies the truth of the first. Using the symbol $\supset$ to mean "implies" and the symbol $\equiv$ to denote equivalence, we have, by definition,

$$K \equiv C$$

when $$K \supset C \quad \text{and} \quad C \supset K.$$

Now, it may easily be shown that

$$K \equiv C$$

also when $-K \supset -C$ and $-C \supset -K.$

Thus, in order to demonstrate the equivalence of K and C, we have to show that a violation of one statement implies a violation of the second, and vice versa.

1   To prove that $-C \supset -K$, consider a refrigerator, shown in the left-hand side of Fig. 7-10, which requires *no work* to transfer Q_2 units of heat from a cold reservoir to a hot reservoir and which therefore violates the Clausius statement. Suppose that a heat engine (on the right) also operates between the same two reservoirs in such a way that heat Q_2 is delivered to the cold reservoir. The engine, of course, does not violate any law, but the refrigerator and engine *together* constitute a self-acting device whose sole effect is to take heat $Q_1 - Q_2$ from the hot reservoir and to convert *all* this heat into work. Therefore the refrigerator and engine together constitute a violation of the Kelvin-Planck statement.

2   To prove that $-K \supset -C$, consider an engine, shown on the left-hand side of Fig. 7-11, which rejects no heat to the cold reservoir and which therefore violates the Kelvin-Planck statement. Suppose that a refrigerator (on the right) also operates between the same two reservoirs and uses up all the work liberated by the engine. The refrigerator violates no law, but the engine and refrigerator *together* constitute a self-acting device whose sole effect is to transfer heat Q_2 from the cold to the hot reservoir. Therefore the engine and refrigerator together constitute a violation of the Clausius statement.

Fig. 7-10   *Proof that* $-C \supset -K$. *The refrigerator on the left is a violation of C; the refrigerator and engine acting together constitute a violation of K.*

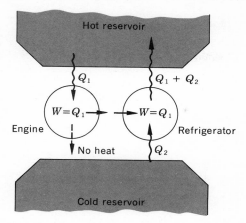

Fig. 7-11   *Proof that* $-K \supset -C$. *The engine on the left is a violation of K; the engine and refrigerator acting together constitute a violation of C.*

We therefore arrive at the conclusion that both statements of the second law are equivalent. It is a matter of indifference which one is used in a particular argument.

PROBLEMS

7-1   Figure P7-1 represents a simplified PV diagram of the Joule ideal-gas cycle. All processes are quasi-static, and C_P is constant. Prove that the

Fig. P7-1   *Joule ideal-gas cycle.*

thermal efficiency of an engine performing this cycle is

$$1 - \left(\frac{P_1}{P_2}\right)^{\frac{\gamma-1}{\gamma}}.$$

7-2   Figure P7-2 represents a simplified PV diagram of the Sargent ideal-gas cycle. All processes are quasi-static, and the heat capacities are

Fig. P7-2   *Sargent ideal-gas cycle.*

constant. Prove that the thermal efficiency of an engine performing this cycle is

$$1 - \gamma\,\frac{\theta_4 - \theta_1}{\theta_3 - \theta_2}.$$

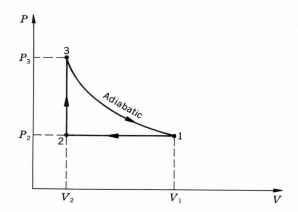

Fig. P7-3

✳7-3   Figure P7-3 represents an imaginary ideal-gas engine cycle. Assuming constant heat capacities, show that the thermal efficiency is

$$\eta = 1 - \gamma \frac{(V_1/V_2) - 1}{(P_3/P_2) - 1}.$$

7-4   An ideal-gas engine operates in a cycle which, when represented on a PV diagram, is a rectangle. Call P_1, P_2 the lower and higher pressures, respectively; call V_1, V_2 the lower and higher volumes, respectively.

(a)   Calculate the work done in one cycle.

(b)   Indicate which parts of the cycle involve heat flow into the gas, and calculate the amount of heat flowing into the gas in one cycle. (Assume constant heat capacities.)

(c)   Show that the efficiency of this engine is

$$\eta = \frac{\gamma - 1}{\dfrac{\gamma P_2}{P_2 - P_1} + \dfrac{V_1}{V_2 - V_1}}.$$

7-5   A vessel contains 600 cm³ of helium gas at 2°K and $\frac{1}{36}$ atm. Take the zero of internal energy of helium to be at this point.

(a)   The temperature is raised at constant volume to 288°K. Assuming helium to behave like an ideal monatomic gas, how much heat is absorbed, and what is the internal energy of the helium? Can this energy be regarded as stored heat or stored work?

(b)   The helium is now expanded adiabatically to 2°K. How much work is done, and what is the new internal energy? Has heat been converted into work without compensation, thus violating the second law?

(c)   The helium is now compressed isothermally to its original volume. What are the quantities of heat and work in this process? What is the efficiency of the cycle? Plot on a PV diagram.

7-6   Derive the expression for the efficiency of an ideal engine operating in an air-standard Diesel cycle, Eq. (7-4).

7-7

(a)   Assume an ideal gas to undergo the idealized Stirling engine cycle shown in Fig. 7-1b with perfect regeneration. Show that

$$\eta = 1 - \frac{\theta_C}{\theta_H}.$$

(b)   If this cycle is reversed, calculate the coefficient of performance.

7-8   In the tropics the water near the surface of the ocean is warmer than the deep water. Would an engine operating between these two levels violate the second law?

7-9   A storage battery is connected to a motor, which is used to lift a weight. The battery remains at constant temperature by receiving heat from the outside air. Is this a violation of the second law? Why?

7-10   There are many paramagnetic solids whose internal energy is a function of temperature only, like an ideal gas. In an isothermal demagnetization, heat is absorbed from one reservoir and converted completely into work. Is this a violation of the second law? Why?

7-11   Would an atomic-energy power plant violate either the first law or the second law of thermodynamics? Explain.

8.

REVERSIBILITY AND
THE KELVIN TEMPERA-
TURE SCALE

8-1   Reversibility and Irreversibility

In thermodynamics, work is a macroscopic concept. The performance of work may always be described in terms of the raising or lowering of an object or the winding or unwinding of a spring, i.e., by the operation of a device that serves to increase or decrease the potential energy of a mechanical system. Imagine, for the sake of simplicity, a suspended object coupled by means of suitable pulleys to a system so that any work done by or on the system can be described in terms of the raising or lowering of the object. Imagine, further, a series of reservoirs which may be put in contact with the system and in terms of which any flow of heat to or from the system may be described. We shall refer to the suspended object and the series of reservoirs as the *local surroundings* of the system. The local surroundings are, therefore, those parts of the surroundings which interact *directly* with the system. Other mechanical devices and reservoirs which are accessible and which *might* interact with the system constitute the *auxiliary surroundings* of the system— or, for want of a better expression, the *rest of the universe*. The word "universe" is used here in a very restricted technical sense, with no cosmic or celestial implications. The universe merely means a finite portion of the world consisting of the system and those surroundings which may interact with the system.

Now suppose that a process occurs in which (1) the system proceeds from an initial state i to a final state f; (2) the suspended object is lowered to an extent that W units of work are performed; and (3) a transfer of heat Q takes place from the system to the series of reservoirs. If, at the conclusion of this process, the system may be restored to its initial state i, the object lifted to its former level, and the reservoirs caused to part with the same amount of heat Q, without producing any changes in any other mechanical device or reservoir in the universe, the original process is said to be *reversible*. In other words, *a reversible process is one that is performed in such a way that, at the conclusion of the process, both the system and the local surroundings may be restored to their initial states, without producing any changes in the rest of the universe.* A process that does not fulfill these stringent requirements is said to be *irreversible*.

The question immediately arises as to whether natural processes, i.e., the familiar processes of nature, are reversible or not. We shall show that it is a consequence of the second law of thermodynamics that all natural processes are irreversible. By considering representative types of natural processes and examining the features of these processes which are responsible for their irreversibility, we shall then be able to state the conditions under which a process may take place reversibly.

8-2   External Mechanical Irreversibility

There is a large class of processes involving the isothermal transformation of work through a system (which remains unchanged) into internal energy of a reservoir. This type of process is depicted schematically in Fig. 8-1 and is illustrated by the following five examples:

1   Irregular stirring of a viscous liquid in contact with a reservoir.
2   Coming to rest of a rotating or vibrating liquid in contact with a reservoir.
3   Inelastic deformation of a solid in contact with a reservoir.
4   Transfer of electricity through a resistor in contact with a reservoir.
5   Magnetic hysteresis of a material in contact with a reservoir.

In order to restore the system and its local surroundings to their initial states without producing changes elsewhere, Q units of heat would have to be

Fig. 8-1   *Isothermal transformation of work through a system (which remains unchanged) into internal energy of a reservoir.*

Fig. 8-2   *Adiabatic transformation of work into internal energy of a system.*

extracted from the reservoir and converted completely into work. Since this would involve a violation of the second law, all processes of the above type are irreversible.

Another set of processes involves the adiabatic transformation of work into internal energy of a system. This is depicted schematically in Fig. 8-2 and is illustrated by the following examples, similar to the preceding list:

1   Irregular stirring of a viscous thermally insulated liquid.
2   Coming to rest of a rotating or vibrating thermally insulated liquid.
3   Inelastic deformation of a thermally insulated solid.
4   Transfer of electricity through a thermally insulated resistor.
5   Magnetic hysteresis of a thermally insulated material.

A process of this type is accompanied by a rise of temperature of the system from, say, θ_i to θ_f. In order to restore the system and its local surroundings to their initial states without producing changes elsewhere, the internal energy of the system would have to be decreased by extracting $U_f - U_i$ units of heat, thus lowering the temperature from θ_f to θ_i, and this heat would have to be completely converted into work. Since this violates the second law, all processes of the above type are irreversible.

The transformation of work into internal energy either of a system or of a reservoir is seen to take place through the agency of such phenomena as viscosity, friction, inelasticity, electric resistance, and magnetic hysteresis. These effects are known as *dissipative effects,* and the work is said to be dissipated. Processes involving the dissipation of work into internal energy are said to exhibit *external mechanical irreversibility.* It is a matter of everyday experience that dissipative effects, particularly friction, are always present in moving devices. Friction, of course, may be reduced considerably by suitable lubrication, but experience has shown that it can never be completely eliminated. If it could, a movable device could be kept in continual operation without violating either of the two laws of thermodynamics. Such a continual motion is known as *perpetual motion of the third kind.*

8-3   Internal Mechanical Irreversibility

The following very important natural processes involve the transformation of internal energy of a system into mechanical energy and then back into internal energy again:

1   Ideal gas rushing into a vacuum (free expansion).
2   Gas seeping through a porous plug (throttling process).
3   Snapping of a stretched wire after it is cut.
4   Collapse of a soap film after it is pricked.

We shall prove the irreversibility of only the first.

During a free expansion, no interactions take place, and hence there are no local surroundings. The only effect produced is a change of state of an ideal gas from a volume V_i and temperature θ to a larger volume V_f and the same temperature θ. To restore the gas to its initial state, it would have to be compressed isothermally to the volume V_i. If the compression were performed quasi-statically and there were no friction between the piston and cylinder, an amount of work W would have to be done by some outside mechanical device, and an equal amount of heat would have to flow out of the gas into a reservoir at the temperature θ. If the mechanical device and the reservoir are to be left unchanged, the heat would have to be extracted from the reservoir and converted completely into work. Since this last step is impossible, the process is irreversible.

In a free expansion, immediately after the stopcock is opened, there is a transformation of some of the internal energy into kinetic energy of "mass motion" or "streaming," and then this kinetic energy is dissipated through viscosity into internal energy again. Similarly, when a stretched wire is cut, there is first a transformation of internal energy into kinetic energy of irregular motion and of vibration and then the dissipation of this energy through inelasticity into internal energy again. In all the processes, the first energy transformation takes place as a result of mechanical instability, and the second by virtue of some dissipative effect. A process of this sort is said to exhibit *internal mechanical irreversibility*.

8-4   External and Internal Thermal Irreversibility

Consider the following processes involving a transfer of heat between a system and a reservoir by virtue of a *finite* temperature difference:

1   Conduction or radiation of heat from a system to a cooler reservoir.
2   Conduction or radiation of heat through a system (which remains unchanged) from a hot reservoir to a cooler one.

To restore, at the conclusion of a process of this type, both the system and its local surroundings to their initial states without producing changes elsewhere, heat would have to be transferred by means of a self-acting device from a cooler to a hotter body. Since this violates the second law (Clausius statement), all processes of this type are irreversible. Such processes are said to exhibit *external thermal irreversibility*.

A process involving a transfer of heat between parts of the same system because of nonuniformity of temperature is also obviously irreversible by virtue of the Clausius statement of the second law. Such a process is said to exhibit *internal thermal irreversibility*.

8-5   Chemical Irreversibility

Some of the most interesting processes that go on in nature involve a spontaneous change of internal structure, chemical composition, density, crystal form, etc. Some important examples follow.

Formation of new chemical constituents:
1   All chemical reactions.   are irreversible

Mixing of two different substances:
2   Diffusion of two dissimilar inert ideal gases.
3   Mixing of alcohol and water.

Sudden change of phase:
4   Freezing of supercooled liquid.
5   Condensation of supersaturated vapor.

Transport of matter between phases in contact:
6   Solution of solid in water.
7   Osmosis.

Such processes are by far the most difficult to handle and must, as a rule, be treated by special methods. Such methods constitute what is known as chemical thermodynamics and are discussed in the last few chapters of this book. It can be shown that the diffusion of two dissimilar inert ideal gases is equivalent to two independent free expansions. Since a free expansion is irreversible, it follows that diffusion is irreversible. The student will have to accept at present the statement that the above processes are irreversible. Processes that involve a spontaneous change of chemical structure, density, phase, etc., are said to exhibit *chemical irreversibility*.

8-6   Conditions for Reversibility

Most processes that occur in nature are included among the general types of process listed in the preceding articles. Living processes, such as cell division, tissue growth, etc., are no exception. If one takes into account all the interactions that accompany living processes, such processes are irreversible. It is a direct consequence of the second law of thermodynamics that *all natural spontaneous processes are irreversible.*

A careful inspection of the various types of natural process shows that all involve one or both of the following features:

1   The conditions for mechanical, thermal, or chemical equilibrium, i.e., thermodynamic equilibrium, are not satisfied.
2   Dissipative effects, such as viscosity, friction, inelasticity, electric resistance, and magnetic hysteresis, are present.

For a process to be reversible, it must not possess these features. If a process is performed quasi-statically, the system passes through states of thermodynamic equilibrium, which may be traversed just as well in one direction as in the opposite direction. If there are no dissipative effects, all the work done by the system during the performance of a process in one direction can be returned to the system during the reverse process. We are led, therefore, to the conclusion that a process will be reversible when (1) it is performed quasi-statically and (2) it is not accompanied by any dissipative effects.

Since it is impossible to satisfy these two conditions perfectly, it is obvious that a reversible process is purely an ideal abstraction, extremely useful for theoretical calculations (as we shall see) but quite devoid of reality. In this sense, the assumption of a reversible process in thermodynamics resembles the assumptions made so often in mechanics, such as those which refer to weightless strings, frictionless pulleys, and point masses.

A heat reservoir was defined as a body of very large mass capable of absorbing or rejecting an unlimited supply of heat without suffering appreciable changes in its thermodynamic coordinates. The changes that do take place are so very slow and so minute that dissipative actions never develop. *Therefore, when heat enters or leaves a reservoir, the changes that take place in the reservoir are the same as those which would take place if the same quantity of heat were transferred reversibly.*

It is possible in the laboratory to approximate the conditions necessary for the performance of reversible processes. For example, if a gas is confined in a cylinder equipped with a well-lubricated piston and is allowed to expand very slowly against an opposing force provided either by an object suspended from a frictionless pulley or by an elastic spring, the gas undergoes an approximately reversible process. Similar considerations apply to a wire and to a surface film.

A reversible transfer of electricity through an electric cell may be imagined as follows: Suppose that a motor whose coils have a negligible resistance is caused to rotate until its back emf is only slightly different from the emf of the cell. Suppose further that the motor is coupled either to an object suspended from a frictionless pulley or to an elastic spring. If neither the cell itself nor the connecting wires to the motor have appreciable resistance, a reversible transfer of electricity takes place.

In order to arrive at conclusions concerning the equilibrium states of thermodynamic systems, it is often necessary to invoke some sort of process in which the system passes through these states. To assume the process to be quasi-static only, often is not sufficient, for if dissipative processes are present there may be heat flows or internal energy changes of neighboring systems (envelopes, containers, surroundings) that may limit the validity of the argument. In order to ensure that equilibrium states of the system *only* are considered—without having to take account of the effect of dissipated work in the system itself or in some other neighboring body—it is useful to invoke the concept of a *reversible process*, even though this assumption may at times seem a bit drastic.

8-7   Existence of Reversible Adiabatic Surfaces

Up to this point, the only consequence of the second law of thermodynamics that has been drawn is the irreversibility of natural, spontaneous processes. To develop further consequences, it has been customary to proceed along either of two lines: the engineering method, due to Carnot, Kelvin, and Clausius; and the axiomatic method, due to the Greek mathematician C. Caratheodory.† The engineering method is based upon the Kelvin-Planck formulation of the second law or its equivalent, the Clausius statement. One starts first by defining a particularly simple reversible cycle called the *Carnot cycle* and then proving that an engine operating in this cycle between reservoirs at two different temperatures is more efficient than any other engine operating between the same two reservoirs. After proving that all Carnot engines operating between the same two reservoirs have the same efficiency, regardless of the substance undergoing the cycle, the Kelvin temperature scale is defined so as to be independent of the properties of any particular kind of thermometer. A theorem called the *Clausius theorem* is then derived, and from it the existence of the entropy function. The engineering method of developing the consequences of the Kelvin-Planck or Clausius statements of

† C. Caratheodory, *Math. Ann.*, **67**:355 (1909) (in German).

the second law is rigorous and general. If one is interested in the design and manufacture of engines and refrigerators, it is essential to employ principles that hold regardless of the nature of the materials involved. If, however, one is interested in the behavior of systems, their coordinates, their equations of state, their properties, their processes, etc., *apart* from their use in the cylinders of engines and refrigerators, then it is desirable to adopt a method more closely associated with the coordinates and equations of actual systems.

In the first decade of the twentieth century Caratheodory, to replace the Kelvin-Planck and Clausius statements of the second law, presented this axiom: *In the neighborhood (however close) of any equilibrium state of a system of any number of thermodynamic coordinates, there exist states that cannot be reached (are inaccessible) by reversible adiabatic processes.* He showed how to derive the Kelvin temperature scale from this axiom and how to derive every other consequence of the engineering method. Physicists (Born, Ehrenfest, Landé) recognized the importance of Caratheodory's work, but since the mathematics needed to deal with Caratheodory's axiom presented much more difficulty than the simple manipulations involving outputs and inputs of engines and refrigerators, other physicists were slow in adopting his methods. In recent years, mainly because of the activities of Pippard, Turner, Landsberg, and Sears,† the mathematical machinery of the Caratheodory method has been considerably simplified, and now it appears that *the axiom itself can be dispensed with entirely.* All the consequences of the Caratheodory axiom follow directly from the Kelvin-Planck statement of the second law.

Consider a system described with the aid of five thermodynamic coordinates: the empiric temperature t, measured on *any* scale whatsoever; two generalized forces Y and Y'; and two corresponding generalized displacements X and X'. For such a system, the first law for a reversible process is

$$dQ = dU + Y\,dX + Y'\,dX',$$

and because of the existence of two equations of state, only three of the coordinates are independent. At first, let us choose these coordinates to be U, X, and X'. A system of three independent variables is chosen for two reasons: (1) it enables us to use simple three-dimensional graphs, and (2) all conclusions concerning the mathematical properties of the differential dQ will hold equally well for all systems with *more or fewer* than three independent variables.

In Fig. 8-3, the three independent variables U, X, and X' are plotted along three rectangular axes, and an arbitrarily chosen equilibrium state i is indi-

---

† A. B. Pippard, "Elements of Classical Thermodynamics," Cambridge University Press, New York, 1957, p. 38; L. A. Turner, *Am. J. Phys.*, **28**:781 (1960); P. T. Landsberg, *Nature*, **201**:485 (1964); F. W. Sears, *Am. J. Phys.*, **31**:747 (1963).

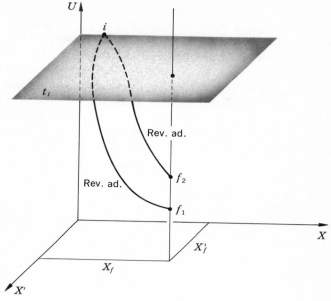

Fig. 8-3   *Both f_1 and f_2, lying on a line of constant X and X', cannot be reached by reversible adiabatic processes from i.*

cated. Let f_1 be an equilibrium state that the system can reach by means of a reversible adiabatic process. Through f_1 draw a vertical line for which the values of X and X' are constant at every point. Let f_2 be any other equilibrium state on this vertical line. We now proceed to prove that *both states f_1 and f_2 cannot be reached by reversible adiabatic processes* from i. Assume that it *is* possible for the system to proceed along either of the two reversible adiabatic paths $i \rightarrow f_1$ or $i \rightarrow f_2$. Let the system start at i, proceed to f_1, then to f_2, and then back to i along $f_2 \rightarrow i$, which, being a reversible path, can be traversed in either direction. Since f_2 lies above f_1, the system undergoes an *increase* of energy at constant X and X', during which process no work is done. It follows from the first law that *heat Q must be absorbed* in the process $f_1 \rightarrow f_2$. In the reversible adiabatic processes, however, no heat is transferred but *work W is done*. In the entire cycle if_1f_2i, there is no energy change, and therefore $Q = W$. The system has thus performed a cycle in which the sole effect is the absorption of heat and the conversion of this heat completely into work. Since this violates the Kelvin-Planck statement of the second law, it follows that *both f_1 and f_2 cannot be reached by reversible adiabatic processes. Only one point on the line of constant X and X' can be reached by a reversible adiabatic process from i.*

For a different line (different X_f and X'_f), there would be another single point accessible from i by a reversible adiabatic process, and so on. A few such points, f_1, f_2, etc., are shown in Fig. 8-4. *The locus of all points accessible from i by reversible adiabatic processes is a space of dimensionality one less than three; in other words, these points lie on a two-dimensional surface.* If the system were described with the aid of four independent coordinates, the states accessible from any given equilibrium state i by reversible adiabatic processes would lie on a three-dimensional hypersurface, and so on.

In what is to follow, it is more convenient to choose as one of the independent coordinates the empiric temperature t instead of the energy U. Since, for a given i, a reversible adiabatic surface has been shown to exist in a UXX' space, such a surface must also exist in a tXX' space, although its shape might be quite different.

With a system of three independent coordinates t, X, and X', the reversible adiabatic surface comprising all the equilibrium states that are accessible from i by reversible adiabatic processes may be expressed by the equation

$$\sigma(t,X,X') = \text{const.,} \qquad (8\text{-}1)$$

where σ represents some as yet undetermined function. Surfaces correspond-

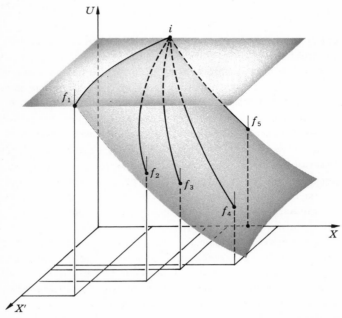

Fig. 8-4   *All states that can be reached by reversible adiabatic processes starting at i lie on a surface.*

Fig. 8-5   *If two reversible adiabatic surfaces could intersect, it would be possible to violate the second law by performing the cycle if$_1$f$_2$i.*

ing to other initial states would be represented by different values of the constant.

Reversible adiabatic surfaces cannot intersect, for if they did it would be possible, as shown in Fig. 8-5, to proceed from an initial equilibrium state i on the curve of intersection to two different final states f_1 and f_2, having the same X_f and X'_f, along reversible adiabatic paths. We have just shown that this is impossible.

8-8   Integrability of dQ

It has been emphasized that dW and dQ are inexact differentials; there are *no* functions W and Q representing, respectively, the work and heat of a body. When a system can be described with the aid of two independent thermodynamic coordinates, say, a temperature t (on any scale) and a generalized displacement X, then if Y is the generalized force,

$$dQ = dU + Y \, dX.$$

Regarding U as a function of t and X, we get

$$đQ = \left(\frac{\partial U}{\partial t}\right)_X dt + \left[Y + \left(\frac{\partial U}{\partial X}\right)_t\right] dX,$$

where $(\partial U/\partial t)_X$, Y, and $(\partial U/\partial X)_t$ are known functions of t and X. A reversible adiabatic process for this system is represented by the equation

$$\left(\frac{\partial U}{\partial t}\right)_X dt + \left[Y + \left(\frac{\partial U}{\partial X}\right)_t\right] dX = 0, \tag{8-2}$$

Solving for dt/dX, we get

$$\left(\frac{dt}{dX}\right)_{ad} = -\frac{Y + (\partial U/\partial X)_t}{(\partial U/\partial t)_X}.$$

The right-hand member is known as a function of t and X, and therefore the derivative dt/dX, representing the slope of an adiabat on a tX diagram, is known at all points. Equation (8-2) has therefore a solution consisting of a family of curves, and the curve through any one point may be written

$$\sigma(t,X) = \text{const.}$$

A set of curves is obtained when different values are assigned to the constant. *The existence of the family of curves $\sigma(t,X) = $ const., representing reversible adiabatic processes, follows from the fact that there are only two independent coordinates, and not from any law of physics.*

When three or more independent coordinates are needed to describe a system, the situation is quite different. The second law of thermodynamics is *needed* to enable us to conclude that:

Through any arbitrary initial-state point, all reversible adiabatic processes lie on a surface, and reversible adiabatics through other initial states determine a family of nonintersecting surfaces.

Consider a system whose coordinates are the empiric temperature t, two generalized forces Y and Y', and two generalized displacements X and X'. The first law for a reversible process is expressed by the equation

$$đQ = dU + Y\,dX + Y'\,dX', \tag{8-3}$$

where U, Y, and Y' are functions of t, X, and X'. Since the t, X, X' space is subdivided into a family of nonintersecting reversible adiabatic surfaces,

$$\sigma(t,X,X') = \text{const.},$$

where the constant can take on various values σ_1, σ_2, . . . , any point in this space may be determined by specifying the value of σ along with X and X', so that we may regard the internal energy function U as well as Y and Y' as functions of σ, X, and X'. Then,

$$dU = \frac{\partial U}{\partial \sigma}\, d\sigma + \frac{\partial U}{\partial X}\, dX + \frac{\partial U}{\partial X'}\, dX',$$

and
$$dQ = \frac{\partial U}{\partial \sigma}\, d\sigma + \left(Y + \frac{\partial U}{\partial X}\right) dX + \left(Y' + \frac{\partial U}{\partial X'}\right) dX'. \tag{8-4}$$

Since the coordinates σ, X, and X' are independent variables, this equation must be true for all values of $d\sigma$, dX, and dX'. Suppose that two of the differentials, $d\sigma$ and dX, are zero and that dX' is not. The provision that $d\sigma = 0$ (or $\sigma = $ const.) is the condition for an adiabatic process in which $dQ = 0$, and therefore the coefficient of dX' must vanish. If we take $d\sigma$ and dX' to be zero, then by the same reasoning the coefficient of dX must vanish. It follows therefore that, in order for the coordinates σ, X, X' to be independent, and also for dQ to be zero whenever $d\sigma$ is zero, the equation for dQ must reduce to the form

$$dQ = \left(\frac{\partial U}{\partial \sigma}\right)_{X,X'} d\sigma, \tag{8-5}$$

If we *define* a function λ by the equation

$$\lambda = \left(\frac{\partial U}{\partial \sigma}\right)_{X,X'}, \tag{8-6}$$

we get the result

$$\boxed{dQ = \lambda\, d\sigma.} \tag{8-7}$$

According to its definition, given in Eq. (8-6), λ is a function of σ, X, and X'. Since σ is a function of t, X, and X', however, we may imagine X' to be eliminated, with the result that λ is a function of t, σ, and X.

It is seen from Eq. (8-7) that the function $1/\lambda$ is an integrating factor, such that when dQ is multiplied by $1/\lambda$ the result is an exact differential $d\sigma$. Now, an infinitesimal of the type

$$P\, dx + Q\, dy + R\, dz + \cdots ,$$

known as a *linear differential form* or a *Pfaffian expression*, when it involves three or more independent variables, does *not* admit, in general, of an integrating factor. *It is only because of the existence of the second law that the differential form for*

Fig. 8-6   *Two reversible adiabatic surfaces, infinitesimally close. When the process is represented by a curve connecting the two surfaces, heat* $dQ = \lambda\, d\sigma$ *is transferred.*

dQ *referring to a physical system of any number of independent coordinates possesses an integrating factor.*

Two infinitesimally neighboring reversible adiabatic surfaces are shown in Fig. 8-6. One surface is characterized by a constant value of the function σ, and the other by a slightly different value $\sigma + d\sigma$. In any process represented by a curve *on* either of the two surfaces $dQ = 0$. When a reversible process is represented by a curve *connecting* the two surfaces, however, heat $dQ = \lambda\, d\sigma$ is transferred. All curves joining the two surfaces represent processes with the same $d\sigma$, *but the values of* λ *are different.*

8-9   Physical Significance of λ

The various infinitesimal processes that may be chosen to connect the two neighboring reversible adiabatic surfaces shown in Fig. 8-6 involve the same change of σ but take place at different values of λ, because λ is a function of t, σ, and X. To find the temperature dependence of λ, we go back to the fundamental concept of temperature as the property of a system determining thermal equilibrium between it and another system. Let us therefore consider two systems, each of three independent coordinates (for mathematical generality), in contact through a diathermic wall, as depicted schematically in Fig. 8-7. The two systems are assumed to be at all times in thermal equilibrium having a common temperature t, and together they constitute a composite system with five independent coordinates.

1   *Main system.*   The three independent coordinates are t, X, and X', and the reversible adiabatic surfaces are specified by different values of the function σ of t, X, and X'. When heat dQ is transferred, σ changes by $d\sigma$, and $dQ = \lambda\, d\sigma$ where λ is a function of t, σ, and X.

2   *Reference system.*†   The three independent coordinates are t, $\hat{X}$, and $\hat{X}'$, and the reversible adiabatic surfaces are specified by different values of the function $\hat{\sigma}$ of t, $\hat{X}$, and $\hat{X}'$. When heat $d\hat{Q}$ is transferred, $\hat{\sigma}$ changes by $d\hat{\sigma}$, and $d\hat{Q} = \hat{\lambda}\, d\hat{\sigma}$ where $\hat{\lambda}$ is a function of t, $\hat{\sigma}$, and $\hat{X}$.

3   *Composite system.*   The five independent coordinates are t, X, X', $\hat{X}$, and $\hat{X}'$, and the reversible adiabatic hypersurfaces are specified by different values of the function $\boldsymbol{\sigma}$ of these independent variables.

Using the equation for σ of the main system, we may express X' in terms of t, σ, and X. Similarly, using the equation for $\hat{\sigma}$ of the reference system, $\hat{X}'$

† The diacritical mark or accent over the symbols referring to the reference system is called a *circumflex*.

Fig. 8-7   *Two systems in thermal equilibrium, constituting a composite system receiving heat from a reservoir.*

may be expressed in terms of t, $\acute{\sigma}$, and $\hat{X}$. The primed quantities X' and $\hat{X}'$ may therefore be eliminated from the expression for σ of the composite system, and σ may be regarded as a function of t, σ, $\acute{\sigma}$, X, and $\hat{X}$. For an infinitesimal process between two neighboring reversible adiabatic hypersurfaces specified by σ and $\sigma + d\sigma$, the heat transferred is $dQ = \lambda\, d\sigma$, where λ is also a function of t, σ, $\acute{\sigma}$, X, and $\hat{X}$. We have

$$d\sigma = \frac{\partial \sigma}{\partial t}\, dt + \frac{\partial \sigma}{\partial \sigma}\, d\sigma + \frac{\partial \sigma}{\partial \acute{\sigma}}\, d\acute{\sigma} + \frac{\partial \sigma}{\partial X}\, dX + \frac{\partial \sigma}{\partial \hat{X}}\, d\hat{X}. \qquad (8\text{-}8)$$

Now suppose that, in a reversible process, there is a transfer of heat dQ between the composite system and an external reservoir, as shown in Fig. 8-7, with heats dQ and $d\hat{Q}$ being transferred, respectively, to the main and to the reference systems. Then,

$$dQ = dQ + d\hat{Q},$$

and

$$\lambda\, d\sigma = \lambda\, d\sigma + \hat{\lambda}\, d\acute{\sigma},$$

or

$$d\sigma = \frac{\lambda}{\lambda}\, d\sigma + \frac{\hat{\lambda}}{\lambda}\, d\acute{\sigma}. \qquad (8\text{-}9)$$

Comparing the two expressions for $d\sigma$ given by Eqs. (8-8) and (8-9), we get

$$\frac{\partial \sigma}{\partial t} = 0, \qquad \frac{\partial \sigma}{\partial X} = 0, \qquad \text{and} \qquad \frac{\partial \sigma}{\partial X} = 0;$$

therefore σ does *not* depend on t, X, or $\hat{X}$ but only on σ and $\acute{\sigma}$. That is,

$$\sigma = \sigma(\sigma, \acute{\sigma}). \qquad (8\text{-}10)$$

Again comparing the two expressions for $d\sigma$, we see that

$$\frac{\lambda}{\lambda} = \frac{\partial \sigma}{\partial \sigma} \qquad \text{and} \qquad \frac{\hat{\lambda}}{\lambda} = \frac{\partial \sigma}{\partial \acute{\sigma}}; \qquad (8\text{-}11)$$

therefore the two ratios λ/λ and $\hat{\lambda}/\lambda$ are also independent of t, X, and $\hat{X}$. These two ratios depend only on the σ's, but each *separate* λ *must depend on temperature as well*. [For example, if λ depended only on σ and on nothing else, then since $dQ = \lambda\, d\sigma$, dQ would equal $f(\sigma)\, d\sigma$, which is an exact differential!] In order, therefore, for each λ to depend on temperature, and at the same time for the ratios of the λ's to depend only on the σ's, the λ's *must* have the following structure:

$$\lambda = \varphi(t)f(\sigma),$$

$$\hat{\lambda} = \varphi(t)\hat{f}(\dot{\sigma}),$$

and

$$\boldsymbol{\lambda} = \varphi(t)g(\sigma,\dot{\sigma}). \tag{8-12}$$

(The quantity λ cannot contain X, nor can $\hat{\lambda}$ contain $\hat{X}$, since $\lambda/\boldsymbol{\lambda}$ and $\hat{\lambda}/\boldsymbol{\lambda}$ must be functions of the σ's only.)

Referring now only to our main system as representative of any system of any number of independent coordinates, we have, from the top line of Eq. (8-12),

$$\boxed{dQ = \varphi(t)f(\sigma)\, d\sigma.} \tag{8-13}$$

Since $f(\sigma)\, d\sigma$ is an exact differential, the quantity $1/\varphi(t)$ *is an integrating factor for dQ.* It is an extraordinary circumstance that not only does an integrating factor exist for the dQ of any system, but *this integrating factor is a function of temperature only and is the* same *function for all systems!* This universal character of $\varphi(t)$ enables us to define an *absolute temperature.*

The fact that a system of *two* independent variables has a dQ which always admits an integrating factor regardless of the second law is interesting, of course; but *its importance in physics* is not established until it is shown that the integrating factor is a function of temperature *only* and that it is the *same* function for all systems.

8-10   Kelvin Temperature Scale

Consider a system of three independent variables t, X, and X', for which two isothermal surfaces and reversible adiabatic surfaces are drawn in Fig. 8-8. Suppose there is a reversible isothermal transfer of heat Q between the system and a reservoir at the temperature t, so that the system proceeds from a state b, lying on a reversible adiabatic surface characterized by the value σ_{I}, to another state c, lying on another reversible adiabatic surface specified by σ_{II}. Then, since Eq. (8-13) tells us that $dQ = \varphi(t)f(\sigma)\, d\sigma$ we have

$$Q = \varphi(t) \int_{\sigma_{\mathrm{I}}}^{\sigma_{\mathrm{II}}} f(\sigma)\, d\sigma \qquad \text{(at const. } t\text{)}.$$

For any reversible isothermal process $a \rightarrow d$ at the temperature t_3 *between the same two reversible adiabatic surfaces,* the heat Q_3 is

$$Q_3 = \varphi(t_3) \int_{\sigma_{\mathrm{I}}}^{\sigma_{\mathrm{II}}} f(\sigma)\, d\sigma \qquad \text{(at const. } t_3\text{)}.$$

Fig. 8-8   *Two isothermal heat transfers, Q at t from b to c and Q_3 at t_3 from a to d,* between the same two reversible adiabatic surfaces σ_I and σ_{II}. *The cycle abcda is a Carnot cycle.*

Taking the ratio of Q to Q_3, we get

$$\frac{Q}{Q_3} = \frac{\varphi(t)}{\varphi(t_3)} = \frac{\text{a function of the temp. at which } Q \text{ is transferred}}{\text{the } same \text{ function of temp. at which } Q_3 \text{ is transferred}};$$

therefore we define the ratio of two Kelvin temperatures T/T_3 by the relation

$$\boxed{\frac{Q \text{ (between } \sigma_I \text{ and } \sigma_{II} \text{ at } T)}{Q_3 \text{ (between } \sigma_I \text{ and } \sigma_{II} \text{ at } T_3)} = \frac{T}{T_3}.} \qquad (8\text{-}14)$$

Thus, *two temperatures on the Kelvin scale are to each other as the heats transferred between the same two reversible adiabatic surfaces at these two temperatures.* It is seen that the Kelvin temperature scale is independent of the peculiar characteristics of any particular substance. It therefore supplies exactly what is lacking in the ideal-gas scale.

If the temperature T_3 is taken arbitrarily to be the triple point of water (the standard fixed point) and T_3 is chosen to have the value 273.16°K, then the Kelvin temperature is defined to be

$$\boxed{T = 273.16°K \; \frac{Q}{Q_3}}$$

(between the same two re-
versible adiabatic surfaces).   (8-15)

To measure a Kelvin temperature, we must therefore measure or calculate
the heats transferred at the unknown temperature and at the triple point of
water during reversible isothermal processes between the same two reversible
adiabatic surfaces. Comparing this equation with the corresponding equation
for the ideal-gas temperature

$$\theta = 273.16° \; \frac{\lim (PV)}{\lim (PV)_3} ,$$

it is seen that, in the Kelvin scale, Q plays the role of a "thermometric property." This does not have the objection attached to a coordinate of an arbitrarily chosen thermometer, however, inasmuch as Q/Q_3 is independent of
the nature of the system.

It follows from Eq. (8-15) that the heat transferred isothermally between
two given reversible adiabatic surfaces decreases as the temperature decreases.
Conversely, the smaller the value of Q, the lower the corresponding T. The
smallest possible value of Q is zero, and the corresponding T is absolute zero.
Thus, *if a system undergoes a reversible isothermal process between two reversible
adiabatic surfaces without transfer of heat, the temperature at which this process takes
place is called absolute zero.*

It should be noticed that the definition of absolute zero holds for all substances and is therefore independent of the peculiar properties of any one
arbitrarily chosen substance. Furthermore, the definition is in terms of purely
macroscopic concepts. No reference is made to molecules or to molecular
energy. Whether absolute zero may be achieved experimentally is a question
that we shall defer until a later chapter.

8-11 Equality of Ideal-gas Temperature and Kelvin Temperature

For the sake of generality, systems with three or more independent coordinates have been used in most of the discussions in this chapter. The systems
encountered most frequently in practical applications of thermodynamics,
however, usually have no more than two independent variables. In such
cases, isothermal and reversible adiabatic surfaces degenerate into plane
curves such as those shown on the θV diagram of an ideal gas in Fig. 8-9.

Fig. 8-9   *Two isotherms, at θ and at θ₃, between two reversible adiabatics of an ideal gas. abcda is a Carnot cycle.*

For any infinitesimal reversible process of an ideal gas, the first law may be written

$$dQ = C_V \, d\theta + P \, dV.$$

When this equation is applied to the isothermal process $b \rightarrow c$, the heat transferred is found to be

$$Q = \int_{V_b}^{V_c} P \, dV = nR\theta \ln \frac{V_c}{V_b}.$$

Similarly, for the isothermal process $a \rightarrow d$, the heat transferred is

$$Q_3 = nR\theta_3 \ln \frac{V_d}{V_a}.$$

Therefore,

$$\frac{Q}{Q_3} = \frac{\theta \ln (V_c/V_b)}{\theta_3 \ln (V_d/V_a)}.$$

Since the process $a \rightarrow b$ is adiabatic, we may write for any infinitesimal portion

$$C_V \, d\theta = -P \, dV = -\frac{nR\theta}{V} \, dV.$$

Integrating from a to b, we get

$$\frac{1}{nR}\int_{\theta_3}^{\theta} C_V \frac{d\theta}{\theta} = \ln \frac{V_a}{V_b}.$$

Similarly, for the adiabatic process $d \to c$,

$$\frac{1}{nR}\int_{\theta_3}^{\theta} C_V \frac{d\theta}{\theta} = \ln \frac{V_d}{V_c}.$$

Therefore, $\ln \dfrac{V_a}{V_b} = \ln \dfrac{V_d}{V_c}$ and $\ln \dfrac{V_c}{V_b} = \ln \dfrac{V_d}{V_a}$,

and we get, finally,

$$\frac{Q}{Q_3} = \frac{\theta}{\theta_3}.$$

Since, however, the Kelvin temperature scale is defined by the same sort of equation, we have

$$\frac{\theta}{\theta_3} = \frac{T}{T_3}.$$

If θ and T refer to any temperature and if θ_3 and T_3 refer to the triple point of water,

$$\theta_3 = T_3 = 273.16°K,$$

and

$$\boxed{\theta = T.}$$ (8-14)

The Kelvin temperature is therefore numerically equal to the ideal-gas temperature and, in the proper range, may be measured with a gas thermometer.

PROBLEMS

8-1   A gas is contained within a cylinder-piston combination. In the following five sets of conditions, tell (1) whether $dW = P\,dV$ or not and (2) whether the process is reversible, quasi-static, or irreversible:

(a)   There is no external pressure on the piston and no friction between the piston and the cylinder wall.

(b)   There is no external pressure, and friction is small.

(c)   The piston is jerked out faster than the average molecular speed.

(d)   The friction is adjusted to allow the gas to expand slowly.

(e)   There is no friction, but the external pressure is adjusted to allow the gas to expand slowly.

8-2   Continuing the reasoning at the beginning of Art. 8-8 concerning a system of two independent variables, show that the expression for dQ admits an integrating factor.

8-3   Consider the differential (or Pfaffian) expression

$$yz\ dx + dy + dz.$$

To determine whether an integrating factor exists, we investigate the possible solutions of the Pfaffian equation

$$yz\ dx + dy + dz = 0. \tag{P8-1}$$

(a)   Holding x constant, show that the resulting equation has a solution

$$y + z = F(x),$$

but that this cannot be a solution of Eq. (P8-1).

(b)   Holding z constant, show that the resulting equation has a solution

$$y = G(z)e^{-zx},$$

but that this cannot be a solution of Eq. (P8-1).

(c)   Do the two "cuts" (x = const. and z = const.) produce a smooth surface?

(d)   Does an integrating factor exist?

8-4   Determine whether the Pfaffian equation

$$y\ dx + x\ dy + 2z\ dz = 0$$

has a solution; and if so, find the equation of the family of surfaces.

8-5   Consider the Pfaffian expression

$$a^2y^2z^2\ dx + b^2z^2x^2\ dy + c^2x^2y^2\ dz.$$

(a)   By inspection and guessing, find an integrating factor.

(b)   Find the equation of the family of surfaces satisfying the Pfaffian equation obtained by setting the expression equal to zero.

8-6   The expression for $\hat{\lambda}$ given in Eq. (8-12) enables one to write $d\hat{Q} = \varphi(t)\hat{f}(\hat{\sigma})\ d\hat{\sigma}$, which is of the same form as Eq. (8-13). The expression for λ, however, would give an equation for dQ of the same form as Eq. (8-13), *provided that* $g(\sigma,\acute{\sigma}) = f(\sigma)$. The purpose of this problem is to lead the way toward a proof of the functional dependence of $g(\sigma,\acute{\sigma})$ on σ.

(a) Show that $f = g \dfrac{\partial \sigma}{\partial \sigma}$ and $\hat{f} = g \dfrac{\partial \sigma}{\partial \acute{\sigma}}$.

(b) Differentiate f with respect to $\acute{\sigma}$ and equate to zero. Differentiate $\hat{f}$ with respect to σ and equate to zero.

(c) Subtract the two equations of part (b).

(d) Rewrite part (c) in the form of a determinant, and interpret the result.

⋆**8-7**   A Carnot cycle, as shown in Figs. 8-8 and 8-9, consists of a reversible adiabatic process from a lower temperature T_C to a higher temperature T_H, then a reversible isothermal process at T_H in which heat Q_H is transferred, then a reversible adiabatic process from T_H to T_C, and finally a reversible isothermal process at T_C in which heat Q_C is transferred. Draw qualitatively a Carnot cycle for the following:

(a) An ideal gas on a PV diagram.

(b) A liquid in equilibrium with its vapor on a PV diagram.

(c) A reversible electric cell whose emf is a function of temperature only, on an $\mathcal{E}Z$ diagram, assuming reversible adiabatics to have a positive slope.

(d) A paramagnetic substance obeying Curie's law on an $\mathcal{H}M$ diagram, assuming $\mathcal{H}/T$ to be practically constant during reversible adiabatic processes.

8-8   Apply the definition of the Kelvin scale to *any* Carnot cycle and calculate the following:

(a) The efficiency of a Carnot engine.

(b) The coefficient of performance of a Carnot refrigerator.

8-9   Which is the more effective way to increase the efficiency of a Carnot engine: to increase T_H while keeping T_C constant; or to decrease T_C while keeping T_H constant?

8-10   Cause a gas whose equation of state is $P(v - b) = R\theta$ and whose molar energy is a function of θ only to undergo a Carnot cycle, and prove that $\theta = T$.

9.

ENTROPY

9-1   The Concept of Entropy

In a system of any number of independent variables, all states accessible from a given initial state by reversible adiabatic processes lie on a surface (or hypersurface) $\sigma(t,X,X', \ldots) = $ const. The entire t, X, X', $\ldots$ space may be conceived as being crossed by many nonintersecting surfaces of this kind, each corresponding to a different value of σ. In a *reversible nonadiabatic* process involving a transfer of heat dQ, a system in a state represented by a point lying on a surface σ will change until its state point lies on another surface $\sigma + d\sigma$. We have seen that

$$dQ = \lambda \, d\sigma,$$

where $1/\lambda$, the integrating factor of dQ, is given by

$$\lambda = \varphi(t)f(\sigma),$$

and therefore

$$dQ = \varphi(t)f(\sigma) \, d\sigma.$$

Since the Kelvin temperature T is defined so that $T/T' = dQ/dQ'$, with $d\sigma$ being the same for both heat transfers, it follows that

$$T = k\varphi(t),$$

where k is an arbitrary constant. Therefore,

$$\frac{dQ}{T} = \frac{1}{k}f(\sigma) \, d\sigma.$$

Since σ is an actual function of t, X, X', . . . , the right-hand member is an exact differential, which we may designate by dS; whence

$$dS = \frac{dQ_R}{T},$$ (9-1)

where the subscript R is written to emphasize that dQ *must* be transferred reversibly. The quantity S is called the *entropy* of the system, and dS is an infinitesimal *entropy change* of the system. In a finite change of state from i to f, the entropy change is $S_f - S_i$, where

$$S_f - S_i = {_R}\!\int_i^f \frac{dQ}{T}.$$ (9-2)

The entropy of a system is a function of the thermodynamic coordinates whose change *is equal to the integral of* dQ_R/T *between the terminal states, integrated along any reversible path connecting the two states.* It is important to understand that only an entropy *change* is defined, not an absolute entropy—just as in the case of the internal energy function, whose *change* is defined as the adiabatic work but whose absolute value is undefined.

A third relation may be obtained by integrating Eq. (9-1) around a reversible cycle, so that the initial and final entropies are the same. For a reversible cycle, we get

$$_R\!\oint \frac{dQ}{T} = 0,$$ (9-3)

an equation known as the *Clausius theorem*.

The concept of entropy was first introduced into theoretical physics by R. J. Clausius about the middle of the nineteenth century. Until this time there had been much confusion concerning the relation between heat and work and their roles in the operation of a heat engine. The great French engineers Carnot, Petit, Clément, and Désormes had little knowledge of the first law of thermodynamics. Carnot believed that the work output of an engine was the result of an amount of heat leaving a hot reservoir and the same amount of heat entering a cold reservoir. Petit and Clément computed the efficiency of a heat engine by calculating the work done *only* in the power stroke without considering, as Carnot insisted one must do, the entire cycle. In the words of Mendoza, "In the hands of Clapeyron, Kelvin, and Clausius, thermodynamics began to make headway only when it was divorced from engine design."

Clausius proved the existence of an entropy function by first deriving his theorem [Eq. (9-3); see Prob. 9-1] and then applying it to a cycle consisting of a reversible path R_1 between two equilibrium states i and f, followed by another reversible path R_2 bringing the system back to i. For this cycle,

$$_R\oint \frac{dQ}{T} = \,_{R_1}\!\int_i^f \frac{dQ}{T} + \,_{R_2}\!\int_f^i \frac{dQ}{T} = 0,$$

or

$$_{R_1}\!\int_i^f \frac{dQ}{T} = \,_{R_2}\!\int_i^f \frac{dQ}{T} = \text{independent of path.}$$

It follows that there exists a function S whose change is

$$S_f - S_i = \,_R\!\int_i^f \frac{dQ}{T}.$$

The derivation of the Clausius theorem, the properties of Carnot engines on which the theorem is based, and Clausius' derivation of the existence of an entropy function are in every way equivalent to and as general as the methods of Caratheodory. The only superiority of the Caratheodory approach is that it focuses the attention on the system, its coordinates, its states, etc., whereas these are apt to be overlooked in the engineering approach. Physicists and engineers should appreciate both points of view.

9-2   Entropy of an Ideal Gas

If a system absorbs an infinitesimal amount of heat dQ_R during a reversible process, the entropy change of the system is equal to

$$dS = \frac{dQ_R}{T}.$$

If dQ_R is expressed as a sum of differentials involving thermodynamic coordinates, then, upon dividing by T, the expression may be integrated and the entropy of the system obtained. As an example of this procedure, consider one of the expressions for dQ_R of an ideal gas, namely,

$$dQ_R = C_P\,dT - V\,dP.$$

Dividing by T, we get

$$\frac{dQ_R}{T} = C_P \frac{dT}{T} - \frac{V}{T} dP,$$

or

$$dS = C_P \frac{dT}{T} - nR \frac{dP}{P}.$$

Let us now calculate the entropy change ΔS of the gas between an arbitrarily chosen *reference state* with coordinates T_r, P_r and any other state with coordinates T, P. Integrating between these two states, we get

$$\Delta S = \int_{T_r}^{T} C_P \frac{dT}{T} - nR \ln \frac{P}{P_r}.$$

Suppose we ascribe to the reference state an entropy S_r and chose *any arbitrary numerical value* for this quantity. Then an entropy S may be associated with the other state where $S - S_r = \Delta S$. To make the discussion simpler, let C_P be constant. Then,

$$S - S_r = C_P \ln \frac{T}{T_r} - nR \ln \frac{P}{P_r},$$

which may be rewritten thus:

$$S = C_P \ln T - nR \ln P + (S_r - C_P \ln T_r + nR \ln P_r).$$

Denoting the quantity in parentheses by the *constant* S_0, we get finally

$$S = C_P \ln T - nR \ln P + S_0.$$

Substituting for T and P thousands of different values, we may calculate thousands of corresponding values of S which, after tabulation, constitute an *entropy table*. Any one value from this table, taken alone, will have no meaning. The difference between two values, however, will be an actual entropy change.

Let us now return to the original differential equation,

$$dS = C_P \frac{dT}{T} - nR \frac{dP}{P}.$$

Again, for simplicity, assuming C_P to be constant, we may take the indefinite integral and obtain

$$S = C_P \ln T - nR \ln P + S_0,$$

where S_0 is the constant of integration. Since this is precisely the equation obtained previously, we see that, in taking the indefinite integral of dS, we do not obtain an "absolute entropy," but merely an entropy referred to a nonspecified reference state whose coordinates are contained within the constant of integration. Thus, for an ideal gas,

$$S = \int C_P \frac{dT}{T} - nR \ln P + S_0. \tag{9-4}$$

To calculate the entropy of an ideal gas as a function of T and V, we use the other expression for dQ_R of an ideal gas. Thus,

$$\frac{dQ_R}{T} = C_V \frac{dT}{T} + \frac{P}{T} dV,$$

and
$$dS = C_V \frac{dT}{T} + nR \frac{dV}{V}.$$

Proceeding in the same way as before, we get for the entropy, referred to an unspecified reference state, the expression

$$S = \int C_V \frac{dT}{T} + nR \ln V + S_0, \tag{9-5}$$

which becomes, if C_V is constant,

$$S = C_V \ln T + nR \ln V + S_0.$$

9-3   *TS* **Diagram**

For each infinitesimal amount of heat that enters a system during an infinitesimal portion of a reversible process, there is an equation

$$dQ_R = T \, dS.$$

It follows therefore that the total amount of heat transferred in a reversible process is given by

$$Q_R = \int_i^f T \, dS.$$

This integral can be interpreted graphically as the area under a curve on a diagram in which T is plotted along the Y axis and S along the X axis. The nature of the curve on the TS diagram is determined by the kind of reversible process that the system undergoes. Obviously, an isothermal process is a horizontal line.

In the case of a reversible adiabatic process, we have

$$dS = \frac{dQ_R}{T},$$

and

$$dQ_R = 0;$$

whence, if T is not zero,

$$dS = 0$$

and S is constant. Therefore, during a reversible adiabatic process, the entropy of a system remains constant; or in other words, the system undergoes an *isentropic process*. An isentropic process on a TS diagram is obviously a vertical line.

If two equilibrium states are infinitesimally near, then

$$dQ = T \, dS,$$

and

$$\frac{dQ}{dT} = T \frac{dS}{dT}.$$

At constant volume,

$$\boxed{\left(\frac{dQ}{dT}\right)_V = C_V = T\left(\frac{\partial S}{\partial T}\right)_V;} \qquad (9\text{-}6)$$

and at constant pressure,

$$\boxed{\left(\frac{dQ}{dT}\right)_P = C_P = T\left(\frac{\partial S}{\partial T}\right)_P.} \qquad (9\text{-}7)$$

If the temperature variation of C_V is known, the entropy change during an isochoric process may be calculated from the equation

$$S_f - S_i = \int_i^f \frac{C_V}{T} \, dT \qquad \text{(isochoric).} \qquad (9\text{-}8)$$

Similarly, for an isobaric process,

$$S_f - S_i = \int_i^f \frac{C_P}{T}\, dT \qquad \text{(isobaric).} \qquad (9\text{-}9)$$

The above equations provide a general method for calculating an entropy change but no way of calculating the absolute entropy of a system in a given state. If a set of tables is required that is to be used to obtain entropy differences and not absolute entropy, then it is a convenient procedure to choose an arbitrary standard state and calculate the entropy change of the system from this standard state to all other states. Thus, in the case of water, the standard state is chosen to be that of saturated water at $0.01°C$ and its own vapor pressure 4.58 mm, and all entropies are referred to this state.

The slope of a curve on a TS diagram representing a reversible isochoric process, from Eq. (9-6), is

$$\left(\frac{\partial T}{\partial S}\right)_V = \frac{T}{C_V};$$

and from Eq. (9-7), the slope of a reversible isobar is

$$\left(\frac{\partial T}{\partial S}\right)_P = \frac{T}{C_P}.$$

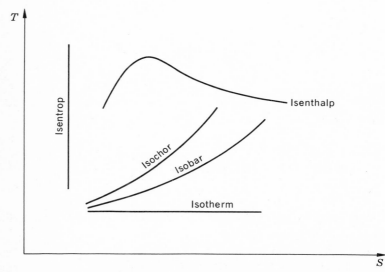

Fig. 9-1   *Curves representing reversible processes of a hydrostatic system on a TS diagram.*

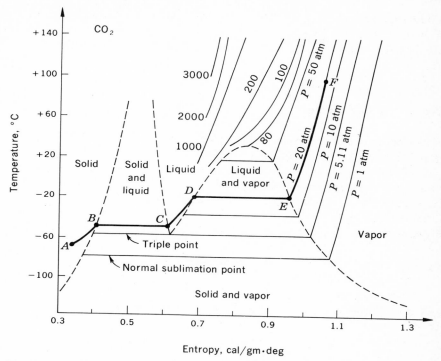

Fig. 9-2   *TS diagram for CO_2. (The two dashed lines bounding the solid-liquid region are a guess.)*

Curves representing various types of processes of a hydrostatic system are shown on a *TS* diagram in Fig. 9-1.

The *TS* diagram for a substance such as CO_2 is shown in Fig. 9-2. The curve from *A* to *F* is a typical isobar representing a series of reversible isobaric processes in which solid is transformed finally into vapor. Thus,

> *AB* = isobaric heating of solid to its melting point.
> *BC* = isobaric isothermal melting.
> *CD* = isobaric heating of liquid to its boiling point.
> *DE* = isobaric isothermal vaporization.
> *EF* = isobaric heating of vapor (superheating).

The area under the line *BC* represents the heat of fusion at the particular temperature, and the area under the line *DE* represents the heat of vaporization. Similarly, the heat of sublimation is represented by the area under any sublimation line. It is obvious from the diagram that the heat of vaporization becomes zero at the critical point and, also, that the heat of sublimation is equal to the sum of the heat of fusion and the heat of vaporization at the triple point.

9-4   Carnot Cycle

During a part of the cycle performed by the system in an engine, some heat is absorbed from a hot reservoir; during another part of the cycle, a smaller amount of heat is rejected to a cooler reservoir. The engine is therefore said to operate between these two reservoirs. Since it is a fact of experience that some heat is always rejected to the cooler reservoir, the efficiency of an actual engine is never 100 percent. If we assume that we have at our disposal two reservoirs at given temperatures, it is important to answer the following questions: (1) What is the maximum efficiency that can be achieved by an engine operating between these two reservoirs? (2) What are the characteristics of such an engine? (3) Of what effect is the nature of the substance undergoing the cycle?

The importance of these questions was recognized by Nicolas Léonard Sadi Carnot, a brilliant young French engineer who in the year 1824, before the first law of thermodynamics was firmly established, described in a paper entitled "Réflexions sur la puissance motrice du feu" an ideal engine operating in a particularly simple cycle known today as the *Carnot cycle*. A general Carnot cycle is depicted in Fig. 8-8, and one executed by an ideal gas with only two independent variables in Fig. 8-9.

An engine operating in a Carnot cycle is called a *Carnot engine*. A Carnot engine operates between two reservoirs in a particularly simple way. *All the heat that is absorbed is absorbed at a constant high temperature, namely, that of the hot reservoir. Also, all the heat that is rejected is rejected at a constant lower temperature, that of the cold reservoir.* Since all four processes are reversible, the Carnot cycle is a reversible cycle.

If an engine is to operate between only two reservoirs and still operate in a reversible cycle, then it must be a Carnot engine. For example, if an Otto cycle were performed between only two reservoirs, the heat transfers in the two isochoric processes would involve finite temperature differences and, therefore, could not be reversible. Conversely, if the Otto cycle were performed reversibly, it would require a series of reservoirs, not merely two. The expression "Carnot engine," therefore, means "a reversible engine operating between only two reservoirs."

A Carnot engine absorbing heat Q_H from a hot reservoir at T_H and rejecting heat Q_C to a cooler reservoir at T_C has an efficiency η equal to $1 - Q_C/Q_H$.

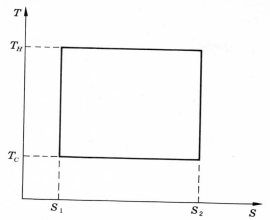

Fig. 9-3   *A Carnot cycle of any system of any number of independent coordinates when represented on a TS diagram is a rectangle.*

Since, between the same two isentropic surfaces,

$$\frac{Q_C}{Q_H} = \frac{T_C}{T_H},$$

$$\eta \text{ (Carnot)} = 1 - \frac{T_C}{T_H}. \qquad (9\text{-}10)$$

For a Carnot engine to have an efficiency of 100 percent, T_C must be zero. Since nature does not provide us with a reservoir at absolute zero, a heat engine with 100 percent efficiency is a practical impossibility.

A temperature-entropy diagram is particularly suited to display the characteristics of a Carnot cycle. The two reversible adiabatic processes are vertical lines, and the two reversible isothermal processes are horizontal lines lying between the two vertical lines, so that the Carnot cycle is represented by a rectangle, as shown in Fig. 9-3. This is true regardless of the nature of the system and of the number of independent thermodynamic coordinates.

9-5   Entropy and Reversibility

In order to understand the physical meaning of entropy and its significance in the world of science, it is necessary to study all the entropy changes that take place when a system undergoes a process. If we calculate the entropy change of the system and add to this the entropy change of the local surroundings, we obtain a quantity that is the sum of all the entropy changes brought about by this particular process. We may call this the *entropy change of the universe* due to the process in question.

When a finite amount of heat is absorbed or rejected by a reservoir, extremely small changes in the coordinates take place in every unit of mass. The entropy change of a unit of mass is therefore very small. Since the total mass of a reservoir is large, however, the total entropy change is finite. Suppose that a reservoir is in contact with a system and that heat Q is absorbed by the reservoir at the temperature T. The reservoir undergoes nondissipative changes determined entirely by the quantity of heat absorbed. Exactly the same changes *in the reservoir* would take place if the same amount of heat Q were transferred reversibly. Hence the entropy change of the reservoir is Q/T. Therefore, *whenever a reservoir absorbs heat Q at the temperature T from any system during any kind of process, the entropy change of the* reservoir *is Q/T.*

Consider now the entropy change of the universe that is brought about by the performance of any reversible process. The process will, in general, be accompanied by a flow of heat between a system and a set of reservoirs ranging in temperature from T_i to T_f. During *any* infinitesimal portion of the process, an amount of heat dQ_R is transferred between the system and one of the reservoirs at the temperature T. Let dQ_R be a positive number. If dQ_R is absorbed by the system, then

$$dS \text{ of the system} = + \frac{dQ_R}{T},$$

$$dS \text{ of the reservoir} = - \frac{dQ_R}{T},$$

and the entropy change of the universe $\Sigma\, dS$ is zero. If dQ_R is rejected by the system, then obviously

$$dS \text{ of the system} = - \frac{dQ_R}{T},$$

$$dS \text{ of the reservoir} = + \frac{dQ_R}{T},$$

and the entropy change of the universe $\Sigma\, dS$ is again zero. If dQ_R is zero, then neither the system nor the reservoir will have an entropy change, and the entropy change of the universe is still zero. Since this is true for any infinitesimal portion of the reversible process, it is true for all such portions; therefore we may conclude that, *when a reversible process is performed, the entropy of the universe remains unchanged.*

9-6   Entropy and Irreversibility

When a system undergoes an irreversible process between an initial equilibrium state and a final equilibrium state, the entropy change of the system is equal to

$$\Delta S \text{ (system)} = S_f - S_i = {}_R\!\int_i^f \frac{\mathrm{d}Q}{T},$$

where R indicates *any reversible process arbitrarily chosen* by which the system may be brought from the given initial state to the given final state. No integration is performed over the original irreversible path. The irreversible process is replaced by a reversible one. This can easily be done when the initial and the final state of the system are equilibrium states. When either the initial or the final state is a nonequilibrium state, special methods must be used. At first, we shall limit ourselves to irreversible processes all of which involve initial and final states of equilibrium.

Processes exhibiting external mechanical irreversibility   (*a*) Those involving the isothermal dissipation of work through a system (which remains unchanged) into internal energy of a reservoir, such as:

1   Irregular stirring of a viscous liquid in contact with a reservoir.
2   Coming to rest of a rotating or vibrating liquid in contact with a reservoir.
3   Inelastic deformation of a solid in contact with a reservoir.
4   Transfer of electricity through a resistor in contact with a reservoir.
5   Magnetic hysteresis of a material in contact with a reservoir.

In the case of any process involving the isothermal transformation of work W through a system into internal energy of a reservoir, there is no entropy change of the system because the thermodynamic coordinates do not change. There is a flow of heat Q into the reservoir where $Q = W$. Since the reservoir absorbs Q units of heat at the temperature T, its entropy change is $+Q/T$ or $+W/T$. The entropy change of the universe is therefore W/T, which is a positive quantity.

(*b*) Those involving the adiabatic dissipation of work into internal energy of a system, such as:

1   Irregular stirring of a viscous thermally insulated liquid.
2   Coming to rest of a rotating or vibrating thermally insulated liquid.
3   Inelastic deformation of a thermally insulated solid.

4   Transfer of electricity through a thermally insulated resistor.
5   Magnetic hysteresis of a thermally insulated material.

In the case of any process involving the adiabatic transformation of work W into internal energy of a system whose temperature rises from T_i to T_f at constant pressure, there is no flow of heat to or from the surroundings, and therefore the entropy change of the local surroundings is zero. To calculate the entropy change of the system, the original irreversible process must be replaced by a reversible one that will take the system from the given initial state (temperature T_i, pressure P) to the final state (temperature T_f, pressure P). Let us replace the irreversible performance of work by a reversible isobaric flow of heat from a series of reservoirs ranging in temperature from T_i to T_f. The entropy change of the system will then be

$$\Delta S \text{ (system)} = {}_R\!\int_{T_i}^{T_f} \frac{dQ}{T}.$$

For an isobaric process,
$$dQ_R = C_P \, dT,$$

and
$$\Delta S \text{ (system)} = \int_{T_i}^{T_f} C_P \frac{dT}{T}.$$

Finally, if C_P is assumed constant,

$$\Delta S \text{ (system)} = C_P \ln \frac{T_f}{T_i},$$

and the entropy change of the universe is $C_P \ln (T_f/T_i)$, which is a positive quantity.

Processes exhibiting internal mechanical irreversibility   Those involving the transformation of internal energy of a system into mechanical energy and then back into internal energy again, such as:

1   Ideal gas rushing into a vacuum (free expansion).
2   Gas seeping through a porous plug (throttling process).
3   Snapping of a stretched wire after it is cut.
4   Collapse of a soap film after it is pricked.

In the case of a free expansion of an ideal gas, the entropy change of the local surroundings is zero. To calculate the entropy change of the system, the free expansion must be replaced by a reversible process that will take the gas from its original state (volume V_i, temperature T) to the final state (volume V_f, temperature T). Evidently, the most convenient reversible process is a reversible isothermal expansion at the temperature T from a volume V_i to the volume V_f. The entropy change of the system is then

$$\Delta S \text{ (system)} = {}_R\!\int_{V_i}^{V_f} \frac{dQ}{T}.$$

For an isothermal process of an ideal gas,

$$dQ_R = P\,dV,$$

and

$$\frac{dQ_R}{T} = nR\frac{dV}{V};$$

whence

$$\Delta S \text{ (system)} = nR \ln \frac{V_f}{V_i}.$$

The entropy change of the universe is therefore $nR \ln (V_f/V_i)$, which is a positive number.

Processes exhibiting external thermal irreversibility   Those involving a transfer of heat by virtue of a finite temperature difference, such as:

1   Conduction or radiation of heat from a system to its cooler surroundings.
2   Conduction or radiation of heat through a system (which remains unchanged) from a hot reservoir to a cooler one.

In the case of the conduction of Q units of heat through a system (which remains unchanged) from a hot reservoir at T_1 to a cooler reservoir at T_2, the following steps are obvious:

$$\Delta S \text{ (system)} = 0,$$

$$\Delta S \text{ (hot reservoir)} = -\frac{Q}{T_1},$$

$$\Delta S \text{ (cold reservoir)} = +\frac{Q}{T_2},$$

and

$$\Sigma\, \Delta S = \Delta S \text{ (universe)} = \frac{Q}{T_2} - \frac{Q}{T_1}.$$

Processes exhibiting chemical irreversibility   Those involving a spontaneous change of internal structure, chemical composition, density, etc., such as:

1   A chemical reaction.
2   Diffusion of two dissimilar inert ideal gases.
3   Mixing of alcohol and water.
4   Freezing of supercooled liquid.

5   Condensation of a supersaturated vapor.
6   Solution of a solid in water.
7   Osmosis.

Assuming the diffusion of two dissimilar inert ideal gases to be equivalent to two separate free expansions, for one of which

$$\Delta S = nR \ln \frac{V_f}{V_i} ,$$

and taking a mole of each gas with $V_i = v$ and $V_f = 2v$, we obtain

$$\Sigma \, \Delta S = 2R \ln 2,$$

which is a positive number. All the results of this article are summarized in Table 9-1.

Table 9-1   Entropy Change of the Universe Due to Natural Processes

Type of irreversibility	Irreversible process	Entropy change of the system ΔS (syst.)	Entropy change of the local surroundings ΔS (surr.)	Entropy change of the universe $\Sigma \, \Delta S$
External mechanical irreversibility	Isothermal dissipation of work through a system into internal energy of a reservoir	0	$\dfrac{W}{T}$	$\dfrac{W}{T}$
	Adiabatic dissipation of work into internal energy of a system	$C_P \ln \dfrac{T_f}{T_i}$	0	$C_P \ln \dfrac{T_f}{T_i}$
Internal mechanical irreversibility	Free expansion of an ideal gas	$nR \ln \dfrac{V_f}{V_i}$	0	$nR \ln \dfrac{V_f}{V_i}$
External thermal irreversibility	Transfer of heat through a medium from a hot to a cooler reservoir	0	$\dfrac{Q}{T_2} - \dfrac{Q}{T_1}$	$\dfrac{Q}{T_2} - \dfrac{Q}{T_1}$
Chemical irreversibility	Diffusion of two dissimilar inert ideal gases	$2R \ln 2$	0	$2R \ln 2$

9-7   Entropy and Nonequilibrium States

The calculation of the entropy changes associated with the irreversible processes discussed in Art. 9-6 presented no special difficulties because, in all cases, the system either did not change at all (in which case only the entropy changes of reservoirs had to be calculated) or the terminal states of a system were equilibrium states that could be connected by a suitable reversible process. Consider, however, the following process involving internal thermal irreversibility. A thermally conducting bar, brought to a nonuniform temperature distribution by contact at one end with a hot reservoir and at the other end with a cold reservoir, is removed from the reservoirs and then thermally insulated and kept at constant pressure. An internal flow of heat will finally bring the bar to a uniform temperature, but the transition will be from an initial nonequilibrium state to a final equilibrium state. It is obviously impossible to find one reversible process by which the system may be brought from the same initial to the same final state. What meaning, therefore, may be attached to the entropy change associated with this process?

Let us consider the bar to be composed of an infinite number of infinitesimally thin sections, each of which has a different initial temperature but all of which have the same final temperature. Suppose we imagine all the sections to be insulated from one another and kept at the same pressure and then each section to be put in contact successively with a series of reservoirs ranging in temperature from the initial temperature of the particular section to the common final temperature. This defines an infinite number of reversible isobaric processes, which may be used to take the system from its initial nonequilibrium state to its final equilibrium state. We shall now define the entropy change as the result of integrating dQ/T over all these reversible processes. In other words, in the absence of one reversible process to take the system from i to f, we conceive of an infinite number of reversible processes—one for each volume element.

As an example, consider the uniform bar of length L depicted in Fig. 9-4. A typical volume element at x has a mass

$$dm = \rho A \, dx,$$

where ρ is the density and A the cross-sectional area. The heat capacity of the section is

$$c_P \, dm = c_P \rho A \, dx.$$

Let us suppose that the initial temperature distribution is linear, so that the

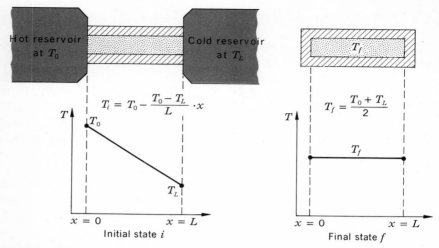

Fig. 9-4   *Process exhibiting internal thermal irreversibility.*

section at x has an initial temperature

$$T_i = T_0 - \frac{T_0 - T_L}{L} x.$$

If no heat is lost and if we assume for the sake of simplicity that the thermal conductivity, density, and heat capacity of all sections remain constant, then the final temperature will be

$$T_f = \frac{T_0 + T_L}{2}.$$

Integrating dQ/T over a reversible isobaric transfer of heat between the volume element and a series of reservoirs ranging in temperature from T_i to T_f, we get, for the entropy change of *this one volume element,*

$$c_P \rho A \, dx \int_{T_i}^{T_f} \frac{dT}{T} = c_P \rho A \, dx \ln \frac{T_f}{T_i}$$

$$= c_P \rho A \, dx \ln \frac{T_f}{T_0 - \dfrac{T_0 - T_L}{L} x}$$

$$= -c_P \rho A \, dx \ln \left(\frac{T_0}{T_f} - \frac{T_0 - T_L}{L T_f} x \right).$$

Upon integrating over the whole bar, the total entropy change is

$$\Sigma \, \Delta S = -c_P \rho A \int_0^L \ln \left(\frac{T_0}{T_f} - \frac{T_0 - T_L}{LT_f} x \right) dx,$$

which, after integration† and simplification, becomes

$$\Sigma \, \Delta S = C_P \left(1 + \ln T_f + \frac{T_L}{T_0 - T_L} \ln T_L - \frac{T_0}{T_0 - T_L} \ln T_0 \right).$$

To show that the entropy change is positive, let us take a convenient numerical case such as $T_0 = 400°K$, $T_L = 200°K$; whence $T_f = 300°K$. Then,

$$\Sigma \, \Delta S = 2.30 C_P \left(\frac{1}{2.30} + 2.477 + 2.301 - 2 \times 2.602 \right)$$

$$= 0.019 C_P.$$

The same method may be used to compute the entropy change of a system during a process from an initial nonequilibrium state characterized by a nonuniform pressure distribution to a final equilibrium state where the pressure is uniform. Examples of such processes are given in the problems at the end of this chapter.

9-8   Principle of the Increase of Entropy

The entropy change of the universe associated with each of the irreversible processes treated up to now was found to be positive. We are led to believe, therefore, that whenever an irreversible process takes place the entropy of the universe increases. To establish this proposition, known as the *entropy principle*, in a general manner, it is sufficient to confine our attention to adiabatic processes only, since we have already seen that the entropy principle is true for all processes involving the irreversible transfer of heat. We start the proof by considering the special case of an adiabatic irreversible process between two equilibrium states of a system.

1. Let the system, as usual, have three independent coordinates T, X, and X' and let the initial state be represented by point i on the diagram shown in Fig. 9-5. Suppose that the system undergoes an *irreversible adiabatic process* to

$$\dagger \int \ln (a + bx) \, dx = \frac{1}{b} (a + bx) \ln (a + bx) - x.$$

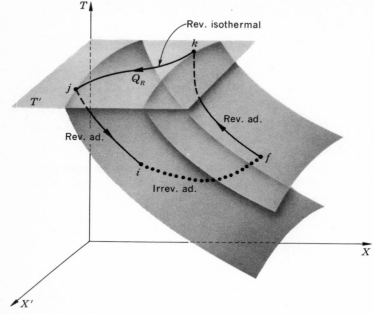

Fig. 9-5   *The process $i \rightarrow f$ is irreversible and adiabatic. The cycle ifkji contradicts the second law unless $S_f > S_i$.*

the state f; then the entropy change is

$$\Delta S = S_f - S_i.$$

A temperature change may or may not have taken place. Whether or not, let us cause the system to undergo a *reversible adiabatic process* $f \rightarrow k$ in such a direction as to bring its temperature to that of any arbitrarily chosen reservoir, say, at T'. Now suppose that the system is brought into contact with the reservoir and caused to undergo a *reversible isothermal process* $k \rightarrow j$ until its entropy is the same as at the beginning. A final *reversible adiabatic process* $j \rightarrow i$ will now bring the system back to its original state. The net entropy change for the cycle is zero, and entropy changes take place only during the two processes $i \rightarrow f$ and $k \rightarrow j$. Consequently

$$(S_f - S_i) + (S_j - S_k) = 0.$$

If ΔS denotes the entropy change associated with the irreversible part of the cycle ($\Delta S = S_f - S_i$), it follows that

$$\Delta S = S_k - S_j.$$

The only heat transfer Q_R that has taken place in the cycle is during the isothermal process $k \rightarrow j$, where

$$Q_R = T'(S_j - S_k).$$

A net amount of work W (net) has been done in the cycle, where

$$W \text{ (net)} = Q_R.$$

It is clear from the second law of thermodynamics that the heat Q_R cannot have entered the system—that is, Q_R cannot be positive—for then we would have a cyclic process in which no effect has been produced other than the extraction of heat from a reservoir and the performance of an equivalent amount of work. Therefore $Q_R \leq 0$, and

$$T'(S_j - S_k) \leq 0,$$

and finally, $\hspace{4em} \Delta S \geq 0.$

2. If we assume that the original irreversible adiabatic process took place without any change in entropy, then it would be possible to bring the system back to i by means of one reversible adiabatic process. Moreover, since the net heat transferred in this cycle is zero, the net work would also be zero. Therefore, under these circumstances, the system and its surroundings would have been restored to their initial states without producing changes elsewhere, which implies that the original process was reversible. Since this is contrary to our original assertion, the entropy of the system cannot remain unchanged. Therefore,

$$\Delta S > 0. \hspace{6em} (9\text{-}11)$$

3. Let us now suppose that the system is not homogeneous and not of uniform temperature and pressure and that it undergoes an irreversible adiabatic process in which mixing and chemical reaction may take place. If we assume that the system may be subdivided into parts (each one infinitesimal, if necessary) and that it is possible to ascribe a definite temperature, pressure, composition, etc., to each part, so that each part shall have a definite entropy depending on its coordinates, then we may define the entropy of the whole system as the sum of the entropies of its parts. If we now assume that it is possible to take *each part* back to its initial state by means of the reversible processes described above in (1), using the same reservoir for each part, then it follows that ΔS of the whole system is positive.

It should be emphasized that we have had to make two assumptions, namely, (1) that the entropy of a system may be defined by subdividing the system into parts and summing the entropies of these parts and (2) that reversible processes may be found or imagined by which mixtures may be unmixed and reactions may be caused to proceed in the opposite direction. The justification for these assumptions rests to a small extent on experimental grounds. Thus, in a later chapter, there will be described a device involving semipermeable membranes whereby a mixture of two different inert ideal gases may be separated reversibly. A similar device through which a chemical reaction may be caused to proceed reversibly in any desired direction may also be conceived. Nevertheless, the main justification for these assumptions, and therefore for the entropy principle, lies in the fact that they lead to results in complete agreement with experiment; for the experimental physicist, this is sufficient.

4. As the last step in our argument, let us consider an assemblage of systems *and* reservoirs in an adiabatic enclosure. All heat transfers involving finite temperature differences involve net entropy increases, and all adiabatic processes involving irreversible state changes, mixing, chemical reactions, etc., are also attended by net entropy increases. The adiabatic enclosure constitutes the "universe" since it includes all systems and reservoirs that interact during the process under consideration. It follows, therefore, that the behavior of the *entropy of the universe* as a result of *any* kind of process may now be represented in the following succinct manner:

$$\Sigma \, \Delta S \geq 0, \tag{9-12}$$

where the equality sign refers to reversible processes and the inequality sign to irreversible processes.

9-9   Engineering Applications of the Entropy Principle

Whenever irreversible processes take place, the entropy of the universe increases. In the actual operation of a device such as an engine or a refrigerator, it is often possible to calculate the sum of all the entropy changes. The fact that this sum is positive enables us to draw useful conclusions concerning the behavior of the device. Two important examples from the field of mechanical engineering will illustrate the power and simplicity of the entropy principle.

1. Consider a heat engine undergoing *any arbitrary cycle*, as shown in Fig. 9-6a, extracting heat Q from a reservoir at T_H delivering an amount of work W, and rejecting heat $Q - W$ to a colder reservoir at T_C. According to the

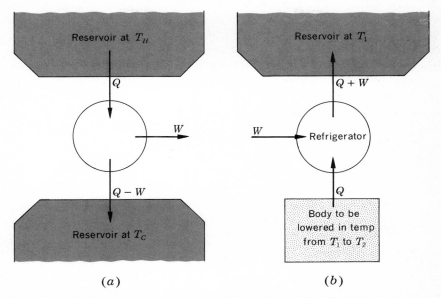

Fig. 9-6   (a) *Engine operating between reservoirs at T_H and T_C. (b) Refrigerator operating between a reservoir at T_1 and a finite body and lowering the temperature of the body from T_1 to T_2.*

entropy principle,

$$\Sigma \, \Delta S \text{ (universe)} = \frac{Q - W}{T_C} - \frac{Q}{T_H} \geq 0,$$

or

$$W \leq Q - \frac{T_C}{T_H} Q;$$

whence

$$W_{\max} = Q \left(1 - \frac{T_C}{T_H} \right).$$

Since $W_{\max}/Q$ is the maximum efficiency of an engine extracting Q from a reservoir at T_H and rejecting heat to a reservoir at T_C, and since $1 - T_C/T_H$ was shown, in Eq. (9-10), to be the efficiency of a Carnot engine, we have the result that *the maximum efficiency of any engine operating between two reservoirs is that of a Carnot engine operating between the same two reservoirs.*

2. Suppose it is desired to freeze water or to liquefy air, i.e., to lower the temperature of a body of finite mass from the temperature T_1 of its surroundings to any desired temperature T_2. A refrigerator operating in a cycle between a reservoir at T_1 and the body itself is utilized, and after a finite number of complete cycles has been traversed, a quantity of heat Q has been removed from the body, a quantity of work W has been supplied to the

refrigerator, and a quantity of heat $Q + W$ has been rejected to the reservoir, as shown in Fig. 9-6(b). Listing the entropy changes, we have

$$\Delta S \text{ of the body} = S_2 - S_1,$$
$$\Delta S \text{ of the refrigerant} = 0,$$

and $\qquad\qquad \Delta S \text{ of the reservoir} = \dfrac{Q + W}{T_1}.$

Applying the entropy principle,

$$S_2 - S_1 + \frac{Q + W}{T_1} \geq 0;$$

whence $\qquad\qquad W \geq T_1(S_1 - S_2) - Q.$

It follows that the smallest possible value for W is

$$W \text{ (min)} = T_1(S_1 - S_2) - Q.$$

If tables of the thermodynamic properties of the material are available, a knowledge of the initial and final states is all that is needed to read from the tables the values of $S_1 - S_2$ and, if the body undergoes an isobaric process, of Q. The calculated value of W (min) is used to provide an estimate of the minimum cost of operation of the refrigeration plant.

9-10   Entropy and Unavailable Energy

Suppose that a quantity of heat Q may be extracted from a reservoir at the temperature T and that it is desired to convert as much as possible of this heat into work. If T_0 is the temperature of the *coldest* reservoir at hand, then

$$W \text{ (max)} = Q \left(1 - \frac{T_0}{T}\right),$$

which represents the maximum amount of energy available for work when Q units of heat are extracted from a reservoir at T. It is obvious, therefore, that any energy which resides within the reservoir at T_0 and which may be extracted only in the form of heat is in a form in which it is completely unavailable for work. The potential energy, however, of a frictionless mechanical device (as measured from the position of lowest potential energy) is in a form in which it is completely available for work. It is desired to establish the proposition that, *whenever an irreversible process takes place, the effect on the universe is the same as that which would be produced if a certain quantity of energy were converted from a form in which it was completely available for work into a form in which it is completely unavailable for work. This amount of energy E is T_0 times the entropy change of the universe brought about by the irreversible process.*

Since the general proof of this proposition is somewhat abstract, let us consider first a special case, namely, the irreversible conduction of heat under a finite temperature gradient. Suppose that heat Q is conducted along a bar from a region at temperature T_1 to a region at temperature T_2. After conduction has taken place, we have heat Q available at the lower temperature T_2, of which the following amount is available for work:

$$\text{Max work after conduction} = Q\left(1 - \frac{T_0}{T_2}\right).$$

If conduction had not taken place, heat Q would have been available at the higher temperature T_1, and the maximum amount of work that could have been obtained from this is

$$\text{Max work before conduction} = Q\left(1 - \frac{T_0}{T_1}\right).$$

Evidently, the amount of energy E that has become unavailable for work is the difference

$$
\begin{aligned}
E &= Q\left(1 - \frac{T_0}{T_1}\right) - Q\left(1 - \frac{T_0}{T_2}\right) \\
&= T_0\left(\frac{Q}{T_2} - \frac{Q}{T_1}\right) \\
&= T_0\,\Delta S \qquad \text{(universe)}.
\end{aligned}
$$

The proposition is therefore seen to be true for the special case of heat conduction. Since it is not possible to handle all irreversible processes in this simple manner, we shall have to adopt a more abstract point of view in order to establish the proposition generally.

Consider a mechanical device such as a suspended object or a compressed spring capable of doing work on a system. Suppose the system is in contact with a reservoir at the temperature T. The mechanical device and the reservoir at T constitute the *local surroundings* of the system. Suppose an irreversible process takes place in which the mechanical device does work W on the system, the internal energy of the system changes from U_i to U_f, and heat Q is transferred between the system and the reservoir. Then the first law demands that

$$Q = U_f - U_i + W,$$

and the second law that

$$S_f - S_i \text{ (system and local surroundings)} > 0.$$

Now suppose that it is desired to produce exactly the same changes in the system and the local surroundings which resulted from the performance of the irreversible process, *but by reversible processes only*. This would require, in general, the services of Carnot engines and refrigerators, which, in turn, would have to be operated in conjunction with an auxiliary mechanical device and an auxiliary reservoir. The auxiliary mechanical device may be considered, as usual, to be either a suspended object or a compressed spring. For the auxiliary reservoir let us choose the one whose temperature is the lowest at hand, say, T_0. These constitute the *auxiliary surroundings*. With the aid of suitable Carnot engines and refrigerators all operating in cycles, in conjunction with the auxiliary surroundings, it is now possible to produce in the system and the local surroundings, by reversible processes only, the same changes that were formerly brought about by the irreversible process. If this is done, the entropy change of the system and the local surroundings is the same as before, since they have gone from the same initial states to the same final states. The auxiliary surroundings, however, must undergo an equal and opposite entropy change, because the net entropy change of the universe during reversible processes is zero.

Since the entropy change of the system and local surroundings is positive, the entropy change of the auxiliary surroundings is negative. Therefore the reservoir at T_0 must have rejected a certain amount of heat, say, E. Since no extra energy has appeared in the system and local surroundings, the energy E must have been transformed into work on the auxiliary mechanical device. We have the result therefore that, *when the same changes which were formerly produced in a system and local surroundings by an irreversible process are brought about reversibly, an amount of energy E leaves an auxiliary reservoir at T_0 in the form of heat and appears in the form of work on an auxiliary mechanical device.* In other words, energy E is converted from a form in which it was completely unavailable for work into a form in which it is completely available for work. Since the original process was not performed reversibly, the energy E was not converted into work, and therefore E *is the energy that is rendered unavailable for work* because of the performance of the irreversible process.

It is a simple matter to calculate the energy that becomes unavailable during an irreversible process. If the same changes are brought about reversibly, the entropy change of the system and local surroundings is the same as before, namely, $S_f - S_i$. The entropy change of the auxiliary surroundings is merely the entropy change of the auxiliary reservoir due to the rejection of E units of heat at the temperature T_0, that is, $-E/T_0$. Since the sum of the entropy changes of the system, local surroundings, and auxiliary surroundings is zero, we have

$$S_f - S_i - \frac{E}{T_0} = 0;$$

whence

$$\boxed{E = T_0(S_f - S_i).}$$
(9-13)

Therefore, *the energy that becomes unavailable for work during an irreversible process is T_0 times the entropy change of the universe that is brought about by the irreversible process.* Since no energy becomes unavailable during a reversible process, it follows that *the maximum amount of work is obtained when a process takes place reversibly.*

Since irreversible processes are continually going on in nature, energy is continually becoming unavailable for work. This conclusion, known as the *principle of the degradation of energy* and first developed by Kelvin, provides an important physical interpretation of the entropy change of the universe. It must be understood that energy which becomes unavailable for work is not energy which is lost. The first law is obeyed at all times. Energy is merely transformed from one form into another. In picturesque language, one may say that energy is "running downhill."

9-11   Entropy and Disorder

It has been emphasized that work, as it is used in thermodynamics, is a macroscopic concept. There must be changes that are describable by macroscopic coordinates. Haphazard motions of individual molecules against intermolecular forces do not constitute work. Work involves order or orderly motion. Whenever work is dissipated into internal energy, the disorderly motion of molecules is increased. Thus, during either the isothermal or adiabatic dissipation of work into internal energy, the disorderly motion of the molecules of either a reservoir or a system is increased. Such processes therefore involve a transition from order to disorder. Similarly, two gases that are mixed represent a higher degree of disorder than when they are separated. It is possible to regard all natural processes from this point of view, and in all cases the result obtained is that *there is a tendency on the part of nature to proceed toward a state of greater disorder.*

The increase of entropy of the universe during natural processes is an expression of this transition. In other words, we may state roughly that *the entropy of a system or of a reservoir is a measure of the degree of molecular disorder existing in the system or reservoir*. To put these ideas on a firm foundation, the concept of disorder must be properly defined. It will be shown in the next chapter that the disorder of a system may be calculated by the theory of probability and expressed by a quantity Ω known as the *thermodynamic probability*. The relation between entropy and disorder is then shown to be

$$S = \text{const. ln } \Omega. \tag{9-14}$$

By means of this equation a meaning may be given to the entropy of a system in a nonequilibrium state. That is, a nonequilibrium state corresponds to a certain degree of disorder and, therefore, to a definite entropy.

9-12   Entropy and Direction; Absolute Entropy

The second law of thermodynamics provides an answer to the question that is not contained within the scope of the first law: In what direction does a process take place? The answer is that a process always takes place in such a direction as to cause an increase in the entropy of the universe. In the case of an isolated system, it is the entropy of the system that tends to increase. To find out, therefore, the equilibrium state of an isolated system, it is necessary merely to express the entropy as a function of certain coordinates and to apply the usual rules of calculus to render the function a maximum. When the system is not isolated but instead, let us say, is maintained at constant temperature and pressure, there are other entropy changes to be taken into account. It will be shown later, however, that there exists another function, referring to the system alone and known as the *Gibbs function*, whose behavior determines equilibrium under these conditions.

In practical applications of thermodynamics, one is interested only in the amount by which the entropy of a system changes in going from an initial to a final state. In cases where it is necessary to perform many such calculations with the minimum of effort—for example, in steam engineering, in problems in refrigeration and gas liquefaction, etc.— it is found expedient to set up an *entropy table* in which the "entropy" of the system in thousands of different states is represented by appropriate numbers. This is done by assigning the value zero to the entropy of the system in an arbitrarily chosen standard state and calculating the entropy change from this standard state to all other states. When this is done, it is understood that one value of what is listed as "the entropy" has no meaning but that the difference between two values is actually the entropy change.

It is a very interesting and also a very important question in physics as to whether there exists an absolute standard state of a system in which the entropy is really zero, so that the number obtained by calculating the entropy change from the zero state to any other represents the "absolute entropy" of the system. It was first suggested by Planck that the entropy of a single crystal of a pure element at the absolute zero of temperature should be taken to be zero. Zero entropy, however, has statistical implications implying, in a rough way, the absence of all molecular, atomic, electronic, and nuclear disorder. Before any meaning can be attached to the idea of zero entropy, one must know all the factors that contribute to the disorder of a system. An adequate discussion requires the application of quantum ideas to statistical mechanics.

Fowler and Guggenheim, who have considered the subject exhaustively, summarize the situation as follows:

> We may assign, if we please, the value zero to the entropy of all perfect crystals of a single pure isotope of a single element in its idealized state at the absolute zero of temperature, but even this has no theoretical significance on account of nuclear spin weights. For the purpose of calculating experimental results, some conventional zero must be chosen, and the above choice or a similar one is thus often convenient. But its conventional character will no longer be so likely to be overlooked that any importance will in the future be attached to absolute entropy, an idea which has caused much confusion and been of very little assistance in the development of the subject.

9-13   Entropy Flow and Entropy Production

Consider the conduction of heat along a copper wire that lies between a hot reservoir at temperature T_1 and a cooler reservoir at T_2. Suppose the heat current or rate of flow of heat is represented by the symbol I_Q. In unit time, the hot reservoir undergoes a decrease of entropy I_Q/T_1, the copper wire suffers no entropy change because, once in the steady state, its coordinates do not change, and the cooler reservoir undergoes an entropy increase I_Q/T_2. The entropy change of the universe per unit time is $I_Q/T_2 - I_Q/T_1$, which is of course positive.

This process may be considered, however, from a point of view in which the attention is focused on the wire, rather than on the universe. Since the hot reservoir underwent an entropy decrease, we may say that it lost entropy to the wire, or that *there was a flow of entropy into the wire* equal to I_Q/T_1 per unit time. Since the cooler reservoir underwent an entropy increase, we may say that the reservoir gained entropy from the wire, or that *there was a flow of entropy out of the wire* equal to I_Q/T_2 per unit time. But I_Q/T_2 is greater than I_Q/T_1, and hence this point of view leads us to a situation in which the *flow of entropy out of the wire exceeds the flow in.* If entropy is to be regarded as a quantity that can flow, it is necessary to assume that entropy is produced or generated inside the wire at a rate sufficient to compensate for the difference between the rate of outflow and the rate of inflow. If the rate of production of entropy within the wire is written $dS/d\tau$, we have

$$\frac{dS}{d\tau} = \frac{I_Q}{T_2} - \frac{I_Q}{T_1} = I_Q \frac{T_1 - T_2}{T_1 T_2},$$

and if the temperatures of the reservoirs are $T + \Delta T$ and T, so that only a small temperature difference exists across the wire,

$$\frac{dS}{d\tau} = I_Q \frac{\Delta T}{T^2} = \frac{I_Q}{T} \frac{\Delta T}{T}.$$

Since I_Q stands for a heat current, we may interpret I_Q/T as an entropy current I_S, or

$$I_S = \frac{I_Q}{T}.$$

We have therefore the result that, when heat is conducted along a wire across which there is a temperature difference ΔT, *entropy flows through the wire at a rate I_S and entropy is produced within the wire at a rate*

$$\frac{dS}{d\tau} = I_S \frac{\Delta T}{T}.$$

Suppose now that an electric current I is maintained in this same copper wire by virtue of a difference of potential $\Delta\mathcal{E}$ across its ends, while the wire is in contact with a reservoir at the temperature T. Electrical energy of amount $I \Delta\mathcal{E}$ is dissipated in the wire per unit time, and heat flows out of the wire at the same rate $I \Delta\mathcal{E}$, since the wire itself undergoes no energy change. The reservoir undergoes an increase of entropy $I \Delta\mathcal{E}/T$ per unit time, and there is no entropy change of the wire. Hence the entropy change of the universe per unit time is $I \Delta\mathcal{E}/T$, which is positive. Changing our point of view, as before, to a consideration of the wire, we may say that there was no flow of entropy into the wire, but that entropy flowed out at the rate $I \Delta\mathcal{E}/T$. To provide for this outflow of entropy, we assume an entropy production inside the wire at the rate

$$\frac{dS}{d\tau} = I \frac{\Delta\mathcal{E}}{T}.$$

If, now, *both* a heat current and an electric current exist in the wire simultaneously, we may say that entropy is being generated within the wire by virtue of *both processes* at a rate given by

$$\frac{dS}{d\tau} = I_S \frac{\Delta T}{T} + I \frac{\Delta \mathcal{E}}{T}.$$

$$(9\text{-}15)$$

It is an interesting fact of experimental physics that, in the absence of a potential difference, a heat current depends only on the temperature difference; but when there is a potential difference as well, the heat current (also the entropy current) depends on *both* the temperature difference and the potential difference. Similarly, when both temperature and potential differences exist across a wire, the electric current also depends on *both* of these differences. The heat flow (and entropy flow) and the electricity flow are irreversible *coupled flows*, which exist by virtue of a departure from equilibrium conditions in the wire. If the departure from equilibrium is not too great, it may be assumed that both I_S and I are *linear* functions of the temperature and potential differences. Thus,

$$I_S = L_{11} \frac{\Delta T}{T} + L_{12} \frac{\Delta \mathcal{E}}{T}$$

$$(9\text{-}16)$$

and

$$I = L_{21} \frac{\Delta T}{T} + L_{22} \frac{\Delta \mathcal{E}}{T}$$

$$(9\text{-}17)$$

are the famous *Onsager equations*, which express the linearity between the flows (or currents) and the *generalized forces* $\Delta T/T$ and $\Delta \mathcal{E}/T$. The L's are coefficients connected with electric resistance, thermal conductivity, and the thermoelectric properties of the wire. Only three of the four L's are independent, for it can be proved rigorously by means of statistical mechanics that, if the departure from equilibrium is small,

$$L_{12} = L_{21},$$

$$(9\text{-}18)$$

which is known as *Onsager's reciprocal relation*.

By means of this strange point of view involving entropy flow and entropy production, and with the aid of Onsager's equations and reciprocal relation, the famous equations for a thermocouple will be derived in Chap. 13.

PROBLEMS

9-1   Fig. P9-1 represents schematically a system undergoing a reversible cycle during which heat transfers Q_1, Q_2, . . . , take place between it and a

Fig. P9-1   *System undergoing a reversible cycle.*

set of reservoirs at T_1, T_2, . . . , where any T is the temperature of the system at the moment it is exchanging heat with the reservoir at T. (If the cycle were not reversible, the temperature of a reservoir and that of the system would not necessarily be the same.) Some Q's are positive and some are negative. Let C_1, C_2, . . . , represent devices each of which operates in a Carnot cycle either as an engine or as a refrigerator, between one of the reservoirs and a common reservoir at T'. Suppose each device is arranged so that in one or more complete cycles it exchanges the same amount of heat with its reservoir that the reservoir exchanges with the system, so that *each reservoir is left unchanged.* Let Q'_1, Q'_2, . . . , be the heats exchanged between the Carnot devices and the common reservoir. By invoking the second law of thermodynamics, derive Clausius' theorem,

$$_R\oint \frac{dQ}{T} = 0.$$

9-2

(*a*) Derive the expression for the efficiency of a Carnot engine directly from a *TS* diagram.

(*b*) Compare the efficiencies of cycles *A* and *B* of Fig. P9-2.

 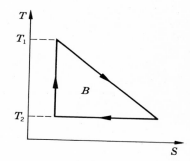

Fig. P9-2

9-3   Draw rough *TS* diagrams for the following ideal gas cycles: Stirling, Otto, and Diesel; a rectangle on a *PV* diagram; a "right triangle" on a *PV* diagram in which the base is an isobaric, the altitude an isochoric, and the "hypotenuse" an adiabatic.

9-4   Given a system whose coordinates are the temperature T, any number of generalized forces Y, Y', . . . , and their corresponding generalized displacements X, X', ...

(*a*) Prove that

$$\frac{1}{T} = \left(\frac{\partial S}{\partial U}\right)_{X,X',\ldots}.$$

(*b*) What is the expression for $1/T$ of a fluid?

(*c*) Of a paramagnetic gas?

9-5   For an ideal gas with constant heat capacities, show that

(*a*) The entropy is given by

$$S = C_V \ln P + C_P \ln V + \text{const.}$$

(b)   The adiabatic compressibility is

$$\kappa_S = -\frac{1}{V}\left(\frac{\partial V}{\partial P}\right)_S = \frac{1}{\gamma P}.$$

(c)   If a gas is both ideal and paramagnetic, obeying Curie's law, show that the entropy is given by

$$S = C_{V,M} \ln T + nR \ln V - \frac{M^2}{2C_C} + \text{const.},$$

where $C_{V,M}$ is the heat capacity at constant volume and magnetization, assumed constant, and C_C is the Curie constant.

9-6   An electric current of 10 A is maintained for 1 s in a resistor of 25 Ω while the temperature of the resistor is kept constant at 27°C.

(a)   What is the entropy change of the resistor?

(b)   What is the entropy change of the universe?

The same current is maintained for the same time in the same resistor, but now thermally insulated, whose initial temperature is 27°C. If the resistor has a mass of 10 g and $c_P = 0.84$ J/g · deg:

(c)   What is the entropy change of the resistor?

(d)   What is the entropy change of the universe?

9-7

(a)   A kilogram of water at 273°K is brought into contact with a heat reservoir at 373°K. When the water has reached 373°K, what is the entropy change of the water? Of the heat reservoir? Of the universe?

(b)   If the water had been heated from 273 to 373°K by first bringing it in contact with a reservoir at 323°K and then with a reservoir at 373°K, what would have been the entropy change of the universe?

(c)   Explain how the water might be heated from 273 to 373°K with almost no change of entropy of the universe.

9-8   A body of constant heat capacity C_P and at a temperature T_i is put in contact with a reservoir at a higher temperature T_f. The pressure remains constant while the body comes to equilibrium with the reservoir. Show that the entropy change of the universe is equal to

$$C_P[x - \ln (1 + x)],$$

where $x = -(T_f - T_i)/T_f$. Prove that this entropy change is positive.

9-9   According to Debye's law, the molar heat capacity at constant volume of a diamond varies with the temperature as follows:

$$c_V = 3R\frac{4\pi^4}{5}\left(\frac{T}{\Theta}\right)^3.$$

What is the entropy change in units of R of a diamond of 1.2 g mass when it is heated at constant volume from 10 to 350°K? Atomic weight of carbon is 12, and Θ is 2230°K.

9-10   Calculate the entropy change of the universe as a result of each of the following processes:

(a)   A copper block of 400 g mass and with a total heat capacity at constant pressure of 150 J/deg at 100°C is placed in a lake at 10°C.

(b)   The same block, at 10°C, is dropped from a height of 100 m into the lake.

(c)   Two such blocks, at 100 and 0°C, are joined together.

9-11   What is the entropy change of the universe as a result of each of the following processes?

(a)   A capacitor of capacitance 1 μF is connected to a 100-V reversible battery at 0°C.

(b)   The same capacitor, after being charged to 100 V, is discharged through a resistor kept at 0°C.

9-12   Thirty-six grams of water at a temperature of 20°C is converted into steam at 250°C at constant atmospheric pressure. Assuming the heat capacity per gram of liquid water to remain practically constant at 4.2 J/g · deg and the heat of vaporization at 100°C to be 2260 J/g, and using Table 5-2, calculate the entropy change of the system.

9-13   Ten grams of water at 20°C is converted into ice at -10°C at constant atmospheric pressure. Assuming the heat capacity per gram of liquid water to remain constant at 4.2 J/g · deg and that of ice to be one-half of this value, and taking the heat of fusion of ice at 0°C to be 335 J/g, calculate the total entropy change of the system.

9-14   A thermally insulated cylinder closed at both ends is fitted with a frictionless heat-conducting piston which divides the cylinder into two parts. Initially the piston is clamped in the center with 1 liter of air at 300°K and 2 atm pressure on one side and 1 liter of air at 300°K at 1 atm pressure on the other side. The piston is released and reaches equilibrium in pressure and temperature at a new position. Compute the final pressure and temperature and the total increase of entropy. What irreversible process has taken place?

9-15   A cylinder closed at both ends, with adiabatic walls, is divided into two parts by a movable frictionless *adiabatic* piston. Originally the pressure, volume, and temperature are the same on both sides of the piston (P_0, V_0, T_0). The gas is ideal, with C_V independent of T and $\gamma = 1.5$. By means of a heating coil in the gas on the left-hand side, heat is slowly supplied to the gas on the left until the pressure reaches $27P_0/8$. In terms of nR, V_0, and T_0:

(a)   What is the final right-hand volume?

(b)   What is the final right-hand temperature?

(c)   What is the final left-hand temperature?

(d)   How much heat must be supplied to the *gas* on the left? (Ignore the coil!)

(e)   How much work is done on the gas on the right?

(f)   What is the entropy change of the gas on the right?

(g)   What is the entropy change of the gas on the left?

(h)   What is the entropy change of the universe?

9-16   A piece of hot metal (mass m, specific heat at instant pressure c_P, temperature T_i) is immersed in a cooler liquid (m', c'_P, T'_i) adiabatically and isobarically. Prove that the condition of equilibrium, namely, $T_f = T'_f$, may be obtained by rendering the entropy change of the universe a maximum subject to the condition that the heat lost by the metal equals the heat gained by the liquid.

9-17   A mass m of water at T_1 is isobarically and adiabatically mixed with an equal mass of water at T_2. Show that the entropy change of the universe is

$$2mc_P \ln \frac{(T_1 + T_2)/2}{\sqrt{T_1 T_2}},$$

and prove that this is positive by drawing a semicircle of diameter $T_1 + T_2$.

9-18   In the expression for the entropy change of the bar in Art. 9-7, let $(T_0 - T_L)/T_0$ be designated by the symbol a.

(a)   Show that $S_f - S_i = C_P \left[1 + \ln \left(1 - \dfrac{a}{2} \right) + \dfrac{1}{a} \ln (1 - a) \right.$

$$\left. - \ln (1 - a) \right].$$

(b)   Show that $S_f - S_i = 0.307 C_P$ when $a = 1$.

(c)   Show that $S_f - S_i$ is positive for all permissible values of a.

(d)   Solve the problem of Art. 9-7 when only the hot reservoir is removed, and show that the entropy change of the universe is

$$C_P \left(1 + \frac{T_0 - T_L}{2 T_L} - \frac{T_0}{T_0 - T_L} \ln \frac{T_0}{T_L} \right).$$

9-19   Using the entropy principle, given in Eq. (9-12), prove:

(a)   The Kelvin-Planck statement of the second law.

(b)   The Clausius statement of the second law.

9-20   A body of finite mass is originally at a temperature T_1, which is higher than that of a reservoir at temperature T_2. Suppose an engine operates in a cycle between the body and the reservoir until it lowers the temperature of the body from T_1 to T_2, thus extracting heat Q from the body. If the engine does work W, then it will reject heat $Q - W$ to the reservoir at T_2. Applying the entropy principle, prove that the maximum work obtainable from the engine is

$$W \text{ (max)} = Q - T_2(S_1 - S_2),$$

where $S_1 - S_2$ is the entropy decrease of the body.

9-21   Two identical bodies of constant heat capacity at temperatures T_1 and T_2, respectively, are used as reservoirs for a heat engine. If the bodies remain at constant pressure and undergo no change of phase, show that the amount of work obtainable is

$$W = C_P(T_1 + T_2 - 2T_f),$$

where T_f is the final temperature attained by both bodies. Show that, when W is a maximum,

$$T_f = \sqrt{T_1 T_2}.$$

9-22   Two identical bodies of constant heat capacity are at the same initial temperature T_i. A refrigerator operates between these two bodies until one body is cooled to temperature T_2. If the bodies remain at constant pressure and undergo no change of phase, show that the minimum amount of work needed to do this is

$$W \text{ (min)} = C_P \left(\frac{T_i^2}{T_2} + T_2 - 2T_i \right).$$

9-23   Consider any system immersed in a medium at the constant temperature T_0 and suppose that *the only reservoir with which the system may exchange heat is this medium.* Let the system undergo a process involving the absorption of heat Q, the performance of work W, and a change of entropy $S_f - S_i$. Show that:

(a) $- \dfrac{U_f - U_i + W}{T_0} + S_f - S_i \geq 0.$

(b) $W \text{ (max)} = U_i - T_0 S_i - (U_f - T_0 S_f).$

(c) $T_0 \, \Delta S \text{ (universe)} = W \text{ (max)} - W \text{ (actual)}.$

9-24   When both a heat current and an electric current are maintained in the same wire simultaneously by a temperature difference ΔT and a potential difference $\Delta \mathcal{E}$, prove that

(a) $\left(\dfrac{\partial I_s}{\partial \, \Delta \mathcal{E}} \right)_{\Delta T} = \left(\dfrac{\partial I}{\partial \, \Delta T} \right)_{\Delta \mathcal{E}}.$

(b) $L_{11} = KA/\Delta x$, where K is the thermal conductivity and A and Δx are the area and length, respectively, of the wire.

(c) $L_{22} = T/R'$, where R' is the electric resistance of the wire.

9-25   Show that, in the case of irreversible coupled flows of heat and electricity,

(a) $T^2 \dfrac{dS}{d\tau} = L_{11}(\Delta T)^2 + (L_{12} + L_{21})\, \Delta T\, \Delta \mathcal{E} + L_{22}(\Delta \mathcal{E})^2.$

(b) $\dfrac{\partial}{\partial \Delta \mathcal{E}}\left(T\dfrac{dS}{d\tau}\right)_{\Delta T} = 2I$ and $\dfrac{\partial}{\partial \Delta T}\left(T\dfrac{dS}{d\tau}\right)_{\Delta \mathcal{E}} = 2I_s.$

(c)   Show that, with ΔT fixed, the equilibrium state obtained when $I = 0$ involves a minimum rate of entropy production.

(d)   Show that, with $\Delta \mathcal{E}$ fixed, the equilibrium state obtained when $I_s = 0$ involves a minimum rate of entropy production.

9-26   Three identical finite bodies of constant heat capacity are at temperatures 300, 300, and 100°K. If no work or heat is supplied from the outside, what is the highest temperature to which any one of the bodies can be raised by the operation of heat engines or refrigerators?

10.

STATISTICAL
MECHANICS

10-1   Fundamental Principles

In the treatment of kinetic theory given in Chap. 6, the molecules of an ideal gas could not be regarded as completely independent of one another, for then they could not arrive at an equilibrium distribution of velocities. It was therefore assumed that interaction *did* take place, but only during collisions with other molecules and with the walls. To describe this limited form of interaction we refer to the molecules as "weakly interacting" or "quasi-independent." The treatment of strongly interacting particles is beyond the scope of the present discussion.

The molecules of an ideal gas have another characteristic besides their quasi-independence. They are *indistinguishable*, because they are not localized in space. It was emphasized in Chap. 6 that the molecules have neither a preferred location nor a preferred velocity. The particles occupying regular lattice sites in a crystal are distinguishable, however, because they are constrained to oscillate about fixed positions; therefore one particle can be distinguished from its neighbors by its location. The statistical treatment of an ideal crystal as a number of distinguishable, quasi-independent particles will be given in the next chapter. In this chapter we shall confine our attention to the indistinguishable, quasi-independent particles of an ideal gas.

Suppose that a monatomic ideal gas consists of N particles, where N, as usual, is an enormous number—say, about 10^{20}. Let the gas be contained in a cubical enclosure whose edge has a length L, and let the energy ϵ of any particle, as a first step, be entirely kinetic energy of translation. In the x direction,

$$\epsilon_x = \tfrac{1}{2}m\dot{x}^2 = \frac{(m\dot{x})^2}{2m} = \frac{p_x^2}{2m},$$

where p_x is the x component of the momentum. If the particle is assumed to move freely back and forth between two planes a distance L apart, the simplest form of quantum mechanics provides that, in a complete cycle (from one wall to the other and back again, or a total distance of $2L$), the constant momentum p_x multiplied by the total path $2L$ is an integer n_x times Planck's constant h. Thus,

$$p_x \cdot 2L = n_x h.$$

Substituting this result into the previous equation, we get

$$\epsilon_x = n_x^2 \frac{h^2}{8mL^2},$$

or

$$n_x = \frac{L}{h} \sqrt{8m\epsilon_x}.$$

The allowed values of kinetic energy ϵ_x are *discrete*, corresponding to integer values of n_x; but when n_x changes by unity, the corresponding change in ϵ_x is very small, because n_x itself is exceedingly large. To see that a typical value of n_x is very large, consider a cubical box containing gaseous helium at 300°K, whose edge is, say, 10 cm. It was shown in Chap. 6 that the average energy associated with each translational degree of freedom is $\frac{1}{2}kT$. Then,

$$\epsilon_x = \tfrac{1}{2}kT = \tfrac{1}{2} \times 1.4 \times 10^{-16} \frac{\text{erg}}{\text{deg}} \times 300 \text{ deg}$$

$$= 2.1 \times 10^{-14} \text{ erg},$$

and

$$n_x = \frac{10 \text{ cm}}{6.6 \times 10^{-27} \text{ erg} \cdot \text{s}} \sqrt{8 \times 6.6 \times 10^{-24} \text{ g} \times 2.1 \times 10^{-14} \text{ erg}}$$

$$= \frac{10 \times 10.5 \times 10^{-19}}{6.6 \times 10^{-27}}$$

$$\approx 10^9.$$

Therefore, the change of energy when n_x changes by unity is so small that, for most practical purposes, the energy may be assumed to vary continuously. This will be of advantage later on, when it will be found useful to replace a sum by an integral.

Taking into account the three components of momentum, we get for the total kinetic energy of a particle

$$\epsilon = \frac{p_x^2 + p_y^2 + p_z^2}{2m} = \frac{h^2}{8mL^2} (n_x^2 + n_y^2 + n_z^2). \tag{10-1}$$

The specification of an integer for each n_x, n_y, and n_z is a specification of a *quantum state* of a particle. All states characterized by values of the *n*'s such that $n_x^2 + n_y^2 + n_z^2 = $ const. will have the same energy. To use an example given by Guggenheim,[†] the states corresponding to the values of n_x, n_y, and n_z in Table 10-1 all have the energy $\epsilon = 66h^2/8mL^2$. There are twelve quan-

Table 10-1 $n_x^2 + n_y^2 + n_z^2 = 66$

	1	2	3	4	5	6	7	8	9	10	11	12
n_x	8	1	1	7	1	4	7	4	1	5	5	4
n_y	1	8	1	4	7	1	1	7	4	5	4	5
n_z	1	1	8	1	4	7	4	1	7	4	5	5

tum states associated with the same *energy level*, and we therefore refer to this energy level as having a *degeneracy* of 12. In any actual case, $n_x^2 + n_y^2 + n_z^2$ is an enormous number, so that the degeneracy of an actual energy level is extremely large.

However close they may be, there is still only a discrete number of energy levels for the molecules of an ideal gas. It is the fundamental problem of statistical mechanics to determine, at equilibrium, the *populations* of these energy levels—that is, the number of particles N_1 having energy ϵ_1, the number N_2 having energy ϵ_2, and so on. It is a simple matter to show that (see Prob. 10-2) the number of quantum states g_i corresponding to an energy level i (the degeneracy of the level) is very much larger than the number of particles occupying that level. Thus,

$$g_i \gg N_i. \tag{10-2}$$

It is very unlikely, therefore, that more than one particle will occupy the same quantum state at any one time.

At any one moment, some particles are moving rapidly and some slowly, so that the particles are distributed among a large number of different quantum states. As time goes on, the particles collide with one another and with the walls, or emit and absorb photons, so that each particle undergoes many changes from one quantum state to another. The fundamental assumption of statistical mechanics is that *all quantum states have equal likelihood of being occupied*. The probability that a particle may find itself in a given quantum state is the same for all states.

[†] E. A. Guggenheim, "Boltzmann's Distribution Law," Interscience Publishers, Inc., New York, 1955.

1	2	3	4	5	6	7	8	9	10	11	12	13	14	15	16
	A					B						C			
	A					C						B			
	B					A						C			
	B					C						A			
	C					A						B			
	C					B						A			

Fig. 10-1   *There are six ways in which three* distinguishable *particles A, B, and C can occupy three given quantum states.*

Now consider the N_i particles in any of the g_i quantum states associated with the energy ϵ_i. Any one particle would have g_i choices in occupying g_i different quantum states. A second particle would have the same g_i choices, and so on. The total number of ways in which N_i *distinguishable* particles could be distributed among g_i quantum states would therefore be $g_i^{N_i}$. But the quantity $g_i^{N_i}$ is much too large, since it holds for distinguishable particles such as A, B, and C in Fig. 10-1. This figure shows six different ways in which three distinguishable particles can occupy quantum states 2, 7, and 13. If the particles had no identity, there would be only one way to occupy these particular quantum states. That is, one must divide by 6, which is 3! The number of permutations of N_i distinguishable objects is $N_i!$ If the quantity $g_i^{N_i}$ is divided by this factor, the resulting expression will then hold for indistinguishable particles. Therefore,

$$\left.\begin{array}{l}\text{No. of ways that } N_i \textit{ indistinguishable}\\ \text{particles can be distributed among } g_i\\ \text{quantum states}\end{array}\right\} = \frac{g_i^{N_i}}{N_i!}. \qquad (10\text{-}3)$$

It should be pointed out that the N indistinguishable, quasi-independent particles were assumed to be contained within a cubical box only for the sake of simplicity. A rectangular box with three different dimensions could easily have been chosen, in which case Eq. (10-3) would be unchanged.

10-2   Equilibrium Distribution

We have seen that, in the case of an ideal gas, there are many quantum states corresponding to the same energy level and that the degeneracy of each level is much larger than the number of particles which would be found in any one level at any one time. The specification, at any one moment, that there are

N_1 particles in energy level ϵ_1 with degeneracy g_1

N_2 particles in energy level ϵ_2 with degeneracy g_2

.   .   .

.   .   .

.   .   .

N_i particles in energy level ϵ_i with degeneracy g_i

.   .   .

.   .   .

.   .   .

in a container of volume V when the gas has a total number of particles N and an energy U is a description of a *macrostate* of the gas. The number of ways Ω in which this macrostate may be achieved is given by a product of terms of the type of Eq. (10-3), or

$$\Omega = \frac{g_1^{N_1}}{N_1!} \frac{g_2^{N_2}}{N_2!} \cdot \cdot \cdot \cdot \qquad (10\text{-}4)$$

The quantity Ω is called the *thermodynamic probability* of the particular macro-state. Other names for this quantity are the *number of microstates* and the *number of complexions*. Whatever its name, the larger Ω is, the greater the probability of finding the system of N particles in this state. It is assumed that, if V, N, and U are kept constant, *the equilibrium state of the gas will correspond to that macrostate in which Ω is a maximum*. To find the equilibrium populations of the energy levels, therefore, we look for the values of the individual N's that render Ω—or more simply, $\ln \Omega$—a maximum.

Since $\ln \Omega$ contains factorials of large numbers, it is convenient to use Stirling's approximation, which may be derived in the following way: the natural logarithm of factorial x is

$$\ln (x!) = \ln 2 + \ln 3 + \cdot \cdot \cdot + \ln x.$$

If we draw a series of steps on a diagram, as shown in Fig. 10-2, where the integers are plotted along the x axis and $\ln x$ along the y axis, the area under each step is exactly equal to the natural logarithm, since the width of each step equals unity. The area under the steps from $x = 1$ to $x = x$ is therefore $\ln (x!)$. When x is large, we may replace the steps by a smooth curve, shown

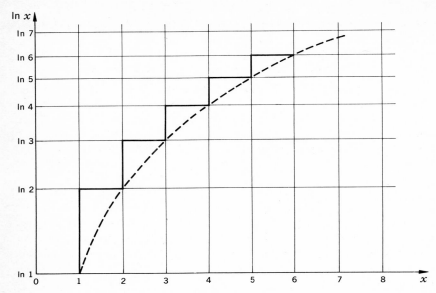

Fig. 10-2   *The area under the dashed curve approximates the area under the steps ($ln\ 2 + ln\ 3 + ln\ 4 + \cdots + ln\ x$) when x is large.*

as a dashed curve in Fig. 10-2; therefore, approximately, when x is large,

$$\ln (x!) \approx \int_1^x \ln x\ dx.$$

Integrating by parts, we get

$$\ln (x!) \approx x \ln x - x + 1.$$

Then, if we neglect 1 compared with x,

$$\boxed{\ln (x!) \approx x \ln x - x.} \qquad (10\text{-}5)$$

This formula is *Stirling's approximation.*

Using Stirling's approximation in Eq. (10-4), we get

$$\ln \Omega = N_1 \ln g_1 - N_1 \ln N_1 + N_1 + N_2 \ln g_2 - N_2 \ln N_2 + N_2 + \cdots$$

$$= \sum N_i \ln g_i - \sum N_i \ln N_i + \sum N_i,$$

or

$$\ln \Omega = \sum N_i \ln \frac{g_i}{N_i} + N, \qquad (10\text{-}6)$$

where we have used the fact that $\Sigma N_i = N$. Our problem now is to render $\ln \Omega$ a maximum subject to the conditions that

$$\Sigma N_i = N = \text{const.,} \tag{10-7}$$

$$\Sigma N_i \epsilon_i = U = \text{const.} \tag{10-8}$$

Before we proceed to solve this problem by the method of Lagrange multipliers, it is important to bear in mind that the ϵ's and g's are constants. The only variables are the populations of the energy levels, and their sum N is constant. Since $dN = 0$, the differential of $\ln \Omega$ is

$$d \ln \Omega = \sum d \left(N_i \ln \frac{g_i}{N_i} \right) = \sum \ln \frac{g_i}{N_i} dN_i + \sum \frac{N_i^2}{g_i} \left(- \frac{g_i}{N_i^2} \right) dN_i$$

$$= \sum \ln \frac{g_i}{N_i} dN_i - d \sum N_i$$

$$= \sum \ln \frac{g_i}{N_i} dN_i. \tag{10-9}$$

Setting the differential of $\ln \Omega$ equal to zero and taking the differential of Eqs. (10-7) and (10-8), we get

$$\ln \frac{g_1}{N_1} dN_1 + \ln \frac{g_2}{N_2} dN_2 + \cdots + \ln \frac{g_i}{N_i} dN_i + \cdots = 0,$$

$$dN_1 + dN_2 + \cdots + dN_i + \cdots = 0,$$

and $\quad \epsilon_1 dN_1 + \epsilon_2 dN_2 + \cdots + \epsilon_i dN_i + \cdots = 0.$

Multiplying the second equation by $\ln A$ and the third by $-\beta$, where $\ln A$ and $-\beta$ are Lagrange multipliers (see Art. 6-3), we get

$$\ln \frac{g_1}{N_1} dN_1 + \ln \frac{g_2}{N_2} dN_2 + \cdots + \ln \frac{g_i}{N_i} dN_i + \cdots = 0,$$

$$\ln A \, dN_1 + \ln A \, dN_2 + \cdots + \ln A \, dN_i + \cdots = 0,$$

and $\quad -\beta\epsilon_1 dN_1 - \beta\epsilon_2 dN_2 - \cdots - \beta\epsilon_i dN_i - \cdots = 0.$

If we add these equations, the coefficient of each dN may be set equal to zero. Taking the ith term,

$$\ln \frac{g_i}{N_i} + \ln A - \beta\epsilon_i = 0,$$

or

$$\ln \frac{N_i}{g_i} - \ln A = -\beta\epsilon_i,$$

or

$$N_i = Ag_i e^{-\beta\epsilon_i}. \tag{10-10}$$

The population of any energy level at equilibrium is therefore seen to be proportional to the degeneracy of the level and to vary exponentially with the energy of the level.

The next step is to determine the physical significance of the Lagrange multipliers A and β.

10-3   Significance of A and β

The population N_i of the ith energy level is given by

$$N_i = Ag_ie^{-\beta\epsilon_i}.$$

Summing over all the energy levels, we get

$$\Sigma N_i = A\Sigma g_ie^{-\beta\epsilon_i},$$

and

$$A = \frac{N}{\Sigma g_ie^{-\beta\epsilon_i}}. \qquad (10\text{-}11)$$

The sum in the denominator plays a fundamental role in statistical mechanics. It was first introduced by Boltzmann, who called it the *Zustandsumme*, or "sum over states." We retain the first letter of *Zustandsumme* as a mathematical symbol, but the accepted English expression for this sum is the *partition function*. Thus,

$$Z = \Sigma g_ie^{-\beta\epsilon_i}, \qquad (10\text{-}12)$$

and

$$A = \frac{N}{Z}. \qquad (10\text{-}13)$$

Substituting this result into Eq. (10-10), we get

$$N_i = N\frac{g_ie^{-\beta\epsilon_i}}{Z}. \qquad (10\text{-}14)$$

It will be shown later that Z is proportional to the volume of the container. Since the properties of a gas depend on temperature as well as on volume, one would expect a relation between β and the temperature. To introduce the concept of temperature into statistical mechanics, we must go back to the fundamental idea of thermal equilibrium between two systems, just like the procedure in Chap. 8 for relating the quantity λ to temperature. Consequently, let us consider an isolated composite system consisting of two samples of ideal gas separated by a diathermic wall, as shown in Fig. 10-3. For the

Fig. 10-3   *An isolated composite system of two samples of ideal gas separated by a diathermic wall. The total energy is constant.*

second sample of gas, the symbols expressing energy levels, populations, etc., are distinguished with a circumflex. The thermodynamic probability of the composite system Ω is the product of the separate thermodynamic probabilities, so that the logarithm is

$$\ln \Omega = \sum N_i \ln \frac{g_i}{N_i} + N + \sum \hat{N}_j \ln \frac{\hat{g}_j}{\hat{N}_j} + \hat{N}.$$

Each sample has a constant number of molecules, so that

$$\Sigma N_i = N = \text{const.}$$

and

$$\Sigma \hat{N}_j = \hat{N} = \text{const.,}$$

but the energy of each sample is *not constant*. Only the total energy of the composite system is constant; thus,

$$\sum N_i \epsilon_i + \sum \hat{N}_j \hat{\epsilon}_j = U = \text{const.}$$

To find equilibrium conditions, we proceed as before and get

$$\sum \ln \frac{g_i}{N_i} dN_i + \sum \ln \frac{\hat{g}_j}{\hat{N}_j} d\hat{N}_j = 0$$

$$\ln A \sum dN_i \qquad\qquad = 0$$

$$\ln \hat{A} \sum d\hat{N}_j = 0$$

$$-\beta \sum \epsilon_i dN_i - \beta \sum \hat{\epsilon}_j d\hat{N}_j = 0.$$

Adding and setting each coefficient of dN and $d\hat{N}$ equal to zero, we get *two* sets of equations,

$$N_i = Ag_i e^{-\beta \epsilon_i}$$

and

$$\hat{N}_j = \hat{A}\hat{g}_j e^{-\beta \hat{\epsilon}_j},$$

where all quantities are different, *except* β. When two systems separated by a diathermic wall come to equilibrium, the temperatures are the same and the β's are the same. The conclusion that β is connected with the temperature is inescapable.

It was shown in Chap. 9 that the entropy of an isolated system increases when the system undergoes a spontaneous, irreversible process. At the conclusion of such a process, when equilibrium is reached, the entropy has the maximum value consistent with its energy and volume. The thermodynamic probability also increases and approaches a maximum as equilibrium is approached. We therefore look for some correlation between S and Ω. Consider two similar systems A and B in thermal contact—one with entropy S_A and thermodynamic probability Ω_A, the other with values S_B and Ω_B. Since entropy is an extensive variable, the total entropy of the composite system is

$$S = S_A + S_B.$$

The thermodynamic probability, however, is the product, or

$$\Omega = \Omega_A \cdot \Omega_B.$$

If we let

$$S = f(\Omega),$$

then,

$$f(\Omega_A \Omega_B) = f(\Omega_A) + f(\Omega_B).$$

The only function that satisfies this relation is the logarithm. Introducing an arbitrary constant k', we may write

$$\boxed{S = k' \ln \Omega} \tag{10-15}$$

for the relation between entropy and thermodynamic probability.

The first law of thermodynamics applied to any infinitesimal process of any hydrostatic system is

$$dQ = dU + P\,dV.$$

If the process takes place between two neighboring equilibrium states, it may be performed reversibly, in which case $dQ = T\,dS$, and

$$dU = T\,dS - P\,dV.$$

If we now specify that the reversible process take place at constant V, we have the important *link between thermodynamics and statistical mechanics:*

$$\frac{1}{T} = \left(\frac{\partial S}{\partial U}\right)_V.$$
(10-16)

Since both S and U may be calculated by statistical mechanics, *the derivative* $(\partial S/\partial U)_V$ *gives the reciprocal of the Kelvin temperature. This is the way in which the macroscopic concept of temperature is injected into statistical mechanics.*

In employing the Lagrange method to find the equilibrium values of the energy level populations [Eqs. (10-9) and (10-10)], we found that

$$d \ln \Omega = \sum \ln \frac{g_i}{N_i} dN_i$$

and
$$\ln \frac{g_i}{N_i} = \beta \epsilon_i - \ln A.$$

Therefore,
$$d \ln \Omega = \sum \beta \epsilon_i \, dN_i - \ln A \sum dN_i$$
$$= \beta \, d \sum \epsilon_i N_i - \ln A \, d \sum N_i$$
$$= \beta \, dU,$$

where U is the total energy of the system. Therefore,

$$\beta = \frac{d \ln \Omega}{dU} = \frac{1}{k'} \frac{d}{dU} k' \ln \Omega = \frac{1}{k'} \left(\frac{\partial S}{\partial U}\right)_V.$$

Since $(\partial S/\partial U)_V = 1/T$, we get the beautiful result

$$\beta = \frac{1}{k'T}.$$
(10-17)

When the actual values of the ϵ's appropriate to an ideal gas are introduced, it will be seen that k' is none other than Boltzmann's constant k.

10-4   Partition Function

We have seen that the population N_i of the ith energy level is

$$N_i = A g_i e^{-\beta \epsilon_i}.$$

Substituting $1/k'T$ for β and N/Z for A, we get

$$N_i = \frac{N}{Z} g_i e^{-\epsilon_i/k'T},$$

(10-18)

where

$$Z = \Sigma g_i e^{-\epsilon_i/k'T}.$$

(10-19)

The partition function Z contains the heart of the statistical information about the particles of the system, so that it is worth while to express other properties of the system, such as U, S, and P, in terms of Z. If we differentiate Z with respect to T, holding V constant, we get

$$\left(\frac{\partial Z}{\partial T}\right)_V = \sum g_i \left(\frac{\epsilon_i}{k'T^2}\right) e^{-\epsilon_i/k'T}$$

$$= \frac{1}{k'T^2} \sum \epsilon_i g_i e^{-\epsilon_i/k'T}$$

$$= \frac{Z}{Nk'T^2} \sum \epsilon_i N_i$$

$$= \frac{ZU}{Nk'T^2}.$$

It follows that

$$U = Nk'T^2 \left(\frac{\partial \ln Z}{\partial T}\right)_V,$$

(10-20)

and U may be calculated once $\ln Z$ is known as a function of T and V. Also,

$$S = k' \ln \Omega,$$

where, according to Eq. (10-6),

$$\ln \Omega = \sum N_i \ln \frac{g_i}{N_i} + N.$$

Hence,

$$S = -k' \sum N_i \ln \frac{N_i}{g_i} + k'N.$$

Substituting for N_i/g_i the value given in Eq. (10-18), we get

$$S = -k' \sum N_i \left(\ln \frac{N}{Z} - \frac{\epsilon_i}{k'T}\right) + k'N$$

and, finally,

$$S = Nk' \ln \frac{Z}{N} + \frac{U}{T} + Nk',$$ (10-21)

which provides us with a method of calculating S once $\ln Z$ is known.

One more equation that is of value is the relation between pressure and the partition function. Since

$$T \, dS = dU + P \, dV,$$

then
$$P = -\frac{dU}{dV} + T\frac{dS}{dV},$$

$$= -\left[\frac{\partial}{\partial V}(U - TS)\right]_T.$$

From the relation between S and the partition function, given in Eq. (10-21), we get

$$U - TS = -Nk'T \ln \frac{Z}{N} - Nk'T;$$

therefore,
$$P = Nk'T\left(\frac{\partial \ln Z}{\partial V}\right)_T,$$ (10-22)

so that again the pressure may be calculated once $\ln Z$ is known as a function of T and V.

This is the advantage of statistical mechanics. It provides us with a simple set of rules for obtaining the properties of a system:

1 Use quantum mechanics to find the ϵ values of the quantum states.
2 Find the partition function Z in terms of T and V.
3 Calculate the energy by differentiating $\ln Z$ with respect to T.
4 Calculate the pressure by differentiating $\ln Z$ with respect to V.
5 Calculate the entropy from Z and U.

10-5   Partition Function of an Ideal Monatomic Gas

To apply the rules laid down in the preceding article to an ideal gas, we must first calculate the appropriate partition function. This was defined to be

$$Z = \sum_{\text{levels}} g_i e^{-\epsilon_i/k'T},$$

where the summation was over all the energy levels. Exactly the same result is obtained if we sum the expression

$$Z = \sum_{\text{states}} e^{-\epsilon_j/k'T}$$

over all quantum states. We at first take into account only the kinetic energy of translation of the particles confined to a rectangular box whose x, y, and z sides are, respectively, a, b, and c. The energy of any quantum state j is given by Eq. (10-1) as

$$\epsilon_j = \frac{h^2}{8m}\left(\frac{n_x^2}{a^2} + \frac{n_y^2}{b^2} + \frac{n_z^2}{c^2}\right),$$

where n_x, n_y, and n_z are quantum numbers specifying the various quantum states. The partition function is therefore a threefold sum: thus,

$$Z = \sum_{n_x=1}^{\infty} \sum_{n_y=1}^{\infty} \sum_{n_z=1}^{\infty} e^{-(h^2/8mk'T)(n_x^2/a^2+n_y^2/b^2+n_z^2/c^2)},$$

or
$$Z = \sum e^{-(h^2/8mk'T)(n_x^2/a^2)} \sum e^{-(h^2/8mk'T)(n_y^2/b^2)} \sum e^{-(h^2/8mk'T)(n_z^2/c^2)}.$$

Since the values of n_x, n_y, and n_z that give rise to appreciable values of the energy are very large and since a change of n_x or n_y or n_z by unity produces a change of energy that is exceedingly small, no error is introduced by replacing each sum with an integral and by writing

$$Z = \left[\int_0^{\infty} e^{-(h^2/8mk'T)(n_x^2/a^2)}\, dn_x\right]\left[\int_0^{\infty} e^{-(h^2/8mk'T)(n_y^2/b^2)}\, dn_y\right]$$
$$\left[\int_0^{\infty} e^{-(h^2/8mk'T)(n_z^2/c^2)}\, dn_z\right].$$

Each integral is of the type listed in Table 6-2:

$$\int_0^{\infty} e^{-ax^2}\, dx = \frac{1}{2}\sqrt{\frac{\pi}{a}}.$$

Therefore,

$$Z = \left[\frac{a}{2}\sqrt{\frac{8\pi mk'T}{h^2}}\right]\left[\frac{b}{2}\sqrt{\frac{8\pi mk'T}{h^2}}\right]\left[\frac{c}{2}\sqrt{\frac{8\pi mk'T}{h^2}}\right],$$

and since $abc = V$,

$$Z = V\left(\frac{2\pi mk'T}{h^2}\right)^{\frac{3}{2}}, \tag{10-23}$$

and

$$\ln Z = \ln V + \tfrac{3}{2} \ln T + \tfrac{3}{2} \ln \left(\frac{2\pi m k'}{h^2} \right).$$

(10-24)

1   *Pressure of an ideal monatomic gas*

$$P = Nk'T \left(\frac{\partial \ln Z}{\partial V} \right)_T$$

$$= Nk'T \left(\frac{1}{V} \right)$$

$$= \frac{N}{V} k'T.$$

(10-25)

Comparing this result with the expression for the pressure $P = NkT/V$ obtained with the kinetic theory of gases, given in Eq. (6-10), where k is Boltzmann's constant, we see that the arbitrary constant k' introduced in the equation $S = k' \ln \Omega$ is none other than the Boltzmann constant, or

$$k' = k = \frac{R}{N_A}.$$

(10-26)

2   *Energy of an ideal monatomic gas*

$$U = NkT^2 \left(\frac{\partial \ln Z}{\partial T} \right)_V$$

$$= NkT^2 \left(\frac{3}{2T} \right)$$

$$= \tfrac{3}{2} NkT.$$

(10-27)

This is exactly the same result which was obtained by the kinetic theory of gases for a monatomic ideal gas and shows that, when particles each having three translational degrees of freedom come to statistical equilibrium, the energy per particle equals $\tfrac{3}{2} kT$.

3   *Entropy of an ideal monatomic gas*

$$S = Nk \ln \frac{Z}{N} + \frac{U}{T} + Nk$$

$$= Nk \left[\ln \frac{V}{N} + \tfrac{3}{2} \ln T + \ln \left(\frac{2\pi m k}{h^2} \right)^{\frac{3}{2}} \right] + \tfrac{3}{2} Nk + Nk$$

$$= Nk \left[\tfrac{3}{2} \ln T + \ln \frac{V}{N} + \ln \left(\frac{2\pi m k}{h^2} \right)^{\frac{3}{2}} + \tfrac{5}{2} \right].$$

If we take 1 mole of gas, $N = N_A$ and $N_A k = R$. Therefore,

$$s = c_V \ln T + R \ln v + R \ln \frac{(2\pi mk/h^2)^{\frac{3}{2}}}{N_A} + \tfrac{5}{2}R. \qquad (10\text{-}28)$$

This expression is to be compared with Eq. (9-5), namely,

$$s = c_V \ln T + R \ln v + s_0,$$

and we see that not only were we able to arrive at this equation by the methods of statistical mechanics but also we were able to calculate the constant s_0. Equation (10-28), which was first obtained by Sackur and Tetrode, usually bears their names.

10-6   Equipartition of Energy

Both kinetic theory and statistical mechanics, when applied to the molecules of an ideal gas (each having three translational degrees of freedom), yield the result that at equilibrium the energy per particle associated with each degree of translational freedom is $\tfrac{1}{2}kT$. The methods of kinetic theory could not be applied to rotational and vibrational degrees of freedom, but the simple statistical method just developed is capable of dealing with all types of molecular energy, not just translational kinetic energy.

The property of the partition function which makes it so useful is that, whenever the energy of a molecule is expressed as a sum of independent terms each referring to a different degree of freedom,

$$\epsilon = \epsilon' + \epsilon'' + \epsilon''' + \cdots ;$$

then,
$$\begin{aligned} Z &= \sum e^{-\epsilon/kT} = \sum e^{-(\epsilon'+\epsilon''+\epsilon'''+\cdots)/kT} \\ &= \sum e^{-\epsilon'/kT} \sum e^{-\epsilon''/kT} \sum e^{-\epsilon'''/kT} \cdots \\ &= Z'Z''Z''' \cdots . \end{aligned} \qquad (10\text{-}29)$$

If the various types of energy are calculated with classical physics, it is a simple matter to derive the *classical* principle of the equipartition of energy. We take Eq. (10-20), namely,

$$U = NkT^2 \left(\frac{\partial \ln Z}{\partial T} \right)_V,$$

and rewrite it thus:

$$\langle \epsilon \rangle = \frac{U}{N} = -\frac{\partial \ln Z}{\partial (1/kT)},$$

$$\langle \epsilon \rangle = -\frac{\partial \ln Z}{\partial \beta}. \tag{10-30}$$

Suppose ϵ to consist of terms representing translational kinetic energy of the type $\frac{1}{2}mw^2$, those representing rotational kinetic energy of the type $\frac{1}{2}I\omega^2$, those representing vibrational energy $\frac{1}{2}m\dot{\xi}^2 + \frac{1}{2}k\xi^2$, etc. All these forms of energy are expressed as squared terms of the type $b_i p_i^2$. Let there be f such terms, or

$$\epsilon = b_1 p_1^2 + b_2 p_2^2 + \cdots + b_f p_f^2.$$

Then, since the partition function is the product of the separate partition functions,

$$Z = \int_0^\infty e^{-\beta b_1 p_1^2}\, dp_1 \int_0^\infty e^{-\beta b_2 p_2^2}\, dp_2 \cdots \int_0^\infty e^{-b_f p_f^2}\, dp_f.$$

Let

$$y_i = \beta^{\frac{1}{2}} p_i \quad \text{and} \quad dy_i = \beta^{\frac{1}{2}}\, dp_i;$$

then

$$\int_0^\infty e^{-\beta b_i p_i^2}\, dp_i = \int_0^\infty e^{-\beta b_i y_i^2/\beta}\, dy_i/\beta^{\frac{1}{2}}$$

$$= \beta^{-\frac{1}{2}} \int_0^\infty e^{-b_i y_i^2}\, dy_i$$

$$= \beta^{-\frac{1}{2}} K_i,$$

where K_i does *not* contain β. The partition function now becomes

$$Z = \beta^{-\frac{1}{2}} K_1 \cdot \beta^{-\frac{1}{2}} K_2 \cdots \beta^{-\frac{1}{2}} K_f,$$

$$= \beta^{-f/2} K_1 K_2 \cdots K_f,$$

where *none of the K's contains β*. Since $\langle \epsilon \rangle = -\partial(\ln Z)/\partial \beta$,

$$\langle \epsilon \rangle = -\frac{\partial}{\partial \beta}\left(-\frac{f}{2}\ln \beta + \ln K_1 + \ln K_2 + \cdots + \ln K_f\right)$$

$$= \frac{f}{2\beta};$$

and since $\beta = 1/kT$,

$$\boxed{\langle \epsilon \rangle = \frac{f}{2} kT.} \tag{10-31}$$

It has therefore been proved that, when a large number of nondistinguishable, quasi-independent particles whose energy is expressed as the sum of f squared terms come to equilibrium, the average energy per particle is f times $\frac{1}{2}kT$.

This is the famous principle of the equipartition of energy that was mentioned but not proved in Art. 6-5. It was stated that the principle broke down badly when applied to polyatomic molecules which have many vibrational degrees of freedom. It is a simple matter to introduce quantum mechanical expressions for the energy of rotation and vibration in the partition function and to calculate the resulting thermodynamic properties. For discussion of this the student is referred to any of the books on statistical mechanics listed in the appendix.

10-7   Statistical Interpretation of Work and Heat

We have been considering the statistical equilibrium of a large number N of nondistinguishable, quasi-independent particles in a cubical container of volume V. The energy levels ϵ_i of individual particles undergoing translational motion only were given by

$$\epsilon_i = \frac{h^2}{8mL^2} (n_x^2 + n_y^2 + n_z^2).$$

Since $L^3 = V$, then $L^2 = V^{\frac{2}{3}}$, and letting B_i be the sum of the squares of the quantum numbers appropriate to the ith energy level, we get

$$\epsilon_i = \frac{h^2}{8m} B_i V^{-\frac{2}{3}}.$$

Given the set of quantum numbers that determines B_i, we may say that the *corresponding energy ϵ_i depends on volume only*. Taking the logarithm of ϵ_i,

$$\ln \epsilon_i = \ln \frac{h^2}{8m} + \ln B_i - \tfrac{2}{3} \ln V.$$

The effect of a small change of V on ϵ is given by taking the differential of this equation; whence

$$\frac{d\epsilon_i}{\epsilon_i} = -\frac{2}{3} \frac{dV}{V}.$$

Therefore,

$$d\epsilon_i = -\frac{2}{3} \frac{\epsilon_i}{V} dV,$$

$$N_i \, d\epsilon_i = -\frac{2}{3} \frac{N_i \epsilon_i}{V} dV,$$

and

$$\sum N_i \, d\epsilon_i = -\frac{2}{3} \frac{U}{V} dV. \qquad (10\text{-}32)$$

Now, it has been shown both by kinetic theory and by statistical mechanics that the pressure of an ideal gas is given by

$$P = \frac{NkT}{V}.$$

Since the energy per particle is translational kinetic energy only, with three degrees of freedom,

$$U = \tfrac{3}{2} NkT.$$

It follows that

$$P = \frac{2}{3} \frac{U}{V}, \tag{10-33}$$

Substituting this result into Eq. (10-32), we get

$$\Sigma N_i \, d\epsilon_i = -P \, dV. \tag{10-34}$$

A change of volume, therefore, causes changes in the energy values of the energy levels, without producing changes in the populations of the levels. When the N_i change and the ϵ_i remain constant, we have from page 261,

$$d \ln \Omega = \beta \, \Sigma \epsilon_i \, dN_i.$$

Since $kd \ln \Omega = dS$, $k \beta \, \Sigma \epsilon_i \, dN_i = dS$, and setting $k\beta$ equal to $1/T$, we get finally,

$$\Sigma \epsilon_i \, dN_i = T \, dS.$$

We see that a reversible heat transfer produces changes in the populations of the energy levels without changes in the energy values of the levels themselves. Thus, the equation $dU = \Sigma \epsilon_i \, dN_i + \Sigma N_i \, d\epsilon_i$ expresses the first and second laws of thermodynamics, with $\Sigma \epsilon_i \, dN_i = T \, dS$ and $\Sigma N_i \, d\epsilon_i = -P \, dV$.

10-8   Disorder, Entropy, and Information

Whenever work or kinetic energy is dissipated within a system because of friction, viscosity, inelasticity, electric resistance, or magnetic hysteresis, the disorderly motions of molecules are increased. Whenever different substances are mixed or dissolved or diffused with one another, the spatial positions of the molecules constitute a more disorderly arrangement. Rocks crumble, iron rusts, some metals corrode, wood rots, leather disintegrates, paint peels, and people age. All these processes involve the transition from some sort of "orderliness" to a greater disorder. This transition is expressed in the language of classical thermodynamics by the statement that the entropy of the universe increases. Molecular disorder and entropy go together, and if we measure disorder by the number of ways a particular macrostate may be achieved, the thermodynamic probability Ω is a measure of disorder. Then the equation $S = k \ln \Omega$ is the simple relation between entropy and disorder.

The number of ways in which a particular macrostate may be achieved can be given another interpretation. Suppose that you are called upon to guess a person's first name. The number of choices of names of men and women is staggeringly large. With no hint or clue, the number of ways in which one can arrive at a name is very large, and the information at one's disposal is small. Suppose, now, that we are told the person is a man. Immediately the number of choices of names is *reduced*, whereas the information is *increased*. Information is increased further if we are told that the man's name starts with H, for then the number of choices (or ways of picking a man's name) is reduced very greatly. It is clear that the *fewer* the number of ways a particular situation or a particular state of a system may be achieved, the greater is the information.

A convenient measure of the information conveyed when the number of choices is reduced from Ω_0 to Ω_1 is given by

$$I = k \ln \frac{\Omega_0}{\Omega_1}.$$

The bigger the reduction, the bigger the information. Since $k \ln \Omega$ is the entropy S, then

$$I = S_0 - S_1,$$

or

$$S_1 = S_0 - I,$$

which can be interpreted to mean that the entropy of a system is reduced by the amount of information about the state of a system. In the words of Brillouin, "Entropy measures the lack of information about the exact state of a system."

As an example of the connection between entropy and information, consider the isothermal compression of an ideal gas (N molecules) from a volume V_0 to a volume V_1. We know that the reduction of entropy is equal to

$$S_0 - S_1 = Nk \ln \frac{V_0}{V_1}.$$

But, when we decrease the volume of the gas, we decrease the number of ways of achieving this state, because there are fewer microstates with position coordinates in the smaller volume. Before the compression, each molecule is known to be in the volume V_0. The number of locations each molecule could occupy is $V_0/\Delta V$, where ΔV is some arbitrary small volume. After the compression, each molecule is to be found in volume V_1, with a smaller number of possible locations $V_1/\Delta V$. It follows that

$$ I = k \ln \frac{\Omega_0}{\Omega_1} = k \ln \frac{V_0/\Delta V}{V_1/\Delta V} = k \ln \frac{V_0}{V_1}, $$

and for the entire gas of N molecules,

$$ I = Nk \ln \frac{V_0}{V_1}, $$

in agreement with the result of classical thermodynamics. The increase of information as a result of the compression is seen to be identical with the corresponding entropy reduction.

The connection between entropy and information can be applied to the problem of *Maxwell's demon*. Maxwell imagined a small creature stationed near a trap door separating two compartments of a vessel containing a gas. Suppose that the demon opened the trap door only when fast molecules approached, thereby allowing the fast molecules to collect in one compartment and slow ones in the other. This would obviously result in a transition from disorder to order—thus violating the second law. According to Brillouin, the demon could not tell the difference between one kind of molecule and another because he and the molecules are in an enclosure at a uniform temperature and all are bathed in isotropic blackbody radiation. The demon could not see the individual atoms. However, suppose that we allow the demon, according to the analysis of Rodd, to use a flashlight whose radiation is not in equilibrium with the enclosure. Then the demon can get information about the molecules and thereby decrease the entropy of the system. But other phenomena come into the discussion: (1) the filament of the lamp in the flashlight undergoes an increase of entropy; (2) a photon scattered by a molecule is absorbed by the demon and serves to increase his entropy; (3) the action of the demon in opening the trap door reduces the number of microstates available to the molecules. (The entropy change of the battery of the flashlight can be ignored.) If all these processes are taken into account and the corresponding entropy changes are calculated from the standpoint of the increase or decrease of information, then Rodd was able to demonstrate that the total entropy change is positive. The second law is not violated.

Much has been written about reversibility and irreversibility, order and disorder, and supposed violations of the second law. It would be hard to find anything in any language to compare with the exposition given in Feynman's "Lectures on Physics" (Chap. 46). This chapter is recommended wholeheartedly to all students—whether naïve or sophisticated in their level of attainment—for its brilliance, its depth, and its human warmth.

PROBLEMS

(Values of constants: $k = 1.38 \times 10^{-16}$ erg/deg and $h = 6.63 \times 10^{-27}$ erg · s.)

10-1   A mercury atom moves in a cubical box whose edge is 1 m long. Its kinetic energy is equal to the average kinetic energy of a molecule of an ideal gas at 1000°K. If the quantum numbers n_x, n_y, and n_z are all equal to n, calculate n.

10-2   The quantum states available for gas molecules of energy ϵ in a cubical box of length L correspond to integer values for each n_x, n_y, and n_z according to Eq. (10-1). In a three-dimensional Euclidean space with coordinates n_x, n_y, and n_z, each unit volume will contain one quantum state. The total number of quantum states g' with energy less than ϵ' is equal to the volume of the positive octant of a sphere of radius $r = L(8m\epsilon_i)^{\frac{1}{2}}/h$. (a) Show that

$$g' = \frac{4\pi V (2m\epsilon')^{\frac{3}{2}}}{3h^3}.$$

In a volume of 1 cm³ of helium gas at 300°K and 1 atm pressure, ϵ' is about 10^{-12} erg. Calculate: (b) g' and (c) the number N of helium atoms. (d) Show that $g' \gg N$.

10-3   Consider a function f defined by the relation

$$f(\Omega_A \Omega_B) = f(\Omega_A) + f(\Omega_B).$$

First differentiate partially with respect to Ω_B, and then with respect to Ω_A. Integrate twice to show that

$$f(\Omega) = \text{const. } \ln \Omega + \text{const.}$$

10-4   Take the expression for the kinetic energy of a particle in a cubical box and imagine a space defined by the cartesian coordinates n_x, n_y, and n_z. Note that a single quantum state occupies unit volume in this space.

(a) Setting $n^2 = n_x^2 + n_y^2 + n_z^2$, show that the number of quantum states in the small interval dn is $\frac{1}{8}(4\pi n^2 \, dn)$.

(b)   Prove that the number of quantum states dg_ϵ in the energy interval $d\epsilon$ is $(2\pi/h^3)V(2m)^{\frac{3}{2}}\epsilon^{\frac{1}{2}}\,d\epsilon$.

(c)   Show that the number of ideal-gas molecules dN_ϵ occupying these quantum states is given by

$$dN_\epsilon = \frac{2N}{\pi^{\frac{1}{2}}}\frac{1}{(kT)^{\frac{3}{2}}}\,\epsilon^{\frac{1}{2}}e^{-\epsilon/kT}\,d\epsilon.$$

(d)   Derive the Maxwellian law of the distribution of speeds, that is, Eq. (6-25).

10-5   In the case of N *distinguishable* particles, the number of ways Ω in which a macrostate defined by N_1 particles in g_1 quantum states with energy ϵ_1; N_2 particles in g_2 quantum states with energy ϵ_2; and so on, may be achieved is given by

$$\Omega = N!\,\frac{g_1^{N_1}g_2^{N_2},\,\cdots}{N_1!N_2!\,\cdots},$$

when $g_i \gg N_i$.

(a)   Using the Stirling approximation, calculate $\ln\Omega$.

(b)   Render $\ln\Omega$ a maximum subject to the equations of constraint $\Sigma N_i = N = $ const. and $\Sigma N_i\epsilon_i = U = $ const., and explain why U and P should be the same as for indistinguishable particles but S should be different.

10-6   Given N indistinguishable, quasi-independent particles capable of existing in energy levels ϵ_1, ϵ_2, . . . , with degeneracies g_1, g_2, . . . , respectively. In any given macrostate in which there are N_1 particles in energy level ϵ_1; N_2 particles with energy ϵ_2; and so on, assume the thermodynamic probability to be given by the Bose-Einstein expression,

$$\Omega_{\mathrm{BE}} = \frac{(g_1 + N_1)!(g_2 + N_2)!\,\cdots}{g_1!N_1!g_2!N_2!\,\cdots}.$$

Using Stirling's approximation and the Lagrange method, render $\ln\Omega_{\mathrm{BE}}$ a maximum subject to $\Sigma N_i = N = $ const. and $\Sigma N_i\epsilon_i = U = $ const., and show that

$$N_i = \frac{g_i}{Ae^{-\beta\epsilon_i} - 1}.$$

10-7   Given the same system as in Prob. 10-6, except that the thermodynamic probability is given by the Fermi-Dirac expression

$$\Omega_{\mathrm{FD}} = \frac{g_1!g_2!\,\cdots}{N_1!(g_1 - N_1)!N_2!(g_2 - N_2)!\,\cdots}.$$

Using Stirling's approximation and the Lagrange method, render $\ln \Omega_{FD}$ a maximum subject to $\Sigma N_i = N = \text{const.}$ and $\Sigma N_i \epsilon_i = U = \text{const.}$, and show that

$$N_i = \frac{g_i}{A e^{-\beta \epsilon_i} + 1}.$$

10-8   Given a gaseous system of N_A indistinguishable, weakly inter-acting diatomic molecules:

(a)   Each molecule may vibrate with the same frequency ν but with an energy ϵ_i, given by

$$\epsilon_i = (\tfrac{1}{2} + i)h\nu \qquad (i = 0, 1, 2, \ldots).$$

Show that the vibrational partition function Z_ν is

$$Z_\nu = \frac{e^{-\frac{1}{2}h\nu/kT}}{1 - e^{-h\nu/kT}}.$$

(b)   Each molecule may rotate, and the rotational partition function Z_r has the same form as that for translation, except that the volume V is replaced by the total solid angle 4π, the mass is replaced by the moment of inertia I, and the exponent $\tfrac{3}{2}$ (referring to three translational degrees of freedom) is replaced by $\tfrac{2}{2}$, since there are only two rotational degrees of freedom. Write the rotational partition function.

(c)   Taking into account translation, vibration, and rotation, calculate the Helmholtz function.

(d)   Calculate the pressure.

(e)   Calculate the energy.

(f)   Calculate the molar heat capacity at constant volume.

11.

PURE SUBSTANCES ✓

11-1   Enthalpy

The laws of thermodynamics were stated and their consequences were developed in a sufficiently general manner to apply to systems of any number of coordinates. When there are three or more independent coordinates, one speaks of isothermal surfaces and isentropic (adiabatic reversible) surfaces. If, as is often the case, there are only two independent coordinates, these surfaces reduce to simple plane curves. The most important system of two independent coordinates is a hydrostatic one, consisting of a single pure substance of constant mass. Once the thermodynamic equations are developed for this system, we shall see how simple it is to write down the analogous equations for any other two-coordinate system.

In discussing some of the properties of gases in Chap. 4, the sum of U and PV appeared several times (see Probs. 4-8, 4-9, and 4-11). It has been found very useful to define a new function H, called the *enthalpy*,† by the relation

$$\boxed{H = U + PV.}$$
(11-1)

In order to study the properties of this function, consider the change in enthalpy that takes place when a system undergoes an infinitesimal process from an initial equilibrium state to a final equilibrium state. We have

$$dH = dU + P\,dV + V\,dP;$$

but

$$dQ = dU + P\,dV.$$

Therefore,

$$dH = dQ + V\,dP.$$
(11-2)

† Pronounced *en-thal'-pi.*

Dividing both sides by dT,

$$\frac{dH}{dT} = \frac{dQ}{dT} + V\frac{dP}{dT}$$

and, at constant P,

$$\left(\frac{\partial H}{\partial T}\right)_P = \left(\frac{dQ}{dT}\right)_P = C_P. \qquad (11\text{-}3)$$

Since

$$dH = dQ + V\,dP,$$

the change in enthalpy during an isobaric process is equal to the heat that is transferred. That is,

$$\left.\begin{aligned} H_f - H_i &= Q, \\ H_f - H_i &= \int_i^f C_P\,dT. \end{aligned}\right\} \quad \text{(isobaric)} \qquad (11\text{-}4)$$

or

Since isobaric processes are much more important in engineering and chemistry than isochoric processes, the enthalpy is of greatest use in these branches of science.

If a pure substance undergoes an infinitesimal reversible process, Eq. (11-2) may be written

$$dH = T\,dS + V\,dP,$$

showing that

$$\left(\frac{\partial H}{\partial S}\right)_P = T \quad \text{and} \quad \left(\frac{\partial H}{\partial P}\right)_S = V. \qquad (11\text{-}5)$$

The relations given in Eqs. (11-5) suggest that the properties of a pure substance could be displayed to advantage on a diagram in which H is plotted as a function of S and P. This three-dimensional graph would be a surface, and T and V would be indicated at any point by the two slopes that determine a plane tangent to the surface at the point.

One of the most interesting properties of the enthalpy function is in connection with a *throttling process*. Imagine a cylinder thermally insulated and equipped with two nonconducting pistons on opposite sides of a porous wall, as shown in Fig. 11-1*i*. The wall, shaded in horizontal lines, is a porous plug, a narrow constriction, or a series of small holes. Between the left-hand piston and the wall there is a gas at a pressure P_i and a volume V_i; and since the right-hand piston is against the wall, with any gas being thus prevented from seeping through, the initial state of the gas is an equilibrium state. Now imagine moving both pistons simultaneously in such a way that a *constant pressure P_i* is maintained on the left-hand side of the wall and a *constant lower pressure P_f* is maintained on the right-hand side. After all the gas has seeped through the porous wall, the final equilibrium state of the system will be as shown in Fig. 11-1*f*. Such a process is a throttling process.

(*i*) Initial state

(*f*) Final state

Fig. 11-1   *Throttling process.*

A throttling process is obviously an irreversible one, since the gas passes through nonequilibrium states on its way from the initial equilibrium state to its final equilibrium state. These nonequilibrium states cannot be described by thermodynamic coordinates, but an interesting conclusion can be drawn about the initial and final equilibrium states. Applying the first law to the throttling process

$$Q = U_f - U_i + W,$$

we have $Q = 0$

and

$$W = \int_0^{V_f} P \, dV + \int_{V_i}^0 P \, dV.$$

Since both pressures remain constant,

$$W = P_f V_f - P_i V_i.$$

The above expression is known in engineering as *flow work*, since it represents the work necessary to keep the gas flowing. Therefore,

$$0 = U_f - U_i + P_f V_f - P_i V_i,$$

or

$$U_i + P_i V_i = U_f + P_f V_f.$$

And, finally,

$$H_i = H_f \qquad \text{(throttling process).} \tag{11-6}$$

In a throttling process, therefore, the initial and final enthalpies are equal. One is not entitled to say that the enthalpy remains constant, since one cannot

High pressure

Fig. 11-2   *Apparatus for performing a continuous throttling process.*

Table 11-1   Comparison of U and H

Internal energy U	Enthalpy H
In general $dU = dQ - P\,dV$ $\left(\dfrac{\partial U}{\partial T}\right)_V = C_V$	In general $dH = dQ + V\,dP$ $\left(\dfrac{\partial H}{\partial T}\right)_P = C_P$
Isochoric process $U_f - U_i = Q$ $U_f - U_i = \displaystyle\int_i^f C_V\,dT$	Isobaric process $H_f - H_i = Q$ $H_f - H_i = \displaystyle\int_i^f C_P\,dT$
Adiabatic process $U_f - U_i = -\displaystyle\int_i^f P\,dV$	Adiabatic process $H_f - H_i = \displaystyle\int_i^f V\,dP$
Free expansion $U_i = U_f$	Throttling process $H_i = H_f$
For an ideal gas $U = \displaystyle\int C_V\,dT + \text{const.}$	For an ideal gas $H = \displaystyle\int C_P\,dT + \text{const.}$
Nearby equil. states $dU = T\,dS - P\,dV$ $T = \left(\dfrac{\partial U}{\partial S}\right)_V$ $-P = \left(\dfrac{\partial U}{\partial V}\right)_S$	Nearby equil. states $dH = T\,dS + V\,dP$ $T = \left(\dfrac{\partial H}{\partial S}\right)_P$ $V = \left(\dfrac{\partial H}{\partial P}\right)_S$

speak of the enthalpy of a system that is passing through such nonequilibrium states. In plotting a throttling process on any diagram, the initial and final equilibrium states may be represented by points. The intermediate states, however, cannot be plotted.

A continuous throttling process may be achieved by a pump that maintains a constant high pressure on one side of a constriction or porous wall and a constant lower pressure on the other side, as shown in Fig. 11-2. For every mole of fluid that undergoes the throttling process, we may write

$$h_i = h_f,$$

where the lower-case letters indicate *molar enthalpy*.

The properties of the enthalpy function must be clearly understood by the student, for they will be used continually throughout the remainder of this book. The comparison of the internal energy and the enthalpy given in Table 11-1 will help the student to remember these properties.

11-2   The Helmholtz and Gibbs Functions

The *Helmholtz function* (sometimes called the *Helmholtz free energy*) is defined as

$$\boxed{F = U - TS.}$$
$$(11-7)$$

For an infinitesimal reversible process,

$$dF = dU - T\,dS - S\,dT,$$

and

$$T\,dS = dU + P\,dV.$$

Hence

$$dF = -S\,dT - P\,dV.$$
$$(11-8)$$

From this it follows: (1) For a *reversible isothermal process*,

$$dF = -P\,dV,$$

or

$$F_f - F_i = -\int_i^f P\,dV.$$
$$(11-9)$$

Hence the change of the Helmholtz function during a reversible isothermal process equals the work done *on* the system. (2) For a *reversible isothermal and isochoric process*,

$$dF = 0,$$

and

$$F = \text{const.}$$
$$(11-10)$$

These properties are of interest in chemistry and are useful in considering chemical reactions that take place isothermally and isochorically. The main importance of the Helmholtz function, however, is in statistical mechanics, where it is closely associated with the partition function Z defined by the equation

$$Z = \Sigma g_i e^{-\epsilon_i/kT},$$

where ϵ_i and g_i represent the energy values and degeneracies, respectively, of the various energy levels of the system of particles. In the case of indistinguishable particles, it was shown in Chap. 10, that the entropy is given by

$$S = Nk \ln \frac{Z}{N} + \frac{U}{T} + Nk. \tag{10-21}$$

Therefore, $F = U - TS = -NkT \ln \dfrac{Z}{N} - NkT$

$$= -kT(N \ln Z - N \ln N + N),$$

or

$$F = -kT(N \ln Z - \ln N!).$$

The relation between Helmholtz function and partition function is even simpler in the case of distinguishable particles (such as those of a crystal, where the particles are localized); namely,

$$F = -NkT \ln Z.$$

Whether the particles are distinguishable or not, the logarithm of the partition function leads directly to the Helmholtz function, and since

$$dF = -S\,dT - P\,dV,$$

the entropy and the pressure may then be calculated by performing the simple differentiations:

$$S = -\left(\frac{\partial F}{\partial T}\right)_V \quad \text{and} \quad P = -\left(\frac{\partial F}{\partial V}\right)_T.$$

The *Gibbs function* (also called the *Gibbs free energy*) is defined as

$$\boxed{G = H - TS.} \tag{11-11}$$

For an infinitesimal reversible process,

$$dG = dH - T\,dS - S\,dT.$$

It will be recalled, however, that

$$dH = T\,dS + V\,dP;$$

$dG = Td\cancel{S} + Vdp - Td\cancel{S} - SdT$

whence

$$dG = -S\,dT + V\,dP. \tag{11-12}$$

In the case of a *reversible isothermal and isobaric process,*

$$dG = 0,$$

and

$$G = \text{const.}$$

This is a particularly important result in connection with processes involving a change of phase. Sublimation, fusion, and vaporization take place isothermally and isobarically and can be conceived of as occurring reversibly. Hence, during such processes, the Gibbs function of the system remains constant. If we denote by the symbols g', g'', and g''' the molar Gibbs functions of a saturated solid, saturated liquid, and saturated vapor, respectively, then the equation of the fusion curve is

$$g' = g'',$$

the equation of the vaporization curve is

$$g'' = g''',$$

and the equation of the sublimation curve is

$$g' = g'''.$$

At the triple point two equations hold simultaneously, namely,

$$g' = g'' = g'''.$$

All the g's can be regarded as functions of P and T only, and hence the two equations above serve to determine the P and T of the triple point uniquely.

The Gibbs function is of the utmost importance in chemistry, since chemical reactions can be conceived of as taking place at constant P and T. It is also of some use in engineering.

11-3   Two Mathematical Theorems

Theorem 1   If a relation exists among x, y, and z, we may imagine z expressed as a function of x and y; whence

$$dz = \left(\frac{\partial z}{\partial x}\right)_y dx + \left(\frac{\partial z}{\partial y}\right)_x dy.$$

If we let

$$M = \left(\frac{\partial z}{\partial x}\right)_y \quad \text{and} \quad N = \left(\frac{\partial z}{\partial y}\right)_x,$$

then

$$dz = M\, dx + N\, dy,$$

where z, M, and N are all functions of x and y. Partially differentiating M with respect to y, and N with respect to x, we get

$$\left(\frac{\partial M}{\partial y}\right)_x = \frac{\partial^2 z}{\partial x\, \partial y} \quad \text{and} \quad \left(\frac{\partial N}{\partial x}\right)_y = \frac{\partial^2 z}{\partial y\, \partial x}.$$

Since the two second derivatives of the right-hand terms are equal, it follows that (if the differential is exact)

$$\boxed{\left(\frac{\partial M}{\partial y}\right)_x = \left(\frac{\partial N}{\partial x}\right)_y.} \qquad (11\text{-}13)$$

This is known as the *condition for an exact differential*.

Theorem 2   If a quantity f is a function of x, y, and z, and a relation exists among x, y, and z, then f may be regarded as a function of *any two* of x, y, and z. Similarly, any one of x, y, and z may be considered to be a function of f and one other of x, y, and z. Thus, regarding x to be a function of f and y,

$$x = x(f, y)$$

$$dx = \left(\frac{\partial x}{\partial f}\right)_y df + \left(\frac{\partial x}{\partial y}\right)_f dy.$$

Considering y to be a function of f and z,

$$y = y(f, z)$$

$$dy = \left(\frac{\partial y}{\partial f}\right)_z df + \left(\frac{\partial y}{\partial z}\right)_f dz.$$

Substituting this expression for dy in the preceding equation, we get

$$dx = \left[\left(\frac{\partial x}{\partial f}\right)_y + \left(\frac{\partial x}{\partial y}\right)_f \left(\frac{\partial y}{\partial f}\right)_z\right] df + \left[\left(\frac{\partial x}{\partial y}\right)_f \left(\frac{\partial y}{\partial z}\right)_f\right] dz.$$

But

$$dx = \left(\frac{\partial x}{\partial f}\right)_z df + \left(\frac{\partial x}{\partial z}\right)_f dz.$$

Equating the dz terms of the last two equations, we get

$$\left(\frac{\partial x}{\partial y}\right)_f \left(\frac{\partial y}{\partial z}\right)_f = \left(\frac{\partial x}{\partial z}\right)_f$$

$$\left(\frac{\partial x}{\partial y}\right)_f \left(\frac{\partial y}{\partial z}\right)_f \left(\frac{\partial z}{\partial x}\right)_f = 1.$$

(11-14)

11-4 Maxwell's Equations

We have seen that the properties of a pure substance are conveniently represented in terms of these four functions:

Internal energy U,
Enthalpy $H = U + PV$,
Helmholtz function $F = U - TS$,
Gibbs function $G = H - TS$.

Any one of these may be regarded as a function of *any two* of P, V, and T. Suppose for example that both U and S are expressed as functions of V and T, thus:

$$U = \text{function of } (V,T),$$

and

$$S = \text{function of } (V,T).$$

The second equation may be imagined to be solved for T in terms of S and V; substituting this value of T in the first equation, we should then have

$$U = \text{function of } (S,V).$$

Consequently, we may go further and say that any one of the eight quantities P, V, T, S, U, H, F, and G may be expressed as a function of *any two others*.

Now imagine a hydrostatic system undergoing an infinitesimal reversible process from one equilibrium state to another:

1   The internal energy changes by an amount

$$dU = dQ - P \, dV$$
$$= T \, dS - P \, dV,$$

where U, T, and P are all imagined to be functions of S and V.

2   The enthalpy changes by an amount

$$dH = dU + P \, dV + V \, dP = T dS - PdV + PdV + VdP$$
$$= T \, dS + V \, dP,$$

where H, T, and V are all imagined to be functions of S and P.

3   The Helmholtz function changes by an amount

$$dF = dU - T \, dS - S \, dT = TdS - PdV - TdS - SdT$$
$$= -S \, dT - P \, dV,$$

where F, S, and P are all imagined to be functions of T and V.

4   The Gibbs function changes by an amount

$$dG = dH - T \, dS - S \, dT$$
$$= -S \, dT + V \, dP,$$

where G, S, and V are all imagined to be functions of T and P.

Since U, H, F, and G are actual functions, their differentials are exact differentials of the type

$$dz = M \, dx + N \, dy,$$

where z, M, and N are all functions of x and y. Therefore,

$$\left(\frac{\partial M}{\partial y} \right)_x = \left(\frac{\partial N}{\partial x} \right)_y.$$

Applying this result to the four exact differentials dU, dH, dF, and dG:

1 $\quad dU = \quad T\,dS - P\,dV;$ hence $\left(\dfrac{\partial T}{\partial V}\right)_S = -\left(\dfrac{\partial P}{\partial S}\right)_V .$

2 $\quad dH = \quad T\,dS + V\,dP;$ hence $\left(\dfrac{\partial T}{\partial P}\right)_S = \left(\dfrac{\partial V}{\partial S}\right)_P .$

3 $\quad dF = -S\,dT - P\,dV;$ hence $\left(\dfrac{\partial S}{\partial V}\right)_T = \left(\dfrac{\partial P}{\partial T}\right)_V .$

$$(11\text{-}15)$$

4 $\quad dG = -S\,dT + V\,dP;$ hence $\left(\dfrac{\partial S}{\partial P}\right)_T = -\left(\dfrac{\partial V}{\partial T}\right)_P .$

The four equations on the right are known as *Maxwell's equations*. These do not refer to a process but express relations which hold at any equilibrium state of a hydrostatic system.

Maxwell's equations are enormously useful, because they provide relationships between measurable quantities and those which either cannot be measured or are difficult to measure. For example, the fourth Maxwell equation,

$$\left(\frac{\partial S}{\partial P}\right)_T = -\left(\frac{\partial V}{\partial T}\right)_P ,$$

may be combined with the statistical interpretation of entropy in order to provide information concerning the volume expansivity β of a pure substance in the following way. If a substance is compressed isothermally and if no unusual molecular rearrangements take place (such as association or dissociation), the molecules merely occupy a smaller volume and are therefore in a more orderly state. In the language of information theory, our knowledge about these molecules is increased. The entropy is therefore decreased, and the derivative $(\partial S/\partial P)_T$ is negative. It follows that $(\partial V/\partial T)_P$ is positive and that the substance must have a positive expansivity.

The Maxwell equations will be used extensively in the remaining portions of this text. They need not be memorized, but they must be readily available. For this purpose, no less than ten mnemonic schemes have been suggested— all in the pages of the *American Journal of Physics*.† The diagram in Fig. 11-3 is based on a sentence due to J. J. Gilvarry, a former student of the author: namely, "*Good Physicists Have Studied Under Very Fine Teachers*." The upper-right and lower-left corners of a square are slightly cut away to provide eight points. Starting at the upper-left point and proceeding clockwise, the first letter of each word of Gilvarry's magic sentence is placed successively at

† The ten references will be found in a note by D. E. Christie, *Am. J. Phys.*, **25**:486 (1957).

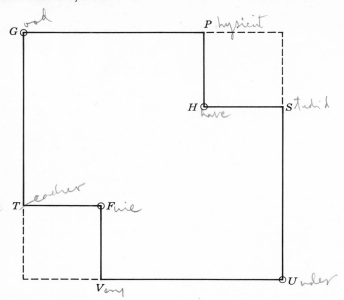

Fig. 11-3   *Mnemonic for obtaining dU, dH, dF, and dG by using the sentence "Good physicists have studied under very fine teachers."*

each point, and the points corresponding to the four functions U, H, F, and G are emphasized. The equations for dU, dH, dF, and dG may now be obtained automatically by noting what the adjacent letters are and where they lie. Thus, to find dU, we look at U and see that S lies above (positive) and V lies to the left (negative). Therefore,

$$dU = +(\ \ ) \, dS - (\ \ ) \, dV.$$

The student is assumed to be able to fill the parentheses. It is an interesting exercise to discover how the Maxwell equations are hidden in the diagram.

11-5   The $T \, dS$ Equations

The entropy of a pure substance can be imagined as a function of T and V; whence

$$dS = \left(\frac{\partial S}{\partial T}\right)_V dT + \left(\frac{\partial S}{\partial V}\right)_T dV,$$

and

$$T \, dS = T \left(\frac{\partial S}{\partial T}\right)_V dT + T \left(\frac{\partial S}{\partial V}\right)_T dV.$$

Since $T\,dS = dQ$ for a reversible process, it follows that

$$T\left(\frac{\partial S}{\partial T}\right)_V = C_V.$$

And, from Maxwell's third equation,

$$\left(\frac{\partial S}{\partial V}\right)_T = \left(\frac{\partial P}{\partial T}\right)_V;$$

whence

$$\boxed{T\,dS = C_V\,dT + T\left(\frac{\partial P}{\partial T}\right)_V dV.}\qquad(11\text{-}16)$$

We shall call the above equation the *first T dS equation*. It is useful in a variety of ways. For example, 1 mole of a van der Waals gas undergoes a reversible isothermal expansion from a volume v_i to a volume v_f. How much heat has been transferred?

For 1 mole,

$$T\,ds = c_V\,dT + T\left(\frac{\partial P}{\partial T}\right)_V dv.$$

Using the van der Waals equation of state,

$$P = \frac{RT}{v - b} - \frac{a}{v^2},$$

and

$$\left(\frac{\partial P}{\partial T}\right)_V = \frac{R}{v - b};$$

hence

$$T\,ds = c_V\,dT + RT\frac{dv}{v - b}.$$

Since T is constant, $c_V\,dT = 0$; and since the process is reversible, $q = \int T\,ds$. Therefore,

$$q = RT \int_{v_i}^{v_f} \frac{dv}{v - b},$$

and finally

$$q = RT \ln\frac{v_f - b}{v_i - b}.$$

If the entropy of a pure substance is regarded as a function of T and P, then

$$dS = \left(\frac{\partial S}{\partial T}\right)_P dT + \left(\frac{\partial S}{\partial P}\right)_T dP,$$

and

$$T\,dS = T\left(\frac{\partial S}{\partial T}\right)_P dT + T\left(\frac{\partial S}{\partial P}\right)_T dP.$$

But

$$T\left(\frac{\partial S}{\partial T}\right)_P = C_P.$$

And, from Maxwell's fourth equation,

$$\left(\frac{\partial S}{\partial P}\right)_T = -\left(\frac{\partial V}{\partial T}\right)_P;$$

whence

$$\boxed{T\,dS = C_P\,dT - T\left(\frac{\partial V}{\partial T}\right)_P dP.} \tag{11-17}$$

This is the *second T dS equation*. A third will be found among the problems at the end of the chapter. Two important applications of the second $T\,dS$ equation follow.

1. *Reversible isothermal change of pressure*   When T is constant,

$$T\,dS = -T\left(\frac{\partial V}{\partial T}\right)_P dP,$$

and

$$Q = -T\int \left(\frac{\partial V}{\partial T}\right)_P dP.$$

Remembering that the volume expansivity is

$$\beta = \frac{1}{V}\left(\frac{\partial V}{\partial T}\right)_P,$$

we obtain

$$Q = -T\int V\beta\,dP,$$

which can be integrated when the dependence of V and β on the pressure is known. In the case of a solid or liquid, neither V nor β is very sensitive to a change in pressure. For example, in the case of mercury, Bridgman found that as the pressure was increased from zero to 1000 atm at 0°C the volume of 1 mole of mercury changed from 14.72 to 14.67 cm³, a change of only

$\frac{1}{3}$ percent; and the volume expansivity changed from 181×10^{-6} deg^{-1} to 174×10^{-6} deg^{-1}, a 4 percent change. The volume and the expansivity of most solids and liquids behave similarly; therefore V and β may be taken out from under the integral sign and replaced by average values, $\bar{V}$ and $\bar{\beta}$. (A bar over a quantity indicates an average value.) We then have

$$Q = -T\bar{V}\bar{\beta} \int_{P_i}^{P_f} dP,$$

or

$$Q = -T\bar{V}\bar{\beta}(P_f - P_i).$$

It is seen from this result that, as the pressure is increased isothermally, heat will flow *out* if $\bar{\beta}$ is positive but that, for a substance with a negative expansivity (such as water between 0 and 4°C), an isothermal increase of pressure causes an absorption of heat.

If the pressure on 0.015 liter of mercury at 0°C is increased reversibly and isothermally from zero to 1000 atm, the heat transferred will be

$$Q = -T\bar{V}\bar{\beta}(P_f - P_i),$$

where $T = 273$ deg, $\bar{V} = 0.015$ liter, $\bar{\beta} = 178 \times 10^{-6}$ deg^{-1}, $P_i = 0$, and $P_f = 1000$ atm. Hence,

$$Q = -273 \text{ deg} \times 0.015 \text{ liter} \times 178 \times 10^{-6} \text{ deg}^{-1} \times 10^3 \text{ atm}$$

$$= -0.730 \text{ liter} \cdot \text{atm} = -0.730 \times 101 \text{ J}$$

$$= -73.7 \text{ J}.$$

It is interesting to compare the heat liberated with the work done during the compression.

$$W = \int P \, dV;$$

and at constant temperature,

$$W = \int \left(\frac{\partial V}{\partial P}\right)_T P \, dP.$$

Recalling the isothermal compressibility, $\kappa = -(1/V)(\partial V/\partial P)_T$, we get

$$W = -\int_{P_i}^{P_f} V\kappa P \, dP.$$

The isothermal compressibility is also fairly insensitive to a change of pressure. Bridgman showed that the compressibility of mercury at 0°C changed from 3.92×10^{-6} to 3.83×10^{-6} atm^{-1} (a 2 percent change) as the pressure was increased from zero to 1000 atm. We may therefore again replace V and κ by average values and obtain

$$W = -\frac{\bar{V}\bar{\kappa}}{2}(P_f^2 - P_i^2);$$

and taking $\bar{\kappa} = 3.88 \times 10^{-6}$ atm^{-1} for mercury, we get

$$W = -\tfrac{1}{2}(0.015 \text{ liter} \times 3.88 \times 10^{-6} \text{ atm}^{-1} \times 10^6 \text{ atm}^2)$$

$$= -0.0291 \text{ liter} \cdot \text{atm}$$

$$= -2.94 \text{ J.}$$

Therefore, it is seen that, when the pressure on 0.015 liter of mercury at 0°C is increased from zero to 1000 atm, 73.7 J of heat is liberated but only 2.94 J of work is done! The extra amount of heat comes, of course, from the store of internal energy, which has changed by an amount

$$\Delta U = Q - W$$

$$= -73.7 + 2.9 = -70.8 \text{ J.}$$

A similar result is obtained in the case of any substance with a positive expansivity. For a substance with a negative expansivity, heat is absorbed and the internal energy is increased.

2. *Reversible adiabatic change of pressure*   Since the entropy remains constant,

$$T \, dS = 0 = C_P \, dT - T \left(\frac{\partial V}{\partial T}\right)_P dP,$$

or

$$dT = \frac{T}{C_P}\left(\frac{\partial V}{\partial T}\right)_P dP = \frac{TV\beta}{C_P} dP.$$

In the case of a solid or liquid, an increase of pressure of as much as 1000 atm produces only a small temperature change. Also, experiment shows that C_P hardly changes even for an increase of 10,000 atm. The above equation, when applied to a solid or a liquid, may therefore be written

$$\Delta T = \frac{T\bar{V}\bar{\beta}}{C_P}(P_f - P_i).$$

It is clear from the above that an adiabatic increase of pressure will produce an increase of temperature in any substance with a positive expansivity and a decrease in temperature in a substance with a negative expansivity.

If the pressure on 0.0015 liter of mercury ($\bar{C}_P = 28.6$ J/deg) at 0°C is

increased isentropically from zero to 1000 atm, the temperature change
will be

$$\Delta T = \frac{273 \text{ deg} \times 0.015 \text{ liter} \times 178 \times 10^{-6} \text{ deg}^{-1} \times 10^3 \text{ atm}}{28.6 \text{ J/deg}}$$

$$= 0.0255 \text{ deg} \frac{\text{liter} \cdot \text{atm}}{\text{J}} = 0.0255 \times 101 \text{ deg}$$

$$= 2.58 \text{ deg.}$$

11-6   Energy Equations

If a pure substance undergoes an infinitesimal reversible process between
two equilibrium states, the change of internal energy is

$$dU = T\, dS - P\, dV.$$

Dividing by dV, we get

$$\frac{dU}{dV} = T \frac{dS}{dV} - P,$$

where U, S, and P are regarded as functions of T and V. If T is held constant,
then the derivatives become partial derivatives, and

$$\left(\frac{\partial U}{\partial V}\right)_T = T\left(\frac{\partial S}{\partial V}\right)_T - P.$$

Using Maxwell's third equation, $(\partial S/\partial V)_T = (\partial P/\partial T)_V$, we get

$$\boxed{\left(\frac{\partial U}{\partial V}\right)_T = T\left(\frac{\partial P}{\partial T}\right)_V - P.} \tag{11-18}$$

We shall call this equation the *first energy equation*. Two examples of its usefulness follow.

1. *Ideal gas*

$$P = \frac{nRT}{V},$$

$$\left(\frac{\partial P}{\partial T}\right)_V = \frac{nR}{V},$$

and

$$\left(\frac{\partial U}{\partial V}\right)_T = T\frac{nR}{V} - P = 0.$$

Therefore U does not depend on V but is a function of T only.

2. *Van der Waals gas (1 mole)*

$$P = \frac{RT}{v-b} - \frac{a}{v^2}$$

$$\left(\frac{\partial P}{\partial T}\right)_v = \frac{R}{v-b},$$

and

$$\left(\frac{\partial u}{\partial v}\right)_T = T\frac{R}{v-b} - \frac{RT}{v-b} + \frac{a}{v^2} = \frac{a}{v^2}.$$

Consequently,

$$du = c_V\, dT + \frac{a}{v^2}\, dv,$$

and

$$u = \int c_V\, dT - \frac{a}{v} + \text{const.}$$

It follows, therefore, that the internal energy of a van der Waals gas increases as the volume increases, with the temperature remaining constant.

The second energy equation shows the dependence of energy on pressure. We start, as usual, with the equation

$$dU = T\, dS - P\, dV,$$

and divide by dP. Then,

$$\frac{dU}{dP} = T\frac{dS}{dP} - P\frac{dV}{dP},$$

where U, S, and V are imagined to be functions of T and P. If T is held constant, then the derivatives become partial derivatives, and

$$\left(\frac{\partial U}{\partial P}\right)_T = T\left(\frac{\partial S}{\partial P}\right)_T - P\left(\frac{\partial V}{\partial P}\right)_T.$$

Using Maxwell's fourth equation, $(\partial S/\partial P)_T = -(\partial V/\partial T)_P$, we get

$$\boxed{\left(\frac{\partial U}{\partial P}\right)_T = -T\left(\frac{\partial V}{\partial T}\right)_P - P\left(\frac{\partial V}{\partial P}\right)_T,}$$

(11-19)

which is the *second energy equation*.

11-7   Heat-capacity Equations

Equating the first and second $T\,dS$ equations,

$$C_P\,dT - T\left(\frac{\partial V}{\partial T}\right)_P dP = C_V\,dT + T\left(\frac{\partial P}{\partial T}\right)_V dV;$$

solving for dT,

$$dT = \frac{T\left(\frac{\partial P}{\partial T}\right)_V}{C_P - C_V}\,dV + \frac{T\left(\frac{\partial V}{\partial T}\right)_P}{C_P - C_V}\,dP.$$

But

$$dT = \left(\frac{\partial T}{\partial V}\right)_P dV + \left(\frac{\partial T}{\partial P}\right)_V dP.$$

Therefore

$$\left(\frac{\partial T}{\partial V}\right)_P = \frac{T\left(\frac{\partial P}{\partial T}\right)_V}{C_P - C_V},$$

and

$$\left(\frac{\partial T}{\partial P}\right)_V = \frac{T\left(\frac{\partial V}{\partial T}\right)_P}{C_P - C_V}.$$

Both the above equations yield the result that

$$C_P - C_V = T\left(\frac{\partial V}{\partial T}\right)_P\left(\frac{\partial P}{\partial T}\right)_V.$$

It was shown in Art. 2-7 that

$$\left(\frac{\partial P}{\partial T}\right)_V = -\left(\frac{\partial V}{\partial T}\right)_P\left(\frac{\partial P}{\partial V}\right)_T,$$

and therefore

$$\boxed{C_P - C_V = -T\left(\frac{\partial V}{\partial T}\right)_P^2\left(\frac{\partial P}{\partial V}\right)_T.} \qquad (11\text{-}20)$$

This is one of the most important equations of thermodynamics, and it shows that:

1   Since $(\partial P/\partial V)_T$ is always negative for all known substances and $(\partial V/\partial T)_P^2$ must be positive, then $C_P - C_V$ can never be negative; or *C_P can never be less than C_V.*

2   As $T \to 0$, $C_P \to C_V$; or *at the absolute zero the two heat capacities are equal.*

3      $C_P = C_V$ when $(\partial V/\partial T)_P = 0$. For example, at 4°C, at which the density of water is a maximum, $C_P = C_V$.

Laboratory measurements of the heat capacity of solids and liquids usually take place at constant pressure and therefore yield values of C_P. It would be extremely difficult to measure with any degree of accuracy the C_V of a solid or liquid. Values of C_V, however, must be known for purposes of comparison with theory. The equation for the difference in the heat capacities is very useful in calculating C_V in terms of C_P and other measurable quantities. Remembering that

$$\beta = \frac{1}{V}\left(\frac{\partial V}{\partial T}\right)_P$$

and

$$\kappa = -\frac{1}{V}\left(\frac{\partial V}{\partial P}\right)_T,$$

we may write the equation in the form

$$C_P - C_V = \frac{TV\left[\frac{1}{V}\left(\frac{\partial V}{\partial T}\right)_P\right]^2}{-\frac{1}{V}\left(\frac{\partial V}{\partial P}\right)_T}$$

$$\boxed{C_P - C_V = \frac{TV\beta^2}{\kappa}.} \tag{11-21}$$

As an example, let us calculate the molar heat capacity at constant volume of mercury at 0°C and 1 atm pressure. From experiment we have $c_P = 28.0$ J/mole · deg, $T = 273$ deg, $v = 0.0147$ liter/mole, $\beta = 181 \times 10^{-6}$ deg^{-1}, and $\kappa = 3.94 \times 10^{-6}$ atm^{-1}. Hence,

$$c_P - c_V = \frac{273 \text{ deg} \times 0.0147 \text{ liter/mole} \times (181)^2 \times 10^{-12} \text{ deg}^{-2}}{3.94 \times 10^{-6} \text{ atm}^{-2}}$$

$$= 0.0336 \frac{\text{liter} \cdot \text{atm}}{\text{mole} \cdot \text{deg}}$$

$$= 3.39 \text{ J/mole} \cdot \text{deg,}$$

and $c_V = 28.0 - 3.4 = 24.6$ J/mole · deg.

Finally, $\gamma = \dfrac{c_P}{c_V} = \dfrac{28.0}{24.6} = 1.14.$

The two $T\,dS$ equations are

$$T\,dS = C_P\,dT - T\left(\frac{\partial V}{\partial T}\right)_P dP,$$

and

$$T\,dS = C_V\,dT + T\left(\frac{\partial P}{\partial T}\right)_V dV.$$

At constant S,

$$C_P\,dT_S = T\left(\frac{\partial V}{\partial T}\right)_P dP_S,$$

and

$$C_V\,dT_S = -T\left(\frac{\partial P}{\partial T}\right)_V dV_S.$$

Dividing,

$$\frac{C_P}{C_V} = -\left[\frac{(\partial V/\partial T)_P}{(\partial P/\partial T)_V}\right]\left(\frac{\partial P}{\partial V}\right)_S.$$

But the quantity in square brackets is equal to $-(\partial V/\partial P)_T$. Therefore,

$$\boxed{\frac{C_P}{C_V} = \frac{(\partial P/\partial V)_S}{(\partial P/\partial V)_T}.}$$

$$(11\text{-}22)$$

The *adiabatic compressibility* is defined as

$$\kappa_S = -\frac{1}{V}\left(\frac{\partial V}{\partial P}\right)_S;$$

and, as usual,

$$\kappa = -\frac{1}{V}\left(\frac{\partial V}{\partial P}\right)_T.$$

We have, therefore,

$$\frac{C_P}{C_V} = \gamma = \frac{\kappa}{\kappa_S}.$$

$$(11\text{-}23)$$

11-8   Heat Capacity at Constant Pressure

The experimental measurement of c_P has already been discussed in Art. 4-7, and the general features of one type of calorimeter suitable for such measurements were described, as well as some details of technique. Data on the heat capacities of elements, alloys, compounds, plastics, etc., taken over as wide a temperature interval as possible, are of great importance in pure science and

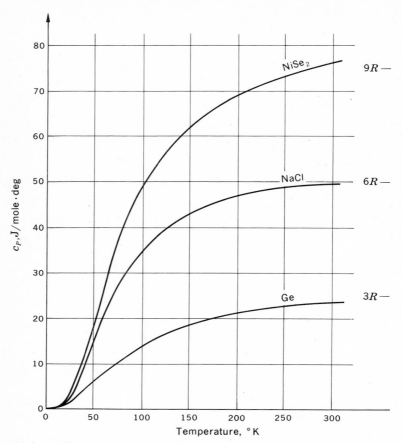

Fig. 11-4   *Heat capacity at constant pressure of crystalline nonmetals. (Ge, Keesom and Seidel; NaCl, Clusius, Goldmann, and Perlick; NiSe₂, Gronvold and Westrum.)* ($R = 8.31$ *J/mole deg.*)

in engineering. To the physicist the most important temperature region is from absolute zero to about room temperature (300°K), so that we shall emphasize this region more than any other. In this range, most materials are in the solid phase. We shall limit ourselves to solids in the form of crystals, either a single crystal or a rod or powder consisting of a large number of small crystals.

The behavior of three different crystalline nonmetals is shown in Fig. 11-4. (Metals exhibit a special behavior because of the effect of free electrons; such behavior will be discussed later in this chapter.) *The c_P of all materials approaches zero as T approaches zero.* In the first 20 to 40 deg, c_P rises rapidly but then bends and begins to flatten out in the neighborhood of room temperature. In none of the three crystals, however, does the c_P curve actually become horizontal.

In the Ge crystal, lattice sites are occupied by single germanium atoms, and therefore 1 mole of Ge consists of N_A vibrating particles, where N_A is Avogadro's number. The value of c_P at room temperature is very nearly equal to $3R$. In NaCl, the lattice sites are occupied by sodium ions and by chlorine ions in a face-centered cubic arrangement. Therefore 1 mole of NaCl consists of N_A sodium ions in addition to N_A chlorine ions, so that altogether there are $2N_A$ vibrating particles. The value of c_P at room temperature is very nearly equal to $6R$. In $NiSe_2$, the lattice sites are occupied by nickel atoms and by selenium atoms, with the center of the line joining the two selenium atoms and the nickel atom forming a face-centered cubic arrangement similar to that of NaCl. In 1 mole of $NiSe_2$, there are $3N_A$ vibrating particles, and the room temperature value of c_P is very nearly equal to $9R$. In all cases, the c_P at room temperature of *exactly N_A atoms or ions* is in the neighborhood of $3R$, about 25 J mole $\cdot$ deg or about 6 cal/mole $\cdot$ deg.

The curves in Fig. 11-4 correspond to crystals that were deliberately chosen to illustrate a regularity at room temperature. There is no magic in the temperature 300°K, however. Not all crystals have values of c_P whose rapid increase is tapering off at 300°K. The c_P of diamond, for example, rises so slowly that at 300°K it is still quite far from the value $3R$. Furthermore, c_P never approaches any value asymptotically but continues to rise at all temperatures. The laws governing the temperature variation of heat capacity cannot be stated simply in terms of c_P. To express experimental results in a neat form and also to appreciate the relation between experiment and theory, it is necessary to study the temperature variation of c_V. For this purpose, we use the thermodynamic formula

$$c_P - c_V = \frac{Tv\beta^2}{\kappa},\qquad(11\text{-}21)$$

which requires a knowledge of the complete temperature dependence of β, κ, and v, as given, for example, for NaCl in Table 11-2, compiled by Meincke and Graham. Before we use this equation, let us first learn something about thermal expansivity and compressibility.

11-9   Thermal Expansivity

In modern experiments on the expansion of solids, the linear expansivity α is usually measured. If the three rectangular dimensions of a solid are L_1, L_2,

Table 11-2   Thermal Properties of NaCl
(*Compiled by P. P. M. Meincke and G. M. Graham.*)

T, °K	c_P, J/mole · deg	β, μ(deg^{-1})	κ, μ(atm^{-1})	v, liter/mole	c_V, J/mole · deg	κ_S, μ(atm^{-1})
10	0.151	0.171	3.94	0.0264	0.151	3.94
20	1.30	1.72	3.94	0.0264	1.30	3.94
30	4.76	7.44	3.94	0.0264	4.76	3.94
40	9.98	17.2	3.94	0.0264	9.97	3.94
50	15.7	29.3	3.95	0.0264	15.7	3.94
60	21.0	41.4	3.97	0.0264	20.9	3.96
70	25.5	52.2	3.99	0.0264	25.3	3.97
80	29.3	61.5	4.01	0.0265	29.1	3.98
90	32.3	69.5	4.03	0.0265	32.0	3.99
100	35.0	75.8	4.05	0.0265	34.7	4.01
125	40.1	88.2	4.09	0.0266	39.5	4.03
150	43.3	96.3	4.12	0.0266	42.4	4.04
175	45.4	103	4.16	0.0267	44.2	4.05
250	48.6	114	4.29	0.0269	46.6	4.11
290	49.2	118	4.36	0.0270	46.7	4.13

and L_3, then

$$V = L_1 L_2 L_3,$$

$$\frac{\partial V}{\partial T} = L_2 L_3 \frac{\partial L_1}{\partial T} + L_1 L_3 \frac{\partial L_2}{\partial T} + L_1 L_2 \frac{\partial L_3}{\partial T},$$

$$\frac{1}{V}\frac{\partial V}{\partial T} = \frac{1}{L_1}\frac{\partial L_1}{\partial T} + \frac{1}{L_2}\frac{\partial L_2}{\partial T} + \frac{1}{L_3}\frac{\partial L_3}{\partial T},$$

and

$$\beta = \alpha_1 + \alpha_2 + \alpha_3,$$

where α_1, α_2, and α_3 are the linear expansivities along the three directions. In the case of quartz, the two linear coefficients perpendicular to the z axis are equal, so that $\beta = 2\alpha_\perp + \alpha_\parallel$. If the solid is isotropic, as in the case of a cubic crystal, $\alpha_1 = \alpha_2 = \alpha_3 = \alpha$ and $\beta = 3\alpha$.

There are four absolute methods of measuring the linear expansivity of solids: X-ray diffraction determinations, interference fringes of visible light, variation of electric capacitance, and variation of intensity of light. Modern methods, particularly those which are used to make measurements in the 0 to 50°K range, involve a lot of auxiliary cryogenic equipment, but the physical principles are easily understood.

In the X-ray diffraction method, the lattice parameter of the specimen crystal is measured as a function of the temperature, using an X-ray beam of known wavelength.

Fig. 11-5   *Modern version of Fizeau interferometric dilatometer. (James and Yates.)*

In Fig. 11-5 there is a rough schematic diagram of an interferometer which is a modification due to James and Yates of a device originally designed by Abbe and Pulfrich. Highly monochromatic light, such as the red light from a low-pressure cadmium lamp, after it has passed through a filter F is concentrated by lens L_1 and reflected from mirror M_1 onto plates P_1 and P_2, which are separated by a ring or cylinder R made of the material whose expansivity is to be studied. The ring and plates are placed at the bottom of a cryostat, where liquid hydrogen or liquid helium is used to provide the low temperatures at which measurements are often made. In Fig. 11-5 all details of the cryostat, heater, thermometer, venting tubes, electric leads, etc., have been omitted. Interference takes place between the rays of light reflected from the bottom of P_1 and the top of P_2, and a camera C is used to photograph the interference fringes. The temperature is varied very slowly from, let us say, 4°K up to room temperature, and the fringe system is photographed at regular intervals.

If N fringes travel across the field of view while the temperature changes from T_0 to T, then the optical path difference has changed by $N\lambda$, where λ is the wavelength of the light, and the thickness of the air space has changed by $N\lambda/2$. If L_0 is the length of the specimen at temperature T_0 and L is the length at T, then

$$\frac{L - L_0}{L_0} = \frac{N\lambda}{2L_0}.$$

If, therefore, $N\lambda/2L_0$ is plotted against T and the slope of the resulting curve is taken at various temperatures, the linear expansivity is obtained. Thus,

$$\alpha = \frac{d}{dT}\left(\frac{N\lambda}{2L_0}\right).$$

In order to avoid the delay involved in photographic processing, R. K. Kirby and his staff at the U.S. National Bureau of Standards have developed a photoelectric interferometer in which the movement of interference fringes is detected by a photomultiplier tube and the number of fringes is automatically plotted on a recorder against the measured temperature of the specimen. Thus, all hand operations are eliminated, and the data are presented on a chart in a form suitable for immediate determination of expansivities.

In the electric method, the expansion of the specimen is communicated to one of the plates of a capacitor, whose other plate is fixed nearby. The change in capacitance is measured by an extremely sensitive bridge; and in the hands of the Australian physicists headed by G. K. White, this method has proved capable of detecting length changes of the order of 10^{-8} cm.

The optical grid method of R. V. Jones, which has been used with great success by Andres in Switzerland, is extraordinarily sensitive. The specimen is connected to one of the grids shown in Fig. 11-6, the other remaining fixed. The left-hand grid is regular, and the one on the right has an irregularity in the middle. In position (a), no light can pass the grids in the lower half; whereas in position (b), in which the right-hand grid has been lowered with respect to the other by one line width, no light can pass the grids in the upper half. In position (c), the two halves are equally transparent, and as a result, the net output of two oppositely connected photocells (one behind the upper half, and the other behind the lower half) is zero. Thus, a change in length of the specimen produces a change in the net output of the two oppositely connected photocells.

The temperature dependence of the volume expansivity of many sub-

(a) (b) (c)

Fig. 11-6   *Optical grid method of measuring thermal expansion. (R. V. Jones.)*

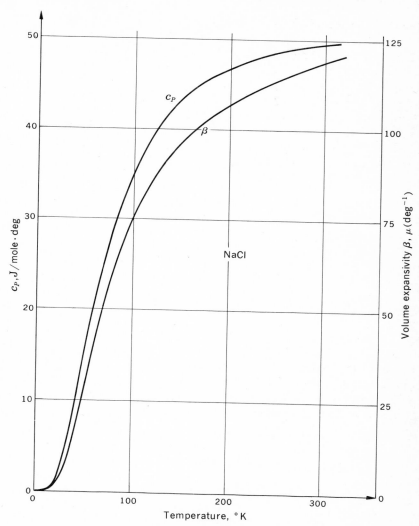

Fig. 11-7   *Temperature dependence of β and of c_P are almost identical. (β, Meincke and Graham; c_P, Clusius, Goldmann, and Perlick.)*

stances is the same as that of NaCl, shown in Fig. 11-7: namely, β is zero at absolute zero, rises rapidly in the interval from 0 to 50°K, then bends and flattens out without actually becoming horizontal. Thus, the temperature behavior of β is almost identical with that of c_P, as shown in Fig. 11-7. Another similarity between β and c_P is the insensitivity of both quantities to changes of pressure.

11-10   Compressibility

Compressibility measurements are made in two ways and for two different reasons. Installations capable of subjecting solids to enormous hydrostatic pressures at constant temperature and capable of providing numerical values of the *isothermal compressibility* at pressures up to about a million atmospheres are used to study phase transitions, changes of crystal structure, and other internal changes of solids and liquids. These are *static measurements*. Measurements of the speed of longitudinal waves in liquids and both longitudinal and transverse waves in solids, at atmospheric or moderate pressures, are *dynamic* in character and provide numerical values of the *adiabatic compressibility* κ_S, where

$$\kappa_S = -\frac{1}{V}\left(\frac{\partial V}{\partial P}\right)_S.$$

It was shown in Chap. 5 that the speed of a longitudinal wave w in a fluid is given by

$$w = \sqrt{\frac{1}{\rho \kappa_S}},$$

where ρ is the density. Measurements of w and ρ are sufficient to provide κ_S of a fluid, but the measurement of κ_S of a crystalline solid is more difficult. It is necessary to measure the speed of transverse waves as well as that of longitudinal waves and, from the two measurements, to calculate two different elastic constants. In the case of NaCl, these quantities are designated c_{11} and c_{12}, and it is shown in books on elasticity that

$$\kappa_S = \frac{3}{c_{11} + 2c_{12}}.$$

Once κ_S is obtained, the isothermal compressibility may be calculated by using the two thermodynamic equations derived in this chapter, namely,

$$c_P - c_V = \frac{Tv\beta^2}{\kappa} \tag{11-21}$$

and

$$c_V\kappa = c_P\kappa_S. \tag{11-23}$$

Substituting for c_V in the first equation the value found from the second, we get

$$c_P - \frac{c_P\kappa_S}{\kappa} = \frac{Tv\beta^2}{\kappa},$$

Fig. 11-8   *Temperature variation of isothermal and adiabatic compressibilities of NaCl.* (*Overton and Swim.*)

which reduces to

$$\kappa - \kappa_S = \frac{Tv\beta^2}{c_P}. \qquad (11\text{-}24)$$

The method of measuring wave velocities that is most suitable for crystalline solids is one which incorporates the familiar radar technique. Short ultrasonic pulses of about 1 μs duration are sent through the crystal by a quartz crystal transducer. After reflection from an end of the crystal, the quartz emitter is used as a receiver. The pulse and the echo are observed on an oscilloscope, and the wave speed is calculated from the dimensions of the crystal and the time delay between pulse and echo. This is the method used by Overton and Swim to obtain the values of κ_S listed in Table 11-2.

The temperature variation of κ_S and κ of NaCl are shown in Fig. 11-8, where it may be seen that both κ_S and κ—unlike c_P and β—do *not* approach zero as T approaches zero. From zero to 40°K, the adiabatic and isothermal compressibilities are nearly equal. At higher temperatures, κ is larger than κ_S, as required by Eq. (11-24).

The molar volume of NaCl is shown in Fig. 11-9, where the temperature variation may be seen to be very similar to that of κ. In a rough sort of way,

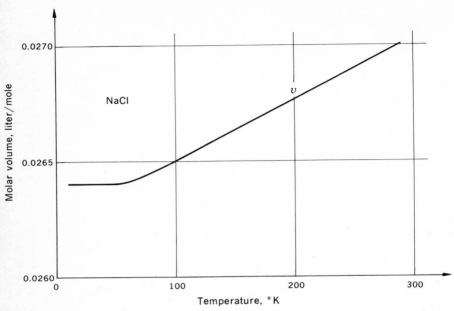

Fig. 11-9   *Temperature variation of molar volume of NaCl, similar to that of isothermal compressibility.* (*Heinglen.*)

c_P and β vary in the same manner, while v and κ are also similar, but with an entirely different kind of temperature variation.

The speed of longitudinal waves in a liquid is usually measured with the aid of an acoustic interferometer such as the one described in Art. 5-9, which was used with helium gas to serve as an absolute thermometer in the range from 4 to 10°K. Results of measurements on water are listed in Table 11-3

Table 11-3   Properties of Water

$T,$ °C	$w,$ km/s	$\beta,$ $\mu(\deg^{-1})$	$c_P,$ J/g · deg	$\rho,$ g/cm³	$\kappa,$ $\mu(\text{atm}^{-1})$	$\kappa_S,$ $\mu(\text{atm}^{-1})$
0	1.404	−67	4.2177	0.99986	51.5	51.5
10	1.448	89	4.1922	0.99973	48.8	48.6
20	1.483	208	4.1819	0.99823	46.4	46.1
30	1.510	304	4.1785	0.99568	45.2	44.5
40	1.530	390	4.1786	0.99225	44.4	43.3
50	1.544	465	4.1807	0.98807	44.3	42.6
60	1.552	522	4.1844	0.98324	44.3	42.0
70	1.555	586	4.1896	0.97781	44.7	41.8
80	1.555	643	4.1964	0.97183	45.4	41.8

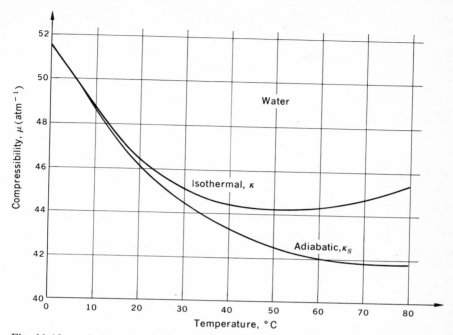

Fig. 11-10   *Isothermal and adiabatic compressibilities of water.*

and are shown in Fig. 11-10. The minimum achieved by the isothermal compressibility of water at about 50°C is quite anomalous. As a rule, the isothermal compressibility of most liquids increases as the temperature is raised and follows a simple exponential equation quite well:

$$\kappa = \kappa_0 e^{bT} \qquad (11\text{-}25)$$

where κ_0 and b are constants. The constant b for mercury is $1.37 \times 10^{-3}\,\mathrm{deg^{-1}}$.

All liquids, including water, become less compressible the more they are compressed; the reciprocal of the isothermal compressibility increases linearly with respect to the pressure, where

$$\frac{1}{\kappa} - \frac{1}{\kappa_0} = cP, \qquad (11\text{-}26)$$

where κ_0 is the compressibility at zero pressure and c is 6.7 for water and 8.2 for mercury.

11-11   Heat Capacity at Constant Volume

The measurement of c_P, β, and κ of crystalline solids both metallic and nonmetallic, particularly at low temperatures, is a constant challenge to experimental physicists throughout the world. This field is still a very active one, for each quantity is of theoretical interest in its own right. Our purpose at present is to use these measurements in conjunction with the thermodynamic equation,

$$c_P - c_V = \frac{Tv\beta^2}{\kappa}, \tag{11-21}$$

to find the complete temperature dependence of c_V. All the measurements on NaCl are listed in Table 11-2, along with the calculated values of c_V, and both c_P and c_V are plotted against T up to 1000°K in Fig. 11-11. Since 1 mole of NaCl consists of $2N_A$ ions, the heat capacities refer to $\frac{1}{2}$ mole, or N_A ions.

At low temperatures, below 100°K, c_P and c_V are practically the same. At

Fig. 11-11   *Temperature variation of c_P and c_V of $\frac{1}{2}$ mole of NaCl. The value of c_V approaches 3R as a limit.*

Fig. 11-12   *Temperature variation of $c_V/3R$ of nonmetals. (1 mole of diamond, $\frac{1}{2}$ mole of RbI, NaCl, MgO, and $\frac{1}{3}$ mole of FeS$_2$.)*

all higher temperatures, while c_P continues to increase, c_V approaches a constant value $3R$, which is called the *Dulong and Petit value*, named after the physicists who first observed that c_P came near this value at about room temperature. We see now that this value is actually approached by c_V and is exceeded only in special situations. The temperature dependence of $c_V/3R$ of five representative nonmetals is shown in Fig. 11-12, where it may be seen that RbI practically reaches the Dulong and Petit value even before room temperature, whereas diamond has reached only one-fifth this value. As a matter of fact, it requires a temperature greater than 2000°K to bring the c_V of diamond near $3R$.

Although the five curves in Fig. 11-12 differ markedly in the temperature at which $c_V \rightarrow 3R$, the curves are still very similar in shape. An experienced experimenter would be led to suspect that there existed a parameter—Θ, let us say—small for RbI and large for diamond, such that c_V is a *universal function* of the ratio $T/Θ$. Such a variation is called a *law of corresponding states*, and we shall see that an approximate law of this sort is provided by theory.

11-12   Statistical Mechanics of a Nonmetallic Crystal

The reason that the c_V of a solid is of more theoretical interest than c_P is that $c_V = (\partial u/\partial T)_V$, where u is the molar internal energy, which may be calculated with the aid of statistical mechanics. In general, this calculation is extremely complicated, because many different phenomena contribute to the internal energy of the solid. Suppose, for example, that the solid is a crystal having a lattice composed of molecules, each of which consists of several atoms; and furthermore, suppose that there is about one free electron per molecule. Then the total internal energy may be due to:

1   Translational motions of the free electrons.
2   Vibrations of the molecules about their equilibrium positions, called briefly *lattice vibrations*.
3   Internal vibrations of atoms within each molecule.
4   Partial rotation of the molecules.
5   Excitation of upper energy levels of the molecules.
6   Anomalous effects.

It is fortunate that all these effects do not take place in all solids. For example, in the case of nonmetals, motions of free electrons do not exist, and in the case of metals the lattice consists of single atoms whose component parts do not rotate or vibrate. Furthermore, all effects do not take place in all temperature ranges. Thus, the motions of the free electrons of metals have an appreciable effect on the heat capacity only at very low temperatures, below about 20°K. Above this temperature, they may be ignored. Similarly, excitation of upper energy levels takes place only at very high temperatures and can therefore be ignored at moderate temperatures.

In this article, let us limit ourselves to a nonmetallic crystal in which the lattice sites are occupied either by a single atom or ion or by a rigid molecule whose internal vibrations, rotations, excitations, etc., may be ignored. We shall refer to the particles occupying lattice sites as *lattice points* and shall assume there are N of them. These lattice points are localized in space and are therefore distinguishable by their positions; furthermore, they are closely packed and interact very strongly with their neighbors. It would seem, at first glance, that the statistical methods described in Chap. 10 as appropriate to indistinguishable, weakly interacting particles are useless here. But this is not the case. Since each lattice point has three coordinates x, y, and z, the system of N lattice points has $3N$ coordinates. If each lattice point undergoes a displacement from its equilibrium position that is small compared with the space between lattice points, the change in potential energy of the crystal would involve many terms involving not only squares of these displacements but product terms as well. In the theory of small oscillations, it is shown that there *always* exists a new set of $3N$ coordinates (linear functions of the original coordinates) such that the potential energy is the sum of exactly $3N$ squared terms. Corresponding to these new coordinates, called *normal coordinates*, there are $3N$ momenta, and the kinetic energy is the sum of $3N$ terms that each contains the square of a momentum.

A particle undergoing simple harmonic motion in the x direction has an energy equal to $\frac{1}{2}kx^2 + (1/2m)p_x^2$. The fact that the energy of N vibrating lattice points is given by $3N$ expressions of this type enables us to conclude that, when N lattice points undergo small displacements, *the motion of the crystal may be described as that of 3N independent simple harmonic oscillators.*

These harmonic oscillators (or *normal modes*) are *not associated with individual lattice points;* each one involves motion of the entire crystal. This conclusion is independent of the type of crystal lattice and is true only when displacements from equilibrium positions are small. When the vibrations get large enough, anharmonic effects take place and the oscillators are no longer independent. Actually, to determine the normal coordinates of a given crystal and to calculate the various frequencies of vibration of the $3N$ normal modes is a very complicated problem in mechanics. It is a fortunate circumstance that considerable information may be obtained by applying statistical mechanics to these normal modes, along with either of two simplifying assumptions—one due to Einstein and the other due to Debye.

Our problem in statistical mechanics has now been reduced to that of $3N$ independent (weakly interacting) but *distinguishable* simple harmonic oscillators. Suppose we have N_ν such oscillators *each vibrating with the same frequency ν.* According to the quantum theory, the energy ϵ of any such oscillator may take on only discrete values:

$$\epsilon_i = (i + \tfrac{1}{2})h\nu \qquad (i = 0, 1, 2, \ldots), \qquad (11\text{-}27)$$

where h is Planck's constant, 6.63×10^{-34} J $\cdot$ s. Suppose that at any moment a macrostate of the crystal is specified by:

N_0 oscillators with energy $\epsilon_0 = \tfrac{1}{2}h\nu$

N_1 oscillators with energy $\epsilon_1 = \tfrac{3}{2}h\nu$

N_2 oscillators with energy $\epsilon_2 = \tfrac{5}{2}h\nu$

. . . .

These energy states are nondegenerate: that is, not more than one quantum state has the same energy. The number of ways in which N_ν vibrators may be distributed among the energy states according to the macrostate specified is the same as the number of ways in which N_ν *distinguishable* objects (colored balls, marked objects, etc.) can be distributed in boxes so that there are N_0 objects in box 0, N_1 objects in box 1, etc. To fix our ideas, suppose that we have only four objects a, b, c, and d to be distributed between two boxes so that one object will be in one box and three in the other. The number of different ways in which four lettered objects may be arranged in sequence is

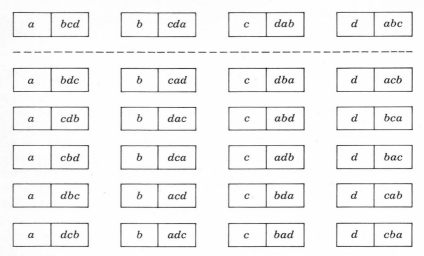

Fig. 11-13 *The number of different microstates corresponding to the macrostate in which one vibrator is in one energy state and three vibrators are in the other energy state is equal to 4!/3! = 4. The four different microstates lie above the dashed line; those below are superfluous.*

$4! = 24$, as shown in Fig. 11-13. Consider the arrangement (microstate) depicted in the upper left-hand corner, where a is in the left box and b, c, and d are in the right one. All the other microstates with a in the left box (depicted beneath the dashed line) are superfluous, since they involve merely a shift of position *within* a box. Of the six arrangements on the left, only one-sixth need be counted or $1/3!$. The same is true of the arrangements involving b in the left box, and so on. The total number of different arrangements is therefore $4!/3! = 4$.

In the general case where N_ν vibrators are distributed among energy states with N_0 vibrators in the state with energy ϵ_0, N_1 in the state with energy ϵ_1, etc., the total number of microstates, or the thermodynamic probability Ω, is given by

$$\Omega = \frac{N_\nu!}{N_1!N_2! \cdots}, \tag{11-28}$$

which is the expression given in Prob. 10-5, where degeneracy was included. The entropy S is expressed as

$$\begin{aligned}
S &= k \ln \Omega \\
&= k(\ln N_\nu! - \ln N_1! - \ln N_2! - \cdots) \\
&= k(N_\nu \ln N_\nu - N_\nu - N_1 \ln N_1 + N_1 - N_2 \ln N_2 + N_2 - \cdots) \\
&= k(N_\nu \ln N_\nu - \Sigma N_i \ln N_i),
\end{aligned}$$

which must be maximized subject to the usual conditions,

$$\Sigma N_i = N_\nu = \text{const.},$$

and
$$\Sigma N_i \epsilon_i = U_\nu = \text{const.}$$

The details of this calculation are identical with those of Chap. 10, and only the results will be given. We get

$$N_i = N_\nu \frac{e^{-\epsilon_i/kT}}{Z_\nu}, \tag{11-29}$$

where Z_ν is the partition function

$$Z_\nu = \Sigma e^{-\epsilon_i/kT}. \tag{11-30}$$

The expressions for energy U_ν and pressure P are the same as for indistinguishable particles, namely,

$$U_\nu = N_\nu kT^2 \left(\frac{\partial \ln Z_\nu}{\partial T}\right)_V, \tag{11-31}$$

and
$$P = N_\nu kT \left(\frac{\partial \ln Z_\nu}{\partial V}\right)_T. \tag{11-32}$$

But the expression for the entropy is simpler:

$$S_\nu = N_\nu k \ln Z_\nu + \frac{U_\nu}{T}. \tag{11-33}$$

The evaluation of the partition function is particularly simple, since it is merely a geometric progression with a ratio less than 1 and an infinite number of terms:

$$Z_\nu = e^{-h\nu/2kT} + e^{-3h\nu/2kT} + e^{-5h\nu/2kT} + \cdots$$
$$= e^{-h\nu/2kT}(1 + e^{-h\nu/kT} + e^{-2h\nu/kT} + \cdots),$$

or
$$Z_\nu = \frac{e^{-h\nu/2kT}}{1 - e^{-h\nu/kT}} \tag{11-34}$$

and
$$\boxed{\ln Z_\nu = -\frac{1}{2}\frac{h\nu}{kT} - \ln\left(1 - e^{-h\nu/kT}\right).} \tag{11-35}$$

The energy U_ν of N_ν simple harmonic vibrators is

$$U_\nu = N_\nu k T^2 \frac{\partial}{\partial T} \ln Z_\nu$$

$$= N_\nu k T^2 \left[\frac{1}{2} \frac{h\nu}{kT^2} - \frac{-e^{-h\nu/kT}(h\nu/kT^2)}{1 - e^{-h\nu/kT}} \right]$$

$$= N_\nu \left(\tfrac{1}{2} h\nu + \frac{h\nu}{e^{h\nu/kT} - 1} \right);$$

therefore the average energy per vibrator is

$$\langle \epsilon \rangle = \frac{U_\nu}{N_\nu} = \frac{h\nu}{2} + \frac{h\nu}{e^{h\nu/kT} - 1}. \tag{11-36}$$

In general, all the $3N$ equivalent simple harmonic oscillators do *not* have the same frequency. Let dN_ν be the number of oscillators whose frequency lies between ν and $\nu + d\nu$. Then

$$dN_\nu = g(\nu) \, d\nu \tag{11-37}$$

where $g(\nu)$, the number of vibrators per unit frequency band, must be determined for a given crystal or class of crystals and must satisfy the condition

$$\int dN_\nu = \int g(\nu) \, d\nu = 3N. \tag{11-38}$$

The energy of N particles of the crystal is then

$$U = \int \langle \epsilon \rangle \, dN_\nu = \int \left(\frac{h\nu}{2} + \frac{h\nu}{e^{h\nu/kT} - 1} \right) g(\nu) \, d\nu, \tag{11-39}$$

and the heat capacity at constant volume of this amount of crystal is

$$C_V = \frac{\partial U}{\partial T} = \int \frac{(1/k)(h\nu/T)^2 e^{h\nu/kT}}{(e^{h\nu/kT} - 1)^2} g(\nu) \, d\nu. \tag{11-40}$$

11-13   Frequency Spectrum of Crystals

The simplest assumption concerning the vibration characteristics of a crystal was that of Einstein, namely, that all the $3N$ equivalent harmonic oscillators had the same frequency ν_E (subscript E for Einstein), as depicted

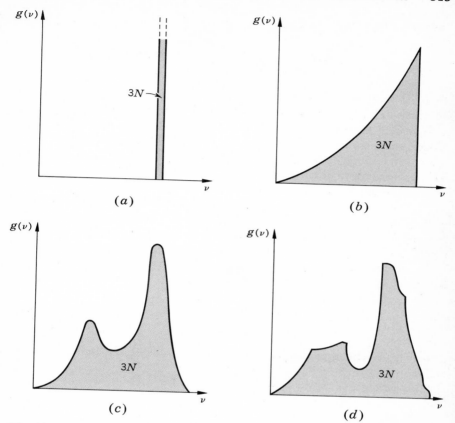

Fig. 11-14   *Frequency spectra of lattice vibrations. (a) Einstein approximation; (b) Debye approximation; (c) Blackman approximation; (d) more rigorous calculation.*

in Fig. 11-14a. Equation (11-40) then reduces to the following simple form:

$$C_V = 3N \frac{k(h\nu_E/kT)^2 e^{h\nu_E/kT}}{(e^{h\nu_E/kT} - 1)^2}.$$

If we define the *Einstein characteristic temperature* Θ_E by the expression

$$\Theta_E = \frac{h\nu_E}{k} \tag{11-41}$$

and let $N = N_A$ (Avogadro's number)—remembering that $N_A k = R$ (the universal gas constant)—we get

$$\frac{c_V}{3R} = \left(\frac{\Theta_E}{T}\right)^2 \frac{e^{\Theta_E/T}}{(e^{\Theta_E/T} - 1)^2}. \tag{11-42}$$

This was the first attempt to apply quantum theory to the specific heat of solids, and although the assumption of equal frequencies for all equivalent harmonic oscillators is far from justified, the Einstein expression has the same general shape as the curves in Fig. 11-12. As $T \to \infty$, then $c_V/3R \to 1$, in agreement with the Dulong and Petit law. As $T \to 0$, then $c_V/3R$ approaches zero, in agreement with experiment; but it approaches zero exponentially, which is faster than experiment indicates.

The next approximation was made by Debye, who calculated a frequency distribution on the assumption that a crystal was a *continuous* medium supporting standing (or stationary) longitudinal and transverse waves. With this assumption it was a simple matter to show that a continuous spectrum of frequencies was present, starting with zero and terminating at a maximum frequency ν_m, according to the simple relation

$$g(\nu) = \frac{9N}{\nu_m^3} \nu^2. \tag{11-43}$$

It may be seen by inspection that $\int g(\nu)\, d\nu$ is equal to $3N$. The Debye approximation is depicted in Fig. 11-14b.

Substituting the Debye approximation into Eq. (11-40), we get

$$\frac{C_V}{3Nk} = \int_0^{\nu_m} \frac{(3\nu^2/\nu_m^3)(h\nu/kT)^2 e^{h\nu/kT}\, d\nu}{(e^{h\nu/kT} - 1)^2}.$$

It is convenient to define a new variable of integration x, where

$$x = \frac{h\nu}{kT} \quad \text{and} \quad x_m = \frac{h\nu_m}{kT} = \frac{\Theta}{T},$$

and the *Debye characteristic temperature*

$$\Theta = \frac{h\nu_m}{k}. \tag{11-44}$$

With these new quantities and with $N = N_A$,

$$\frac{c_V}{3R} = \frac{3}{(\Theta/T)^3} \int_0^{\Theta/T} \frac{x^4 e^x\, dx}{(e^x - 1)^2}. \tag{11-45}$$

As $T \to \infty$, the upper limit of the integral becomes small, and the integrand evaluated at small values of x reduces to x^2 and, when integrated, yields $\frac{1}{3}(\Theta/T)^3$. Therefore $c_V/3R \to 1$, as required by the Dulong and Petit law.

To find the limiting value of $c_V/3R$ as $T \to 0$, it is convenient to express Eq. (11-45) in a different form by integrating by parts.

$$\frac{3}{(\Theta/T)^3} \int_0^{\Theta/T} \frac{x^4 e^x \, dx}{(e^x - 1)^2} = \frac{3}{(\Theta/T)^3} \int_0^{\Theta/T} x^4 \, d\left(\frac{-1}{e^x - 1}\right)$$

$$= \frac{3}{(\Theta/T)^3} \left[\int_0^{\Theta/T} \frac{4x^3 \, dx}{e^x - 1} - \frac{(\Theta/T)^4}{e^{\Theta/T} - 1} \right];$$

therefore,

$$\frac{c_V}{3R} = 4 \cdot \frac{3}{(\Theta/T)^3} \int_0^{\Theta/T} \frac{x^3 \, dx}{e^x - 1} - \frac{3(\Theta/T)}{e^{\Theta/T} - 1}. \tag{11-46}$$

As $T \to 0$,

$$\frac{3(\Theta/T)}{e^{\Theta/T} - 1} \to 0,$$

and

$$\int_0^{\Theta/T} \frac{x^3 \, dx}{e^x - 1} \to \int_0^\infty \frac{x^3 \, dx}{e^x - 1} = 3! \zeta(4),$$

where $\zeta(4)$ is a *Riemann zeta function*,† equal to

$$\zeta(4) = 1 + \frac{1}{2^4} + \frac{1}{3^4} + \cdots = \frac{\pi^4}{90}.$$

Hence

$$\frac{c_V}{3R} \to 4 \cdot \frac{3}{(\Theta/T)^3} \frac{3! \pi^4}{90} = \frac{4\pi^4}{5} \left(\frac{T}{\Theta}\right)^3.$$

Since $4\pi^4/5 = 77.9$, and at low temperatures $c_V = c_P = c$, we may write *Debye's T^3 law* in either of these two forms:

$$\left. \begin{array}{l} \dfrac{c}{3R} = 77.9 \left(\dfrac{T}{\Theta}\right)^3, \\[3mm] c = \dfrac{(125)^3 \text{ mJ}}{\text{mole} \cdot \text{deg}} \left(\dfrac{T}{\Theta}\right)^3. \end{array} \right\} \quad \left(\text{for } \frac{T}{\Theta} < 0.04\right) \tag{11-47}$$

or

The entire course of $c_V/3R$ given by Eq. (11-45) or (11-46) cannot be reduced to a simple form but must be evaluated numerically. The results of

† See Appendix.

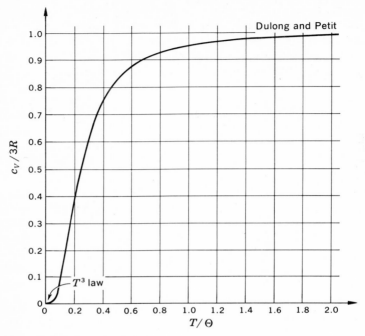

Fig. 11-15   *Debye's heat capacity.*

this calculation are listed in Table 11-4 and are plotted in Fig. 11-15. A more extensive table will be found in the "AIP Handbook."

Table 11-4   Debye's Heat Capacity

$\dfrac{T}{\Theta}$	$\dfrac{c_V}{3R}$	$\dfrac{T}{\Theta}$	$\dfrac{c_V}{3R}$	$\dfrac{T}{\Theta}$	$\dfrac{c_V}{3R}$
0	0	0.175	0.293	0.7	0.916
0.025	0.00122	0.20	0.369	0.8	0.926
0.050	0.00974	0.25	0.503	0.9	0.942
0.075	0.0328	0.3	0.613	1.0	0.952
0.100	0.0758	0.4	0.746	1.2	0.963
0.125	0.138	0.5	0.825	1.5	0.980
0.150	0.213	0.6	0.869	2.0	0.988

The fundamental assumption of the Debye theory, leading to a simple quadratic function for $g(\nu)$, as shown in Fig. 11-14b, is quite crude compared with theoretically derived functions such as that of Blackman shown in Fig. 11-14c. It is quite astonishing that the Debye curve in Fig. 11-15 is in such good agreement with experiment. Only when heat capacities are measured with great accuracy do departures from Debye's curve show up. These are obtained as follows: The accurate experimental value of $c_V/3R$ at a known T is compared with the Debye curve of Fig. 11-15, and the corresponding value of T/Θ is obtained; from this is derived the value of Θ. This is done at a number of temperatures. If all values of Θ so obtained were the same, the Debye theory would hold perfectly. Such is not the case, however, as the experimental points in Fig. 11-16 show. The exact calculation of the frequency spectrum of lattice vibrations is a very complicated and tedious task. The use of modern computers has helped a great deal, and physicists are having reasonable success in explaining experimentally observed heat capacities.

Debye's model, although crude in the medium temperature range, is quite rigorous at very low temperatures, below $\Theta/100$, well within the T^3 region. The reason may be seen in curves (b), (c), and (d) of Fig. 11-14. At very low temperatures, only the small frequencies of lattice vibration are excited, so that only the beginning segments of the curves play a role. No matter how rigorously the calculation of $g(\nu)$ is carried out, the beginning segment of $g(\nu)$ is always quadratic. One would expect therefore that, at very low tem-

Fig. 11-16   *Variation of Θ with T for NaCl. (Curve calculated by Lundquist, Lundstrom, Tenerz, and Waller.)*

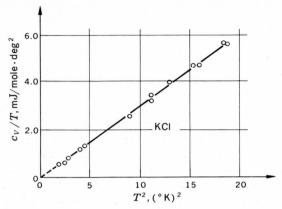

Fig. 11-17   *Verification of Debye T^3 law for KCl. (Keesom and Pearlman.)*

peratures, the Debye T^3 law should be strictly obeyed and also that the value of Θ obtained from such measurements should be the correct value of Θ at absolute zero. Using the T^3 law in the form

$$c_V = \left(\frac{125}{\Theta}\right)^3 T^3 \quad \frac{mJ}{mole \cdot deg},$$

Table 11-5 Θ Values for Nonmetals

Nonmetal	Θ, °K	Nonmetal	Θ, °K
He	26	KF	336
Ne	67	KCl	233
A	93	KBr	174
Kr	72	KI	132
Xe	55	RbCl	165
Se	90	RbBr	131
Te	153	RbI	103
As	282	InSb	200
Ge	363	CaF_2	510
Si	636	SiO_2	470
C (graphite)	420	Fe_2O_3	660
C (diamond)	2230	TiO_2	760
LiF	730	MgO	946
LiCl	422	ZnS	315
NaF	492	FeS_2	637
NaCl	321	$NiSe_2$	297
NaBr	225	$FeSe_2$	366
NaI	164	Bi_2Te_3	155

and dividing both sides by T, we get

$$\frac{c_V}{T} = \left(\frac{125}{\Theta}\right)^3 T^2 \qquad \frac{\text{mJ}}{\text{mole} \cdot \text{deg}^2}.$$

The graph in Fig. 11-17 shows how well the law is obeyed between 0 and 4.5°K for KCl. Values of Θ near absolute zero are given for a number of nonmetals in Table 11-5.

11-14   Thermal Properties of Metals

In a metal crystal the lattice sites are occupied by single metal atoms whose vibrations obey the same laws that have been found to hold for nonmetals. In addition to the lattice vibrations, however, there are free electrons whose number is of the same order of magnitude as the number of atoms and whose motions resemble those of the molecules of a gas. If the classical theory of an ideal gas were valid for the electron gas in a metal, the molar heat capacity at constant volume should be augmented *at all temperatures* by the constant

Fig. 11-18   *Temperature variation of c_P and β of copper is similar to that of nonmetals. (Compare with Fig. 11-7.)*

value $\frac{3}{2}R$. Hence at high temperatures, instead of reaching the Dulong and Petit value $3R$, it should reach the value $\frac{9}{2}R$, or about 37 J/mole · deg; and at low temperatures, c_V should not approach zero as T approaches zero but should approach $\frac{3}{2}R$. The fact that the temperature variation of c_V of metals had the same general features as that of nonmetals remained a puzzle until Sommerfeld applied quantum statistics (Fermi-Dirac statistics) to the free electrons in a metal and showed that the contribution of the electrons to the heat capacity of the metal is linear in T and is appreciable only at low temperatures when the Debye T^3 term becomes small. At higher temperatures, the linear term is small compared with the effect of lattice vibrations. We shall return to this point later, after we have studied other thermal properties of metals.

The c_P and β of metals are insensitive to moderate changes of pressure and vary with temperature in the same way as nonmetals. The graphs for copper (as typical of all metals) in Fig. 11-18, which should be compared with those of NaCl in Fig. 11-7, show that both c_P and β are zero at absolute zero and that, from 0 to 50°K, they rise rapidly. At higher temperatures the curves flatten out but do not approach asymptotic values. The temperature dependence of the β of metals shows a curious regularity, as shown in Fig. 11-19,

Fig. 11-19   *Normal temperature variation of volume expansivity of metals. (NMP, normal melting point.)*

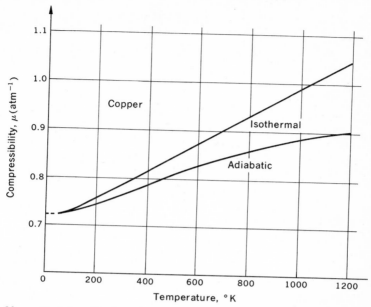

Fig. 11-20   *Variation of isothermal and adiabatic compressibilities of copper with temperature.*

where it may be seen that the higher the melting point, the lower the volume expansivity. As a result, in the temperature interval from absolute zero to the melting point, all metals expand approximately the same fraction of their original volumes. It seems almost as if a metal like tin, realizing it is going to melt soon, expands rapidly with the temperature, whereas platinum, with a high melting point, slows down its rate.

In Fig. 11-20 it may be seen that the isothermal and adiabatic compressibilities of copper vary with the temperature like those of NaCl in Fig. 11-8. The complete temperature dependence of the thermal properties of copper is given in Table 11-6, and c_V is compared with c_P in Fig. 11-21. Notice that the c_V of copper goes somewhat beyond the Dulong and Petit value above 700°K. We shall see later that this additional heat capacity may be attributed to the free-electron gas inside the metal.

The free-electron gas in a metal differs from an ordinary gas in two main respects. In an ordinary gas, the number of quantum states accessible to the gas molecules is very much larger than the number of molecules $(g_i \gg N_i)$, whereas in a metal the number of quantum states and the number of electrons are comparable. Let us see how this comes about. An electron moving more or less freely in a cubical metal of length L and volume $V = L^3$ has a kinetic energy ϵ given by exactly the same expression as that developed in Chap. 10

Table 11-6   Thermal Properties of Copper

T, °K	c_P, J/mole · deg	β, $\mu(\text{deg}^{-1})$	κ, $\mu(\text{atm}^{-1})$	v, cm³/mole	c_V, J/mole · deg	κ_S, $\mu(\text{atm}^{-1})$
50	6.25	11.4	0.722	7.00	6.24	0.721
100	16.1	31.5	0.731	7.01	16.0	0.728
150	20.5	40.7	0.744	7.02	20.3	0.737
200	22.8	45.3	0.759	7.03	22.4	0.744
250	24.0	48.3	0.773	7.04	23.5	0.754
300	24.5	50.4	0.788	7.06	23.8	0.764
500	25.8	54.9	0.850	7.12	24.5	0.806
800	27.7	60.0	0.935	7.26	25.4	0.860
1200	30.2	70.2	1.045	7.45	26.0	0.901

for a molecule moving in a cubical box, namely,

$$\epsilon = \frac{h^2}{8mL^2} (n_x^2 + n_y^2 + n_z^2),$$

where m is the mass of an electron and n_x, n_y, and n_z are very large integers.

Fig. 11-21   *Temperature variation of c_P and c_V of copper.*

Each triplet of values of n_x, n_y, and n_z refers to one quantum state, and all the quantum states referring to one energy ϵ lie on the surface of a sphere of radius r in a space where n_x, n_y, and n_z are cartesian coordinates and

$$r^2 = n_x^2 + n_y^2 + n_z^2.$$

The quantum states referring to an energy interval between ϵ and $\epsilon + d\epsilon$ lie between the spheres of radius r and $r + dr$, and the number of these states is the volume of the positive part of this spherical shell. Since

$$r^2 = \frac{8mL^2}{h^2}\, \epsilon,$$

then

$$2r\, dr = \frac{8mL^2}{h^2}\, d\epsilon,$$

and the volume of the spherical shell between r and $r + dr$ is $4\pi r^2\, dr$. Therefore, the number of quantum states $g\, d\epsilon$ with energy between ϵ and $\epsilon + d\epsilon$ is one-eighth of this volume, or

$$g\, d\epsilon = \tfrac{1}{8} \cdot 4\pi r^2\, dr = \frac{\pi}{4}\, r \cdot 2r\, dr$$

$$= \frac{\pi}{4}\sqrt{\frac{8mL^2}{h^2}}\; \epsilon^{\frac{1}{2}} \frac{8mL^2}{h^2}\, d\epsilon$$

or

$$g = 2\pi V \left(\frac{2m}{h^2}\right)^{\frac{3}{2}} \epsilon^{\frac{1}{2}}. \tag{11-48}$$

The number of quantum states per unit energy interval, g, is seen to depend on $m^{\frac{3}{2}}$. Since an electron has a mass only about $1/10{,}000$ that of, say, a helium atom, it follows that, for a given energy, there may be $(10^{-4})^{\frac{3}{2}}$, or 10^{-6}, fewer quantum states for an electron gas than for an ordinary gas. Also, in a given volume (say, 1 cm³), there may be 10^{19} atoms of helium, but in a metal of the same volume there might be about 10^{23} free electrons, assuming about one free electron per atom of metal. With 10^4 more electrons and about 10^{-6} fewer quantum states, it is clear that the number of electrons and the number of quantum states may be comparable.

Now, according to the Pauli exclusion principle, only two electrons (with opposite spin) can occupy the same quantum state. At a temperature of absolute zero, all the electrons cannot be in the lowest energy state; instead, all energy states are filled to an energy ϵ_F, known as the *Fermi energy*. Suppose that a volume V of metal contains N free electrons. At absolute zero, the number of states occupied by these electrons is $N/2$, where from Eq. (11-48)

$$\frac{N}{2} = 2\pi V \left(\frac{2m}{h^2}\right)^{\frac{3}{2}} \int_0^{\epsilon_F} \epsilon^{\frac{1}{2}} \, d\epsilon,$$

or

$$\frac{N}{V} = \frac{8\pi}{3} \left(\frac{2m}{h^2}\right)^{\frac{3}{2}} \epsilon_F^{\frac{3}{2}}. \tag{11-49}$$

To appreciate how large the Fermi energy is, it is instructive to calculate the temperature of an ordinary gas at which a molecule would have the energy ϵ_F. This temperature, called the *Fermi temperature*, is defined as

$$T_F = \frac{\epsilon_F}{k}, \tag{11-50}$$

where k is Boltzmann's constant. From Eq. (11-49), we get

$$T_F = \left(\frac{3}{8\pi}\right)^{\frac{2}{3}} \frac{h^2}{2mk} \left(\frac{N}{V}\right)^{\frac{2}{3}}. \tag{11-51}$$

The molar volume of copper is 7.2 cm³; and assuming one free electron for every two copper atoms, $N = 3.0 \times 10^{23}$ electrons. Hence,

$$T_F = 0.24 \, \frac{(6.6)^2 \times 10^{-54} \times 12 \times 10^{14}}{2 \times 9.1 \times 10^{-28} \times 1.4 \times 10^{-16}},$$

or

$$T_F \sim 50,000°K.$$

This means that the closely packed electrons in a metal *at absolute zero* have the energy that an ordinary gas would have at 50,000°K! This energy, known as the *zero-point energy* of the electron gas, may be several hundred thousand joules per mole.

When the temperature of the metal is raised to a value T, only electrons whose energies are near ϵ_F can be raised to higher states, so that the increase of energy per unit temperature rise dU/dT, which is the heat capacity, is small. To calculate this electronic contribution to the molar heat capacity of the metal, c_e, it is necessary to develop a statistics of indistinguishable particles obeying the Pauli exclusion principle where $g_i \approx N_i$. First formulated by Fermi and Dirac, this is called the *Fermi-Dirac statistics* (see Prob. 10-7). When a system obeying this type of statistics comes to equilibrium, it is a simple matter to show that the number of particles N_i with energy ϵ_i is given by

$$N_i = \frac{g_i}{e^{(\epsilon_i - \epsilon_F)/kT} + 1},$$

and the energy U of the entire system of N particles is

$$U = \frac{3N/V}{2\epsilon_F^{\frac{3}{2}}} \int_0^\infty \frac{\epsilon^{\frac{3}{2}} \, d\epsilon}{e^{(\epsilon - \epsilon_F)/kT} + 1}.$$

The evaluation of this integral is difficult. When T/T_F is small, the integrand may be expanded in a series and integrated term by term. When only the first two terms are retained,

$$U = \tfrac{3}{5} N\epsilon_F \left[1 + \frac{5\pi^2}{12} \left(\frac{kT}{\epsilon_F} \right)^2 - \cdots \right],$$

and
$$C_V = Nk \frac{\pi^2}{2} \frac{kT}{\epsilon_F} + \cdots \cdot$$

Calling the constant γ', we may write for the molar heat capacity

$$\boxed{c_e = \gamma' T} \qquad \text{(for } T \ll T_F\text{).} \qquad (11\text{-}52)$$

The entire course of c_e is shown in Fig. 11-22, where it may be seen that, when $T \approx T_F$, then $c_e \approx \tfrac{3}{2} R$. In the linear region of the curve,

$$c_e = \left(31 \, \frac{\text{J}}{\text{mole} \cdot \text{deg}} \right) \frac{T}{T_F} \qquad \text{(for } T/T_F < 0.2\text{).}$$

It was mentioned previously that the c_V of copper at 1200°K exceeds the

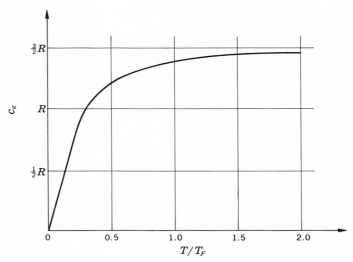

Fig. 11-22   *Temperature variation of heat capacity of an electron gas.*

Dulong and Petit value, as shown in Fig. 11-21. The electronic contribution at this temperature is

$$c_e = \left(31 \; \frac{J}{\text{mole} \cdot \text{deg}} \right) \frac{1200}{50,000} = 0.75 \; \text{J/mole} \cdot \text{deg},$$

and when this is added to the lattice contribution of 25 J/mole · deg, the result 25.8 J/mole · deg is in good agreement with the value 26 J/mole · deg shown in Fig. 11-21.

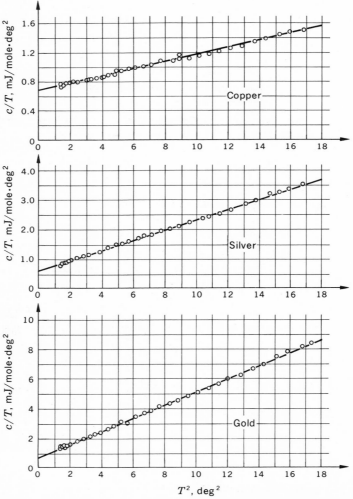

Fig. 11-23   *Heat-capacity measurements of Corak, Garfunkel, Satterthwaite, and Wexler.*

The region of greatest interest in the study of the electron gas in a metal is at low temperatures ($T < \Theta/25$), where Debye's T^3 law holds. In this region, the total heat capacity in mJ/mole $\cdot$ deg is given by

$$c = \left(\frac{125}{\Theta}\right)^3 T^3 + \gamma'T,$$

a relation first derived by Sommerfeld. Dividing by T, we get

$$\frac{c}{T} = \left(\frac{125}{\Theta}\right)^3 T^2 + \gamma'; \tag{11-53}$$

therefore a graph of c/T plotted against T^2 should yield a straight line with a slope equal to $(125/\Theta)^3$ and an intercept γ'. The experimental measurements on copper, silver, and gold made at the Westinghouse laboratories and plotted in Fig. 11-23 verify Eq. (11-53) very well and yield reliable values of Θ and γ'. Values of Θ and γ' of other metals are listed in Table 11-7.

Table 11-7   Debye Temperatures and Electronic Constants of Metals

(*Compiled by N. Pearlman, 1966.*)

Metal	Θ, °K	γ', mJ / mole $\cdot$ deg^2	Metal	Θ, °K	γ', mJ / mole $\cdot$ deg^2	Metal	Θ, °K	γ', mJ / mole $\cdot$ deg^2
3 Li	344	1.63	37 Rb	56	2.4	70 Yb	120	2.9
4 Be	1440	0.17	38 Sr	147	3.6	71 Lu	210	11.3
11 Na	158	1.4	39 Y	280	10.2	72 Hf	252	2.16
12 Mg	400	1.3	40 Zr	291	2.80	73 Ta	240	5.9
13 Al	428	1.35	41 Nb	275	7.79	74 W	400	1.21
19 K	91	2.1	42 Mo	450	2.0	75 Re	430	2.3
20 Ca	230	2.9	44 Ru	600	3.3	76 Os	500	2.4
21 Sc	400	11	45 Rh	480	4.9	77 Ir	420	3.1
22 Ti	420	3.5	46 Pd	274	9.42	78 Pt	240	6.8
23 V	380	9.8	47 Ag	225	0.650	79 Au	164	0.75
24 Cr	630	1.40	48 Cd	209	0.69	80 Hg	72	1.8
25 Mn	410	14	49 In	108	1.6	81 Tl	79	1.5
26 Fe	467	5.0	50 Sn	199	1.78	82 Pb	105	3.0
27 Co	445	4.7	51 Sb	210	0.105	83 Bi	119	0.021
28 Ni	450	7.1	55 Cs	38	3.2	90 Th	170	4.7
29 Cu	343	0.688	56 Ba	110	2.7	92 V	182	10.3
30 Zn	310	0.65	57 La	142	10	94 Pu	160	13
31 Ga	320	0.60	66 Dy	210				
33 As	282	0.20	69 Tm	200	10.5			

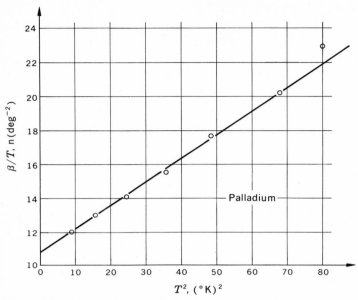

Fig. 11-24   *Thermal expansion of palladium to show the effect of conduction electrons.* (G. K. White, 1961.)

It is an interesting fact that conduction electrons in a metal contribute to the thermal expansion as well as to the heat capacity and, according to the same relation,

$$\beta = aT + bT^3, \qquad (11\text{-}54)$$

where the linear term represents the electronic contribution and the cubic term that due to the lattice. A verification of this equation in the case of palladium is shown in Fig. 11-24, and numerical values of a and b are listed in Table 11-8.

Table 11-8   Expansion of Metals at Low Temperatures
($\beta = aT + bT^3$; *compiled by K. Andres, 1963.*)

Metal	$a,$ $n(\deg^{-2})$	$b,$ $n(\deg^{-4})$	Metal	$a,$ $n(\deg^{-2})$	$b,$ $n(\deg^{-4})$
Mo	1.29	0.0114	Al	3.3	0.072
W	0.09	0.0135	Pb	3	4.20
Re	2.7	0.0204	Mg	3.6	0.126
Pt	6.6	0.177	Ta	3.1	0.096
Cd	0.6	1.14	Pd	10.8	0.129

PROBLEMS

11-1   Show that, for an ideal gas:

(a) $F = \int C_V \, dT - T \int \dfrac{C_V}{T} \, dT - nRT \ln V - \text{const. } T + \text{const.}$

(b) $G = \int C_P \, dT - T \int \dfrac{C_P}{T} \, dT + nRT \ln P - \text{const. } T + \text{const.}$

(c)   Apply the above equations to 1 mole of an ideal monatomic gas.

11-2   Defining the *Massieu function* F_M by the equation

(a)

$$F_M = -\frac{U}{T} + S,$$

show that

$$dF_M = \frac{U}{T^2} \, dT + \frac{P}{T} \, dV.$$

(b)   Defining the *Planck function* F_P by the equation

$$F_P = -\frac{H}{T} + S,$$

show that

$$dF_P = \frac{H}{T^2} \, dT - \frac{V}{T} \, dP.$$

11-3   From the fact that dV/V is an exact differential, derive the relation

$$\left(\frac{\partial \beta}{\partial P}\right)_T = -\left(\frac{\partial \kappa}{\partial T}\right)_P.$$

11-4   Derive the following equations:

(a) $U = F - T\left(\dfrac{\partial F}{\partial T}\right)_V = -T^2\left(\dfrac{\partial F/T}{\partial T}\right)_V.$

(b) $C_V = -T\left(\dfrac{\partial^2 F}{\partial T^2}\right)_V.$

(c) $H = G - T\left(\dfrac{\partial G}{\partial T}\right)_P = -T^2\left(\dfrac{\partial G/T}{\partial T}\right)_P \qquad$ (Gibbs-Helmholtz equation).

(d) $C_P = -T\left(\dfrac{\partial^2 G}{\partial T^2}\right)_P.$

11-5   Derive the third $T \, dS$ equation,

$$T \, dS = C_V\left(\frac{\partial T}{\partial P}\right)_V dP + C_P\left(\frac{\partial T}{\partial V}\right)_P dV,$$

and show that the three $T \, dS$ equations may be written as follows:

(1) $T \, dS = C_V \, dT + \dfrac{\beta T}{\kappa} \, dV,$

(2) $T \, dS = C_P \, dT - V\beta T \, dP,$

(3) $T \, dS = \dfrac{C_V \kappa}{\beta} \, dP + \dfrac{C_P}{\beta V} \, dV.$

11-6   The pressure on 500 g of copper is increased reversibly and iso-thermally from zero to 5000 atm at 100°K. (Assume the density, volume expansivity, isothermal compressibility, and heat capacity to remain practically constant. The values are given in Table 11-6.)

(a)   How much heat is transferred during the compression?

(b)   How much work is done during the compression?

(c)   Determine the change of internal energy.

(d)   What would have been the rise of temperature if the copper had been subjected to a reversible adiabatic compression?

11-7   The pressure on 200 g of water is increased reversibly and iso-thermally from 1 to 3000 atm at 0°C. (Numerical values are given in Table 11-3.)

(a)   How much heat is transferred?

(b)   How much work is done?

(c)   Calculate the change in internal energy.

11-8   The pressure on 1 g of water is increased from 0 to 1000 atm reversibly and adiabatically. Calculate the temperature change when the initial temperature has the three different values given below:

Temperature, °C	Specific volume v, cm³/g	β, $\mu(\deg^{-1})$	c_P, J/g · deg
0	1.000	− 67	4.220
5	1.000	+ 15	4.200
50	1.012	+465	4.180

11-9   A gas obeys the equation $P(v - b) = RT$, where b is constant and has a constant c_V. Show that:

(a) u is a function of T only.

(b) γ is constant.

(c)   A relation that holds during an adiabatic process is

$$P(v - b)^\gamma = \text{const.}$$

11-10   Show that for a gas obeying the van der Waals equation $(P + a/v^2)(v - b) = RT$, with c_V a function of T only, an equation for an adiabatic process is

$$T(v - b)^{R/c_V} = \text{const.}$$

11-11

(a)   Using the virial expansion

$$Pv = RT\left(1 + \frac{B}{v} + \frac{C}{v^2} + \cdots\right),$$

calculate $(\partial u/\partial v)_T$ and its limit as $v \to \infty$.

(b)   Using the same expansion, calculate $(\partial P/\partial v)_T$ and its limit as $v \to \infty$.

(c)   Using (a) and (b), calculate $(\partial u/\partial P)_T$ and its limit as $v \to \infty$. (Compare the solution with the results of Rossini and Frandsen given in Art. 5-2.)

(d)   Using the virial expansion

$$Pv = RT + B'P + C'P^2 + \cdots$$

and bearing in mind that $B' = B$, calculate $(\partial u/\partial P)_T$ directly from Eq. (11-19).

11-12   Show that the differentials of the three thermodynamic functions U, H, and F may be written

$$dU = (C_P - PV\beta)\,dT + V(\kappa P - \beta T)\,dP.$$

$$dH = C_P\,dT + V(1 - \beta T)\,dP.$$

$$dF = -(PV\beta + S)\,dT + PV\kappa\,dP.$$

11-13

(a)   Derive the equation

$$\left(\frac{\partial C_V}{\partial V}\right)_T = T\left(\frac{\partial^2 P}{\partial T^2}\right)_V.$$

(b)   Prove that C_V of an ideal gas is a function of T only.

(c)   In the case of a gas obeying the equation of state

$$\frac{Pv}{RT} = 1 + \frac{B}{v},$$

where B is a function of T only, show that

$$c_V = -\frac{RT}{v}\frac{d^2}{dT^2}(BT) + (c_V)_0,$$

where $(c_V)_0$ is the value at very large volumes.

11-14

(a)   Derive the equation

$$\left(\frac{\partial C_P}{\partial P}\right)_T = -T\left(\frac{\partial^2 V}{\partial T^2}\right)_P.$$

(b)   Prove that C_P of an ideal gas is a function of T only.

(c)   In the case of a gas obeying the equation of state

$$Pv = RT + BP,$$

where B is a function of T only, show that

$$c_P = -T\frac{d^2B}{dT^2}P + (c_P)_0,$$

where $(c_P)_0$ is the value at very low pressures.

11-15   In the accompanying table are listed the thermal properties of liquid neon, compiled by Gladun. Calculate and plot against temperature (a) c_V; (b) κ_S; and (c) γ.

T, °K	ρ, 10^{-2} mole/cm³	β, 10^{-2} deg⁻¹	κ, 10^{-3} atm⁻¹	c_P, J/mole · deg
25	6.15	1.33	0.43	36.6
27	5.99	1.46	0.50	37.6
29	5.81	1.63	0.62	39.2
31	5.62	1.84	0.79	41.2
33	5.40	2.12	1.03	43.9
35	5.17	2.52	1.40	47.7
37	4.91	3.14	2.04	53
39	4.61	4.24	3.4	62
41	4.23	6.8	6.9	82
42	4.00	10	11	100
43	3.68	18	26	160

11-16   Derive the following equations:

(a) $C_V = -T\left(\frac{\partial P}{\partial T}\right)_V\left(\frac{\partial V}{\partial T}\right)_S.$

(b) $\left(\frac{\partial V}{\partial T}\right)_S = -\frac{C_V\kappa}{\beta T}.$

(c) $\frac{(\partial V/\partial T)_S}{(\partial V/\partial T)_P} = \frac{1}{1-\gamma}.$

11-17   Derive the following equations:

(a) $C_P = T\left(\dfrac{\partial V}{\partial T}\right)_P \left(\dfrac{\partial P}{\partial T}\right)_S$.

(b) $\left(\dfrac{\partial P}{\partial T}\right)_S = \dfrac{C_P}{V\beta T}$.

(c) $\dfrac{(\partial P/\partial T)_S}{(\partial P/\partial T)_V} = \dfrac{\gamma}{\gamma - 1}$.

11-18

(a) A measure of the result of a Joule free expansion is provided by the *Joule coefficient* $\eta = (\partial T/\partial V)_U$. Show that:

$$\eta = -\frac{1}{C_V}\left(\frac{\beta T}{\kappa} - P\right).$$

(b) A measure of the result of a Joule-Kelvin expansion (throttling process) is provided by the Joule-Kelvin coefficient $\mu = (\partial T/\partial P)_H$. Show that:

$$\mu = \frac{V}{C_P}(\beta T - 1).$$

11-19   It was shown in Art. 11-12 that the partition function of an Einstein crystal is

$$Z = \frac{e^{-h\nu/2kT}}{1 - e^{-h\nu/kT}}.$$

If the crystal consists of N_A lattice points, calculate (a) the Helmholtz function F; (b) the pressure P; and (c) the entropy S. (d) Express the zero-point energy in terms of Θ_E.

11-20   Using the Debye approximation, show that the total energy U of N_A lattice points ($3N_A$ independent harmonic oscillators) is

$$U = \tfrac{9}{8}R\Theta + \frac{9RT}{(\Theta/T)^3}\int_0^{\Theta/T} \frac{x^3\,dx}{e^x - 1}.$$

What is the interpretation of the term $\tfrac{9}{8}R\Theta$?

11-21   Plot the Einstein $c_V/3R$ curve against T/Θ_E on the same graph as the Debye $c_V/3R$ curve against T/Θ, and then compare the two curves.

11-22   A system consists of N_A distinguishable, independent particles, each of which is capable of existing in only two nondegenerate energy states 0 and ϵ.

(*a*)   What is the partition function?

(*b*)   Calculate the energy.

(*c*)   Calculate c_V.

(*d*)   Plot c_V/R as a function of kT/ϵ from $kT/\epsilon = 0$ to 1.

11-23   Given a crystal obeying Debye's approximation with Θ a function of V only, assume the entropy S to be a function of T/Θ. If Γ is defined by the equation

$$\Gamma = -\frac{d \ln \Theta}{d \ln V},$$

(*a*)   Show that

$$\Gamma = \frac{\beta V}{C_V \kappa}.$$

[*Hint:* Use Maxwell's third equation.]

(*b*)   Calculate Γ of NaCl at a few temperatures using Table 11-2, and plot Γ against T.

(*c*)   Show that

$$\gamma = 1 + \Gamma \beta T.$$

11-24   The partition function of a Debye crystal is

$$\ln Z = -\frac{9}{(\Theta/T)^3} \int_0^{\Theta/T} x^2 \ln (1 - e^{-x}) \, dx.$$

(*a*)   Show that

$$\ln Z = -3 \ln (1 - e^{-\Theta/T}) + \frac{9}{(\Theta/T)^3} \int_0^{\Theta/T} \frac{x^3 \, dx}{e^x - 1}.$$

(*b*)   Calculate the Helmholtz function.

(*c*)   Show that the equation of state of the crystal is given by

$$PV + f(V) = \Gamma(U - U_0),$$

where U_0 is the zero-point energy.

12.

PHASE TRANSITIONS; LIQUID AND SOLID HELIUM

12-1   Joule-Kelvin Effect

In this chapter we shall study the behavior of pure substances during the transition from one phase to another. In the best-known phase transitions, namely, the melting of ice and the vaporization of water, the regions of temperature and pressure are easily accessible without special apparatus. Some of the most interesting materials, however, such as nitrogen, hydrogen, and helium, whose phase transitions contain still unsolved problems, exist only at low temperatures. It is important, therefore, to learn how these low temperatures are achieved and maintained. The first step is to liquefy air, and the most economical way to accomplish this is with the aid of the *Joule-Kelvin effect* or, as it was formerly called, the *porous-plug experiment*.

In the porous-plug experiment a gas is made to undergo a continuous throttling process. By means of a pump, a constant pressure is maintained on one side of a porous plug and a constant lower pressure on the other side. In the original experiments of Joule and Kelvin a cotton plug was used, and the gas flowed through it parallel to the axis of the pipe. In modern measurements a cup of a strong porous material capable of withstanding great force allows the gas to seep through in a radial direction. Rigid precautions are taken to provide adequate thermal insulation for the plug and the portion of the pipe near the plug. Suitable manometers and thermometers are used to measure the pressure and temperature of the gas on both sides of the plug.

The experiment is performed in the following way: The pressure P_i and temperature T_i on the high-pressure side of the plug are chosen arbitrarily. The pressure P_f on the other side of the plug is then set at any value less than P_i, and the temperature of the gas T_f is measured. P_i and T_i are kept the same; P_f is changed to another value, and the corresponding T_f is measured. This is done for a number of different values of P_f, and the corresponding T_f is measured in each case. P_f is the independent variable of the experiment, and T_f is the dependent variable. The results provide a set of discrete points on a TP diagram, one point being P_iT_i and the others being the various P_f's and T_f's indicated in Fig. 12-1 by numbers (1) to (7). Although the points shown in the figure do not refer to any particular gas, they are typical of most gases. It can be seen that, if a throttling process takes place between the states P_iT_i and P_fT_f (3), there is a rise of temperature. Between P_iT_i and P_fT_f (7), however, there is a drop of temperature. In general, the temperature change of a gas upon seeping through a porous plug depends on the three quantities P_i, T_i, and P_f and may be an increase or a decrease, or there may be no change whatever.

According to the principles developed in Art. 11-1, the eight points plotted in Fig. 12-1 represent equilibrium states of some constant mass of the gas (say, 1 g) at which the gas has the same enthalpy. All equilibrium states of the gas corresponding to this enthalpy must lie on some curve, and it is reasonable to assume that this curve can be obtained by drawing a smooth curve through the discrete points. Such a curve is called an *isenthalpic curve*. The student must understand that *an isenthalpic curve is not the graph of a throttling process*. No such graph can be drawn because in any throttling process the intermediate states traversed by a gas cannot be described by means of thermodynamic coordinates. An isenthalpic curve is the locus of all points representing equilibrium states of the same enthalpy. The porous-plug experiment is performed to provide a few of these points, and the rest are obtained by interpolation.

The temperature T_i on the high-pressure side is now changed to another value, with P_i being kept the same. P_f is again varied, and the corresponding T_f's are measured. Upon plotting the new P_iT_i and the new P_f's and T_f's, another discrete set of points is obtained, which determines another isenthalpic curve corresponding to a different enthalpy. In this way, a series

Fig. 12-1   *Isenthalpic states of a gas.*

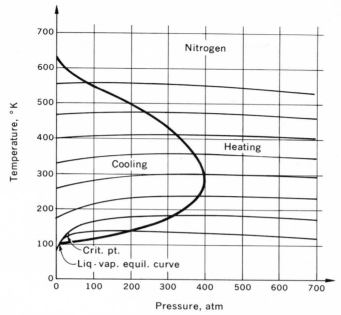

Fig. 12-2   *Isenthalps and inversion curve for nitrogen. (From TS diagram prepared by F. Din, 1958.)*

of isenthalpic curves is obtained. Such a series is shown in Fig. 12-2 for nitrogen.

The numerical value of the slope of an isenthalpic curve on a TP diagram at any point is called the *Joule-Kelvin coefficient* and will be denoted by μ. Thus,

$$\mu = \left(\frac{\partial T}{\partial P}\right)_h. \tag{12-1}$$

The locus of all points at which the Joule-Kelvin coefficient is zero, i.e., the locus of the maxima of the isenthalpic curves, is known as the *inversion curve* and is shown for N_2 in Fig. 12-2 as a heavy closed curve. The region inside the inversion curve, where μ is positive, is called the *region of cooling;* whereas outside, where μ is negative, is the *region of heating*.

If a vertical line is drawn at some arbitrarily chosen pressure, it will intersect the isenthalpic curves at a number of points at which μ may be obtained by measuring the slopes of the isenthalps at these points. We should then have a set of values of μ referring to the same pressure but to different temperatures. This can then be repeated at another pressure.

Since the Joule-Kelvin coefficient involves T, P, and h, we seek a relation among the differentials of T, P, and h. In general, the difference in molar enthalpy between two neighboring equilibrium states is

$$dh = T\,ds + v\,dP,$$

and, according to the second $T\,ds$ equation,

$$T\,ds = c_P\,dT - T\left(\frac{\partial v}{\partial T}\right)_P dP.$$

Substituting for $T\,ds$, we get

$$dh = c_P\,dT - \left[T\left(\frac{\partial v}{\partial T}\right)_P - v \right] dP,$$

or

$$dT = \frac{1}{c_P}\left[T\left(\frac{\partial v}{\partial T}\right)_P - v \right] dP + \frac{1}{c_P}\,dh.$$

Since $\mu = (\partial T/\partial P)_h$,

$$\boxed{\mu = \frac{1}{c_P}\left[T\left(\frac{\partial v}{\partial T}\right)_P - v \right].} \qquad (12\text{-}2)$$

This is the thermodynamic equation for the Joule-Kelvin coefficient. It is evident that, for an ideal gas,

$$\mu = \frac{1}{c_P}\left(T\frac{R}{P} - v \right) = 0.$$

The most important application of the Joule-Kelvin effect is in the liquefaction of gases.

12-2   Liquefaction of Gases by the Joule-Kelvin Effect

An inspection of the isenthalpic curves and the inversion curve of Fig. 12-2 shows that, for the Joule-Kelvin effect to give rise to cooling, the initial temperature of the gas must be below the point where the inversion curve cuts the temperature axis, i.e., below the maximum inversion temperature. For many gases, room temperature is already below the maximum inversion temperature, so that no precooling is necessary. Thus, if air is compressed to a pressure of 200 atm and a temperature of 52°C, then, after

Fig. 12-3 *Isenthalps and inversion curve for hydrogen. (Woolley, Scott, and Brickwedde 1948.)*

throttling to a pressure of 1 atm, it will be cooled to 23°C. On the other hand, if helium originally at 200 atm and 52°C is throttled to 1 atm, its temperature will rise to 64°C.

Figure 12-3 shows that, for the Joule-Kelvin effect to produce cooling in hydrogen, the hydrogen must be cooled below 200°K. Liquid nitrogen is used in most laboratories for this purpose. To produce Joule-Kelvin cooling in helium, the helium is first cooled with the aid of liquid hydrogen. Table 12-1 gives the maximum inversion temperatures of a few gases commonly used in low-temperature work. The inversion curve for helium is shown in Fig. 12-4.

It is clear from Figs. 12-2, 12-3, and 12-4 that, once a gas has been precooled to a temperature lower than the maximum inversion temperature, the optimum pressure from which to start throttling corresponds to a point on the inversion curve. Starting at this pressure and ending at atmospheric pressure, the largest temperature drop is produced. This, however, is not large enough to produce liquefaction. Consequently, the gas that has been cooled by throttling is used to cool the incoming gas, which after throttling

Table 12-1   Maximum Inversion Temperatures

Gas	Maximum inversion temp., °K
Carbon dioxide	~1500
Argon	780
Oxygen	764
Air	659
Nitrogen	621
Neon	231
Hydrogen	202
Helium	~40

becomes still cooler. After many repetitions of these successive coolings, the gas is lowered to such a temperature that after throttling it becomes partly liquefied. The device used for this purpose, a *countercurrent heat exchanger*, is shown in Fig. 12-5.

The gas, after precooling, is sent through the middle tube of a long coil of double-walled pipe. After throttling, it flows back through the outer

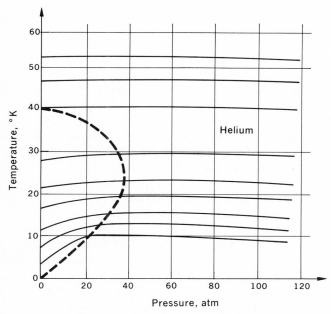

Fig. 12-4   *Isenthalps and inversion curve for helium. (R. W. Hill and O. V. Lounasmaa, 1960.)*

Fig. 12-5   *Liquefaction of a gas by means of Joule-Kelvin effect.*

annular space surrounding the middle pipe. For the heat exchanger to be efficient, the temperature of the gas as it leaves must differ only slightly from the temperature at which it entered. To accomplish this, the heat exchanger must be quite long and well insulated, and the gas must flow through it with sufficient speed to cause turbulent flow, so that there is good thermal contact between the opposing streams of gas.

When the steady state is finally reached, liquid is formed at a constant rate: for every mass unit of gas supplied, a certain fraction y is liquefied, and the fraction $1 - y$ is returned to the pump. Considering only the heat exchanger and throttling valve completely insulated, as shown in Fig. 12-6, we have a process in which the enthalpy of the entering gas is equal to the enthalpy of y units of emerging liquid plus the enthalpy of $1 - y$ units of emerging gas. If

$$h_i = \text{enthalpy of entering gas at } (T_i, P_i),$$

$$h_L = \text{enthalpy of emerging liquid at } (T_L, P_L),$$

and $\qquad h_f = \text{enthalpy of emerging gas at } (T_f, P_f),$

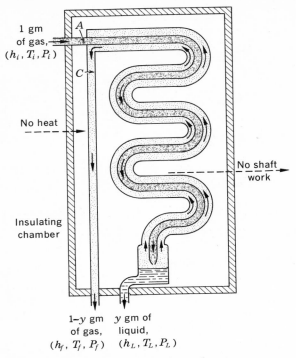

1 gm
of gas,
(h_i, T_i, P_i)

A

C

No heat

No shaft
work

Insulating
chamber

1–y gm   y gm of
of gas,   liquid,
(h_f, T_f, P_f) (h_L, T_L, P_L)

Fig. 12-6   *Throttling valve and heat exchanger in steady state.*

then
$$h_i = y h_L + (1 - y) h_f,$$

or
$$y = \frac{h_f - h_i}{h_f - h_L}. \tag{12-3}$$

Now, in the steady state, h_L is determined by the pressure on the liquid, which fixes the temperature, and hence is constant. h_f is determined by the pressure drop in the return tube and the temperature at C, which is only a little below that at A; hence, it remains constant. h_i refers to a temperature T_i that is fixed, but at a pressure that may be chosen at will. Therefore, the fraction liquefied y may be varied only by varying h_i. Since

$$y = \frac{h_f - h_i}{h_f - h_L},$$

y will be a maximum when h_i is a minimum; and since h_i may be varied only by varying the pressure, the condition that it be a minimum is that

$$\left(\frac{\partial h_i}{\partial P}\right)_{T=T_i} = 0.$$

But

$$\left(\frac{\partial h}{\partial P}\right)_T = - \left(\frac{\partial h}{\partial T}\right)_P \left(\frac{\partial T}{\partial P}\right)_h = -c_P\mu;$$

hence, for y to be a maximum,

$$\mu = 0 \qquad \text{at } T = T_i,$$

or the *point* (T_i, P_i) *must lie on the inversion curve.*

In the design of a gas-liquefaction unit, a *TS* diagram showing isobars and isenthalps is particularly useful. For example, to calculate the fraction liquefied in the steady state y, the three enthalpies h_i, h_f, and h_L may be obtained directly from such a diagram. *TS* diagrams for hydrogen and for helium are shown in Figs. 12-7 and 12-8.

The use of the Joule-Kelvin effect to produce liquefaction of gases has two advantages: (1) There are no moving parts at low temperature that would be difficult to lubricate. (2) The lower the temperature, the larger the drop in temperature for a given pressure drop, as shown by the isenthalps in Figs. 12-2 and 12-3. For the purpose of liquefying hydrogen and helium, however, it has a serious disadvantage: namely, the large amount of pre-cooling that is necessary. The hydrogen must be precooled with liquid nitrogen, and the helium must be precooled with liquid hydrogen, which makes the liquefaction of these gases expensive.

An approximately reversible adiabatic expansion against a piston or a turbine blade always produces a decrease in temperature, no matter what the original temperature. If, therefore, a gas like helium could be made to do external work adiabatically through the medium of an engine or a turbine, then, with the aid of a heat exchanger, the helium could be liquefied without precooling. But this method has the disadvantage that the tempera-ture drop on adiabatic expansion decreases as the temperature decreases.

A combination of both methods has been used successfully. Thus, adiabatic reversible expansion is used to achieve a temperature within the inversion curve, and then the Joule-Kelvin effect completes the liquefaction. Kapitza was the first to liquefy helium in this way, with the aid of a small expansion engine that was lubricated by the helium itself. Later he liquefied air with the aid of a centrifugal turbine only a trifle larger than a watch.

The most significant development in the field of gas liquefaction is the Collins helium liquefier, in which helium undergoes adiabatic expansion in

Fig. 12-7   *Temperature-entropy diagram for hydrogen. (Woolley, Scott, and Brickwedde, 1948.)*

a reciprocating engine. The expanded gas is then used to cool the incoming gas in the usual countercurrent heat exchanger. When the temperature is low enough, the gas passes through a throttling valve, and Joule-Kelvin cooling is used to complete the liquefaction. The unit consists of a four-stage compressor, a gasholder, a purifier, and a cryostat containing the engines, heat exchangers, Dewar flasks, vacuum pumps, and all switches and gauges,

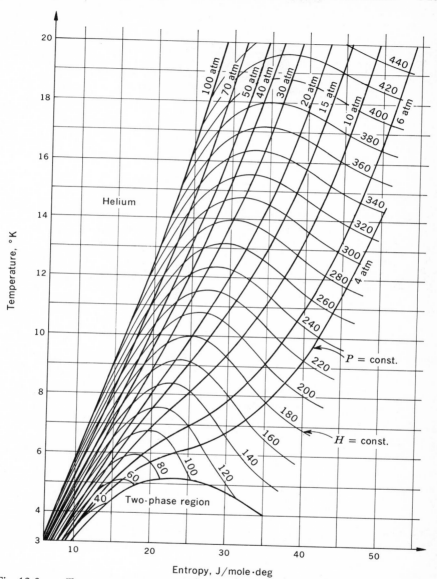

Fig. 12-8   *Temperature-entropy diagram of helium. Lines of constant pressure (P = 4 to 100 atm), and constant enthalpy (H − H₀ = 40 to 440 J/mole) are shown. (R. W. Hill and O. V. Lounasmaa, 1960.)*

Four-stage compressor

(0.5 psig) ↑ ↓ (200 psig)

Hydraulic hoist for maintenance

Low pressure helium gas return (0.5 psig)

Experimental chamber

Low-pressure gas holder

Pressure regulator

Liquid helium drawoff tube

Expansion engines

Joule-Thompson valve

Liquid helium container

Heat exchanger

Helium cylinder (2000 psig)

Helium purifier

Fig. 12-9   *Schematic diagram of Collins helium-liquefying plant.*

as shown in Fig. 12-9. This unit is manufactured by the A. D. Little Co. of Massachusetts.

The simplest laboratory devices for producing small amounts of liquid air are the Stirling refrigerators, which were described in Art. 7-6.

12-3   First-order Transition; Clapeyron's Equation

In the familiar phase transitions—melting, vaporization, and sublimation—as well as in some less familiar transitions, such as from one crystal modification to another, the temperature and pressure remain constant while the entropy and volume change. Consider n_0 moles of material in phase i with molar entropy $s^{(i)}$ and molar volume $v^{(i)}$. Both $s^{(i)}$ and $v^{(i)}$ are functions of T and P and hence remain constant during the phase transition which ends with the material in phase f with molar entropy $s^{(f)}$ and molar volume $v^{(f)}$. (The different phases are indicated by superscripts in order to reserve subscripts for specifying different states of the same phase or different substances.) Let x equal the fraction of the initial phase that has been transformed into the final phase at any moment. Then the entropy and volume of the mixture at any moment—S and V, respectively—are given by

$$S = n_0(1 - x)s^{(i)} + n_0xs^{(f)}$$

and

$$V = n_0(1 - x)v^{(i)} + n_0xv^{(f)},$$

and S and V are seen to be linear functions of x.

If the phase transition takes place reversibly, the heat (commonly known as a *latent heat*) transferred per mole is given by

$$l = T(s^{(f)} - s^{(i)}).$$

The existence of a latent heat, therefore, means that there is a change of entropy. Since

$$dg = -s\,dT + v\,dP,$$

$$s = -\left(\frac{\partial g}{\partial T}\right)_P,$$

and

$$v = \left(\frac{\partial g}{\partial P}\right)_T,$$

we may characterize the familiar phase transitions by either of the following equivalent statements:

1   There are changes of entropy and of volume.
2   The first-order derivatives of the Gibbs function change discontinuously.

Any phase change that satisfies these requirements is known as a *phase change of the first order*. For such a phase change, the temperature variations of G, S, V, and C_P are shown by four crude graphs in Fig. 12-10. The phase transition may be regarded as accomplished reversibly in either direction. The fourth graph showing the behavior of C_P is particularly significant in that the C_P of a *mixture of two phases during the phase transition* is infinite. This is true because the transition occurs at constant T and P. When P is constant, $dT = 0$; or when T is constant $dP = 0$. Therefore,

$$C_P = T\left(\frac{\partial S}{\partial T}\right)_P = \infty, \quad \beta = \frac{1}{V}\left(\frac{\partial V}{\partial T}\right)_P = \infty, \quad \kappa = -\frac{1}{V}\left(\frac{\partial V}{\partial P}\right)_T = \infty.$$

It should be noticed, however, that these statements are true only when both phases are present. As shown in Fig. 12-10d, the C_P of phase (i) remains

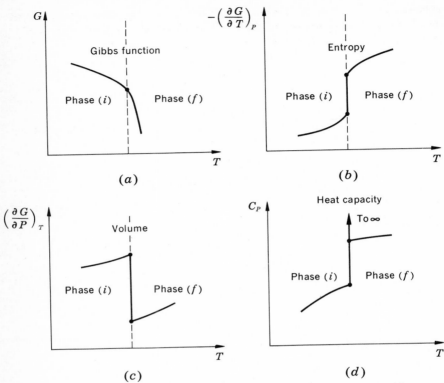

Fig. 12-10   *Characteristics of a first-order phase transition. (a) Gibbs function; (b) entropy; (c) volume; (d) heat capacity.*

finite right up to the transition temperature. It does not "anticipate" the onset of a phase transition by starting to rise before this temperature is reached. This is always true of a first-order transition, but not of all transitions.

The second $T\,dS$ equation provides an indeterminate result when applied to a first-order phase transition. For any small portion,

$$T\,dS = C_P\,dT - TV\beta\,dP,$$

where $C_P = \infty$ and $dT = 0$; also, $\beta = \infty$ and $dP = 0$.

The first $T\,dS$ equation, however, may be integrated through the phase transition. When 1 mole of substance is converted reversibly, isothermally, and isobarically from phase (i) to phase (f), the first $T\,dS$ equation,

$$T\,ds = c_V\,dT + T\left(\frac{\partial P}{\partial T}\right)_V dv,$$

may be integrated with the understanding that the various P's and T's at which a phase transition occurs obey a relation in which P is a function of T only, independent of V, so that $(\partial P/\partial T)_V = dP/dT$. Hence,

$$T(s^{(f)} - s^{(i)}) = T\frac{dP}{dT}(v^{(f)} - v^{(i)}).$$

The left-hand member of this equation is the latent heat per mole, and hence

$$\boxed{\frac{dP}{dT} = \frac{l}{T(v^{(f)} - v^{(i)})}.} \qquad (12\text{-}4)$$

This equation, known as *Clapeyron's equation*, applies to any first-order change of phase or transition that takes place at constant T and P.

It is instructive to derive Clapeyron's equation in another way. It was shown in Chap. 11 that the Gibbs function remains constant during a reversible process taking place at constant temperature and pressure. Hence, for a change of phase at T and P,

$$g^{(i)} = g^{(f)};$$

and for a phase change at $T + dT$ and $P + dP$,

$$g^{(i)} + dg^{(i)} = g^{(f)} + dg^{(f)}.$$

Subtracting, we get

$$dg^{(i)} = dg^{(f)},$$

or

$$-s^{(i)}\, dT + v^{(i)}\, dP = -s^{(f)}\, dT + v^{(f)}\, dP.$$

Therefore,

$$\frac{dP}{dT} = \frac{s^{(f)} - s^{(i)}}{v^{(f)} - v^{(i)}},$$

and, finally,

$$\frac{dP}{dT} = \frac{l}{T(v^{(f)} - v^{(i)})}.$$

12-4   Sublimation; Kirchhoff's Equation

In dealing with phase transitions, it is necessary to indicate in a simple way the initial and final phases and the corresponding heat of transition. The notation used in this book is as follows: A symbol representing any property of the solid phase will be distinguished with a prime; for the liquid phase it will have a double prime, and for the vapor phase a triple prime.

Thus v' stands for the molar volume of a solid, v'' of a liquid, and v''' of a vapor. The heat of sublimation per mole will be l_S, the heat of vaporization (boiling) l_V, and the heat of fusion (melting) l_F. Using this system of notation, Clapeyron's equation for sublimation becomes

$$\frac{dP}{dT} = \frac{l_S}{T(v''' - v')}.$$

Sublimation usually takes place at a low pressure, where the vapor may be regarded as an ideal gas, so that

$$v''' \approx \frac{RT}{P}.$$

Since P is small, v''' is large—indeed, so much larger than the molar volume of the solid that v' may be neglected, or

$$v''' - v' \approx v'''.$$

Clapeyron's equation can then be written

$$l_S = R \frac{dP/P}{dT/T^2}$$

$$= -R \frac{d \ln P}{d(1/T)}$$

$$= -2.30R \frac{d \log P}{d(1/T)},$$

from which it can be seen that l_S is equal to $-2.30R$ times the slope of the curve obtained when $\log P$ is plotted against $1/T$. Vapor pressures of solids are usually measured over only a small range of temperature. Within this range, the graph of $\log P$ against $1/T$ is practically a straight line, or

$$\log P = -\frac{\text{const.}}{T} + \text{const.}$$

For example, within the temperature interval from 700 to 739°K, the vapor pressure of magnesium satisfies with reasonable accuracy the equation

$$\log P = -\frac{7527}{T} + 8.589.$$

In the case of zinc between 575 and 630°K, the vapor pressure is given by

$$\log P = -\frac{6787}{T} + 8.972.$$

Therefore, from 700 to 739°K the heat of sublimation for magnesium is $2.30R \times 7527 = 144$ kJ/mole; for zinc between 575 and 630°K, $l_S = 2.30R \times 6787 = 130$ kJ/mole. At other temperatures, the heat of sublimation is different. If reliable vapor-pressure data existed over other temperature ranges, the temperature variation of l_S could be obtained. As a rule, however, this is impossible because at low temperatures the vapor pressure of a solid is too small to measure. In the following pages we shall derive *Kirchhoff's equation* for the heat of sublimation at any desired temperature.

An infinitesimal change of molar enthalpy between two states of equilibrium of a chemical system is given by

$$dh = T\,ds + v\,dP.$$

Introducing the second $T\,ds$ equation, we get

$$dh = c_P\,dT + \left[v - T\left(\frac{\partial v}{\partial T}\right)_P\right]dP$$
$$= c_P\,dT + v(1 - \beta T)\,dP.$$

A finite change of enthalpy between the two states $P_i T_i$ and $P_f T_f$ is

$$h_f - h_i = \int_i^f c_P\,dT + \int_i^f v(1 - \beta T)\,dP.$$

Let us apply this equation to a solid whose initial state i' is at zero pressure and at a temperature of absolute zero and whose final state f' is that of a saturated solid (solid about to sublime) represented by a point on the solid-saturation curve below the triple point. These two states are shown on a PVT surface in Fig. 12-11. To calculate the enthalpy change from i' to f', we may integrate along any reversible path from i' to f'. The most convenient is the path represented by the two steps $i' \rightarrow A$ and $A \rightarrow f'$, the first being isothermal at absolute zero and the second isobaric at pressure P. Denoting the final enthalpy by h' and the initial by h'_0,

$$h' - h'_0 = \int_{i'}^A v(1 - \beta T)\,dP + \int_A^{f'} c_P\,dT$$
$$= \int_0^P v'\,dP + \int_0^T c'_P\,dT,$$

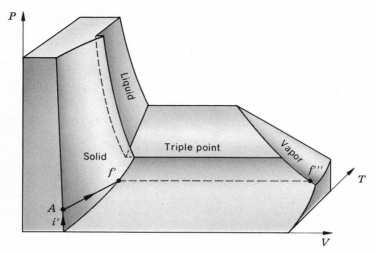

Fig. 12-11   *Portion of PVT surface below the triple point.*

where v' is the molar volume of the solid at absolute zero and c'_P the molar heat capacity at a constant pressure P. Now the pressure at all points on the sublimation curve is very small for most solids. For example, for ordinary ice it ranges from 0 to about 5 mm; for cadmium, from 0 to 0.1 mm. Therefore, if we limit the application of this formula to solids at temperatures where the vapor pressure is very small, we may ignore $\int_0^P v' \, dP$, and

$$h' = \int_0^T c'_P \, dT + h'_0. \tag{12-5}$$

Since the c'_P of a solid does not vary appreciably with the pressure, the value of c'_P at atmospheric pressure may be used in the above integral.

The enthalpy of the saturated vapor indicated by point f''' in Fig. 12-11 may be calculated on the basis of the assumption that the saturated vapor at such a low pressure behaves like an ideal gas. Going back to the general equation $c_P = (\partial h / \partial T)_P$ and remembering that the enthalpy of an ideal gas is a function of the temperature only, we have

$$dh''' = c'''_P \, dT.$$

Integrating from absolute zero to T, we have

$$h''' = \int_0^T c'''_P \, dT + h'''_0, \tag{12-6}$$

where h'''_0 is the molar enthalpy of a saturated vapor at absolute zero.

Consider now the reversible sublimation of 1 mole of a solid at temperature T and pressure P corresponding to the transition from f' to f''' in Fig. 12-11. We have

$$l_S = h''' - h'$$

$$= \int_0^T c_P''' \, dT - \int_0^T c_P' \, dT + h_0''' - h_0'.$$

Since the two integrals approach zero as T approaches zero, it follows that

$$l_S \to h_0''' - h_0' \qquad \text{as } T \to 0,$$

and $h_0''' - h_0'$ *is the heat of sublimation at absolute zero,* which is denoted by l_0. Hence,

$$\boxed{l_S = \int_0^T c_P''' \, dT - \int_0^T c_P' \, dT + l_0.} \tag{12-7}$$

This equation is known as *Kirchhoff's equation.* It is only an approximate equation, being subject to the restrictions that the pressure is low and that the saturated vapor behaves like an ideal gas.

12-5   Vapor-pressure Constant

If the vapor in equilibrium with a solid is assumed to behave like an ideal gas, and if the volume of the solid is neglected in comparison with that of the vapor, Clapeyron's equation becomes

$$\frac{dP}{P} = \frac{l_S}{RT^2} \, dT.$$

If, in addition to these assumptions, we suppose that the vapor pressure is very small, Kirchhoff's equation may be used. Thus,

$$l_S = l_0 + \int_0^T c_P''' \, dT - \int_0^T c_P' \, dT.$$

The molar heat capacity of an ideal gas can be represented as the sum of a constant term and a term that is a function of the temperature. Thus,

$$c_P''' = c_0''' + c_i''', \tag{12-8}$$

where c_0''' is equal to $\frac{5}{2}R$ for all monatomic gases and to $\frac{7}{2}R$ for all diatomic gases except hydrogen. The factor c_i''' has the property that it approaches zero rapidly as T approaches zero. Kirchhoff's equation may therefore be written

$$l_S = l_0 + c_0''' T + \int_0^T c_i''' \, dT - \int_0^T c_P' \, dT;$$

and after substitution in Clapeyron's equation, we get

$$\frac{dP}{P} = \frac{l_0}{RT^2} \, dT + \frac{c_0'''}{RT} \, dT + \frac{\int_0^T c_i''' \, dT}{RT^2} \, dT - \frac{\int_0^T c_P' \, dT}{RT^2} \, dT.$$

Integrating this equation, we get finally

$$\ln P = -\frac{l_0}{RT} + \frac{c_0'''}{R} \ln T + \frac{1}{R} \int_0^T \frac{\int_0^T c_i''' \, dT}{T^2} \, dT - \frac{1}{R} \int_0^T \frac{\int_0^T c_P' \, dT}{T^2} \, dT + i,$$

$$(12\text{-}9)$$

where i is a constant of integration. This relation is not rigorous, but it is accurate enough to be used in conjunction with experimental measurements of the vapor pressure of solids. Such measurements are usually attended by errors that are much greater than those brought about by the simplifying assumptions introduced in the derivation.

If the vapor in equilibrium with a solid is monatomic, c_0''' has the value of $\frac{5}{2}R$ and c_i''' is zero. The equation of the sublimation curve then becomes

$$\ln P = -\frac{l_0}{RT} + \frac{5}{2} \ln T - \frac{1}{R} \int_0^T \frac{\int_0^T c_P' \, dT}{T^2} \, dT + i. \qquad (12\text{-}10)$$

Changing to common logarithms and expressing the pressure in atmospheres, we get

$$\log P = -\frac{l_0}{2.30RT} + \frac{5}{2} \log T - \frac{1}{2.30R} \int_0^T \frac{\int_0^T c_P' \, dT}{T^2} \, dT$$

$$+ \frac{i}{2.30} - \log 1{,}013{,}600.$$

The last two terms are known as the *practical vapor-pressure constant i'*. Thus,

$$i' = \frac{i}{2.30} - \log 1,013,600$$

$$= \frac{i}{2.30} - 6.006.$$

Finally, expressing the pressure in millimeters, introducing the numerical values

$$2.30R = 19.1 \text{ J/mole} \cdot \text{deg}$$

and

$$\log 760 = 2.881,$$

and calling

$$B = \frac{1}{2.30R} \int_0^T \frac{\int_0^T c'_P \, dT}{T^2} \, dT,$$

the equation becomes

$$\log P = -\frac{l_0}{19.1 T} + \frac{5}{2} \log T - B + i' + 2.881.$$

This is the form in which the equation is most useful to the physicist or chemist in the laboratory.

The sublimation equation is used in two ways: (1) to obtain experimental measurements of the vapor-pressure constant i', which are to be compared with theoretical calculations of i'; and (2) to calculate the vapor pressure of a substance at temperatures at which P is too small to measure. In both cases, the integral B must be evaluated on the basis either of experimental measurements of c'_P or of theoretical values for c'_P. In order to do this, c'_P is plotted against T from absolute zero to as high a temperature as is necessary. The area under the curve at various values of T is measured with a planimeter, and the temperature variation of $\int_0^T c'_P \, dT$ is thus obtained. These values are now divided by T^2 and plotted on another graph against T. The area under this new curve at various values of T provides, finally, the temperature variation of B.

If measurements of the vapor pressure exist over a wide temperature range, the numerical value of $\log P - \frac{5}{2} \log T + B$ is plotted against $1/T$. Since

$$\log P - \frac{5}{2} \log T + B = -\frac{l_0}{19.1} \frac{1}{T} + i' + 2.881,$$

the resulting graph is a straight line whose

$$\text{Slope} = -\frac{l_0}{19.1}$$

and

$$\text{Intercept} = i' + 2.881.$$

The data for cadmium are listed in Table 12-2. The vapor-pressure measurements were made by Egerton and Raleigh, and the measurements of B by

Table 12-2   Data for the Determination of i' of Cadmium

T, °K	$\log P$	$\frac{5}{2}\log T$	B	$\log P - \frac{5}{2}\log T + B$	$1/T$
360	−7.44	6.38	1.82	−12.00	0.00278
380	−6.57	6.45	1.88	−11.14	0.00263
400	−5.80	6.50	1.94	−10.36	0.00250
450	−4.17	6.63	2.08	− 8.72	0.00222
500	−2.86	6.75	2.20	− 7.41	0.00200
550	−1.77	6.85	2.32	− 6.30	0.00182
594	−0.99	6.94	2.41	− 5.52	0.00168

Lange and Simon. From the graph shown in Fig. 12-12, l_0 is found to be 112 kJ/mole, and i' to be 1.50.

Fig. 12-12   *Graph for determination of vapor-pressure constant of cadmium.*

The vapor pressure constant i' is connected with the entropy constant of the vapor. To show this correlation, we write the equation

$$\frac{h''' - h'}{T} = s''' - s',$$

where

$$h''' = \int c_P''' \, dT + h_0''' \qquad \text{and} \qquad h' = \int c_P' \, dT + h_0',$$

$$s''' = \int \frac{c_P''' \, dT}{T} - R \ln P + s_0''' \qquad \text{and} \qquad s' = \int \frac{c_P' \, dT}{T} + s_0',$$

subject to the three assumptions made previously. Substituting, we get

$$\frac{1}{T} \int c_P''' \, dT - \frac{1}{T} \int c_P' \, dT + \frac{l_0}{T} = \int \frac{c_P''' \, dT}{T} - R \ln P + s_0''' - \int \frac{c_P' \, dT}{T} - s_0'.$$

For a monatomic vapor $c_P''' = \frac{5}{2}R$; therefore, dividing by R and solving for $\ln P$, we get

$$\ln P = -\frac{l_0}{RT} + \frac{5}{2} \ln T - \frac{1}{R} \left[\int \frac{c_P' \, dT}{T} - \frac{1}{T} \int_0^T c_P' \, dT \right] + \frac{s_0''' - s_0'}{R} + \frac{5}{2}.$$

The two integrals within the bracket may be combined into one double integral, because

$$\int \left(\int c_P' \, dT \right) \frac{dT}{T^2} = -\frac{1}{T} \int c_P' \, dT + \int \frac{c_P' \, dT}{T},$$

by integration by parts. (Let $u = \int c_P' \, dT$ and $dv = dT/T^2$.) Therefore,

$$\ln P = -\frac{l_0}{RT} + \frac{5}{2} \ln T - \frac{1}{R} \int \frac{\int c_P' \, dT}{T^2} \, dT + \frac{s_0''' - s_0'}{R} - \frac{5}{2},$$

and by comparison with Eq. (12-10), it is seen that

$$i' = \frac{s_0''' - s_0'}{R} - \frac{5}{2}. \tag{12-11}$$

Since s_0' is the entropy of a solid at an arbitrarily chosen standard state, it is conventionally set equal to zero, so that

$$i' = \frac{s_0'''}{R} - \frac{5}{2}.$$

In Chap. 10, we calculated the entropy of an ideal monatomic gas and obtained Eq. (10-28), as follows:

$$s = c_V \ln T + R \ln v + R \ln \frac{(2\pi mk/h^2)^{3/2}}{N_A} + \frac{5}{2} R.$$

Dividing by R and replacing v by RT/P, we get

$$\frac{s'''}{R} = \frac{c_P'''}{R} \ln T - \ln P + \ln R \frac{(2\pi mk/h^2)^{3/2}}{N_A} + \frac{5}{2};$$

therefore,

$$i' = \ln \frac{(2\pi m)^{3/2}k^{5/2}}{h^3}. \tag{12-12}$$

Since the mass of a molecule m is proportional to the molecular weight $\mathcal{M}$, we see that the vapor-pressure constant depends on $\mathcal{M}^{3/2}$. A more refined calculation shows that this result is true provided the atom in both the solid and the vapor phases has zero spin and zero angular momentum in its ground state. Limiting ourselves to such substances and evaluating the atomic constants, we get finally

$$i' = -1.589 + \tfrac{3}{2} \log \mathcal{M}. \tag{12-13}$$

A comparison between these theoretical values and the experimental values is given in Table 12-3.

Table 12-3   Calculated and Measured Values of the Vapor-pressure Constant

Substance	Molecular weight $\mathcal{M}$	i' [from Eq. (12-12)]	i' (measured)
He	4.00	−0.69	−0.68
Ne	20.2	0.37	0.39
Mg	24.3	0.49	0.47
A	39.9	0.81	0.81
Zn	65.4	1.13	1.21
Kr	83.7	1.30	1.29
Cd	112	1.49	1.50
Xe	131	1.59	1.60
Hg	201	1.87	1.85

12-6   Measurement of Vapor Pressure

The determination of the heat of sublimation at absolute zero l_0 and the vapor pressure constant i' require accurate measurements of the vapor pressure of solids. It will be seen in Art. 12-7 that the most convenient method of determining the heat of vaporization of a liquid also requires measuring the vapor pressure. It is no wonder that such measurements have engaged the attention of physicists and chemists for many years and still constitute a very active branch of modern thermophysics. Let us consider just a few methods that are commonly used:

1   *Static method.*   When the vapor pressure is within the range from about 10^{-3} to 10^3 mm of Hg, the vessel containing the solid or liquid is connected to a liquid column manometer, and the pressure is obtained directly. There are at least a dozen manometers that are more sensitive (e.g., McLeod gauge, Bourdon gauge, hot-wire, ionization), which enable smaller pressures down to about 10^{-8} mm of Hg to be measured. The static method usually is quite adequate for liquids but often is of little value in measuring the vapor pressure of high-melting-point solids.

2   *Langmuir's evaporation method.*   The solid whose vapor pressure is to be measured is carefully weighed, and its surface area A is determined. It is then placed in an evacuated enclosure and raised to the desired temperature. It evaporates at a constant rate, with the vapor being drawn off. The assumption is made that the rate of evaporation is equal to the rate at which vapor molecules would strike the solid if there were equilibrium between the solid and the vapor. This rate was shown in Chap. 6 (Prob. 6-5e) to be equal to $P/\sqrt{2\pi mkT}$; hence the rate of loss of mass per unit area of surface $\dot{M}/A$ is

$$\frac{\dot{M}}{A} = P\sqrt{\frac{\mathcal{M}}{2\pi RT}} \qquad \text{or} \qquad P = \frac{\dot{M}}{A}\sqrt{\frac{2\pi RT}{\mathcal{M}}},$$

where $\mathcal{M}$ is the molecular weight. This method is very useful when the substance is a high-melting-point wire.

3   *Knudsen's effusion method.*   This is a variation of the Langmuir method in which the weight and area of the solid do not have to be measured. Instead, the evaporating vapor is allowed to pass through an opening of known area and is then condensed in a cold trap. A measurement of the mass of condensed vapor after a time interval provides the quantity $\dot{M}$.

There are many very ingenious methods involving optical absorption, rotation of the direction of vibration of linearly polarized light, measurement of radioactivity, isotope exchange, etc., but these are of interest only to research workers in this field. None of the methods is as simple as it may sound, and all are attended by errors that may go as high as 5 or 10 percent. A critical account of all this work, along with extensive tables, is given in a fine book by A. N. Nesmeyanov ("Vapor Pressure of the Elements," Academic Press, New York, 1963).

The complete temperature dependence of vapor pressure requires a formula with four adjustable constants. Many formulas have been suggested, but the one found most satisfactory by Nesmeyanov is

$$\log P = A - \frac{B}{T} + CT + D \log T. \tag{12-14}$$

Values of the constants and of l_0 are given in his book.

A curious regularity has been found between l_0 and the limit (as $T \to 0$) of the ratio c_V/β. In Table 12-4, values of these two quantities are given for 20 metallic elements. The graph drawn in Fig. 12-13 shows that

$$l_0 \approx \frac{3}{5}\left(\frac{c_v}{\beta}\right)_0, \tag{12-15}$$

Table 12-4   Ratio of Heat Capacity to Expansivity and Heat of Sublimation of Metals

[$(c_V/\beta)_0$ is due to R. K. Kirby; l_0 is due to A. N. Nesmeyanov.]

Metal	$(c_V/\beta)_0$, kJ/mole	l_0, kJ/mole	Metal	$(c_V/\beta)_0$, kJ/mole	l_0, kJ/mole
Ag	470	284	Na	120	108
Al	374	312	Nb	1150	722
Au	632	367	Pb	332	197
Be	513	321	Pd	725	382
Cd	302	112	Pt	964	555
Cu	500	338	Sn	507	302
In	343	238	Ta	1280	780
Fe	700	436	Th	835	470
Li	177	160	Ti	943	472
Mg	340	146	Zn	288	131

Fig. 12-13   *Heat of sublimation at absolute zero is proportional to* $(c_V/\beta)_0$.

12-7   Vaporization

The heat of vaporization of liquids with normal boiling points from, let us say, 250 to about 550°K is generally measured directly with a calorimeter resembling that shown in Fig. 12-14. The sample liquid L_2 is contained in a small vessel and has immersed in it a small heating coil R_2. Completely surrounding this vessel is a temperature bath consisting of a mixture of air and the vapor of another liquid L_1. By choosing a suitable liquid L_1 and keeping it at its boiling point by means of the heating coil R_1 in the presence of air at the proper pressure, the temperature bath may be maintained at any desired temperature. At this chosen temperature, the liquid L_2 is in equilibrium with its vapor. The small vessel containing L_2 communicates with another vessel on the outside (not shown in the figure), which may be maintained at any desired temperature by a separately controlled heating or cooling device.

If the temperature of the outside container is maintained at less than that of L_2, a pressure gradient is produced, and some of L_2 will distill over. By maintaining a small current I in the heating coil R_2, the temperature of L_2 is kept equal to that of its surroundings, and the energy necessary to vaporize it is thus supplied. There is therefore a steady distillation of L_2 into the outside container, with the heat of vaporization being supplied by the heating coil

Fig. 12-14   *Apparatus for measuring heat of vaporization.*

R_2 and the heat of condensation being withdrawn by the surroundings of the outside container. Moreover, all the energy supplied by the heater R_2 is used to vaporize L_2, since there is no heat loss between the inner tube and its surroundings. Consequently, if n moles are vaporized in a time τ, the heat of vaporization per mole is

$$l_V = \frac{\mathscr{E} I \tau}{n}.$$

Of much more interest are the cryogenic liquids with normal boiling points in the neighborhood of 100°K or less. For these liquids, one needs the sort of information found in engineering handbooks—that is, the pressure, entropy, enthalpy, and volume of both saturated liquid and saturated vapor at temperatures from the triple point to the critical point. A few such tables are now available, and the heat of vaporization may be obtained by performing the subtraction $h''' - h''$. In Table 12-5, vaporization data for some simple liquids, obtained from thermodynamic tables prepared by F. Din, are listed. In Fig. 12-15, the heat of vaporization l_V divided by the critical temperature T_C has been plotted against the quantity $P(v''' - v'')/T$ from about $0.5 T_C$ to $0.98 T_C$. It may be seen that the points for five gases lie on a common straight line, and therefore one is led to assume that similar points for other simple liquids would lie on the same straight line. By the term "simple" we mean liquids such as Kr, Xe, and O_2 whose molecules have no dipole moment (or at least only a small one) and do not associate in the liquid or the vapor

Table 12-5   **Vaporization Data†**

Substance	T, °K	T/T_C	l_V, J/mole	l_V/T_C, J/mole · deg	P, atm	$v''' - v''$, liter/mole	$\dfrac{P(v''' - v)''}{T}$, J/mole · deg
N₂	63.2	0.501	6200	49.1	0.124	41.9	8.31
$T_C = 126.2$°K	77.4	0.612	5580	44.2	1	6.06	7.93
$P_C = 33.5$ atm	94.1	0.745	4980	39.4	5	1.33	7.16
	104	0.823	4430	35.1	10	0.655	6.38
	111	0.879	3880	30.7	15	0.399	5.45
	116	0.918	3290	26.0	20	0.262	4.58
	120	0.950	2630	20.8	25	0.173	3.65
	124	0.981	1840	14.6	30	0.102	2.50
A	83.8	0.556	6610	43.8	0.679	9.93	8.18
$T_C = 151$°K	87.3	0.580	6520	43.2	1	6.97	8.10
$P_C = 48$ atm	106	0.704	5860	38.8	5	1.55	7.41
	117	0.777	5290	35.0	10	0.769	6.66
	124	0.823	4820	31.9	15	0.494	6.05
	130	0.863	4350	28.8	20	0.347	5.42
	135	0.896	3880	25.7	25	0.255	4.99
	139	0.924	3420	22.6	30	0.192	4.20
	146	0.970	2510	16.6	40	0.107	2.98
CO	72.4	0.544	6480	48.7	0.3	19.0	8.00
$T_C = 133$°K	81.6	0.614	6050	45.5	1	6.32	7.85
$P_C = 34.5$ atm	99.0	0.745	5130	38.6	5	1.30	6.65
	109	0.820	4500	33.8	10	0.650	6.04
	115	0.865	4130	31.1	14	0.449	5.54
	120	0.902	3750	28.2	18	0.326	4.96
	126	0.948	2800	21.0	25	0.185	3.71
	130	0.977	1990	15.0	30	0.109	2.55

† Taken from F. Din (ed.), "Thermodynamic Functions of Gases," Butterworth Scientific Publications, London, 1956.

phase. Determining the slope of the line in Fig. 12-15 to be 5.4, we may write

$$\frac{l_V/T_C}{P(v''' - v'')/T} = 5.4 \qquad \left(\text{for } 0.5 < \frac{T}{T_C} < 1\right). \qquad (12\text{-}16)$$

This relation may be regarded as a law of corresponding states. In the present form it is of limited usefulness, however, since it involves a knowledge of so many quantities. It is therefore of interest to examine the consequences of this strange proportionality. We first write Clapeyron's equation in the form

$$\frac{dP/P}{dT/T^2} = \frac{l_V}{P(v''' -- v'')/T} = \frac{(l_V/T_C)\,T_C}{P(v''' - v'')/T}.$$

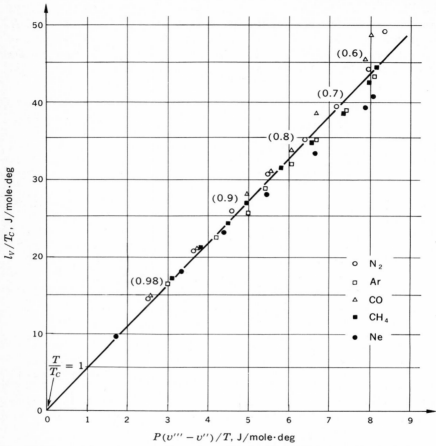

Fig. 12-15 *A law of corresponding states valid at reduced temperature between about 0.5 and 1.*

Notice that the right-hand member is equal to $5.4 T_C$. The resulting equation,

$$\frac{dP}{P} = 5.4 T_C \frac{dT}{T^2},$$

may be integrated from T to T_C and from P to P_C, provided that T/T_C is not less than 0.5. Hence,

$$\ln \frac{P_C}{P} = 5.4 T_C \left(\frac{1}{T} - \frac{1}{T_C} \right)$$

or

$$\ln \frac{P}{P_C} = 5.4 \left(1 - \frac{T_C}{T} \right) \quad \left(\text{for } 0.5 < \frac{T}{T_C} < 1 \right). \qquad (12\text{-}17)$$

Equation (12-17) is a genuine *law of corresponding states*, expressed in terms of reduced temperature and reduced pressure. It was first suggested by E. A. Guggenheim, who plotted the logarithm of the reduced vapor pressure against the reciprocal of the reduced temperature for seven simple liquids, as shown in Fig. 12-16. The points are seen to fall well along one straight line whose equation is

$$\ln \frac{P}{P_c} = 5.3 \left(1 - \frac{T_c}{T} \right) \qquad \left(\text{for } 0.55 < \frac{T}{T_c} < 1 \right),$$

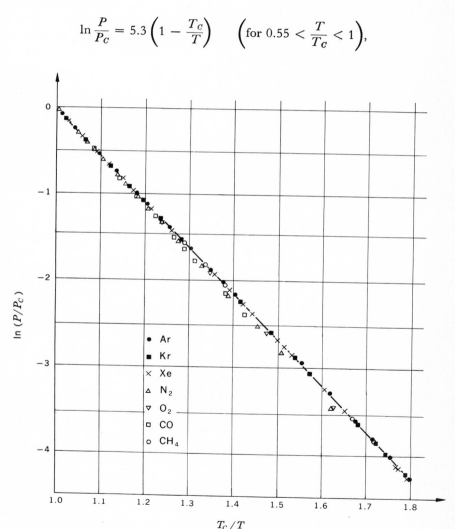

Fig. 12-16   *A law of corresponding states for simple liquids.* (E. A. Guggenheim, "*Thermodynamics*," *Interscience, 1957.*)

and the numerical agreement with Eq. (12-17) is quite satisfactory. It is conceivable that liquids whose molecules have large electric dipole moments and exert unusual forces on one another will obey a law of corresponding states with a different numerical constant.

There is another interesting consequence of the law of corresponding states, as given in Eq. (12-17), which is brought to light if we restrict ourselves to a *small region of temperature* far enough from the critical point to allow us to regard l_V as constant, say, around the normal boiling point. In this region, v'' is negligible compared with v''', and the vapor pressure is small enough to approximate that of an ideal gas, or $v''' = RT/P$. Under these circumstances, Clapeyron's equation becomes

$$\frac{dP}{dT} = \frac{l_V}{RT^2/P},$$

or

$$\frac{l_V}{R} = -\frac{d \ln P}{d(1/T)} = -\frac{d \ln (P/P_C)}{d(1/T)}.$$

If we integrate this equation over a very small temperature range around T_B, where l_V has the constant value l_{VB}, we get

$$\ln \frac{P}{P_C} = \text{const.} - \frac{l_{VB}}{RT}. \tag{12-18}$$

Table 12-6   Heat of Vaporization at the Normal Boiling Point, l_{VB}

Liquid	T_B, °K	T_C, °K	T_B/T_C	l_{VB}/R, °K	$\dfrac{l_{VB}}{RT_B}$
Ne	27.1	44.7	0.606	210	7.7
N_2	77.4	126	0.614	676	8.8
CO	81.7	133	0.614	725	8.9
A	87.3	151	0.578	786	9.1
F_2	86	144	0.597	786	9.2
O_2	90.2	155	0.582	822	9.1
CH_4	112	191	0.586	988	8.8
Kr	120	209	0.574	1090	9.1
Xe	165	290	0.570	1530	9.2
C_2H_4	170	282	0.582	1640	9.6
C_2H_6	185	306	0.604	1770	9.6
HCl	189	325	0.582	1920	10.1
HBr	206	363	0.568	2120	10.3
Cl_2	239	417	0.574	2460	10.3
CS_2	319	552	0.578	3220	10.1

In Table 12-6, the normal boiling points of 12 simple liquids are listed along with their critical points, and the reduced normal boiling points, T_B/T_C, are seen to lie between 0.57 and 0.61, within the range of the law of corresponding states. Therefore, comparing Eqs. (12-17) and (12-18), we get

$$\frac{l_{VB}}{R} = 5.4T_C. \qquad (12\text{-}19)$$

Using the data in Table 12-6, a graph of l_{VB}/R vs. T_C is shown in Fig. 12-17, and again a single straight line is found for fifteen simple liquids. The slope

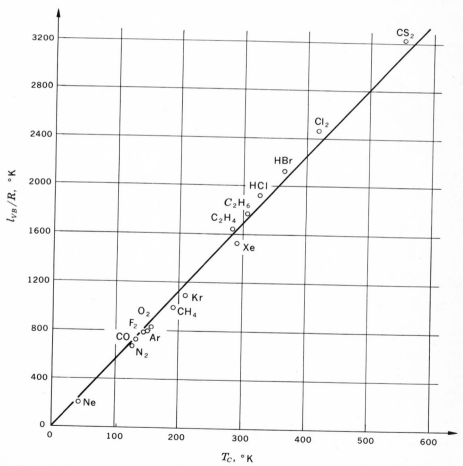

Fig. 12-17   *A law of corresponding states for heat of vaporization of simple liquids at a reduced temperature of about 0.6.*

of this line is found to be 5.6, in fair agreement with the expected value. (The agreement would be perfect if only the first nine liquids were considered.)

Since the reduced boiling point of many liquids is in the neighborhood of 0.6, Eq. (12-19) may be regarded as a law of corresponding states, with the statement:

$$l_{VB} \text{ (at } T/T_C \sim 0.6) = 5.4RT_C.$$

Referring to Table 12-6, note that the ratio given in the last column, constituting the entropy change due to vaporization at the normal boiling point, is *not* constant but increases with T_B. The increase is small, however, so that a rough approximation is provided by taking l_V/RT_B to be about 9—a working rule known as *Trouton's rule*, which is useful in cases where T_C is not known.

12-8   Critical State

The liquid and vapor phases of a substance may coexist in equilibrium at a constant temperature and pressure over a wide range of volumes from v'', where there is practically all liquid, to v''', where there is practically all vapor. At a higher temperature and pressure, v'' increases and v''' decreases. At the critical point, the two volumes (and therefore also the two densities) coincide. On a Pv diagram, the critical point is the limiting position as two points lying on a horizontal line approach each other. Hence, at the critical point, the critical isotherm has a horizontal tangent, or $(\partial P/\partial v)_{T_C} = 0$. As is evident from Fig. 12-18, the critical isotherm must have a point of inflection at the critical point, and therefore $(\partial^2 P/\partial v^2)_{T_C} = 0$.

At all points within the region of coexistence of the liquid and vapor phases, including the critical point, the three physical properties $c_P = T(\partial S/\partial T)_P$, $\beta = (1/v)(\partial v/\partial T)_P$, and $\kappa = -(1/v)(\partial v/\partial P)_T$ are all *infinite*. On the other hand, c_V is finite, so that $\gamma = c_P/c_V$ is also infinite.

To measure precise values of P_C, v_C, and T_C, it is necessary to determine exactly *when* the critical state is reached. For this purpose, the material is raised in temperature slowly and uniformly in a sealed tube of constant volume. Consider the tube filled so that the meniscus separating the phases is initially near the top of the tube. When the temperature is raised, the liquid will expand and the meniscus will rise to the top of the tube as the last of the vapor condenses, according to the dashed line $1 \rightarrow 2$ in Fig. 12-18. If the tube is filled so that the initial position of the meniscus is near the bottom, then the meniscus will fall to the bottom as the last of the liquid vaporizes,

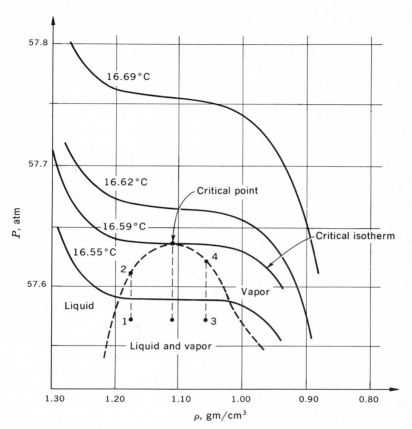

Fig. 12-18   *Isotherms of xenon near the critical point.* (*H. W. Habgood and W. G. Schneider, 1954.*)

according to the dashed line $3 \rightarrow 4$ of Fig. 12-18. To observe the critical point, the tube must be filled so that the meniscus will remain in about the middle of the tube, as shown by the dashed line passing through the critical point. As the critical point is approached, observation becomes difficult because of the following factors:

1   Since the compressibility is infinite, the gravitational field of the earth causes large density gradients from top to bottom. These may be offset somewhat by taking observations of the tube in both vertical and horizontal positions.

2   Since the heat capacity is infinite, thermal equilibrium is difficult to achieve. It is necessary to keep the system at a constant temperature (within 10^{-2} or even 10^{-3} deg) for a long time and to stir constantly.

3   Since the thermal expansivity is infinite, small temperature changes of a local mass element within the system produce large volume changes, and therefore there are violent density fluctuations, which give rise to a large amount of light scattering, so that the material becomes almost opaque. This phenomenon is called *critical opalescence*.

The critical pressure may be measured at the same time as the critical temperature by noting the pressure at which the meniscus disappears. The critical volume, however, is much more difficult to determine. This measurement is carried out most commonly by measuring the densities of both saturated liquid and saturated vapor as a function of temperature to as close to the critical temperature as possible. The vapor and liquid densities are then plotted against temperature, and a line representing the arithmetic average of these densities is constructed as shown in Fig. 12-19. This last line is usually called the *rectilinear diameter*, and experiment shows it to be virtually linear. Extrapolation to the critical temperature yields the critical density.

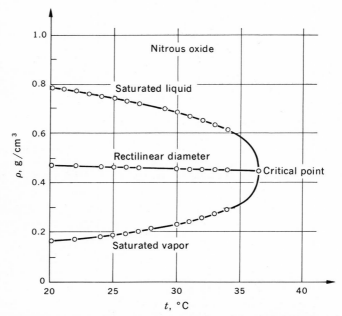

Fig. 12-19   *Measurements of liquid and vapor densities of nitrous oxide, and extrapolation of the mean density through the critical point.* (D. Cook, 1953.)

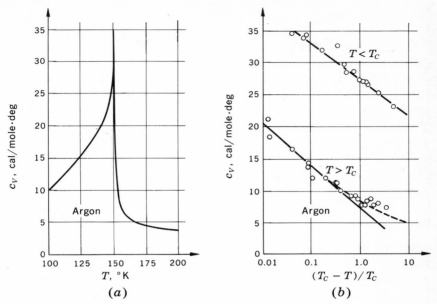

Fig. 12-20   (a) C_V of argon below and above the critical point. (b) C_V of argon varies as log $(T_c - T)$. (M. I. Bagatskii, A. V. Voronel', and V. G. Gusak, 1963.)

The density-temperature relationship for the saturated phases as shown in Fig. 12-19 was for a time believed to show irregularities near the critical point. However, the curve is now believed to be smooth, as shown.

The dashed vertical line $1 \rightarrow 2$ in Fig. 12-18 represents a constant-volume increase of temperature at a volume less than the critical volume. If the heat capacity c_V is measured along this line, it will be found to be quite large, because heat is required not only to raise the temperature but also to change the relative proportions of liquid and vapor. As the liquid saturation curve is crossed at point 2, c_V would be expected to take a sudden drop. Of particular interest is the behavior of the c_V vs. T curve at the critical volume, very close to the critical point. This was first done in 1963 by Bagatskii, Voronel', and Gusak, who showed that the c_V of argon varied as the logarithm of $(T_C - T)$, as shown in Fig. 12-20.

Using a temperature-measuring technique in which a change of 10^{-6} deg Kelvin could be detected, Moldover and Little also measured c_V above and below the critical point of both He^4 and He^3. Their results again indicate that c_V varies as log $(T_C - T)$, and therefore c_V has a logarithmic singularity at the critical point. This sort of behavior is peculiar to a type of phase transition called a *lambda transition*, which will be discussed in Art. 12-10.

12-9   Fusion

The simplest method of measuring the heat of fusion of a solid is to supply electrical energy at a constant rate and to measure the temperature at convenient time intervals. Plotting the temperature against the time, a heating curve is obtained in which the phase transition appears as a straight line at constant temperature, of length $\Delta\tau$ as measured along the time axis. The apparatus, shielding, precautions, etc., are exactly the same as those required in the measurement of heat capacity, which were described in Chap. 4. If n moles of solid melt in time $\Delta\tau$, with electrical energy supplied at the rate $\mathcal{E}I$, then

$$l_F = \frac{\mathcal{E}I\,\Delta\tau}{n}.$$

If T_M is the normal melting point of a solid and l_{FM} is the latent heat of fusion at the normal melting point, the entropy change associated with melting at this temperature is l_{FM}/RT_M, expressed in units of R. This entropy change is listed in Table 12-7 for 15 nonmetallic solids and 15 metals, and it may be seen that metals show more of a regularity than nonmetals. Very roughly, l_{FM}/RT_M is about 1 for metals.

Table 12-7   Entropy Change Accompanying Fusion at the Normal Melting Point T_M

Nonmetal	T_M, °K	l_{FM}, kJ/mole	$\dfrac{l_{FM}}{RT_M}$	Metal	T_M, °K	l_{FM}, kJ/mole	$\dfrac{l_{FM}}{RT_M}$
O_2	54.4	0.444	0.98	Hg	234	2.30	0.98
N_2	63.2	0.722	1.37	Cs	302	2.14	0.85
CO	68.1	0.838	1.48	Rb	312	2.34	0.90
A	83.8	1.18	1.70	K	336	2.32	0.83
C_2H_6	89.9	2.86	3.83	Na	371	2.61	0.85
CH_4	90.7	0.944	1.25	Li	454	3.02	0.80
C_2H_4	104	3.35	3.88	Cd	594	5.78	1.17
Kr	116	1.64	1.70	Pb	601	4.86	0.97
Xe	161	2.30	1.72	Zn	692	7.29	1.27
Cl_2	172	6.41	4.49	Mg	923	7.33	0.96
CCl_4	250	2.47	1.19	Ag	1233	11.3	1.10
CH_4ON_2	406	14.5	4.30	Au	1336	12.8	1.15
$CaCl_2$	1055	28.8	3.28	Cu	1356	13.0	1.15
Ge	1210	31.8	2.71	Be	1556	11.7	0.91
Si	1683	46.4	2.76	Ni	1728	17.6	1.23

Fig. 12-21   *Blocked-capillary method of measuring melting pressure.*

The various pressures and temperatures at which the solid and liquid phases coexist in equilibrium determine the melting curve, and one of the first tasks of the experimenter is to determine the equation of this curve. In the region of low temperatures, the melting temperatures and pressures are often measured by the *blocked-capillary* method, illustrated in Fig. 12-21. The material in the gaseous phase is compressed to a high pressure and is forced into a steel capillary, part of which is immersed in a low-temperature bath whose temperature may be adjusted to any desired value by careful choice of the bath liquid and its pressure. Two manometers, M_1 before the bath and M_2 after, communicate with the capillary. The melting pressure associated with the temperature of the bath is the maximum reading of M_2. Four typical melting curves, those of neon, argon, krypton, and xenon, are shown in Fig. 12-22.

In 1929 F. E. Simon and G. Glatzel suggested an equation that has been fairly successful in representing the data on melting curves, as follows:

$$P - P_3 = a[(T/T_3)^c - 1] \qquad (12\text{-}20)$$

where T_3 and P_3 are the coordinates of the triple point, and a and c are constants that also depend on the substance. At the high pressures, P_3 is negligible, so that the equation is usually used in the form

$$P/a = (T/T_3)^c - 1.$$

The values of a and c for the four condensed inert gases shown in Fig. 12-22 are listed in Table 12-8, and those for many other solids have been given by S. E. Babb, Jr., in an article in the *Reviews of Modern Physics* (April, 1963).

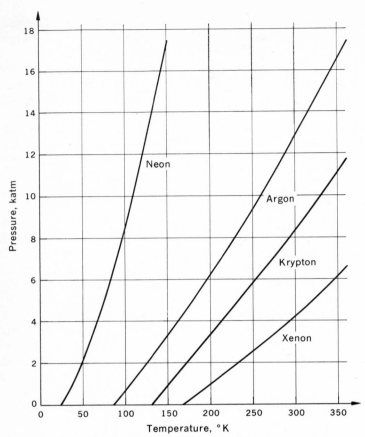

Fig. 12-22   *Melting curves of neon, argon, krypton, and xenon. (S. E. Babb, Rev. Mod. Phys., April, 1963; G. L. Pollack, Rev. Mod. Phys., July, 1964.)*

Table 12-8   Melting Parameters of Condensed Inert Gases

Solidified inert gas	T_3, °K	P_3, atm	a, atm	c
Ne	24.6	0.426	1022	1.6
Ar	83.8	0.681	2240	1.5
Kr	116	0.723	3010	1.4
Xe	161	0.806	3410	1.31

The slope of the melting curve is negative for those few substances like ice I which contract upon melting. This behavior is shown by Bi, Ge, Si, and Ga and requires values of T in Simon's equation less than T_3. Consequently the values of a are negative. The various values of a and c for four of the forms of ice are shown in Fig. 12-23. In Fig. 12-24 are shown the enormous pressures and temperatures needed to produce gaseous and liquid carbon and also the solid crystalline form of diamond.

Theories concerning the exact processes that take place when a solid melts have engaged the attention of physicists for many years. It was first

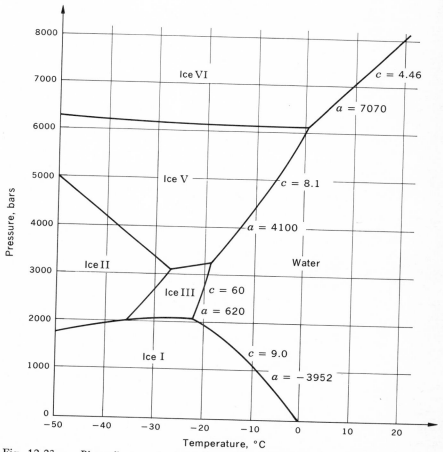

Fig. 12-23   *Phase diagram of water, with melting parameters of ice I, III, V, and VI.* (1 bar = 10^6 dyn/cm².)

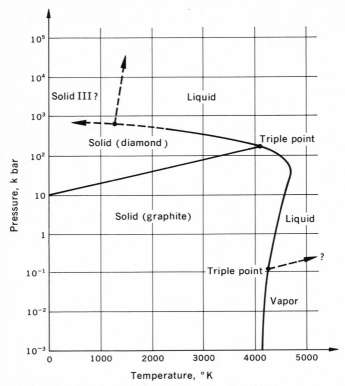

Fig. 12-24   *Phase diagram for carbon. (1 k bar = 10^6 dyn/cm^2.)*

suggested by Lindemann that a solid melts when the amplitude of the lattice vibrations becomes large enough to break down the attractive forces holding the lattice together; in more picturesque language, "In melting, a solid shakes itself to pieces." With this point of view, Lindemann derived the formula

$$\frac{\mathcal{M}v^{2/3}\Theta^2}{T_M} = \text{const.,} \tag{12-21}$$

where $\mathcal{M}$ and v are the molecular weight and molar volume, Θ is the Debye characteristic temperature, and T_M is the melting temperature. This relation holds quite well for many metals and nonmetals, but there are a few of each that depart radically from the formula. This suggests that the melting process is not exclusively a question of lattice vibrations. Dislocations and vacancies in the crystal lattice, as well as the quantities specifying the law of force among the molecules of both solid and liquid, are all considered to play a role. On the basis of such ideas, it is possible to provide a slight theoretical foundation for the Simon equation; as of 1968, however, no complete theory of fusion has been developed.

12-10   Higher-order Transitions

The processes of sublimation, vaporization, and fusion were called phase transitions of the first order because the first-order derivatives of the Gibbs function, $S = -(\partial G/\partial T)_P$ and $V = (\partial G/\partial P)_T$, underwent finite changes during the transition. In contrast, there are many phase transitions in which the entropy and the volume are the *same* at the end of the transition as they were in the beginning. In such phase changes, T, P, G, S, and V remain unchanged, and therefore H, U, and F also remain unchanged. If C_P, κ, and β undergo *finite* changes in such a transition, then, since

$$\frac{C_P}{T} = \left(\frac{\partial S}{\partial T}\right)_P = \frac{\partial}{\partial T}\left(-\frac{\partial G}{\partial T}\right) = -\frac{\partial^2 G}{\partial T^2},$$

$$\kappa V = -\left(\frac{\partial V}{\partial P}\right)_T = -\frac{\partial}{\partial P}\left(\frac{\partial G}{\partial P}\right) = -\frac{\partial^2 G}{\partial P^2},$$

and

$$\beta V = \left(\frac{\partial V}{\partial T}\right)_P = \frac{\partial}{\partial T}\left(\frac{\partial G}{\partial P}\right) = \frac{\partial^2 G}{\partial T\, \partial P},$$

there would be finite changes of the second-order derivatives of the Gibbs function. Such a transition is called a *second-order phase transition*. This transition was first suggested by Ehrenfest, who derived two simple equations that expressed the constancy of S and V. It was first thought that there were many examples of second-order transitions; but as experimental measurements were made closer and closer to the transition temperature (sometimes to within a millionth of a degree!), neither C_P nor β was found to achieve a finite value at the beginning or at the end of the phase transition. It may be that there is only one example of a second-order phase transition, namely, the change from superconductivity to normal conductivity in zero magnetic field. Since this transition will be considered in some detail in Chap. 15, we shall reserve discussion of second-order transitions until then.

By far the most interesting higher-order phase transition is that called the *lambda transition*, characterized by the following:

1   T, P, and G remain constant.
2   S and V (also U, H, and F) remain constant.
3   C_P, β, and κ are infinite.

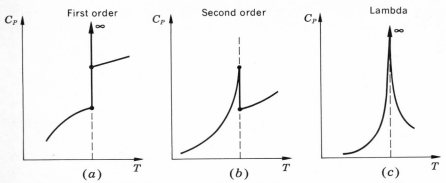

Fig. 12-25   *Distinguishing characteristic among the three types of phase transitions.* (*a*) *First-order;* (*b*) *second-order;* (*c*) *lambda.*

A graph of C_P against T serves to distinguish among the three types of transitions, as shown in Fig. 12-25. The name "lambda transition" is accounted for by the fact that the shape of the $C_P - T$ curve in the third graph resembles the Greek letter lambda. Among the many examples of λ transitions are: (1) "order-disorder" transformations in alloys; (2) the onset of ferroelectricity in certain crystals such as Rochelle salt; (3) the transition from ferromagnetism to paramagnetism at the Curie point; (4) a change of orientation of an ion in a crystal lattice, such as the ammonium chloride transition; and— most interesting of all—(5) the transition from ordinary liquid helium (liq. He I) to superfluid helium (liq. He II) at a temperature and corresponding pressure known as a *lambda point*.

It may be seen in Fig. 12-25*a* that, as a substance in any one phase approaches the temperature at which a first-order phase transition is to occur, its C_P remains finite up to the transition temperature. It becomes infinite only when a small amount of the other phase is present, and its behavior *before* this takes place shows no evidence of any premonition of the coming event. In the case of a λ transition, however, as is evident in Fig. 12-25*c*, C_P starts to rise before the transition point is reached, as though the substance, in the form of only one phase, "anticipated" the coming phase transition. Because the molecules of substances undergoing λ transitions interact strongly with one another, even at distances beyond those of their nearest neighbors, a rigorous statistical treatment is very difficult. The one physical process that has yielded to mathematical solution, namely, the transition from ferromagnetism to paramagnetism according to a simple model known as the *two-dimensional Ising model*, shows the typical anticipatory rise of C_P before the λ transition occurs.

The temperatures and pressures at which the λ transition takes place in

He^4 constitute the λ line shown on the phase diagram of Fig. 12-26a. If we define a new variable t, where

$$t = T - T_\lambda,$$

the slope of the λ line at any point, dP/dT $(= P'_\lambda)$, will be the same at a corresponding point on the parallel curve where the temperature $T = T_\lambda + t$, since the dashed curve marked $t = t$ is merely the λ line shifted a distance t to the right. We shall limit ourselves to very small values of t.

On the entropy curve of Fig. 12-26b, the slope of the dashed curve marked $t = t$ is the same as that of the curve $t = 0$ (S'_λ) at a point at the same pressure, since t is very small. The same is true on the volume diagram of Fig. 12-26c. With these facts in mind, let us use the second $T\,dS$ equation to represent a

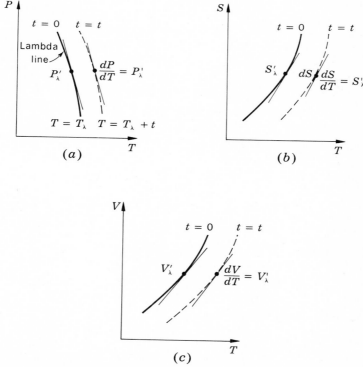

Fig. 12-26   (a) *The λ line of He^4 on a phase diagram. (b), (c) Entropy and volume at points on the λ line. The slope of a curve at a small temperature difference t above (or below) the λ line is the same as that at a corresponding point on the λ line.*

small entropy change *on the dashed entropy curve* of Fig. 12-26*b*, where $T = T_\lambda + t$. Using small letters to indicate molar quantities,

$$ds = \frac{c_P}{T}\, dT - v\beta\, dP,$$

or

$$\frac{c_P}{T} = \frac{ds}{dT} + v\beta\, \frac{dP}{dT}.$$

Since ds/dT and dP/dT are the same, respectively, as the slopes at the corresponding points on the curves where $T = T_\lambda$, we have

$$\frac{c_P}{T} = s'_\lambda + v\beta P'_\lambda. \tag{12-22}$$

This equation is true whether $T > T_\lambda$ or $T < T_\lambda$, and it shows that c_P/T should vary linearly with $v\beta$ as the transition is approached (either from above or below) with a slope equal to P'_λ. Using t as a convenient parameter, experimental measurements of c_P and β as a function of t, when combined, should yield a linear relation between c_P/T and $v\beta$. Because it is not convenient to measure the c_P of liquid helium, the molar heat capacity at constant saturation c_S is usually measured, and c_P is calculated from a simple relation that

Fig. 12-27   *Specific heat of liquid helium II vs. log $|T - T_\lambda|$. (Kellers, Fairbank, and Buckingham; Hill, Lounsamaa, and Kojo; and Kramers, Wasscher, and Gorter.)*

Fig. 12-28   *Volume expansivity of liquid helium II vs. log* $|T - T_\lambda|$. (*Atkins and Edwards; Chase and Maxwell; Kerr and Taylor.*)

can be found in the problems at the end of this chapter. In the case of liquid helium, the correction is quite small.

The variation of c_S of liquid helium II with t is shown in Fig. 12-27, and the variation of β of liquid helium II with t is seen in Fig. 12-28, where the dependence on the logarithm of t, characteristic of λ transitions, is displayed even down to $t = 10^{-6}$ deg. The expected linear relation between c_P/T and $v\beta$ is shown in Fig. 12-29. Some numerical values at three points on the λ line are given in Table 12-9.

Table 12-9   Quantities at Three Points on the λ Line of He^4

P_λ, atm	T_λ, °K	ρ_λ, g/cm³	$P'_\lambda = (dP/dT)_\lambda$ atm/deg	$v'_\lambda = (\partial v/\partial T)_\lambda$ cm³/g · deg	$s'_\lambda = (\partial s/\partial T)_\lambda$ J/g · deg²
0.05	2.172	0.146	−130	13	2.3
13	2.00	0.167	− 75	2.7	0.9
29.7	1.762	0.180	− 60	1.5	0.6

Fig. 12-29   *Straight-line relation between c_P/T and β of liquid helium II.*

12-11   Liquid and Solid Helium

Any temperature and pressure at which three phases of the same substance may coexist in equilibrium are a triple point. Water and many other substances have several triple points, but only one triple point refers to the equilibrium of solid, liquid, and vapor phases. Every material that has been studied has such a triple point, with the exception of helium. As the vapor of liquid He^4 is pumped away, the remaining liquid gets colder; and at the λ point, liquid helium II forms, so that the λ point may be regarded as a triple point for liquid I, liquid II, and vapor, as shown in Fig. 12-30.

The zero-point energy of liquid helium is about 210 J/mole, or about three times as large as the heat of vaporization. If a crystal were to form, it would

Fig. 12-30   *Phase diagram of He⁴.*

be unstable under its own vapor pressure; therefore, as the vapor above liquid helium is pumped away, helium remains a liquid down to the lowest temperatures yet achieved (∼10⁻⁶ °K). To produce solid helium, it is necessary to bring the helium atoms closer together, to the point where attractive forces may produce cohesion. This requires an increase of pressure above 25 atm, so that there is an *upper triple point* where two liquids and a solid may coexist in equilibrium. As a matter of fact, the phase diagram of Fig. 12-30 shows the presence of two different crystal structures for solid He⁴, hexagonal close-packed (abbreviated hcp) and body-centered cubic (abbreviated bcc).

About one part in a million of He⁴ is the light isotope He³, shown in Fig. 12-31, along with that of He⁴. Three features are quite striking:

1   The normal boiling point of He³ (at which the vapor pressure is 760 mm) is 3.2°K, so that by pumping the He³ vapor away tempera-

tures may be produced which are lower than those obtainable with He⁴. Thus, by lowering the vapor pressure of He³ to 0.024 mm, a temperature of 0.4°K can be reached. To reach the same temperature with He⁴ would require lowering the vapor pressure to 2.7×10^{-7} mm, which is out of the question.

2 He³ has no triple points at all.

3 The melting curve, which is the locus of points representing temperatures and pressures at which solid and liquid He³ are in equilibrium, *shows a minimum* at about 0.3°K.

Both liquid He⁴ and liquid He³ show a negative thermal expansivity at temperatures above about 1°K.

In the region of high pressures, from 100 to 5000 atm, other crystal structures form in both He⁴ and He³, as shown in Fig. 12-32. The heat capacity of

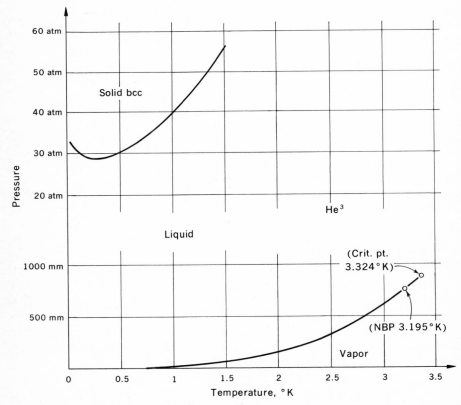

Fig. 12-31   *Phase diagram of He³.*

Fig. 12-32   *Phase diagrams for He⁴ and He³ at high pressures. (A. F. Schuch and R. L. Mills, 1962.)*

these solids has been measured and found to obey a Debye T^3 law, with a Debye Θ depending both on T and on the molar volume v. The temperature dependence is such as to enable an extrapolation to be made to zero temperature, so that the volume dependance of Θ_0 can be studied. This is shown in Fig. 12-33, and the curves have a twofold purpose:

1   By using the result of Prob. 11-20, namely, that the zero-point energy of a crystal is $\frac{9}{8}R\Theta_0$, one can calculate the zero-point energy of solid helium and compare it with that of liquid helium. At $\Theta_0 = 30°$K, $\frac{9}{8}R\Theta \sim 270$ J/mole; and at $\Theta_0 = 110°$K, $\frac{9}{8}R\Theta_0 \sim 1000$ J/mole. Both of these extreme values *exceed* the zero-point energy of the liquid.

2   By using the result of Prob. 11-23, namely, that the Gruneisen Γ is given by

$$\Gamma = -\frac{d \ln \Theta_0}{d \ln v},$$

in conjunction with the curves in Fig. 12-33, the result is obtained that $\Gamma \sim 2.5$.

The transition between the solid and liquid phases of He^4 and of He^3 is particularly interesting. The latent heat of fusion may be calculated from experimental values of $v'' - v'$ and of dP/dT, using Clapeyron's equation. The results of such calculations by Simon and Swenson on He^4 and by Dugdale on He^3 are shown in Fig. 12-34. Notice that, in both cases, the latent heat becomes practically zero at low temperatures, whereas $P(v'' - v')$ does not. As a result, the energy difference $u'' - u' = l_F - P(v'' - v')$ becomes negative, indicating that *the energy of solid helium is greater than that of liquid helium* at the same temperature. The melting of solid helium at such temperatures is a purely mechanical process, since there is practically no latent heat in this temperature region. An isothermal reduction in pressure produces melting; conversely, an isothermal increase of pressure produces solidification.

Fig. 12-33   *Debye Θ_0 as a function of volume for solid He^4 and He^3. (Heltemes and Swenson, 1962; Dugdale and Franck, 1964.)*

Fig. 12-34   *Energy relations for liquid and solid helium, calculated with the aid of Clapeyron's equation and the first law. (a) He⁴ (F. E. Simon and C. A. Swenson); (b) He³ (J. S. Dugdale).*

Another interesting characteristic of solid helium is that its compressibility is greater than that of liquid helium.

PROBLEMS

12-1

(*a*)   Show that in a Joule-Kelvin expansion, no temperature change occurs if $(\partial v/\partial T)_P = v/T$.

(*b*)   Show that

$$\mu c_P = T^2 \left[\frac{\partial(v/T)}{\partial T} \right]_P.$$

In the region of moderate pressures, the equation of state of 1 mole of a gas may be written

$$Pv = RT + B'P + C'P^2,$$

where the second and third virial coefficients B' and C' are functions of T only.

(c)   Show that, as the pressure approaches zero,

$$\mu c_P \to T\frac{dB'}{dT} - B'.$$

(d)   Show that the equation of the inversion curve is

$$P = -\frac{B' - T(dB'/dT)}{C' - T(dC'/dT)}.$$

12-2   The Joule-Kelvin coefficient μ is a measure of the temperature change during a throttling process. A similar measure of the temperature change produced by an isentropic change of pressure is provided by the coefficient μ_S, where

$$\mu_S = \left(\frac{\partial T}{\partial P}\right)_S.$$

Prove that

$$\mu_S - \mu = \frac{V}{C_P}.$$

12-3   According to Hill and Lounasmaa, the equation of the helium inversion curve is

$$P = -21.0 + 5.44T - 0.132T^2,$$

where P is given in atmospheres.
  (a)   What is the maximum inversion temperature?
  (b)   What point on the inversion curve has the maximum pressure?
12-4   Saturated liquid carbon dioxide at a temperature of 293°K and a pressure of 56.5 atm undergoes throttling to a pressure of 1 atm. The temperature of the resulting mixture of solid and vapor is 195°K. What fraction is vaporized? (The enthalpy of saturated liquid at the initial state is 24,200 J/mole, and the enthalpy of saturated solid at the final state is 6750 J/mole. The heat of sublimation at the final state is 25,100 J/mole.)
12-5   Prove that, during a phase transition of the first order, (a) the entropy of the entire system is a linear function of the total volume; (b) the energy change is given by

$$\Delta U = L\left(1 - \frac{d\ln T}{d\ln P}\right).$$

12-6   Iodine crystals have an atomic weight of 127 g/mole and a specific heat of 0.197 J/g · deg. Iodine vapor may be assumed to be an ideal diatomic gas with a constant c_P. At 301°K, the vapor pressure is 515 dyn/cm²; at

299°K, it is 435 dyn/cm². Compute the latent heat of sublimation (a) at 300°K; (b) at absolute zero; and (c) at 200°K.

12-7 The heat of sublimation of zinc at 600°K is found to be 130 kJ/mole. The heat capacity of solid zinc is such that

$$\int_0^{600} c_P' \, dT = 13{,}800 \text{ J/mole,}$$

and B at 600°K is 1.96. The vapor pressure of zinc at 600°K is 4.67×10^{-3} mm of Hg. Assuming zinc vapor to be an ideal gas, calculate (a) the heat of sublimation at absolute zero, and (b) the vapor-pressure constant.

12-8 The vapor pressure in millimeters of Hg of solid ammonia is given by $\ln P = 23.03 - 3754/T$, and that of liquid ammonia by $\ln P = 19.49 - 3063/T$.

(a) What is the temperature of the triple point?

(b) What are the three latent heats at the triple point?

12-9 The triple point of hydrogen is at $T_3 = 14$°K. The density of solid H_2 at this point is 0.0810 g/cm³; that of liquid H_2 is 0.0710 g/cm³. The vapor pressure of the liquid is given by

$$\ln P \text{ (atm)} \approx 6.8 - \frac{122}{T} - 0.3 \ln T,$$

and the melting temperature is given by

$$T_M = 14 + \frac{P \text{ (atm)}}{33}.$$

(a) Compute the three latent heats at the triple point in terms of R, to within 5 percent.

(b) Compute the slope of the vapor pressure curve of the solid at T_3.

12-10 The intensity I of the atomic beam emerging from a narrow slit in an oven containing a solid in equilibrium with its vapor at the temperature T was shown in Chap. 6 to be

$$I = \frac{P}{\sqrt{2\pi m k T}},$$

where m is the atomic mass, k is Boltzmann's constant, and P is the vapor pressure. If the molar latent heat is l, the molar volume of the solid is negligible, and the vapor behaves like an ideal gas, show that

$$\frac{1}{I}\frac{dI}{dT} = \frac{1}{T}\left(\frac{l}{RT} - \frac{1}{2}\right).$$

12-11   Some of the properties of saturated water and steam near the critical point are given in the accompanying table:

Properties of Saturated Water and Steam

T, °K	P, 10^6 dyn/cm²	v'', cm³/g	v''', cm³/g	h'', J/g	h''', J/g
473	15.550	1.1565	127.2	852.39	2793
523	39.776	1.2512	50.06	1085.8	2801
573	85.917	1.4036	21.64	1344.9	2749
623	165.37	1.741	8.80	1671.2	2564
647	221.29	3.1	3.1	2085	2085

Plot l_V/T_c against $P(v''' - v'')/T$, determine the slope, and compare it with that of Fig. 12-15.

12-12   In Fig. P12-1 several examples of two neighboring phase transitions—one at (T,P) and the other at $(T + dT, P + dP)$—are shown on an

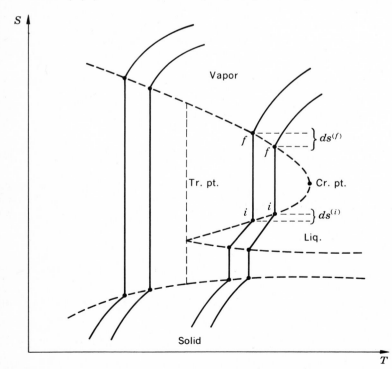

Fig. P12-1

ST diagram. The heat capacity at constant saturation is defined as

$$c_{sat}^{(i)} = T \frac{ds^{(i)}}{dT},$$

and

$$c_{sat}^{(f)} = T \frac{ds^{(f)}}{dT}.$$

Show that

(a) $$\frac{dl}{dT} - \frac{l}{T} = c_{sat}^{(f)} - c_{sat}^{(i)}.$$

(b) $$c_{sat} = c_P - Tv\beta \frac{dP}{dT}.$$

(c) $$\frac{dl}{dT} = c_P^{(f)} - c_P^{(i)} + l \left(\frac{1}{T} - \frac{(v\beta)^{(f)} - (v\beta)^{(i)}}{v^{(f)} - v^{(i)}} \right).$$

12-13   Consider two neighboring vaporizations—one at (T,P) and the other at $(T + dT, P + dP)$. Assuming $v''' \gg v''$ and $v''' = RT/P$, show that the *expansivity at constant saturation* of the vapor is

$$\frac{1}{v'''} \left(\frac{dv'''}{dT} \right)_{sat} = \frac{1}{T} \left(1 - \frac{l_V}{RT} \right).$$

12-14   Using the van der Waals equation of state

$$P = \frac{RT}{v - b} - \frac{a}{v^2},$$

show that

$$P_C = \frac{a}{27b^2}, \qquad v_C = 3b, \qquad T_C = \frac{8a}{27bR},$$

and calculate $RT_C/P_C v_C$.

12-15   Using the Dieterici equation of state

$$P = \frac{RT}{v - b} e^{-a/RTv},$$

show that

$$P_C = \frac{a}{4e^2 b^2}, \qquad v_C = 2b, \qquad T_C = \frac{a}{4Rb},$$

and calculate $RT_C/P_C v_C$.

12-16   When lead is melted at atmospheric pressure, the melting point is $600°K$, the density decreases from 11.01 to 10.65 g/cm^3, and the latent heat of fusion is 24.5 J/g. What is the melting point at a pressure of 100 atm?

12-17   Water at its freezing point (T_i, P_i) completely fills a strong steel container. The temperature is reduced to T_f at constant volume, with the pressure rising to P_f.

(a)   Show that the fraction y of water that freezes is given by

$$y = \frac{v_f'' - v_i''}{v_f'' - v_f'}.$$

(b)   State explicitly the simplifying assumptions that must be made in order that y may be written

$$y = \frac{v''[\beta''(T_f - T_i) - \kappa''(P_f - P_i)]}{v_f'' - v_f'}.$$

(c)   Calculate y for $i = 0°C$, 1 atm; $f = -5°C$, 590 atm; $\beta'' = -67 \times 10^{-6}$ deg^{-1}; $\kappa'' = 12.2$ $\mu(\text{atm}^{-1})$; $v_f'' - v_f' = -0.102$ cm^3/g.

12-18

(a)   Prove that, for a single phase,

$$\left(\frac{\partial P}{\partial T}\right)_S = \frac{c_P}{Tv\beta}.$$

(b)   Calculate $(\partial P/\partial T)_S$ for ice at $-3°C$, where $c_P = 2.01$ J/g · deg, $v = 1.09$ cm^3/g, and $\beta = 158$ $\mu(\text{deg}^{-1})$.

(c)   Ice is originally at $-3°C$ and 1 atm. The pressure is increased adiabatically until the ice reaches the melting point. At what temperature and pressure is this melting point? [*Hint:* At what point does a line whose slope is $(\partial P/\partial T)_S$ cut a line whose slope is that of the fusion curve, -133 atm/deg?]

12-19   Fig. P12-2 shows a thermodynamic surface for water viewed from the high-temperature end. Consider 1 g of ice in the state i ($P_i = 1$ atm, $T_i = 273°K$). If the ice undergoes an isentropic compression to a state f:

(a)   Why is the state f in the mixture region? In other words, why does some of the ice melt?

(b)   Show that the fraction x of ice that is melted is given by

$$x = \frac{s_f' - s_i'}{s_f'' - s_f'}.$$

(c)   State explicitly the simplifying assumptions that must be made in order that x may be written

$$x = -\frac{c_P'(T_f - T_i) - T_f v'\beta'(P_f - P_i)}{(l_F)_f}.$$

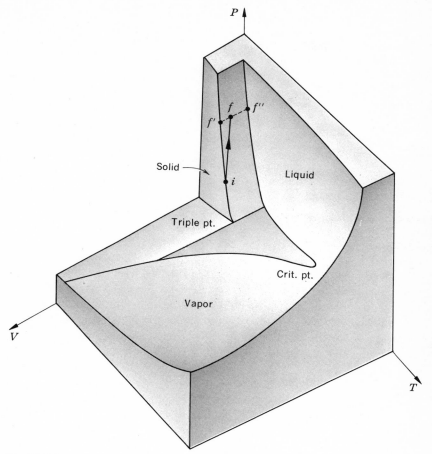

Fig. P12-2

(d)   Calculate x when $T_f = 272°K$, $P_f = 133$ atm, $c'_P = 2.01$ J/g · deg, $v' = 1.09$ cm³/g, $\beta' = 158$ $\mu(\deg^{-1})$, $(l_F)_f = 331$ J/g.

12-20   A steel bar in the form of a rectangular parallelepiped of height a and breadth b is embedded in a cake of ice as shown in Fig. P12-3. With the aid of an external magnetic field, a constant force $\mathscr{F}$ is exerted downward on the bar. The whole system is at 0°C.

(a)   Show that the *decrease* in temperature of the ice directly under the bar is

$$\Delta T = \frac{\mathscr{F}T(v' - v'')}{bcl_F}.$$

Fig. P12-3

(*b*)   Ice melts (see Prob. 12-19) under the bar, and all the water thus formed is forced to the top of the bar, where it refreezes. This phenomenon is known as *regelation*. Heat is therefore liberated above the bar, is conducted through the metal and a layer of water under the metal, and is absorbed by the ice under the layer of water. Show that the speed with which the bar sinks through the ice is

$$\frac{dy}{d\tau} = \frac{U'T(v' - v'')\mathscr{F}}{\rho l_F^2 bc},$$

where U' is the overall heat-transfer coefficient of the composite heat-conducting path consisting of the metal and the water layer. U' is given by

$$\frac{1}{U'} = \frac{x_m}{K_m} + \frac{x_w}{K_w},$$

where x_m and x_w are the thicknesses of metal and water layer, respectively, and K_m and K_w are their respective thermal conductivities.

(*c*)   Assuming the water layer to have a thickness of about 10^{-3} cm and a thermal conductivity of about 6×10^{-3} W/cm · deg, and the bar to be 10 cm long, with a and b each equal to 1 mm, with what speed will the bar descend when $\mathscr{F} = 10^7$ dyn? (The thermal conductivity of steel is 0.6 W/cm · deg.)

12-21   A substance undergoes a phase transition at the temperatures and pressures indicated by the points on the curves in Fig. 12-26a, b, and c.

Choose any point where the slope is $(dP/dT)_\lambda$ in (a); $(ds/dT)_\lambda$ in (b); and $(dv/dT)_\lambda$ in (c). *Near* this point, where $T = T_\lambda + t$, show that:

(a)
$$\frac{c_V}{T} = \left(\frac{ds}{dT}\right)_\lambda - \frac{\beta}{\kappa}\left(\frac{dv}{dT}\right)_\lambda.$$

(b)
$$\beta = \frac{1}{v}\left(\frac{dv}{dT}\right)_\lambda - \kappa\left(\frac{dP}{dT}\right)_\lambda.$$

12-22   In a second-order phase transition, $s^{(i)} = s^{(f)}$ at (T,P), and $s^{(i)} + ds^{(i)} = s^{(f)} + ds^{(f)}$ at $(T + dT, P + dP)$.
  (a) Prove that

$$\frac{dP}{dT} = \frac{1}{Tv}\frac{c_P^{(f)} - c_P^{(i)}}{\beta^{(f)} - \beta^{(i)}}.$$

In a second-order phase transition, $v^{(i)} = v^{(f)}$ at (T,P), and $v^{(i)} + dv^{(i)} = v^{(f)} + dv^{(f)}$ at $(T + dT, P + dP)$.
  (b) Prove that

$$\frac{dP}{dT} = \frac{\beta^{(f)} - \beta^{(i)}}{\kappa^{(f)} - \kappa^{(i)}}.$$

(These are *Ehrenfest's equations*.)
  12-23   For a two-phase system in equilibrium, P is a function of T only; therefore,

$$\left(\frac{\partial P}{\partial T}\right)_V = \left(\frac{\partial P}{\partial T}\right)_S = \frac{dP}{dT}.$$

For such a system show that

$$\frac{C_V}{\kappa_S} = TV\left(\frac{dP}{dT}\right)^2,$$

regardless of the type of transition between the phases.

13.

SPECIAL TOPICS

13-1   Stretched Wire

In the case of an infinitesimal reversible process of a stretched wire, the two laws of thermodynamics yield the equation

$$T \, dS = dU - \mathscr{F} \, dL.$$

Therefore, to obtain any desired equation for a stretched wire, it is necessary merely to choose the corresponding equation for a hydrostatic system and replace P by $-\mathscr{F}$ and V by L. Thus, the second $T \, dS$ equation becomes

$$T \, dS = C_{\mathscr{F}} \, dT + T \left(\frac{\partial L}{\partial T} \right)_{\mathscr{F}} d\mathscr{F}. \tag{13-1}$$

The application of this equation to isothermal and adiabatic processes is exemplified by some of the problems at the end of the chapter.

13-2   Surface Film

To obtain any desired equation for a surface film, it is necessary merely to replace V by A and P by $-\mathscr{S}$ in the corresponding equation for a hydrostatic system. Thus, the first $T \, dS$ equation becomes

$$T \, dS = C_A \, dT - T \left(\frac{\partial \mathscr{S}}{\partial T} \right)_A dA. \tag{13-2}$$

Imagine a small amount of liquid in the form of a droplet with a very small surface film. Suppose that, with the aid of a suitable wire framework, the surface film is expanded isothermally until the area A is very much larger than the original value. Then, *if the surface tension is a function of the temperature only,* the heat transferred is

$$Q = -T \frac{d\mathscr{S}}{dT} (A - 0),$$

and the work done is

$$W = -\mathscr{S} (A - 0).$$

From the first law,

$$U - U_0 = \left(\mathscr{S} - T \frac{d\mathscr{S}}{dT} \right) A,$$

where U_0 is the energy of the liquid with practically no surface and U is the energy of the liquid with the surface of area A. Hence,

$$\boxed{\frac{U - U_0}{A} = \mathscr{S} - T \frac{d\mathscr{S}}{dT}.} \qquad (13\text{-}3)$$

The left-hand member is interpreted as the energy per unit area associated with the surface only, i.e., the *surface energy per unit area.* It is seen that $(U - U_0)/A$ has the same dimensions as $\mathscr{S}$; that is, ergs per square centimeter equals dynes per centimeter. With the aid of the above equation, the surface energy per unit area of a film may be calculated once the surface tension has been measured as a function of temperature.

At the critical temperature, the surface tension of all liquids is zero. The surface tension of a pure liquid in equilibrium with its vapor can usually be

Table 13-1   Surface Tension, Surface Energy, and Heat of Vaporization of Water

$T,$ °K	$\mathscr{S},$ dyn/cm	$\dfrac{U - U_0}{A},$ ergs/cm²	$l_v,$ kJ/g
273	75.5	143	2.50
373	51.5	138	2.26
473	29.0	129	1.94
523	18.9	122	1.72
573	9.6	111	1.40
623	1.6	80	0.89
647	0	0	0

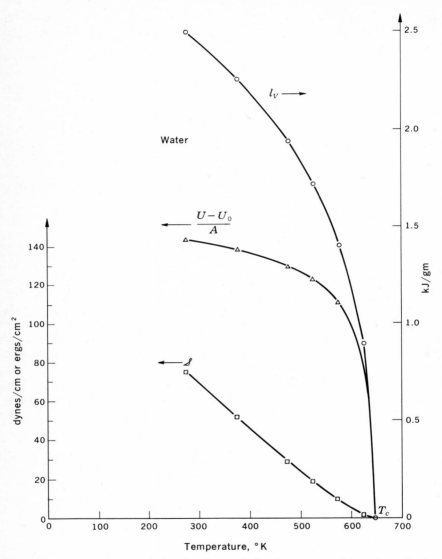

Fig. 13-1   *Temperature variation of surface tension, surface energy, and heat of vaporization of water.*

represented by a formula of the type

$$\mathscr{S} = \mathscr{S}_0 \left(1 - \frac{t}{t_C} \right)^n,$$

where $\mathscr{S}_0$ is the surface tension at 0°C, t_C is the critical temperature, and n is a constant between 1 and 2. For example, in the case of water, $\mathscr{S}_0 = 75.5$ dyn/cm, $t_C = 374$°C, and $n = 1.2$. Since $d\mathscr{S}/dT$ is the same as $d\mathscr{S}/dt$, all the quantities necessary to calculate $(U - U_0)/A$ are at hand. The data for water are given in Table 13-1, and both $\mathscr{S}$ and $(U - U_0)/A$ are plotted in Fig. 13-1. If one compares the surface-energy curve with the heat-of-vaporization curve in Fig. 13-1, it will be seen that both quantities vary with the temperature in a similar manner, both becoming zero at the critical temperature.

13-3 Reversible Cell

Equations for a reversible cell composed of solids and liquids only may be obtained from corresponding equations for a chemical system by replacing V by Z and P by $-\mathscr{E}$. Thus, the first $T\, dS$ equation becomes

$$T\, dS = C_Z\, dT - T \left(\frac{\partial \mathscr{E}}{\partial T} \right)_Z dZ; \qquad (13\text{-}4)$$

and for a saturated reversible cell whose emf depends on the temperature only, the equation becomes

$$T\, dS = C_Z\, dT - T \frac{d\mathscr{E}}{dT}\, dZ.$$

In the case of a *reversible isothermal transfer of a quantity of electricity* $Z_f - Z_i$,

$$Q = -T \frac{d\mathscr{E}}{dT} (Z_f - Z_i),$$

where $Z_f - Z_i$ is negative when positive electricity is transferred externally from the positive to the negative electrode. During this process, the cell delivers an amount of work

$$W = -\mathscr{E}(Z_f - Z_i).$$

If jN_F coulombs of positive electricity are transferred from positive to negative externally, where j is the valence and N_F is Faraday's constant, then

$$Z_f - Z_i = -jN_F;$$

whence

$$Q = jN_F T \frac{d\mathcal{E}}{dT},$$

and

$$W = jN_F\mathcal{E}.$$

From the first law, the change in internal energy is

$$U_f - U_i = -jN_F \left(\mathcal{E} - T\frac{d\mathcal{E}}{dT}\right).$$

When a process takes place at constant pressure with a negligible volume change, the change of internal energy is equal to the change of enthalpy. For

$$H = U + PV$$

and

$$dH = dU + P\,dV + V\,dP,$$

whence, under the conditions mentioned,

$$dH = dU.$$

For the reversible transfer of jN_F coulombs of electricity through a reversible cell whose volume does not change appreciably at constant atmospheric pressure, we may therefore write

$$H_f - H_i = -jN_F \left(\mathcal{E} - T\frac{d\mathcal{E}}{dT}\right).$$

In order to interpret this change of enthalpy, let us take the particular case of the Daniell cell. The transfer of positive electricity externally from the copper to the zinc electrode is accompanied by the reaction

$$Zn + CuSO_4 \rightarrow Cu + ZnSO_4.$$

When jN_F coulombs are transferred, 1 mole of each of the initial constituents disappears, and 1 mole of each of the final constituents is formed. The change of enthalpy in this case is equal to the enthalpy of 1 mole of each of the final constituents minus the enthalpy of 1 mole of each of the initial constituents at the same temperature and pressure. This is called the *heat of reaction* and is denoted by ΔH. Therefore,

$$\Delta H = -jN_F \left(\mathcal{E} - T\frac{d\mathcal{E}}{dT} \right). \qquad (13\text{-}5)$$

In the case of a saturated reversible cell in which gases are liberated, it can be shown rigorously (see Prob. 13-20) that

$$\Delta H = -jN_F \left[\mathcal{E} - T\left(\frac{\partial \mathcal{E}}{\partial T}\right)_P \right]. \qquad (13\text{-}6)$$

The important feature of this equation is that it provides a method of measuring the heat of reaction of a chemical reaction without resorting to calorimetry. If the reaction can be made to proceed in an electric cell, all that is necessary is to measure the emf of the cell as a function of the temperature at constant atmospheric pressure. The heat of reaction is therefore measured with a potentiometer and a thermometer. Both measurements can be made with great accuracy; hence this method yields by far the most accurate values of the heat of reaction. It is interesting to compare values of ΔH obtained electrically with those measured calorimetrically. This is shown for a number of cells in Table 13-2. Most of the values of ΔH are negative. A negative ΔH indicates a rejection of heat, i.e., an exothermic reaction.

Table 13-2   Reversible Cells (N_F = **96,500 C/mole**)

Reaction	T, °K	Va-lence, j	Emf $\mathcal{E}$, V	$\dfrac{d\mathcal{E}}{dT}$ mV/deg	ΔH (electric method), kJ/mole	ΔH (calori-metric method), kJ/mole
$Zn + CuSO_4 = Cu + ZnSO_4$	273	2	1.0934	−0.453	−235	−232
$Zn + 2AgCl = 2Ag + ZnCl_2$	273	2	1.0171	−0.210	−207	−206
$Cd + 2AgCl = 2Ag + CdCl_2$	298	2	0.6753	−0.650	−168	−165
$Pb + 2AgI = 2Ag + PbI_2$	298	2	0.2135	−0.173	− 51.1	− 51.1
$Ag + \frac{1}{2}Hg_2Cl_2 = Hg + AgCl$	298	1	0.0455	+0.338	+ 5.45	+ 3.77
$Pb + Hg_2Cl_2 = 2Hg + PbCl_2$	298	2	0.5356	+0.145	− 96.0	− 98.0
$Pb + 2AgCl = 2Ag + PbCl_2$	298	2	0.4900	−0.186	−105	−104

13-4   Fuel Cell

In the reversible cells listed in Table 13-2 and also in the well-known automobile battery, the reactants and the products of reaction are stored within

Fig. 13-2   *Schematic diagram of a hydrogen-oxygen fuel cell.*

the cell itself. In a modern development, called a *fuel cell*, the reactants are fed to the cell in a steady stream and the products are continually withdrawn, while the cell delivers a steady current to an external load. A typical fuel cell is depicted schematically in Fig. 13-2. The electrolyte is an aqueous solution of potassium hydroxide chosen to provide an abundant supply of hydroxyl ions. The electrodes are of metal or carbon specially baked, impregnated, and treated so that multitudinous pores are produced, each of which is a few microns in diameter. The pores are small enough to allow the electrolyte to be drawn in by capillary action and to prevent the hydrogen present at one electrode and the air at the other electrode from blowing through.

Within the pores of the negative electrode, hydrogen gas is adsorbed in the form of hydrogen atoms, which combine with OH ions to form water and electrons. The electrons move through the electrode to the external circuit while the water mixes with the hydrogen stream and is removed. Within the pores of the positive electrode, adsorbed oxygen molecules combine with water and electrons to form hydroxyl ions and perhydroxyl ions O_2H^-. By action of a suitable catalyst, the perhydroxyl ions decompose into an additional hydroxyl ion and an oxygen atom. The oxygen atoms thus formed unite to form oxygen molecules. The net effect of the reactions within the pores of both electrodes is the reaction

$$H_2 + \tfrac{1}{2}O_2 = H_2O,$$

for which the following quantities apply: The heat of reaction ΔH at 1 atm and 298°K is -286 kJ/mole. To maintain isothermal conditions at 298°K, heat Q must be transferred between the cell and its surroundings equal to -48 kJ/mole. The work output W ($= jN_F\mathcal{E}$) of the fuel cell is therefore

$$jN_F\mathcal{E} = Q - \Delta H$$

$$= (-48 + 286) \text{ kJ/mole;}$$

whence
$$\mathcal{E} = \frac{238,000 \text{ J/mole}}{2 \times 96,500 \text{ C/mole}}$$

$$= 1.23 \text{ V.}$$

The actual terminal voltage of this cell when delivering current is lower than 1.23 V, not only because of the Ir drop within the cell but also because of the failure to achieve isothermal conditions. The operation of the cell requires that the electrodes have pores of just the right size, that they be impregnated with just the right catalyst to initiate the decomposition of perhydroxyl ions, and that no impurities poison the surfaces and stop the reaction. To solve all these problems is a very difficult task, and much work remains to be done toward their solution.

13-5   Dielectric in a Parallel-plate Capacitor

Consider a capacitor consisting of two parallel conducting plates of area A, whose linear dimensions are large in comparison with their separation l, filled with an isotropic solid or liquid dielectric. If a potential difference $\mathcal{E}$ is established across the plates, one plate is given a charge $+Z$ and the other $-Z$. If the charge of the capacitor is changed by an amount dZ, the work done is

$$dW = -\mathcal{E} \, dZ,$$

the minus sign indicating that an increase of charge (positive dZ) requires work done *on* the capacitor. Work supplied by an outside source accomplishes two objectives: (1) an increase in the electric field E in the space between the two plates, and (2) an increase in the polarization of the dielectric. We therefore seek to find the contribution of each of these terms to the total work $-\mathcal{E} \, dZ$.

If E is the electric intensity in the dielectric, then the potential difference

$$\mathcal{E} = El.$$

Also, $Z = C\mathcal{E}$, where the capacitance is given as

$$C = \frac{\epsilon_r A}{4\pi l},$$

with ϵ_r equal to the *dielectric coefficient*, or *relative permittivity*. Therefore,

$$Z = \frac{\epsilon_r A}{4\pi l} El;$$

and since the displacement $D = \epsilon_r E$,

$$Z = \frac{A}{4\pi} D,$$

and

$$dZ = \frac{A}{4\pi} dD.$$

We have, therefore,

$$dW = -\mathcal{E}\, dZ$$
$$= -El \frac{A}{4\pi} dD;$$

and since the volume $V = Al$,

$$\boxed{dW = -\frac{V}{4\pi} E\, dD} \qquad \text{(total).} \qquad (13\text{-}7)$$

This expression is equivalent to $-\mathcal{E}\, dZ$ and represents the total work done on or by the capacitor when the displacement is changed by an amount dD. But

$$D = E + 4\pi \frac{P'}{V}, \qquad (13\text{-}8)$$

where P' is the polarization, i.e., the total electric moment of the dielectric produced either by orientation of elementary dipoles or by the production of induced dipoles. Therefore,

$$dW = -\frac{V}{4\pi} E\, dE - E\, dP',$$

where the first term represents the work required to increase the field by an amount dE, and the second that required to increase the polarization of the dielectric by dP'. If there were no matter present in the space between the plates, the first term would represent the total work; therefore the work done *by the dielectric* is

$$\boxed{dW = -E\,dP'} \qquad \text{(dielectric only).} \qquad (13\text{-}9)$$

The close parallelism between the electric and the magnetic situations is emphasized in Table 13-3.

Table 13-3   Comparison of Magnetic and Electric Systems

	Magnetic	Electric
Total work	$-\dfrac{V}{4\pi}\,\mathcal{H}\,dB$	$-\dfrac{V}{4\pi}\,E\,dD$
Work done to increase the field	$-\dfrac{V}{4\pi}\,\mathcal{H}\,d\mathcal{H}$	$-\dfrac{V}{4\pi}\,E\,dE$
Work done by the material	$-\mathcal{H}\,dM$	$-E\,dP'$

The thermodynamic coordinates of a dielectric are therefore E, P', and T, and an equation of state is a relation among them. If the temperature is not too low, a typical equation of state is

$$\frac{P'}{V} = \left(a + \frac{b}{T}\right) E.$$

The thermodynamic equations appropriate to a dielectric may be easily obtained from those of a chemical system by replacing P by $-E$, and V by P'. Thus, the second $T\,dS$ equation becomes

$$T\,dS = C_E\,dT + T\left(\frac{\partial P'}{\partial T}\right)_E dE.$$

This equation may be applied to (1) a reversible isothermal change of field or (2) a reversible adiabatic change of field. The temperature change accompanying the second process is known as the *electrocaloric effect*. Changes of polarization that accompany changes of temperature are sometimes known as *pyroelectric effects*.

Fig. 13-3   *Relation between piezoelectric, thermoelastic, and pyroelectric effects.*

13-6   Piezoelectric Effect

An elastic substance describable with the aid of the coordinates $\mathcal{F}$, L, T undergoes adiabatic temperature changes or isothermal entropy changes when the tension or the length is changed. Such effects may be called *thermoelastic*. An isotropic dielectric whose coordinates are E, P', T undergoes adiabatic temperature changes or isothermal entropy changes when the electric intensity or the polarization is changed. Such effects may be called *pyroelectric*. If a system in an electric field undergoes isothermal or adiabatic changes of polarization when the tension is varied, or isothermal or adiabatic changes of tension when the electric intensity is varied, the system is said to be *piezoelectric*. These phenomena are called *piezoelectric effects*. (The first two syllables are pronounced like "pie" and "ease.")

It may be seen from Fig. 13-3 that piezoelectric effects are really a combination of thermoelastic and pyroelectric effects. The simplest type of piezoelectric material under the simplest type of stress—say, a pure tension in only one direction and in a uniform electric field in that direction—is described with the aid of the five coordinates $\mathcal{F}$, L, E, P', T. In actual cases of crystals such as rochelle salt, quartz, and ammonium dihydrogen phosphate, one is concerned with several components of stress and of strain, with each component related to the field as well as to the several components of the other, so that the equations are quite involved. We limit ourselves here to the simplest possible situation.

For an infinitesimal reversible process, the first and second laws yield

$$T \, dS = dU - \mathcal{F} \, dL - E \, dP'.$$

The entropy is a function of three variables, any one of the following sets: $T, \mathcal{F}, E$; $T, \mathcal{F}, P'$; T, L, E; or T, L, P'. Choosing the first set, we get

$$T \, dS = T \left(\frac{\partial S}{\partial T} \right)_{\mathcal{F}, E} dT + T \left(\frac{\partial S}{\partial \mathcal{F}} \right)_{E, T} d\mathcal{F} + T \left(\frac{\partial S}{\partial E} \right)_{T, \mathcal{F}} dE.$$

The first expression on the right is easily recognized as the heat capacity at constant tension and field; thus,

$$T\left(\frac{\partial S}{\partial T}\right)_{\mathscr{F},E} = C_{\mathscr{F},E}.$$

The other two derivatives may be evaluated most readily with the aid of a *piezoelectric Gibbs function*, thus:

$$G' = U - TS - \mathscr{F}L - EP'.$$

Taking the differential of this function, we get

$$dG' = dU - T\, dS - S\, dT - \mathscr{F}\, dL - L\, d\mathscr{F} - E\, dP' - P'\, dE;$$

and realizing that

$$T\, dS = dU - \mathscr{F}\, dL - E\, dP',$$

we get

$$dG' = -S\, dT - L\, d\mathscr{F} - P'\, dE.$$

Three results follow:

1. At const. $\mathscr{F}$, $dG'_{\mathscr{F}} = -S\, dT_{\mathscr{F}} - P'\, dE_{\mathscr{F}}$, $\left(\dfrac{\partial S}{\partial E}\right)_{T,\mathscr{F}} = \left(\dfrac{\partial P'}{\partial T}\right)_{E,\mathscr{F}}.$

2. At const. E, $dG'_E = -S\, dT_E - L\, d\mathscr{F}_E$, $\left(\dfrac{\partial S}{\partial \mathscr{F}}\right)_{T,E} = \left(\dfrac{\partial L}{\partial T}\right)_{\mathscr{F},E}.$

3. At const. T, $dG'_T = -L\, d\mathscr{F}_T - P'\, dE_T$, $\left(\dfrac{\partial L}{\partial E}\right)_{T,\mathscr{F}} = \left(\dfrac{\partial P'}{\partial \mathscr{F}}\right)_{T,E}.$

Using results (1) and (2), the expression for $T\, dS$ becomes

$$\boxed{T\, dS = C_{\mathscr{F},E}\, dT + T\left(\frac{\partial L}{\partial T}\right)_{\mathscr{F},E} d\mathscr{F} + T\left(\frac{\partial P'}{\partial T}\right)_{\mathscr{F},E} dE,} \qquad (13\text{-}10)$$

which may be used to calculate isothermal entropy changes or adiabatic temperature changes when $\mathscr{F}$ or E or both are changed.

Result (3) is a relation between what are known as *piezoelectric coefficients*,

$$\left(\frac{\partial L}{\partial E}\right)_{T,\mathscr{F}} = \left(\frac{\partial P'}{\partial \mathscr{F}}\right)_{T,E},$$

since one expresses the effect of a change of electric field on the length, and the other the effect of a change of tension on the polarization.

If the other sets of coordinates are used, different functions are appropriate, the $T\,dS$ equations are different, and different piezoelectric coefficients are obtained, as shown in Table 13-4.

Table 13-4   Alternate Expressions for the Piezoelectric Effect

Coordinates	(1) Appropriate thermodynamic function, (2) $T\,dS$ equation, and (3) relation between piezoelectric coefficients
$T, \mathscr{F}, E$	Piezoelectric Gibbs function: $G' = U - TS - \mathscr{F}L - EP'$. $$T\,dS = C_{\mathscr{F},E}\,dT + T\left(\frac{\partial L}{\partial T}\right)_{\mathscr{F},E} d\mathscr{F} + T\left(\frac{\partial P'}{\partial T}\right)_{\mathscr{F},E} dE.$$ Piezoelectric coefficients: $\left(\dfrac{\partial L}{\partial E}\right)_{T,\mathscr{F}} = \left(\dfrac{\partial P'}{\partial \mathscr{F}}\right)_{T,E}$.
$T, \mathscr{F}, P'$	Thermoelastic Gibbs function: $G'' = U - TS - \mathscr{F}L$. $$T\,dS = C_{\mathscr{F},P'}\,dT + T\left(\frac{\partial L}{\partial T}\right)_{\mathscr{F},P'} d\mathscr{F} + T\left(\frac{\partial E}{\partial T}\right)_{\mathscr{F},P'} dP'.$$ Piezoelectric coefficients: $-\left(\dfrac{\partial L}{\partial P'}\right)_{T,\mathscr{F}} = \left(\dfrac{\partial E}{\partial \mathscr{F}}\right)_{T,P'}$.
T, L, E	Pyroelectric Gibbs function: $G''' = U - TS - EP'$. $$T\,dS = C_{L,E}\,dT + T\left(\frac{\partial \mathscr{F}}{\partial T}\right)_{L,E} dL + T\left(\frac{\partial P'}{\partial T}\right)_{L,E} dE.$$ Piezoelectric coefficients: $-\left(\dfrac{\partial P'}{\partial L}\right)_{T,E} = \left(\dfrac{\partial \mathscr{F}}{\partial E}\right)_{T,L}$.
T, L, P'	Helmholtz function: $A = U - TS$. $$T\,dS = C_{L,P'}\,dT + T\left(\frac{\partial \mathscr{F}}{\partial T}\right)_{L,P'} dL + T\left(\frac{\partial E}{\partial T}\right)_{L,P'} dP'.$$ Piezoelectric coefficients: $\left(\dfrac{\partial \mathscr{F}}{\partial P'}\right)_{T,L} = \left(\dfrac{\partial E}{\partial L}\right)_{T,P'}$.

13-7   Thermoelectric Phenomena

When two dissimilar metals or semiconductors are connected and the junctions held at different temperatures, there are five phenomena that take place simultaneously: the Seebeck effect, the Joule effect, the Fourier effect, the Peltier effect, and the Thomson effect. Let us consider each of these effects briefly.

1. *Seebeck effect*   In Fig. 13-4 a thermocouple consisting of two different conductors A and B has its junctions in contact with different heat reservoirs. We call the warmer junction at T the *test junction*, and the other at temperature T_R the *reference* junction. The existence of a thermal emf $\mathcal{E}_{AB}$ in the circuit is known as the *Seebeck effect*. When the temperature of the reference junction is kept constant, the thermal emf is found to be a function of the temperature T of the test junction. This fact enables the thermocouple to be used as a thermometer, as described in Chap. 1.

The Seebeck effect arises from the fact that the density of charge carriers (electrons in a metal) differs from one conductor to another and depends on the temperature. When two different conductors are connected to form two junctions and the two junctions are maintained at different temperatures, diffusion of the charge carriers takes place at the junctions at different rates. There is a net motion of the charge carriers as though they were driven by a nonelectrostatic field. The line integral of this field around the thermocouple is the Seebeck emf.

For a given T_R, $\mathcal{E}_{AB}$ is a function of T. If T_R is changed to another constant value, the relation between $\mathcal{E}_{AB}$ and T is the same except for an additive constant. It follows therefore that the value of $d\mathcal{E}_{AB}/dT$ is independent of T_R and depends only on the nature of A and B and upon T. The derivative $d\mathcal{E}_{AB}/dT$, at any value of T_R, is known as the *thermoelectric power* of the thermocouple.

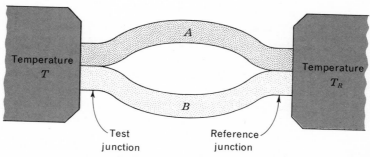

Fig. 13-4   *Thermocouple of conductors A and B with junctions at T and T_R.*

2. *Joule effect*   If the thermal emf $\mathcal{E}_{AB}$ is not balanced by an external emf, a current I exists whose value may be adjusted by varying the external emf. As long as a current exists, electrical energy of amount I^2R is dissipated within the circuit. This is the well-known *Joule effect*.

3. *Fourier effect*   Imagine a thermocouple whose junctions are at temperatures T_1 and T_2, respectively ($T_1 > T_2$), and which has been broken at one point, its two ends being maintained at some intermediate temperature T by means of an insulating reservoir. There is no thermoelectric current, and therefore no Joule effect; but heat is lost by the reservoir at T_1, conducted along both wires, and gained by the reservoir at T_2, with no net gain or loss to the reservoir at T. The wires can be imagined to be suitably lagged so that there is no appreciable lateral transfer of heat across the surfaces of the wires. The phenomenon of heat conduction is called the *Fourier effect*.

4. *Peltier effect*   Imagine a thermocouple with its junctions at the same temperature. If, by means of an outside battery, a current is produced in the thermocouple, the temperatures of the junctions are changed by an amount that is not entirely due to the Joule effect. This additional temperature change is the *Peltier effect*. Allowing for the Joule effect, the heat that must be either supplied or extracted to restore a junction to its initial temperature is called the *Peltier heat*. The Peltier effect takes place whether the current is provided by an outside source or is generated by the thermocouple itself.

The Peltier heat is measured by creating a known current in a junction initially at a known temperature and measuring the rate at which the temperature of the junction changes. The junction itself is used as a sort of calorimeter. From the rate of change of temperature and the heat capacity of the junction, the rate at which heat is transferred is calculated. After subtracting the I^2R loss and correcting for the conducted heat, which was determined from previous experiments, the Peltier heat is finally obtained. Extensive measurements have yielded the following results:

a   The rate at which Peltier heat is transferred is proportional to the first power of the current or equal to πI. The quantity π is called the *Peltier coefficient* and is equal to the heat transferred when unit quantity of electricity traverses the junction.

b   The Peltier heat is reversible. When the direction of the current is reversed, with the magnitude remaining the same, the Peltier heat is the same but in the opposite direction.

c   The Peltier coefficient depends on the temperature and the materials of a junction, being independent of the temperature of the other junction.

d   It is the accepted convention to regard π_{AB} as positive when an electric current from A to B causes an *absorption* of heat by the junction.

5. *Thomson effect*   The conduction of heat along the wires of a thermocouple carrying no current gives rise to a uniform temperature distribution in each wire. If a current exists, the temperature distribution in each wire is altered by an amount that is not entirely due to the Joule effect. This additional change in the temperature distribution is called the *Thomson effect*. Allowing for the Joule effect, the heat that must be either supplied or extracted laterally *at all places along the wires* to restore the initial temperature distribution is called the *Thomson heat*.

To measure the Thomson heat at a small region of any one wire, it is necessary to produce a known temperature gradient in the region and to pass a known current either up or down the gradient. The rate at which Thomson heat is transferred is equal to the rate at which electrical energy is dissipated minus the rate at which heat is conducted. Since the Joule effect can be calculated and the conducted heat is known from previous experiments, the Thomson heat can be obtained. The following conclusions may be drawn from such measurements:

a   The rate at which Thomson heat is transferred into a small region of a wire carrying a current I and supporting a temperature difference dT is equal to $\sigma I\, dT$, where σ is called the *Thomson coefficient*.

b   The Thomson heat is reversible.

c   The Thomson coefficient depends on the material of the wire and on the mean temperature of the small region under consideration.

d   It is the accepted convention to regard σ as positive when a current opposite to the direction of the temperature gradient (low to high temperature) causes an absorption of heat by the conductor.

13-8   Simultaneous Electric and Heat Currents in a Conductor

The application of thermodynamics to the thermocouple has had a long and interesting history. Lord Kelvin was the first to realize that the two irreversible phenomena, the Joule effect and the conduction of heat, could not be eliminated by merely choosing wires of proper dimensions. For, if the wires are made very thin in order to cut down heat conduction, the electric resistance increases; whereas if the wires are made thick to cut down the electric resistance, the heat conduction increases. In spite of this, Kelvin assumed that the irreversible effects could be ignored on the ground that they seemed to be independent of the reversible Peltier and Thomson effects. By considering the purely reversible transfer of unit quantity of electricity through a thermocouple circuit, Kelvin set the sum of all the entropy changes equal to zero and derived relations which have been amply checked and which are undoubtedly correct. The stubborn fact remains, however, that the Seebeck, Peltier, and Thomson effects are inextricably linked with the irreversible effects.

Attempts to resolve these difficulties were made by Bridgman, by Tolman and Fine, and by Meixner, but the results were not entirely free of objection. The solution is to be found in the macroscopic treatment of irreversible coupled flows developed by Onsager, which was introduced briefly in Chap. 9. The following is a simplified version of Onsager's method, based on the work of H. B. Callen.

A small temperature difference ΔT established across a wire disturbs the thermal equilibrium and gives rise to a heat current I_Q. Since a cool reservoir at one end of the wire is gaining entropy *from the wire* at a greater rate than that at which a warmer reservoir at the other end is losing it *to the wire*, we say that entropy is being produced *in the wire* at a rate

$$\frac{dS}{d\tau} = I_Q \frac{\Delta T}{T^2} = I_S \frac{\Delta T}{T},$$

where I_S is the entropy current equal to I_Q/T.

A small potential difference $\Delta \mathscr{E}$ established across a wire disturbs the electrical equilibrium and gives rise to an electric current I. Since a reservoir at temperature T which maintains the wire at a uniform temperature is gaining entropy and there is no entropy input to the wire, we say that entropy is being produced in the wire at a rate

$$\frac{dS}{d\tau} = I \frac{\Delta \mathscr{E}}{T}.$$

When both a temperature difference ΔT and a potential difference $\Delta \mathscr{E}$ exist across the wire, the rate of entropy production is the sum, or

$$\frac{dS}{d\tau} = I_S \frac{\Delta T}{T} + I \frac{\Delta \mathscr{E}}{T}.$$

If departure from equilibrium is not too great, the entropy and electricity flow are coupled in a simple manner, both flows depending *linearly* on both $\Delta T/T$ and $\Delta \mathscr{E}/T$, thus:

$$I_S = L_{11} \frac{\Delta T}{T} + L_{12} \frac{\Delta \mathscr{E}}{T}, \tag{13-11}$$

and

$$I = L_{21} \frac{\Delta T}{T} + L_{22} \frac{\Delta \mathscr{E}}{T}. \tag{13-12}$$

The coefficients L_{11} and L_{22} have simple interpretations in terms of thermal conductivity and electrical conductivity, respectively. The quantities L_{12} and L_{21} are coupling coefficients. They represent the effect of a potential difference on an entropy current and the effect of a temperature difference on an electric current, respectively. Onsager proved by means of the *microscopic* point of view that

$$\boxed{L_{12} = L_{21},}$$

(13-13)

which is now known as *Onsager's reciprocal relation.*

If ΔT is set equal to zero in both Eqs. (13-11) and (13-12), and then the equations are divided, we get

$$\left(\frac{I_S}{I}\right)_{\Delta T=0} = \frac{L_{12}}{L_{22}}.$$

Also, in the absence of an electric current, Eq. (13-12) provides the relation

$$-\left(\frac{\Delta \mathscr{E}}{\Delta T}\right)_{I=0} = \frac{L_{21}}{L_{22}}.$$

Since Onsager's reciprocal relation provides that $L_{12} = L_{21}$, let us write

$$\epsilon = \frac{L_{12}}{L_{22}} = \frac{L_{21}}{L_{22}}.$$

We therefore have two different physical interpretations of the quantity ϵ:

$$\epsilon = \begin{cases} \left(\dfrac{I_S}{I}\right)_{\Delta T=0} = \left(\dfrac{I_Q/T}{I}\right)_{\Delta T=0} \\[2mm] -\left(\dfrac{\Delta \mathscr{E}}{\Delta T}\right)_{I=0} = -\left(\dfrac{d\mathscr{E}}{dT}\right)_{I=0}. \end{cases}$$

(13-14)

Thus, ϵ may be regarded as the *entropy current per unit electric current* at a given temperature, or as the *change of potential difference per unit change of temperature* at zero electric current. Because of this latter physical interpretation, ϵ is called the *Seebeck coefficient* of a substance and is a function of the temperature and the nature of the substance.

13-9   Seebeck and Peltier Effects

Consider the thermocouple depicted in Fig. 13-5. The test junction e of the conductors A and B is maintained at the temperature T while the two

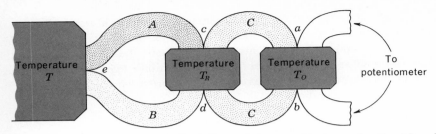

Fig. 13-5   *Thermocouple consisting of wires A and B connected to copper wires C and C, and thence to the binding posts of a potentiometer. (See Fig. 1-11.)*

junctions c and d, each with copper, are maintained at temperature T_R (usually that of an ice bath). The two copper wires marked C are connected to the brass binding posts of a potentiometer, forming two more junctions, each of which is at room temperature T_0. The potentiometer is supposed to be balanced, so that $I = 0$ and $\mathcal{E}_a - \mathcal{E}_b$ is the Seebeck emf $\mathcal{E}_{AB}$.

The second relation in Eq. (13-14), namely,

$$\left(\frac{d\mathcal{E}}{dT}\right)_{I=0} = -\epsilon,$$

may be applied to each of the conductors A, B, and C—the Seebeck coefficients being ϵ_A, ϵ_B, and ϵ_C. Integrating from one end of each wire to the other, we have

$$\mathcal{E}_a - \mathcal{E}_c = \int_{T_0}^{T_R} \epsilon_C \, dT,$$

$$\mathcal{E}_c - \mathcal{E}_e = \int_{T_R}^{T} \epsilon_A \, dT,$$

$$\mathcal{E}_e - \mathcal{E}_d = \int_{T}^{T_R} \epsilon_B \, dT,$$

and
$$\mathcal{E}_d - \mathcal{E}_b = \int_{T_R}^{T_0} \epsilon_C \, dT.$$

When these equations are added, the left side becomes $\mathcal{E}_a - \mathcal{E}_b = \mathcal{E}_{AB}$. On the right side, the first and last terms cancel, so that

$$\boxed{\mathcal{E}_{AB} = \int_{T_R}^{T} (\epsilon_A - \epsilon_B) \, dT.} \tag{13-15}$$

If the Seebeck coefficients of A and B are known as functions of T, the emf of the thermocouple made by joining A and B and holding the junctions at T_R and T could be calculated by performing the integration indicated in Eq. (13-15).

A thermocouple consisting of two metals is well-suited as a thermometer. At low temperatures a highly sensitive potentiometer must be used, and at high temperatures metals with high melting points are essential. Junctions may be made with very low heat capacity, so that they react quickly to changes of temperature. As a result, thermometry has been the main practical application of thermoelectricity since its discovery by Seebeck in 1821. Since

$$\mathscr{E}_{AB} = \int_{T_R}^{T} (\epsilon_A - \epsilon_B) \, dT,$$

it follows that

$$\mathscr{E}_{AB} = \int_{T_R}^{T} (\epsilon_A - \epsilon_C) \, dT - \int_{T_R}^{T} (\epsilon_B - \epsilon_C) \, dT,$$

or

$$\mathscr{E}_{AB} = \mathscr{E}_{AC} - \mathscr{E}_{BC}. \tag{13-16}$$

Therefore, if C is chosen to be platinum, two tables of values of thermal emf—one for metal A and platinum and the other for metal B and platinum —enable one to find $\mathscr{E}_{AB}$. Such tables are given in the "AIP Handbook" for many different metals.

When an electric current traverses a junction of two different conductors at a uniform temperature, the heat that must be supplied or withdrawn, over and above the Joule heat, to keep the junction at a constant temperature is what we have already described above as the Peltier heat. This may be calculated in terms of Seebeck coefficients as follows. Consider the thermo-junction e of Fig. 13-5, depicted in greater detail in Fig. 13-6. Even though the junction is at a uniform temperature, there is a heat current I_{QA} into the junction and a different heat current I_{QB} out of the junction, both carried along with the electric current I, which is taken arbitrarily in the direction from A to B. The difference between I_{QA} and I_{QB} must be transferred, along with I^2R_j (where R_j is the resistance of the junction), in order to keep the

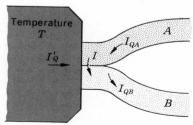

Fig. 13-6   *Thermojunction of conductors A and B at a uniform constant temperature T. The Peltier heat is the difference between I'_Q and I^2R_j.*

temperature constant. Calling this heat current I'_Q, we have

$$I'_Q = I^2 R_j + (I_{QA})_{\Delta T=0} - (I_{QB})_{\Delta T=0}.$$

By definition, the Peltier heat is

$$\pi_{AB} I = I'_Q - I^2 R_j = (I_{QA})_{\Delta T=0} - (I_{QB})_{\Delta T=0}.$$

Since the first part of Eq. (13-14) defines ϵ to be $(I_S/I)_{\Delta T=0}$ and since $I_S = I_Q/T$, it follows that

$$I_{QA} = IT\epsilon_A \qquad \text{and} \qquad I_{QB} = IT\epsilon_B.$$

The Peltier coefficient therefore becomes

$$\boxed{\pi_{AB} = T(\epsilon_A - \epsilon_B).} \tag{13-17}$$

13-10   Thomson Effect and Kelvin Equations

Consider the thermocouple of Fig. 13-7 consisting of wires A and B with the test junction at temperature T' and the reference junction at T_R. If the thermocouple is on open circuit or is connected to a potentiometer that is balanced, there will be no electric current, but there will be a heat current and a temperature distribution throughout the wires. Suppose wire A is now placed in contact *at each point with a heat reservoir of the same temperature as that point*, so that there is no heat exchange between A and the reservoirs. This situation is depicted in Fig. 13-7a, but only one of the reservoirs is shown—the one at temperature T in contact with a small portion of wire A, across which there is a temperature difference ΔT and a potential difference $\Delta \mathcal{E}_A = \epsilon_A \, \Delta T$. The heat current I_Q entering this portion is equal to the heat current leaving the portion.

Now suppose that the potentiometer circuit is opened and an outside generator is connected to wire A (with the aid of connecting wires of the same material as A) and that the terminal voltage of the generator is adjusted until it has exactly the value $\mathcal{E}_A = \mathcal{E}_c - \mathcal{E}_e = \int_{T_0}^{T'} \epsilon_A \, dT$. A current will now exist in wire A of magnitude $I = \mathcal{E}_A/R_A$, and the temperature distribution in wire A will be altered both by Joulean dissipation and by the Thomson effect. Referring to Fig. 13-7b, we see that the small portion of wire A in contact with the reservoir at T has the following characteristics:

1   It supports a temperature difference ΔT.
2   It supports a potential difference $\Delta \mathcal{E}_A = \epsilon_A \, \Delta T$.
3   It carries an electric current $I = \Delta \mathcal{E}_A / \Delta R_A$.
4   A heat current I_Q enters it.
5   A different heat current $I_Q + \Delta I_Q$ leaves it.

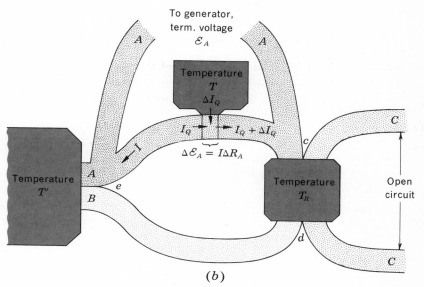

Fig. 13-7   (a) *In the* absence *of an electric current, there is no heat flow between a portion of wire A at temperature T and its heat reservoir at T.* (b) *In the* presence *of an electric current, the heat transfer between a portion of wire A at temperature T and its heat reservoir at T is equal to* $\Delta I_Q = I^2 \, \Delta R - I\sigma_A \, \Delta T$.

6   It exchanges heat $I^2 \Delta R_A$ (Joule effect) and $I\sigma_A \Delta T$ (Thomson effect) with the heat reservoir in contact with it. Therefore,

$$\Delta I_Q = I^2 \Delta R_A - I\sigma_A \Delta T$$

$$= I \Delta\mathcal{E}_A - I\sigma_A \Delta T,$$

or $$\Delta I_Q = I\epsilon_A \Delta T - I\sigma_A \Delta T. \tag{13-18}$$

As before, $I_Q = IT\epsilon_A$, and therefore a small change is given by

$$\Delta I_Q = I\epsilon_A \Delta T + IT \Delta\epsilon_A. \tag{13-19}$$

It follows from Eqs. (13-18) and (13-19) that

$$-I\sigma_A \Delta T = IT \Delta\epsilon_A,$$

or $$\sigma_A = -T\frac{d\epsilon_A}{dT}.$$

Similarly, at a point on wire B that is at temperature T,

$$\sigma_B = -T\frac{d\epsilon_B}{dT};$$

and finally, $$\boxed{\sigma_A - \sigma_B = -T\frac{d}{dT}(\epsilon_A - \epsilon_B).} \tag{13-20}$$

Let us collect the three equations for the three reversible thermoelectric effects:

Seebeck effect

$$\mathcal{E}_{AB} = \int_{T_R}^{T} (\epsilon_A - \epsilon_B)\, dT. \tag{13-15}$$

Peltier effect

$$\pi_{AB} = T(\epsilon_A - \epsilon_B). \tag{13-17}$$

Thomson effect

$$\sigma_A - \sigma_B = -T\frac{d}{dT}(\epsilon_A - \epsilon_B). \tag{13-20}$$

Notice that they are all expressed in terms of the difference of the two Seebeck coefficients, so that if ϵ_A and ϵ_B are known as functions of T, then

$\mathcal{E}_{AB}$ may be obtained by integration, π_{AB}/T without further calculation, and $(\sigma_A - \sigma_B)/T$ by differentiation.

If we differentiate Eq. (13-15) with respect to T, while holding T_R constant, we get $d\mathcal{E}_{AB}/dT = \epsilon_A - \epsilon_B$. Comparing this with Eq. (13-17), we see that

$$\frac{\pi_{AB}}{T} = \frac{d\mathcal{E}_{AB}}{dT}, \qquad (13\text{-}21)$$

which is *Kelvin's first equation.*

If we substitute the value $d\mathcal{E}_{AB}/dT$ for $\epsilon_A - \epsilon_B$ in Eq. (13-20), we get

$$\frac{\sigma_A - \sigma_B}{T} = -\frac{d^2\mathcal{E}_{AB}}{dT^2}, \qquad (13\text{-}22)$$

which is *Kelvin's second equation.* The Kelvin equations have been often verified by experiment.

13-11   Thermoelectric Refrigeration

Metal thermocouples are not suited to extract heat by the Peltier effect because the difference in the Seebeck coefficients is so small. To produce ice cubes, T would have to be about 270°K. Using a current of about 20 A and about 10 thermocouples in series, we could obtain a Peltier heat current equal to

$$\dot{Q} = 270°\text{K}(\epsilon_A - \epsilon_B) \times 20\ \text{A} \times 10.$$

If the thermojunctions were of Cu and Fe, $\epsilon_{Cu} - \epsilon_{Fe} = 13.7\ \mu\text{V/deg}$, and $\dot{Q}$ would be only 0.74 W.

In 1838, Lenz tried thermocouples of Sb and Bi, with

$$\epsilon_{Sb} - \epsilon_{Bi} = 109\ \mu\text{V/deg},$$

and succeeded in converting a drop of water into ice. The large currents needed, the large amount of Fourier conduction, and the large Joulean heat dissipation resulted in a very low coefficient of performance, so that no commercial Peltier refrigerator appeared on the market for over a century after Lenz's experiment. The major breakthrough occurred when semiconducting compounds were found to have large Seebeck coefficients, good electrical conductivity, and poor thermal conductivity. Thus, a thermocouple of

Fig. 13-8   *Schematic diagram of a thermoelectric refrigerator.*

p-type Bi_2Te_3 joined to n-type Bi_2Te_3 has a value of $\epsilon_A - \epsilon_B$ equal to 423 $\mu V/$deg, so that 10 couples at 270°K with a current of 20 A give rise to a Peltier heat current of 23 W. These values make a Peltier refrigerator economically feasible. Such a refrigerator is depicted schematically in Fig. 13-8. Progress in Peltier refrigeration since 1821 is shown in Table 13-5.

Table 13-5   Peltier Refrigeration

Thermojunction	T, °K	I, A	No. of couples	$\epsilon_A - \epsilon_B$, $\mu V/$deg	Peltier heat rate, W
Fe–Cu (1821)	270	20	10	13.7	0.74
Sb–Bi (1838)	270	20	10	109	5.9
$Bi_2Te_3(p)$–$Bi_2Te_3(n)$ (1963)	270	20	10	423	23

13-12   Properties of a System of Photons

The electromagnetic radiation in equilibrium with the interior walls of an evacuated cavity is called *blackbody radiation*. If the walls are at a uniform temperature, the distribution of frequencies and the energy of each frequency band are independent of the nature of the walls and depend only on the temperature and the volume. The quantum picture of the radiation in the cavity is that of a system of photons with many different frequencies, but all moving with a constant speed c and completely independent of one another. All photons of the same frequency constitute a set of particles that satisfies the conditions of *indistinguishability* and *independence* (absence of interaction) better than any system of molecules or electrons.

The most striking peculiarity of a system of photons is that *the total number of photons of all frequencies is not constant*. As equilibrium is approached, photons are absorbed by atoms, and other photons perhaps of different frequencies are reemitted. Therefore, during the approach to equilibrium, although the total *energy* of the photons may remain constant, the total *number* does not.

The number of quantum states associated with the translational kinetic energy of the molecules of a gas is enormously larger than the number of molecules that can occupy these states. Very few of the available states can be occupied at one time, and when a state is occupied, it is most unlikely that it contains more than one molecule. With electrons, however, the number of quantum states and the number of electrons are comparable. The operation of the Pauli exclusion principle, which limits each state to at most two electrons, provides therefore the complete filling of all low-lying states up to a level known as the *Fermi level*. With photons the situation is still different. Since the total number of photons is not constant, there is no clear-cut relation between the number of photons of frequency ν and the number of quantum states g_ν available to these photons. The Pauli principle does not hold for photons, so that *there may be any number of photons in the same energy state*.

The translational kinetic energy of a molecule or an electron moving in a cubical box of side L is given by the familiar expression in Eq. (10-1),

$$\epsilon = \frac{h^2}{8mL^2} (n_x^2 + n_y^2 + n_z^2),$$

where the n's are large integers. If the n's are taken to be rectangular coordinates, the locus of all points in this space corresponding to one value ϵ_i of the energy is the surface of the sphere

$$n_x^2 + n_y^2 + n_z^2 = \frac{8mL^2\epsilon_i}{h^2},$$

with a radius $r = 2L(2m\epsilon_i)^{\frac{1}{2}}/h$. Since the n's are integers, a unit volume in this space contains one quantum state. The number of quantum states $g_i\, d\epsilon_i$

corresponding to an energy lying between ϵ_i and $\epsilon_i + d\epsilon_i$ is $\frac{1}{8}$ the volume of a spherical shell of radius r. Thus,

$$g_i \, d\epsilon_i = \tfrac{1}{8} \cdot 4\pi r^2 \, dr$$

$$= \tfrac{1}{8} \cdot 4\pi \frac{4L^2}{h^2} 2m\epsilon_i \frac{2L}{h} (2m)^{\frac{1}{2}} \tfrac{1}{2} \epsilon_i^{-\frac{1}{2}} \, d\epsilon_i$$

$$= 2\pi L^3 \left(\frac{2m}{h^2}\right)^{\frac{3}{2}} \epsilon_i^{\frac{1}{2}} \, d\epsilon_i.$$

This result appeared in Prob. 10-2 and also in the discussion of free electrons in metals given in Eq. (11-48).

This equation must also hold for photons, but it is not in an appropriate form, since photons have zero rest mass. To apply it to photons, let us rewrite it in terms of momentum p, where $\epsilon = p^2/2m$. Let $g_p \, dp$ represent the number of quantum states corresponding to momenta lying between p and $p + dp$. Then, since $L^3 = V$,

$$g_p \, dp = 2\pi V \left(\frac{2m}{h^2}\right)^{\frac{3}{2}} \frac{p}{(2m)^{\frac{1}{2}}} \frac{1}{2m} 2p \, dp$$

$$= \frac{4\pi V}{h^3} p^2 \, dp.$$

Having gotten rid of m, let us now express our result in terms of frequency ν by using the de Broglie equation,

$$p = \frac{h}{\lambda} = \frac{h\nu}{c}.$$

Let $g_\nu \, d\nu$ be the number of quantum states between ν and $\nu + d\nu$. Then,

$$g_\nu \, d\nu = \frac{4\pi V}{h^3} \frac{h^2 \nu^2}{c^2} \frac{h}{c} \, d\nu.$$

Finally, doubling this result so as to include photons with both kinds of polarization,

$$\boxed{g_\nu \, d\nu = \frac{8\pi V}{c^3} \nu^2 \, d\nu.} \qquad (13\text{-}23)$$

13-13   Bose-Einstein Statistics Applied to Photons

Consider an evacuated cavity with perfectly reflecting walls containing a total of N photons, of which N_ν have a frequency ν. Suppose that within the

cavity there is a speck of coal with negligible heat capacity. As the coal particle absorbs and reemits photons, any resulting change of energy will be so
small that the total energy of the radiation may be regarded as constant. We
require an expression for the number of ways in which N_ν photons may be
distributed among g_ν quantum states with no restriction on the number of
photons in any one state. Let us represent identical indistinguishable photons
by crosses, $\times\times\times$; and quantum states by the spacing between vertical lines,
$\times\times\times|\times|\times\times$, etc. A typical distribution of photons among states would
thus be

$$\times\times\times|\times|\times\times|\times\times\times\times\times|\times\times|\times\times\times.$$

This symbolism represents three photons in the first state, one in the second,
two in the third, etc. Notice that only five vertical lines are needed to represent six states; therefore the total number of symbols needed to represent N_ν
photons and g_ν states is $N_\nu + g_\nu - 1$. The total number of permutations of
$N_\nu + g_\nu - 1$ symbols is $(N_\nu + g_\nu - 1)!$, but this expression is much too
large. To take care of the fact that the photons are indistinguishable, we
must divide by $N_\nu!$; and to show that the lines representing partitions are
indistinguishable, we must divide by $(g_\nu - 1)!$. Very little error is introduced
by replacing $(g_\nu - 1)$ by g_ν; therefore, summing over all the frequencies, the
thermodynamic probability becomes

$$\Omega_{\mathrm{BE}} = \prod^{\nu} \frac{(N_\nu + g_\nu)!}{N_\nu! g_\nu!}. \tag{13-24}$$

This is the probability appropriate to the *Bose-Einstein statistics*.

To find the distribution of photons among the frequencies at equilibrium,
we render $\ln \Omega_{\mathrm{BE}}$ a maximum subject to *only one* restriction, namely, that
$\Sigma N_\nu h\nu = U = $ const. We have

$$\ln \Omega_{\mathrm{BE}} = \Sigma \ln (N_\nu + g_\nu)! - \Sigma \ln N_\nu! - \Sigma \ln g_\nu!;$$

and using Stirling's approximation, $\ln x! = x \ln x - x,$

$$\ln \Omega_{\mathrm{BE}} = \Sigma(N_\nu + g_\nu) \ln (N_\nu + g_\nu) - \Sigma(N_\nu + g_\nu)$$
$$- \Sigma N_\nu \ln N_\nu + \Sigma N_\nu - \Sigma g_\nu \ln g_\nu + \Sigma g_\nu.$$

After some cancellation,

$$\ln \Omega_{\mathrm{BE}} = \Sigma(N_\nu + g_\nu) \ln (N_\nu + g_\nu) - \Sigma N_\nu \ln N_\nu - \Sigma g_\nu \ln g_\nu,$$

and $\quad U = \Sigma N_\nu h\nu.$

Applying the method of Lagrange multipliers, we set

$$d \ln \Omega_{BE} = \sum \left[1 + \ln \left(N_\nu + g_\nu \right) \right] dN_\nu - \sum \left(1 + \ln N_\nu \right) dN_\nu = 0,$$

or $d \ln \Omega_{BE} = \sum \ln \dfrac{N_\nu + g_\nu}{N_\nu} \, dN_\nu = 0,$ (13-25)

with one restriction, namely,

$$dU = \Sigma h\nu \, dN_\nu = 0.$$

Multiplying this last equation by $-\beta$ and adding, we get

$$\ln \left(1 + \frac{g_\nu}{N_\nu} \right) - \beta h\nu = 0,$$ (13-26)

$$1 + \frac{g_\nu}{N_\nu} = e^{\beta h\nu},$$

and
$$N_\nu = \frac{g_\nu}{e^{\beta h\nu} - 1}.$$ (13-27)

To discover the physical significance of β, we consider the system of photons as a thermodynamic system with an entropy $S = k \ln \Omega_{BE}$. Then, from Eq. (13-25),

$$dS = k \, d \ln \Omega_{BE} = k \sum \ln \left(1 + \frac{g_\nu}{N_\nu} \right) dN_\nu;$$

and from Eq. (13-26), at equilibrium,

$$\ln \left(1 + \frac{g_\nu}{N_\nu} \right) = \beta h\nu.$$

Substituting, we get
$$dS = k\Sigma\beta h\nu \, dN_\nu.$$

But since $U = \Sigma N_\nu h\nu$ and $dU = \Sigma h\nu \, dN_\nu,$

$$dS = k\beta \, dU.$$

Inasmuch as the volume is constant, $dS/dU = 1/T$, and

$$\beta = \frac{1}{kT},$$

as always. Substituting into Eq. (13-27) the values of g_ν and β, we get

$$N_\nu = \frac{8\pi V}{c^3} \frac{\nu^2}{e^{h\nu/kT} - 1}.$$

If the energy lying in the frequency range between ν and $\nu + d\nu$ is denoted by $U_\nu \, d\nu$, then

$$U_\nu \, d\nu = N_\nu h\nu \, d\nu,$$
$$= \frac{8\pi Vh}{c^3} \frac{\nu^3 \, d\nu}{e^{h\nu/kT} - 1}.$$

The *spectral energy density* u_ν is defined to be U_ν/V, so that finally

$$u_\nu = \frac{8\pi h}{c^3} \frac{\nu^3}{e^{h\nu/kT} - 1}, \qquad (13\text{-}28)$$

which is *Planck's radiation equation*.

13-14   Optical Pyrometer

The fundamental tool of high-temperature thermometry is a blackbody at the temperature of equilibrium between liquid and solid gold, called the *gold point* (1336°K), originally determined with the aid of a gas thermometer. The construction of the gold-point blackbody used at the U.S. National Bureau of Standards is shown in Fig. 13-9. The energy needed to melt the gold is provided by an electric current in molybdenum windings.

To measure temperatures above the range of thermocouples and resistance thermometers, an *optical pyrometer* is used. As shown in Fig. 13-10, it consists essentially of a telescope T in the tube of which is mounted a filter of red glass and a small electric lamp bulb L. When the pyrometer is directed toward a furnace, an observer looking through the telescope sees the dark lamp filament against the bright background of the furnace. The lamp filament is connected to a battery B and a rheostat R. By turning the rheostat knob, the current in the filament—and hence its brightness—may be gradually increased until the brightness of the filament just matches the brightness of the background. From previous calibration of the instrument at known temperatures, the scale of the ammeter A in the circuit may be marked to read the unknown temperature directly. Since no part of the instrument needs to

Fig. 13-9   *Blackbody at melting point of gold; furnace as used at U.S. National Bureau of Standards.*

come into contact with the hot body, the optical pyrometer may be used at temperatures above the melting points of many metals.

To understand how an optical pyrometer is calibrated at temperatures above the gold point, let us rewrite the Planck equation, Eq. (13-28), in terms of wavelength instead of frequency. Let $u_\lambda \, d\lambda$ be the energy density of the radiation within the wavelength range λ and $\lambda + d\lambda$. Then, since $\nu = c/\lambda$ and $|d\nu| = (c/\lambda^2)|d\lambda|$,

$$u_\lambda \, d\lambda = 8\pi hc \, \frac{\lambda^{-5} \, d\lambda}{e^{hc/\lambda kT} - 1}. \qquad (13\text{-}29)$$

Suppose that an optical pyrometer is sighted on a blackbody at the gold point and that the current necessary to make the lamp filament disappear is noted. Now suppose that another blackbody at a higher temperature T is sighted *with the same pyrometer at the same current setting*, but through a disk equipped with a sector-shaped opening whose angle θ can be varied at will. As the sectored disk rotates rapidly, it transmits the same fraction $\theta/2\pi$ of the radiation of all wavelengths. As θ is made smaller and smaller, the radiation gets dimmer and dimmer until it is the same as that from the gold-point blackbody. When this is the case,

$$\frac{u_\lambda(T_{Au})}{u_\lambda(T)} = \frac{\theta}{2\pi};$$

and using the Planck equation,

$$\frac{e^{c_2/\lambda T} - 1}{e^{c_2/\lambda T_{Au}} - 1} = \frac{\theta}{2\pi}. \tag{13-30}$$

where $c_2 = hc/k = 1.4388$ cm/°K. The wavelength transmitted by the filter is often chosen in the red region, where $\lambda = 6.5 \times 10^{-5}$ cm (6500 Å) and, as mentioned before, $T_{Au} = 1336$°K. Solving Eq. (13-30) for T gives the temperature of the unknown blackbody.

If the red filter transmitted only a very narrow band of wavelengths and if all unknown bodies whose temperatures must be measured were black-bodies, everything would be fine and no further physical ideas or instruments would be needed. This is not the case, however. Elaborate and difficult corrections must be made in order to take into account the finite bandwidth needed for a visual match, as well as the departure from blackbody conditions. These details, however, are for the expert.

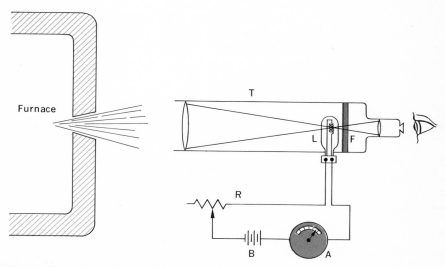

Fig. 13-10   *Main features of optical pyrometer.*

13-15   The Laws of Wien and of Stefan-Boltzmann

The Planck equation, expressed in terms of wavelength, takes the form

$$u_\lambda \, d\lambda = 8\pi hc \, \frac{\lambda^{-5} \, d\lambda}{e^{hc/\lambda kT} - 1}.$$

This is plotted in Fig. 13-11 for seven different temperatures. It can be seen that, the higher the temperature, the smaller the wavelength λ_m at which the energy density is a maximum. To see how λ_m depends on T, we note that u_λ is a maximum when $\lambda^5(e^{hc/\lambda kT} - 1)$ is a minimum. Thus,

$$\frac{d}{d\lambda} \left[\lambda^5 (e^{hc/\lambda kT} - 1) \right] = 0,$$

or

$$5\lambda^4 (e^{hc/\lambda kT} - 1) + \lambda^5 e^{hc/\lambda kT} \left(-\frac{hc}{kT} \frac{1}{\lambda^2} \right) = 0.$$

Fig. 13-11   *Variation of spectral energy density of blackbody radiation at different temperatures, according to Planck equation.*

Fig. 13-12   *Graphical solution of the equation* $1 - e^{-x} = x/5$.

The maximum λ must therefore satisfy the equation

$$1 - e^{-hc/\lambda kT} = \frac{1}{5}\frac{hc}{\lambda kT},$$

or

$$1 - e^{-x} = \frac{x}{5}.$$

This is a transcendental equation whose solution is obtained most simply by plotting two curves, $y = 1 - e^{-x}$ and $y = x/5$, and noting the value x_m at the point of intersection. This is done in Fig. 13-12, where the point of intersection is found to 4.96. Hence,

$$x_m = \frac{hc}{\lambda_m kT} = 4.96,$$

or

$$\lambda_m T = \frac{hc}{4.96k} = \frac{6.63 \times 10^{-27}\ \text{erg}\cdot\text{s} \times 3 \times 10^{20}\ \text{cm/s}}{4.96 \times 1.38 \times 10^{-16}\ \text{erg/deg}};$$

whence

$$\boxed{\lambda_m T = 0.290\ \text{cm}\cdot\text{deg,}} \tag{13-31}$$

which is known as *Wien's law* (pronounced "Veen"). If λ is measured in Angstrom units, where $1\ \text{Å} = 10^{-8}$ cm,

$$\lambda_m T = 0.290 \times 10^8\ \text{Å}\cdot\text{deg.}$$

At $T = 2000°K$, $\lambda_m = 14,500$ Å; whereas at $T = 6000°K$, $\lambda_m \approx 5000$ Å, as shown in Fig. 13-11.

Let us go back to Planck's equation expressed in terms of frequency,

$$u_\nu = \frac{8\pi h}{c^3} \frac{\nu^3}{e^{h\nu/kT} - 1}. \tag{13-28}$$

The *total energy density u* is

$$u = \int_0^\infty u_\nu \, d\nu = \frac{8\pi h}{c^3} \int_0^\infty \frac{\nu^3 \, d\nu}{e^{h\nu/kT} - 1}.$$

If we let $x = h\nu/kT$, then

$$u = \frac{8\pi k^4 T^4}{h^3 c^3} \int_0^\infty \frac{x^3 \, dx}{e^x - 1}.$$

It was mentioned in Art. 11-13, in evaluating the heat capacity of a crystal in the limit as T approaches zero, that

$$\int_0^\infty \frac{x^3 \, dx}{e^x - 1} = 3! \zeta(4)$$

$$= 6 \frac{\pi^4}{90} = \frac{\pi^4}{15}.$$

Hence

$$u = \frac{8\pi^5 k^4}{15 h^3 c^3} T^4. \tag{13-32}$$

Let us accept without proof that the radiant emittance $\mathcal{R}_B$ of the walls of a cavity in which blackbody radiation is in equilibrium is connected with the total energy density u by the following relation:

$$\mathcal{R}_B = \frac{c}{4} u = \frac{2\pi^5 k^4}{15 h^3 c^2} T^4.$$

This is the famous *Stefan-Boltzmann law* mentioned in Chap. 4 and written $\mathcal{R}_B = \sigma T^4$. We have

$$\sigma = \frac{2\pi^5 k^4}{15 h^3 c^2}$$

$$= \frac{2 \times (3.14)^5 \times (1.38)^4 \times 10^{-64} (\text{erg/deg})^4}{15 \times (6.63)^3 \times 10^{-81} (\text{erg} \cdot \text{s})^3 \times 9 \times 10^{20} (\text{cm/s})^2}$$

$$= 5.67 \times 10^{-5} \frac{\text{erg}}{\text{s} \cdot \text{cm}^2 \cdot \text{deg}^4},$$

which is in good agreement with experimental values.

13-16 Radiation Pressure; Blackbody Radiation as a Thermodynamic System

The quantum picture of the radiation in an enclosure is very similar to that of a gas. If the volume is V, we imagine photons of many different frequencies and pick out as a sample N_ν photons of frequency ν. Each photon has an energy $h\nu$ and a constant speed c. A photon has no rest mass. Its mass is due entirely to its speed, so that $mc^2 = h\nu$, or

$$m = \frac{h\nu}{c^2}.$$

In the kinetic theory of an ideal gas that was treated in Chap. 6, the pressure exerted by N molecules on a wall of an enclosure of volume V was shown to be [see Eq. (6-8)]

$$P = \frac{1}{3}\left(\frac{N}{V}\right)m\langle w^2\rangle,$$

where $\langle w^2\rangle$ was the average of the square of the speed. Since all photons have speed c, we get for the contribution to the pressure P_ν of those photons with frequency ν the expression

$$P_\nu = \frac{1}{3}\frac{N_\nu}{V}\frac{h\nu}{c^2}c^2$$

$$= \frac{1}{3}\frac{N_\nu h\nu}{V} = \frac{1}{3}u_\nu$$

and, for the total pressure,

$$P = \tfrac{1}{3}\Sigma u_\nu,$$

or

$$\boxed{P = \frac{u}{3}.}\tag{13-33}$$

Blackbody radiation is therefore completely specified by the pressure of the radiation, the volume of the radiation, and the temperature of the walls with which the radiation is in equilibrium. This temperature is sometimes called the *temperature of the radiation*, for convenience. Strictly speaking, it is not the radiation to which the temperature applies, but the matter in equilibrium with the radiation.

Since blackbody radiation is described by the coordinates P, V, and T, it may be treated as a hydrostatic system, and any one of the equations derived in Chap. 11 may be applied to it. A particularly important result can be obtained from the energy equation

$$\left(\frac{\partial U}{\partial V}\right)_T = T\left(\frac{\partial P}{\partial T}\right)_V - P.$$

Since $U = Vu$ and $P = u/3$, where u is a function of T only, the energy equation becomes

$$u = \frac{T}{3}\frac{du}{dT} - \frac{u}{3}$$

and reduces to

$$\frac{du}{u} = 4\frac{dT}{T}.$$

Integrating the above, we get

$$\ln u = \ln T^4 + \ln b,$$

or

$$u = bT^4,$$

which is in agreement with Eq. (13-32).

Since $P = u/3$ and $u = bT^4$, the equation of state of blackbody radiation takes the interesting form

$$P = \frac{b}{3} T^4, \tag{13-34}$$

and

$$\left(\frac{\partial P}{\partial T}\right)_V = \frac{dP}{dT} = \frac{4}{3} bT^3.$$

Also, since $U = VbT^4$,

$$C_V = \left(\frac{\partial U}{\partial T}\right)_V = 4VbT^3. \tag{13-35}$$

The first $T\,dS$ equation,

$$T\,dS = C_V\,dT + T\left(\frac{\partial P}{\partial T}\right)_V dV,$$

therefore becomes

$$T\,dS = 4VbT^3\,dT + \tfrac{4}{3}bT^4\,dV, \tag{13-36}$$

which may be used in two ways.

1. *Reversible isothermal change of volume*   If blackbody radiation, in equilibrium with the walls of a cavity at temperature T, is caused to expand

isothermally, heat will have to be supplied to the walls to keep the temperature constant. Thus,

$$T \, dS = \tfrac{4}{3} b T^4 \, dV,$$

and

$$Q = \tfrac{4}{3} b T^4 (V_f - V_i).$$

2. *Reversible adiabatic change of volume*   Suppose that blackbody radiation, in equilibrium with an extremely small piece of matter such as a grain of coal, is contained in a cylinder with perfectly reflecting walls. If the radiation is caused to expand against a piston, the expansion will be adiabatic, since there is no exchange of energy between the walls and the radiation. The work done on the surroundings is accomplished at the expense of the internal energy of both the piece of coal and the radiation. If the grain of coal has an extremely minute mass, its heat capacity may be regarded as negligible in comparison with that of the radiation. During the expansion, the radiation is always in equilibrium with the coal; but since the energy density of the radiation is decreasing, the temperature of the coal also decreases. The final temperature of the coal can be found by setting $dS = 0$ in the first $T \, dS$ equation. Thus,

$$\tfrac{4}{3} b T^4 \, dV = -4 V b T^3 \, dT,$$

or

$$\frac{dV}{V} = -3 \frac{dT}{T};$$

and after integration,

$$V T^3 = \text{const.} \tag{13-37}$$

The above equation shows that, if the volume of blackbody radiation were increased adiabatically by a factor of 8, the radiation would then be capable of existing in equilibrium with matter at a temperature which is one-half the original temperature.

PROBLEMS

13-1   The tension in a steel wire of length 1 m, diameter 1 mm, and temperature 300°K is increased reversibly and isothermally from zero to 10^8 dyn. Assume the following quantities to remain constant: $\rho = 7.86 \text{ g/cm}^3$; $\alpha = 12.0 \times 10^{-6} \text{ deg}^{-1}$; $Y = 2.00 \times 10^{12} \text{ dyn/cm}^2$; $C_{\mathscr{F}} = 0.482 \text{ J/g} \cdot \text{deg}$.

    (a)   How much heat in joules is transferred?
    (b)   How much work in joules is done?
    (c)   What is the change in internal energy?
    (d)   What would be the temperature change if the process were performed isentropically?

13-2   The equation of state of an ideal elastic cylinder is

$$\mathcal{F} = KT\left(\frac{L}{L_0} - \frac{L_0^2}{L^2}\right),$$

where K is a constant and L_0, the length at zero tension, is a function of T only. If the cylinder is stretched reversibly and isothermally from $L = L_0$ to $L = 2L_0$, show that:

(a)   The heat transferred is

$$Q = -KTL_0(1 - \tfrac{5}{2}\alpha_0 T),$$

where α_0, the linear expansivity at zero tension, is expressed as

$$\alpha_0 = \frac{1}{L_0}\frac{dL_0}{dT}.$$

(b)   The change of internal energy is

$$\Delta U = +\tfrac{5}{2}KT^2 L_0 \alpha_0.$$

13-3   In the case of the ideal elastic substance whose equation of state is given in Prob. 13-2, prove that:

(a) $\left(\dfrac{\partial U}{\partial L}\right)_T = AY\alpha_0 T.$

(b) $\left(\dfrac{\partial U}{\partial \mathcal{F}}\right)_T = L\alpha_0 T.$

13-4   An ideal elastic cylinder has the equation of state given in Prob. 13-2. When the length is changed isentropically, a temperature change occurs. This is called the *elastocaloric effect*. The magnitude of this effect is expressed by the quantity $(\partial T/\partial L)_S$.

(a)   Derive the expression

$$\left(\frac{\partial T}{\partial L}\right)_S = \frac{KT}{C_L}\left[\left(\frac{L}{L_0} - \frac{L_0^2}{L^2}\right) - \alpha_0 T\left(\frac{L}{L_0} + \frac{2L_0^2}{L^2}\right)\right],$$

where C_L is the heat capacity at constant length of the entire cylinder.

(b)   Assume the following values for a certain sample of rubber: $T = 300°K$ (practically constant), $K = 1.33 \times 10^3$ dyn/deg,

$$\alpha_0 = 5 \times 10^{-4} \text{ deg}^{-1},$$

$C_L = 2$ J/deg. Calculate $(\partial T/\partial L)_S$ for values of L/L_0 equal to 1, 1.1, 1.5, and 2.

13-5   When rubber is unstretched, X-ray diffraction experiments indicate an amorphous structure. When it is stretched isothermally, a crystalline structure is found, indicating that the large chainlike molecules are oriented.

(a)   Is $(\partial S/\partial \mathcal{F})_T$ positive or negative?

(b)   Prove that the linear expansivity of *stretched* rubber is negative.

13-6   A reversible cell whose emf depends only on T undergoes an isothermal transfer of jN_F coulombs of electricity.

(a)   Show that $\Delta S = jN_F \dfrac{d\mathcal{E}}{dT}$.

(b)   Show that $\Delta G = -jN_F\mathcal{E}$.

(c)   If ΔG and ΔH are found to approach the same value as T approaches zero, what conclusion may be drawn concerning $\lim\limits_{T \to 0} \Delta S$?

13-7   When zinc sulfate (valence $= 2$) reacts chemically with copper, at a temperature of 273°K and at atmospheric pressure, the heat evolved in the reaction is 2.31×10^8 J/kmole. The emf of a Daniell cell at 273°K is 1.0934 V, and the emf decreases with temperature at the rate of 4.533×10^{-4} V/deg. How does the calculated heat of reaction compare with the measured value?

13-8   The emf of the cell Zn, $ZnCl_2$, Hg_2Cl_2, Hg is given by the equation

$$\mathcal{E} = 1.0000 + 0.000094(t - 15).$$

Write the reaction, and calculate the heat of reaction at 100°C.

13-9

(a)   Prove that, for a dielectric,

$$\left(\frac{\partial U}{\partial E}\right)_T = T\left(\frac{\partial P'}{\partial T}\right)_E + E\left(\frac{\partial P'}{\partial E}\right)_T.$$

(b)   Assuming the equation of state to be

$$P' = \chi VE,$$

where the susceptibility χ is a function of T only, and the volume V is constant, show that the energy per unit volume of the dielectric is equal to

$$\frac{U}{V} = f(T) + \frac{E^2}{2}\left(\chi + T\frac{d\chi}{dT}\right),$$

where $f(T)$ is an undetermined function of temperature.

(c)   Prove that the energy per unit volume of an electric field in a vacuum is

$$\frac{E^2}{8\pi}.$$

(d)   Using the relation $\epsilon_r = 1 + 4\pi\chi$, show that the *total* energy per unit volume

$$\frac{U}{V} \text{ (dielectric plus field)} = f(T) + \frac{\epsilon_r E^2}{8\pi}\left(1 + \frac{T}{\epsilon_r}\frac{d\epsilon_r}{dT}\right).$$

13-10

(a)   Show that for a dielectric the difference in the heat capacities is given by

$$C_E - C_{P'} = T\frac{(\partial P'/\partial T)_E}{(\partial P'/\partial E)_T}.$$

(b)   If $P' = \chi VE$, show that

$$\frac{C_E - C_{P'}}{V} = \frac{T}{\chi}\left(\frac{d\chi}{dT}\right)^2 E^2.$$

(c)   If $\chi = C/T$, show that

$$\frac{C_E - C_{P'}}{V} = \frac{\chi}{T}E^2.$$

13-11   In the case of a dielectric whose equation of state is $P' = CVE/T$, show that:

(a)   The heat transferred in a reversible isothermal change of field is

$$Q = -\frac{CV}{2T}(E_f^2 - E_i^2).$$

(b)   The small temperature change accompanying a reversible adiabatic change of field is

$$\Delta T = \frac{CV}{2C_E T}(E_f^2 - E_i^2).$$

13-12   A KCl crystal doped with Li ions was found to have a heat capacity equal to AT^3 and a polarization $P' = (N\mu^2/3kT)E$, where N is the concentration of Li ions, μ the electric dipole moment of each Li ion, and k is Boltzmann's constant. If the initial electric field E_i is adiabatically reduced to zero, show that the resulting temperature change ΔT (with $\Delta T \ll T_i$) is given by

$$\Delta T = \frac{N\mu^2 E_i^2}{6kAT^4}.$$

This result, called the *electrocaloric effect*, was observed by G. Lombardo and R. O. Pohl in 1965. If $T = 2°K$ and $N\mu^2/6kA = 1.6 \times 10^{-8}$ cm$^2 \cdot$ deg^5/V^2, calculate ΔT at the following values of E_i: 0.5, 1, 5, and 10 kV/cm.

13-13   I. Shepard and G. Feher, in 1965, observed the *piezocaloric effect*. Derive an expression for this effect in zero electric field.

13-14   The difference between the Seebeck coefficients for Bi and Pb is given by -43.7 μV/deg $-$ $(0.47$ μV/deg$^2)t$, where t is the Celsius temperature.

(a) Calculate the thermal emf of a Bi-Pb thermocouple with the reference junction at 0°C and the test junction at 100°C.

(b) What is the Peltier coefficient of the test junction at 100°C? What Peltier heat would be transferred at this junction by an electric current of 10 A in 5 min? Would this heat go into or out of the junction?

(c) What is the difference between the Thomson coefficients at points at 50°C?

13-15   The thermal emf of a Ni-Pb thermocouple is given by (19.1 μV/ deg)t $-$ $(0.030$ μV/deg$^2)t^2$ when the reference junction is at 0°C.

(a) What is π at 127°C?

(b) What is $\sigma_{Ni} - \sigma_{Pb}$ at 57°C?

13-16

(a) What would be the characteristics of a thermocouple where $\sigma_A - \sigma_B = 0$?

(b) Would this thermocouple make a good thermometer?

13-17   Integrate Eq. (13-20) from a reference temperature T_R to any temperature T, and derive the equation

$$\mathcal{E}_{AB} = (\pi_{AB})_T - (\pi_{AB})_{T_R} + \int_{T_R}^{T} (\sigma_A - \sigma_B) \, dT.$$

(a) Interpret this equation in terms of a Seebeck emf, two Peltier emf's, and two Thomson emf's.

(b) Interpret this equation in terms of the first law of thermodynamics, neglecting irreversible effects.

(c) If three different wires A, B, and C are joined in series, with all junctions at the same temperature, prove that

$$(\pi_{AB})_T + (\pi_{BC})_T + (\pi_{CA})_T = 0.$$

(d)   Two wires A and B form a junction at the temperature T. The other ends of A and B are joined by a wire C forming two junctions, both at T_R. Prove that

$$\mathscr{E}_{ABC} = \mathscr{E}_{AB}.$$

What is the importance of this result?

13-18   In Fig. P13-1 is depicted an idealized apparatus similar to that used to explain a throttling process. There is, however, a big difference. The throttling process is strictly adiabatic, whereas the gas flowing through the porous plug in Fig. P13-1 is maintained at a *constant temperature* and pressure on the left side and at a constant *higher* temperature on the right. If the pores in the plug are small enough, the pressure on the right will be found to be higher than that on the left. This process is called *thermal effusion* or the *Knudsen effect*.

Fig. P13-1   *Thermal effusion (Knudsen effect) of a gas through a porous plug.*

Suppose that both pistons are moved to the right simultaneously, thereby maintaining a constant pressure P on the left and a constant pressure $P + \Delta P$ on the right. Under these circumstances, let n moles of gas be transferred in time τ. In this time, suppose the gas loses heat Q at temperature T and gains heat $Q + \Delta Q$ at the temperature $T + \Delta T$.

(a)   Show that the entropy produced in time τ is

$$\Delta S = Q \frac{\Delta T}{T^2} - \frac{\Delta Q}{T} + n \, \Delta s.$$

(b)   Apply the first law and obtain

$$\Delta Q = n \, \Delta h.$$

(c)   Show that

$$\frac{\Delta S}{\tau} = \frac{Q}{\tau}\frac{\Delta T}{T^2} - \frac{n}{\tau}\frac{v}{T}\Delta P$$

$$= I_S \frac{\Delta T}{T} - I_n v \frac{\Delta P}{T}.$$

(d)   Express I_S and $-I_n$ as linear functions of $\Delta T/T$ and $\Delta P/T$.

(e)   Show that

$$\frac{L_{12}}{L_{22}} = -\left(\frac{I}{I_n v}\right)_{\Delta T=0},$$

and

$$\frac{L_{21}}{L_{22}} = -\left(\frac{\Delta P}{\Delta T}\right)_{I_n=0}.$$

(f)   Show that

$$\left(\frac{\Delta P}{\Delta T}\right)_{I_n=0} = \frac{(I_S/I_n)_{\Delta T=0}}{v} = \frac{S^*}{v}.$$

(g)   The quantity S^* is the entropy accompanying the transport of 1 mole of gas through the plug. It is found from kinetic theory to be $R/2$. Prove that

$$\frac{P_1}{P_2} = \sqrt{\frac{T_1}{T_2}},$$

where the subscripts 1 and 2 refer to opposite sides of the plug.

(h)   Derive the preceding equation by using the result of Prob. 6-5e.

13-19   A thermodynamic system is described with the aid of the five coordinates P, V, T, $\mathscr{Y}$, X, where

$$T\,dS = dU + P\,dV - \mathscr{Y}\,dX.$$

Prove that, if $G = U + PV - TS$, as usual:

(a) $dG = -S\,dT + V\,dP + \mathscr{Y}\,dX.$

(b) $-\left(\dfrac{\partial S}{\partial P}\right)_{X,T} = \left(\dfrac{\partial V}{\partial T}\right)_{X,P}.$

(c) $-\left(\dfrac{\partial S}{\partial X}\right)_{P,T} = \left(\dfrac{\partial \mathscr{Y}}{\partial T}\right)_{P,X}.$

(d) $\left(\dfrac{\partial V}{\partial X}\right)_{T,P} = \left(\dfrac{\partial \mathscr{Y}}{\partial P}\right)_{T,X}.$

13-20   Using the five coordinates P, V, T, $\mathscr{E}$, Z to describe a reversible cell in which gases may be liberated, show that:

(a) $dG = -S\,dT + V\,dP + \mathcal{E}\,dZ.$

(b) $-\left(\dfrac{\partial S}{\partial Z}\right)_{T,P} = \left(\dfrac{\partial \mathcal{E}}{\partial T}\right)_{P,Z}.$

(c) $dH = T\,dS + V\,dP + \mathcal{E}\,dZ.$

(d) $\left(\dfrac{\partial H}{\partial Z}\right)_{T,P} = \mathcal{E} - T\left(\dfrac{\partial \mathcal{E}}{\partial T}\right)_{P,Z}.$

(e)   For a saturated cell, $\Delta H = -\dfrac{jN_F}{J}\left[\mathcal{E} - T\left(\dfrac{\partial \mathcal{E}}{\partial T}\right)_P\right].$

13-21   Using the five coordinates P, V, T, $\mathcal{S}$, A to describe a surface film and its accompanying liquid, show that:

(a) $dG = -S\,dT + V\,dP + \mathcal{S}\,dA.$

(b) $\left(\dfrac{\partial \mathcal{S}}{\partial P}\right)_{T,A} = \left(\dfrac{\partial V}{\partial A}\right)_{T,P}.$

13-22   Fill in the empty boxes in this table:

	Ideal gas molecules	Conduction electrons	Photons in an evacuated cavity
How does N_i compare with g_i?			
What is the expression for g_i?			
What fraction of these states is filled?			
How many particles are in each filled state?			
Is $\Sigma N_i = $ const.?			
What kind of statistics is appropriate?			

13-23

(a)   The spectral energy curve of sunlight has a maximum at a wavelength of 4840 Å. Assuming the sun to be a blackbody, what is the temperature of its emitting surface?

(b)   What is the energy density of the sun's radiation?

(c)   What is the radiation pressure exerted by the sun's radiation?

13-24   The volume of the blackbody radiation contained in a cavity with walls at a temperature of 2000°K is increased reversibly and isothermally from 10 to 1000 cm³.

(*a*)   How much heat is transferred?

(*b*)   What is the change of energy of the radiation?

(*c*)   How much work was done?

(*d*)   If the expansion were performed reversibly and adiabatically, what would be the final temperature of the radiation?

13-25   Prove that, for blackbody radiation,

(*a*) $PV^{\frac{4}{3}}$ = const., for an isentropic process.

(*b*) $\dfrac{S}{V} = \frac{4}{3}bT^3$.

(*c*) $C_P = \infty$.

(*d*) $G = 0$.

14.

PARAMAGNETISM, CRYOGENICS, NEGATIVE TEMPERATURES, AND THE THIRD LAW

14-1   Atomic Magnetism

An atom or molecule in its lowest energy state and uninfluenced by its neighbors or by an external magnetic field may have a net magnetic moment by virtue of two kinds of electronic processes: (1) orbital motion of one or more electrons, and (2) uncompensated spins of one or more electrons. These two effects are specified by the resultant orbital quantum number L and the net-spin quantum number S. The resultant of L and S is denoted by J. It is often the case that the orbital quantum number L is zero, in which case the atomic magnetism is due entirely to electron spin, since $J = S$.

When atoms or molecules are moving freely in the *gaseous* phase, the magnetic moment of the gas is determined by the L and S values of each *neutral* atom or molecule. Thus, oxygen gas is paramagnetic, because the resultant orbital quantum number of each neutral oxygen molecule is zero, and $S = 1$ for the ground state of the molecule. At lower temperatures, when atomic particles coalesce to form crystals, the atomic structures that occupy the various lattice sites are rarely neutral. In the sodium chloride crystal, the lattice sites are occupied by positive sodium ions and negative chlorine ions. Each of these ions has an inert-gas configuration of closed electron shells, with $L = 0$, $S = 0$, and $J = 0$. In a crystal where two or more valence electrons are removed from one atom and taken up by another, the resulting structures may again have an inert-gas configuration with no resultant magnetic moment.

There are some atoms, however, such as Cr and Fe, each with three valence electrons which exist as *trivalent ions* in the crystalline phase and do *not* have an inert-gas structure because *the third electron shell is incomplete*. These trivalent ions Cr^{+++} and Fe^{+++} have magnetic moments. The effect of orbital motions is said to be *quenched* by the fields of neighboring ions, but there remains a net electron spin S, so that $J = S$. The rare-earth atoms are particularly interesting in that, when their valence electrons are removed, the resulting ion lacks an inert-gas configuration because of incomplete filling of the $4f$ electron shell. In the particular case of gadolinium, which in the crystalline state is in the form of a trivalent ion Gd^{+++}, the ground state has an L value equal to zero, so that again $J = S$.

When an atom, molecule, or ion possesses a resultant magnetic moment in its lowest energy level and is sufficiently removed from its neighbors to be only weakly influenced by neighboring magnetic fields, it behaves in a simple way when subjected to an external magnetic field. The level splits into a number of separate states, each of which is characterized by a *magnetic quantum number m*. The allowed, discrete values of m correspond to discrete orientations of the magnetic-moment vector with respect to the external magnetic field. These values of m vary in *integral* steps from $-J$ to $+J$. Thus, when Fe^{+++} in its lowest energy level, with $J = \frac{5}{2}$, is subjected to a magnetic field $\mathcal{H}$, this level is split into six different energy states with m equal to

$$-\tfrac{5}{2}, \ -\tfrac{3}{2}, \ -\tfrac{1}{2}, \ +\tfrac{1}{2}, \ +\tfrac{3}{2}, \ +\tfrac{5}{2}.$$

When $\mathcal{H} = 0$, these six states all have the same energy, and therefore the lowest energy level of Fe^{+++} has a degeneracy of 6, or $2J + 1$. The effect of an external magnetic field is to remove this degeneracy.

If the energy of the lowest level is arbitrarily set equal to zero, then the magnetic potential energy of the ion in any one of the magnetic states is equal to

$$\epsilon_i = -g\mu_B \mathcal{H} m_i, \tag{14-1}$$

where μ_B is the Bohr magneton,

$$\mu_B = \frac{eh}{4\pi mc} = 0.927 \times 10^{-20} \text{ erg/Oe,}$$

and $\mathcal{H}$ is the *local* magnetic field to which the ion is subjected and which is practically equal to the external magnetic field when the sample of crystal is a long cylinder parallel to $\mathcal{H}$. The quantity g is called the *Landé splitting factor*. In the case of a crystal whose internal magnetic field (created by other magnetic ions) is *isotropic*, $g = 2$ when $L = 0$. The minus sign in Eq. (14-1) merely indicates that positive values of m correspond to orientations of the magnetic-moment vector with a component *in the direction* of $\mathcal{H}$, and these orientations involve a *decrease* of energy. When the orientations of the ion are such as to have components antiparallel to the field, then m is negative, and the potential energy of the ion is increased. Think of the magnetic ion as a small compass needle. If held perpendicular to a magnetic

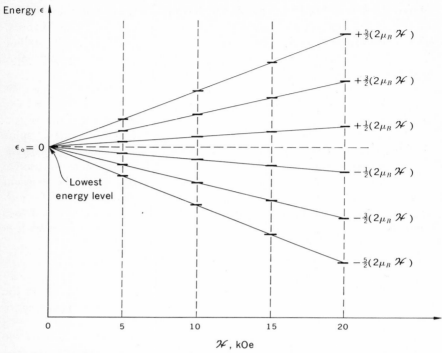

Fig. 14-1   *Splitting of the lowest energy level of Fe^{+++} ion in a magnetic field into six separate energy states.*

field and then allowed to undergo a quasi-static rotation till its magnetic moment is parallel to the field, it will do work on its surroundings and undergo a decrease in energy. To point a compass needle antiparallel to a magnetic field, work would have to be done *on* the needle in twisting it against an opposing torque, and its potential energy would therefore increase.

The magnetic splitting, proportional to the external magnetic field $\mathcal{H}$, is shown for Fe^{+++} in Fig. 14-1, and some of the electronic data for the lowest energy level of four important trivalent magnetic ions existing inside a crystal lattice are listed in Table 14-1.

The upper energy levels of an atom or ion are also split into a number of separate magnetic energy states by an external magnetic field. In the case of a gas supporting an electric discharge in a narrow tube placed between the poles of a strong electromagnet, atoms in one of the magnetic energy states of an upper energy level may undergo a transition to a magnetic state of a lower energy level and emit a spectral line. What was, in the absence of the magnetic field, a single spectral line now becomes a number of spectral

Table 14-1   Magnetic Ions in Paramagnetic Salts

Paramagnetic salt	Magnetic ion	S	L	J	g
$Cr_2(SO_4)_3 \cdot K_2SO_4 \cdot 24H_2O$ (chromium potassium alum)	Cr^{+++}	$\frac{3}{2}$	0 (quenched)	$\frac{3}{2}$	2
$Fe_2(SO_4)_3 \cdot (NH_4)_2SO_4 \cdot 24H_2O$ (iron ammonium alum)	Fe^{+++}	$\frac{5}{2}$	0 (quenched)	$\frac{5}{2}$	2
$Gd_2(SO_4)_3 \cdot 8H_2O$ (gadolinium sulphate)	Gd^{+++}	$\frac{7}{2}$	0	$\frac{7}{2}$	2
$2Ce(NO_3)_3 \cdot 3Mg(NO_3)_2 \cdot 24H_2O$ (cerium magnesium nitrate, CMN)	Ce^{+++}	$\frac{1}{2}$	3	$\frac{5}{2}$	$(\perp)1.84$ $(\parallel)0.02$

lines. This apparent "splitting" of a spectral line into a pattern of lines is called the *Zeeman effect*.

It may be seen in Fig. 14-1 that at a low value of $\mathscr{H}$ the six magnetic states are close together, so that, if $\Delta\epsilon$ is the energy difference between any two adjacent states, $\Delta\epsilon$ is very small. If $\mathscr{H}$ is 1 kOe,

$$\Delta\epsilon = 2\mu_B\mathscr{H} = 2 \times 0.927 \times 10^{-20} \text{ erg/Oe} \times 10^3 \text{ Oe}$$

$$\approx 0.2 \times 10^{-16} \text{ erg.}$$

At a temperature of 1°K,

$$kT = 1.38 \times 10^{-16} \text{ erg/deg} \times 1 \text{ deg}$$

$$\approx 1.4 \times 10^{-16} \text{ erg.}$$

Hence, at $T = 1°K$ and $\mathscr{H} = 10^3$ Oe,

$$\Delta\epsilon < kT \qquad \text{(for } \mathscr{H} = 1 \text{ kOe).}$$

In a large magnetic field, however, say, $\mathscr{H} = 20$ kOe, $\Delta\epsilon = 4 \times 10^{-16}$ erg, and kT at 1°K is still 1.4×10^{-16} erg, so that

$$\Delta\epsilon > kT \qquad \text{(for } \mathscr{H} = 20 \text{ kOe).}$$

In the paramagnetic crystals listed in Table 14-1, the distribution of magnetic ions among the various magnetic states is given by the Boltzmann equation,

$$N_i \propto e^{-\epsilon_i/kT}.$$

Therefore, when $\Delta\epsilon < kT$, all the six closely packed states that exist in a weak field may be populated almost equally. Since each state corresponds to a different orientation with regard to the external magnetic field, the *net magnetic polarization* or *magnetization M* of the crystal would then be very small. When the field is strong enough to make $\Delta\epsilon > kT$, however, only the lowest state, with energy $-J \cdot 2\mu_B\mathscr{H}$, will be populated. Since this state corresponds to the ions lining up parallel to the external magnetic field, the magnetization M would have its largest, or *saturation*, value M_{sat}.

14-2   Statistical Mechanics of a Magnetic-ion Subsystem

The ions occupying lattice sites in a typical crystal such as sodium chloride are localized (and therefore distinguishable) and tremendously influenced by their neighbors. When the vibration characteristics of the crystal *as a whole* are analyzed, it is found that there are three times as many normal modes as lattice points and that these $3N$ normal modes may be treated statistically as $3N$ distinguishable but *weakly interacting* harmonic oscillators. Upon making use of the appropriate expression for the thermodynamic probability (see Art. 11-12) and performing the usual operations, the Boltzmann equation was found to apply.

The paramagnetic crystals of greatest use in practical thermodynamics contain paramagnetic ions surrounded by a very large number of nonmagnetic particles, as shown in Table 14-1. Each chromium ion in $Cr_2(SO_4)_3 \cdot K_2SO_4 \cdot 24H_2O$ is surrounded by 1 potassium atom, 2 sulfur atoms, 20 oxygen atoms, and 24 hydrogen atoms—a total of 47 nonmagnetic particles. In other words, the chromium ions are very dilute and far apart, so that magnetic interaction among them is very weak. The same is true of the magnetic ions in the other three salts listed in Table 14-1. The behavior of the magnetic ions in a dilute paramagnetic salt is almost gaslike in the weakness of interaction, but the ions are, of course, distinguishable by their positions. We may therefore apply the statistical method appropriate to these distinguishable, weakly interacting particles.

Consider a piece of crystal containing N magnetic ions and about fifty times as many nonmagnetic particles. Let us suppose that the temperature of the crystal is so low (in the neighborhood of 1°K) that *the vibrational energy and the heat capacity of everything but the magnetic ions may be ignored*. The N magnetic ions constitute a *subsystem* with which there is associated a temperature T of its own, which may or may not be the same as the temperature of the rest of the crystal. The *magnetization* (or *total magnetic moment*) M of the ions has nothing to do with the rest of the crystal, and the external magnetic field $\mathscr{H}$ produces no effect on the rest of the crystal. In other words, *the magnetic ions form a subsystem with its own identity, describable with the aid of its coordinates* $\mathcal{H}$, *M, and T, as though the rest of the crystal were a container.* The magnetic potential energy ϵ_i of any ion is equal to $-g\mu_B\mathcal{H}m_i$, but this is not the only energy possessed by the ion.

It has been mentioned that the lowest energy level of a magnetic ion in the absence of an external magnetic field has a $(2J + 1)$-fold degeneracy which is removed by the splitting action of the magnetic field. *Even in the absence of an external magnetic field, there are internal fields which provide some splitting of the lowest energy level.* There are, of course, the very weak magnetic fields provided by the other relatively distant magnetic ions, but the effect of these fields is small and sometimes may be neglected in comparison with the much stronger effect of the *electric field* in the crystal. This field is due to the positive and negative charges of the ions in the lattice, and the interaction between an atom or ion and an electric field, known as the *Stark effect,* is similar to the Zeeman effect in that some or all of the degeneracy of an energy level may be removed by the *electric splitting* of the level into a number of electric states.

We have seen that a magnetic field $\mathcal{H}$ gives rise to magnetic states whose separation is given by $\Delta\epsilon = 2\mu_B\mathcal{H}$. It is often convenient to express this "splitting energy" in terms of a temperature T, where $kT = 2\mu_B\mathcal{H}$. The magnetic splitting of a field of, say, 20 kOe would correspond to a temperature

$$T = \frac{2\mu_B\mathcal{H}}{k} = \frac{2 \times 0.917 \times 10^{-20} \text{ erg/Oe} \times 20 \times 10^3 \text{ Oe}}{1.38 \times 10^{-16} \text{ erg/deg}},$$

or $\quad T \approx 3°\text{K}.$

The Stark-effect splitting in most crystals is of the order of a tenth or a hundredth of a degree or less. Sometimes the entire degeneracy of the lowest energy level is not completely removed by the crystalline field, and the level is split into only a few electric states. This splitting is much too small to show in Fig. 14-1 at the point where $\mathcal{H} = 0$. Suppose, for the sake of simplicity, we assume that the effect of the crystalline field is to provide only two states whose energies are zero and δ_1, and whose degeneracies are g_0 and g_1. *In zero magnetic field* and at temperatures far below δ_1/k, most of the ions would be in the lower energy state; whereas at temperatures much higher than δ_1/k, the two states would be about equally populated.

To apply statistical mechanics rigorously to a paramagnetic crystal, taking into account (1) the magnetic-ion subsystem in a field $\mathcal{H}$, (2) its magnetic and electric interaction with the lattice when $\mathcal{H} = 0$, and (3) its mechanical and thermal interaction with the lattice, is a complicated problem requiring the use of a statistical device known as a *canonical ensemble.* For details of this calculation, the reader is referred to Chap. 20 of P. M. Morse's "Thermal

Physics." Much can be done and understood, however, by applying the simple method of dealing with localized, weakly interacting particles that was used in Chap. 11 with a crystal.

Let ϵ_i stand for the *total* energy of a paramagnetic ion, equal to the sum of the energy δ_i due to crystalline field splitting and the magnetic potential energy $-g\mu_B\mathcal{H}m_i$ due to the presence of a magnetic field $\mathcal{H}$. Thus

$$\epsilon_i = \delta_i - g\mu_B\mathcal{H}m_i, \tag{14-2}$$

where δ_i has only two values, 0 and δ_1, and m_i ranges in integral steps from $-J$ to $+J$. Let $N_1, N_2, \ldots N_i, \ldots$ be the instantaneous, nonequilibrium populations of the various energy states. In the systems we have studied up to this point, namely, an ideal gas, a nonmetallic crystal, a metallic crystal, and a photon gas, it was found possible to interpret the sum $\Sigma N_i\epsilon_i$ unambiguously as the internal energy U. This is *not* the case, however, with a paramagnetic ion subsystem in a magnetic field, where

$$\Sigma N_i\epsilon_i = \Sigma N_i\delta_i - \mathcal{H}\Sigma N_i g\mu_B m_i.$$

The sum in the second term on the right is seen to be the magnetization M, so that the entire second term, $-\mathcal{H}M$, is the *magnetic potential energy* of a paramagnetic system of magnetization M in a field $\mathcal{H}$, a quantity which cannot be included within an expression for internal energy. We are forced to conclude, therefore, that the first sum on the right is the internal energy, or

$$U = \Sigma N_i\delta_i.$$

The sum $\Sigma N_i\epsilon_i$ is therefore

$$\Sigma N_i\epsilon_i = U - \mathcal{H}M. \tag{14-3}$$

If our system of paramagnetic ions approaches equilibrium (1) adiabatically ($dQ = 0$) and (2) at constant field ($d\mathcal{H} = 0$), then

$$d\Sigma N_i\epsilon_i = dU - \mathcal{H}\,dM - M\,d\mathcal{H}$$
$$= dQ - M\,d\mathcal{H}$$
$$= 0,$$

or $\Sigma N_i\epsilon_i$ *remains constant.*

For a system of N *localized*, weakly interacting ions, the entropy is given by

$$S = k \ln \frac{N!}{N_1! N_2! \cdots},$$

where $\Sigma N_i = N =$ constant. Using the Stirling approximation, and taking the differential, we get

$$dS = -k\Sigma \ln N_i \, dN_i.$$

If equilibrium is approached adiabatically, at constant $\mathscr{H}$ and at constant N, we have the usual three equations to satisfy:

$$-k\Sigma \ln N_i \, dN_i = 0,$$

$$\Sigma \epsilon_i \, dN_i = 0,$$

$$\Sigma dN_i = 0.$$

Using the Lagrange method, we get

$$N_i = Ae^{-\beta \epsilon_i},$$

where

$$A = \frac{N}{Z},$$

and

$$Z = \Sigma e^{-\beta \epsilon_i}.$$

Substituting the equilibrium values of the N's into the expression for dS, it is a simple matter to show that

$$\beta = \frac{1}{kT},$$

and therefore

$$N_i = \frac{N}{Z} e^{-\epsilon_i/kT}.$$

Substituting these values of the N's into the expression for the entropy, we get

$$S = Nk \ln Z + \frac{\Sigma N_i \epsilon_i}{T}.$$

Since $\Sigma N_i \epsilon_i = U - \mathscr{H}M$, we get

$$S = Nk \ln Z + \frac{U - \mathscr{H}M}{T},$$

or

$$U - TS - \mathscr{H}M = -NkT \ln Z.$$

The function on the left is the analog of the Gibbs function and is therefore the *magnetic Gibbs function*,

$$G^* = U - TS - \mathcal{H}M, \tag{14-4}$$

and we get finally

$$\boxed{G^* = -NkT \ln Z.} \tag{14-5}$$

Now, $dG^* = dU - T\,dS - \mathcal{H}\,dM - S\,dT - M\,d\mathcal{H},$

and since $T\,dS = dU - \mathcal{H}\,dM,$

$$dG^* = -S\,dT - M\,d\mathcal{H}.$$

Therefore,

$$M = -\left(\frac{\partial G^*}{\partial \mathcal{H}}\right)_T;$$

consequently,

$$\boxed{M = NkT\left(\frac{\partial \ln Z}{\partial \mathcal{H}}\right)_T.} \tag{14-6}$$

Also,

$$S = -\left(\frac{\partial G^*}{\partial T}\right)_{\mathcal{H}},$$

and therefore

$$\boxed{S = NkT\left(\frac{\partial \ln Z}{\partial T}\right)_{\mathcal{H}} + Nk \ln Z.} \tag{14-7}$$

Finally,

$$U = G^* + TS + \mathcal{H}M$$

$$= -NkT \ln Z + NkT^2\left(\frac{\partial \ln Z}{\partial T}\right)_{\mathcal{H}} + NkT \ln Z + \mathcal{H}M,$$

and

$$\boxed{U = NkT^2\left(\frac{\partial \ln Z}{\partial T}\right)_{\mathcal{H}} + \mathcal{H}M.} \tag{14-8}$$

The four boxed equations will enable us to find all the desirable information about our magnetic-ion subsystem, once we have our partition function expressed as a function of T and $\mathcal{H}$. Since $\epsilon_i = \delta_i - g\mu_B\mathcal{H}m_i,$

$$Z = \Sigma g_i e^{-(\delta_i - g\mu_B\mathcal{H}m_i)/kT}$$

$$= \Sigma g_i e^{-\delta_i/kT}\Sigma e^{g\mu_B\mathcal{H}m_i/kT},$$

or

$$Z = Z_{\text{int}}Z_{\mathcal{H}}. \tag{14-9}$$

We have simplified matters by assuming that the crystal field splitting gives rise to only two states: one of energy zero and degeneracy g_0, and the other of energy δ_1 and degeneracy g_1. Then,

$$Z_{\text{int}} = g_0 + g_1 e^{-\delta_1/kT}, \tag{14-10}$$

which is a function of T only.

In the next section, we shall evaluate $Z_{\mathscr{H}}$, which will be found to be a function of $\mathscr{H}/T$.

14-3   Magnetic Moment of a Magnetic-ion Subsystem

The magnetic part of the partition function of a magnetic-ion subsystem is given by

$$Z_{\mathscr{H}} = \Sigma e^{g\mu_{\text{B}}\mathscr{H}m_i/kT}. \tag{14-11}$$

If we let

$$a = \frac{g\mu_{\text{B}}\mathscr{H}}{kT}, \tag{14-12}$$

then, since m_i can take on the values $-J, -J+1, \ldots, J-1, J$, we find

$$Z_{\mathscr{H}} = \sum_{m_i=-J}^{m_i=+J} e^{am_i} = e^{-aJ} + e^{-a(J-1)} + \cdots + e^{aJ}.$$

This is a finite geometric progression with a ratio e^a; hence,

$$Z_{\mathscr{H}} = \frac{e^{-aJ} - e^{a(J+1)}}{1 - e^a}.$$

Multiplying numerator and denominator by $e^{-a/2}$, we get

$$Z_{\mathscr{H}} = \frac{e^{-a(J+\frac{1}{2})} - e^{a(J+\frac{1}{2})}}{e^{-a/2} - e^{a/2}},$$

or

$$Z_{\mathscr{H}} = \frac{\sinh (J + \frac{1}{2})a}{\sinh \frac{1}{2}a}. \tag{14-13}$$

Therefore,

$$\boxed{\ln Z = \ln \sinh (J + \tfrac{1}{2})a - \ln \sinh \frac{a}{2} + \ln (g_0 + g_1 e^{-\delta_1/kT}).} \tag{14-14}$$

Since $a = g\mu_{\text{B}}\mathscr{H}/kT$, $\ln Z$ is seen to be a function of $\mathscr{H}$ and T.

We are now in a position to evaluate M with the aid of Eq. (14-6).

$$\begin{aligned} M &= NkT \left(\frac{\partial \ln Z}{\partial \mathscr{H}} \right)_T = NkT \left(\frac{\partial \ln Z_{\mathscr{H}}}{\partial \mathscr{H}} \right)_T \\ &= NkT \left[\frac{d \ln Z_{\mathscr{H}}}{da} \left(\frac{\partial a}{\partial \mathscr{H}} \right)_T \right] = NkT \left(\frac{g\mu_B}{kT} \frac{d \ln Z_{\mathscr{H}}}{da} \right) \\ &= Ng\mu_B \frac{d}{da} [\ln \sinh (J + \tfrac{1}{2})a - \ln \sinh \tfrac{1}{2}a] \\ &= Ng\mu_B \left[\frac{(J + \tfrac{1}{2}) \cosh (J + \tfrac{1}{2})a}{\sinh (J + \tfrac{1}{2})a} - \frac{\tfrac{1}{2} \cosh \tfrac{1}{2}a}{\sinh \tfrac{1}{2}a} \right]. \end{aligned}$$

Finally, $M = Ng\mu_B J \left\{ \frac{1}{J} \left[(J + \tfrac{1}{2}) \coth (J + \tfrac{1}{2})a - \tfrac{1}{2} \coth \tfrac{1}{2}a \right] \right\}.$ (14-15)

The quantity in curved brackets is called the *Brillouin function* $B_J(a)$, named after L. Brillouin, who first extended the classical theory of paramagnetism (due to Langevin) to include quantum ideas. Therefore,

$$\boxed{M = Ng\mu_B J B_J(a),} \qquad (14\text{-}16)$$

where $B_J(a) = \frac{1}{J} \left[(J + \tfrac{1}{2}) \coth (J + \tfrac{1}{2})a - \tfrac{1}{2} \coth \tfrac{1}{2}a \right].$ (14-17)

Before we consider the consequences of Brillouin's equation for M, let us examine the mathematical features of the Brillouin function, which is plotted in Fig. 14-2 for a number of values of J. By definition,

$$\coth x = \frac{\cosh x}{\sinh x} = \frac{e^x + e^{-x}}{e^x - e^{-x}},$$

and for $x \gg 1$, $e^x \gg e^{-x}$, so that $\coth x = 1$. Therefore, for large values of a,

$$B_J(a) = \frac{1}{J} \left[(J + \tfrac{1}{2}) - \tfrac{1}{2} \right] = 1 \qquad (\text{for } a \gg 1).$$

Since $a = g\mu_B \mathscr{H}/kT$, large values of a are achieved

when $\dfrac{g\mu_B \mathscr{H}}{kT} \gg 1,$

or $\dfrac{\mathscr{H}}{T} \gg \dfrac{k}{g\mu_B} \gg \dfrac{1.38 \times 10^{-16} \text{ erg/deg}}{2 \times 0.927 \times 10^{-20} \text{ erg/Oe}},$

or $\dfrac{\mathscr{H}}{T} \gg 7 \text{ kOe/deg}.$

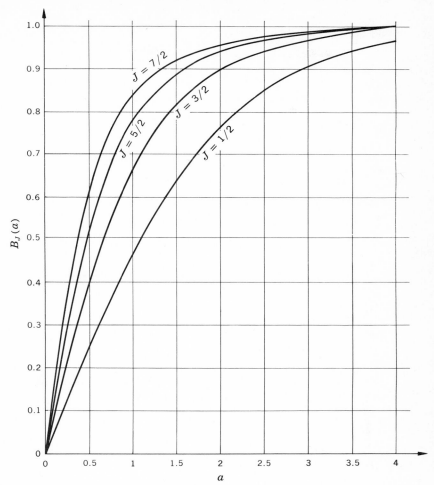

Fig. 14-2   *The Brillouin function.*

Since $M = N\mu_B g J B_J(a)$, it follows that at values of $\mathcal{H}/T$ greatly in excess of 7 kOe/deg, the magnetization M has its saturation value M_{sat} where $M_{\text{sat}} = N g \mu_B J$, and the *magnetization per magnetic ion expressed in terms of Bohr magnitons*, $M_{\text{sat}}/N\mu_B$, becomes

$$\frac{M_{\text{sat}}}{N\mu_B} = gJ \qquad (\text{for } \mathcal{H}/T \gg 7 \text{ kOe/deg}).$$

This conclusion was tested by W. E. Henry with the first three salts listed

Fig. 14-3   *Plot of magnetization per magnetic dipole, expressed in Bohr magnetons, against* $\mathcal{H}/T$ *for (I) chromium potassium alum* $(J = \frac{3}{2})$*; (II) iron ammonium alum* $(J = \frac{5}{2})$*; and (III) gadolinium sulfate* $(J = \frac{7}{2})$*. The points are experimental results of W. E. Henry (1952), and the solid curves are graphs of the Brillouin equation.*

in Table 14-1. The experimental results, plotted in Fig. 14-3, agree very well with the Brillouin equation and with the limiting value of $M/N\mu_B$.

When $x \ll 1$, it is easy to show that

$$\coth x = \frac{1}{x} + \frac{x}{3}.$$

Therefore, for small values of a,

$$B_J(a) = \frac{1}{J}\left\{(J + \tfrac{1}{2})\left[\frac{1}{(J + \tfrac{1}{2})a} + \tfrac{1}{3}(J + \tfrac{1}{2})a\right] - \tfrac{1}{2}\left[\frac{2}{a} + \frac{a}{6}\right]\right\}$$

$$= \frac{1}{J}\left\{\tfrac{1}{3}(J + \tfrac{1}{2})^2 a - \frac{a}{12}\right\}$$

$$= \frac{a}{3J}(J^2 + J + \tfrac{1}{4} - \tfrac{1}{4}),$$

and finally, $\qquad\qquad B_J(a) = \dfrac{J + 1}{3}\, a \qquad$ (for $a \ll 1$).

Small values of a are achieved when

$$\frac{\mathcal{H}}{T} \ll 7 \text{ kOe/deg.}$$

When this is the case,

$$M = Ng\mu_{\mathrm{B}}J\,\frac{J + 1}{3}\,a = \frac{Ng^2\mu_{\mathrm{B}}^2 J(J + 1)\mathcal{H}}{3kT},$$

or $\qquad$ $\boxed{M = \dfrac{Ng^2\mu_{\mathrm{B}}^2 J(J + 1)}{3k}\,\dfrac{\mathcal{H}}{T}}$ $\qquad\left(\text{for } \dfrac{\mathcal{H}}{T} \ll 7 \text{ kOe/deg}\right).$ $\qquad$ (14-18)

This is Curie's equation, and the Curie constant C_C is seen to be

$$\boxed{C_C = \frac{N\mu_{\mathrm{B}}^2 g^2 J(J + 1)}{3k}.}$$
$\qquad\qquad\qquad\qquad$ (14-19)

A mass of crystal containing exactly N_A (Avogadro's number) magnetic ions is known as 1 *gram-ion*. The gram-ionic masses of the four crystals listed in Table 14-1 are given in Table 14-2. The Curie constant per g $\cdot$ ion is given

Table 14-2   Curie Constants and Heat-capacity Constants

Paramagnetic salt	m, gram-ionic mass of crystal	$J(J + 1)$	C_C (measured) cm$^3 \cdot$ deg / g $\cdot$ ion	C_C (calculated) cm$^3 \cdot$ deg / g $\cdot$ ion	A/R, deg^2
$Cr_2(SO_4)_3 \cdot K_2SO_4 \cdot 24H_2O$	499	3.75	1.84	1.88	0.018
$Fe_2(SO_4)_3 \cdot (NH_4)_2SO_4 \cdot 24H_2O$	482	8.75	4.39	4.38	0.013
$Gd_2(SO_4)_3 \cdot 8H_2O$	373	15.75	7.80	7.87	0.35
$2Ce(NO_3)_3 \cdot 3Mg(NO_3)_2 \cdot 24H_2O$	765		~ 0 (∥) 0.317 (⊥)		6.1×10^{-6}

by

$$C_C = \frac{6.02 \times 10^{23} \, 1/g \cdot \text{ion} \times (0.927)^2 \times 10^{-40} \, \text{erg}^2/\text{Oe}^2}{3 \times 1.38 \times 10^{-16} \, \text{erg/deg}} \, g^2 J(J + 1).$$

Upon recalling that the unit Oe^2 has the same dimensions as erg/cm^3, the gram-ionic Curie constant becomes

$$C_C = 0.125 \, \frac{\text{cm}^3 \cdot \text{deg}}{\text{g} \cdot \text{ion}} \, g^2 J(J + 1) \tag{14-20}$$

and provides the calculated values in Table 14-2. The agreement with the measured values is very good.

14-4   Thermal Properties of a Magnetic-ion Subsystem

The internal energy of a magnetic-ion subsystem is given by Eq. (14-8), namely,

$$U = NkT^2 \left(\frac{\partial \ln Z}{\partial T} \right)_{\mathscr{H}} + \mathscr{H}M.$$

We have

$$\left(\frac{\partial \ln Z}{\partial T} \right)_{\mathscr{H}} = \frac{d \ln Z_{\mathscr{H}}}{da} \left(\frac{\partial a}{\partial T} \right)_{\mathscr{H}} + \frac{d \ln Z_{\text{int}}}{dT}$$

$$= JB_J(a) \left(-\frac{g\mu_B \mathscr{H}}{kT^2} \right) + \frac{d}{dT} [\ln (g_0 + g_1 e^{-\delta_1/kT})]$$

$$= -\frac{g\mu_B \mathscr{H}}{kT^2} \, JB_J(a) + \frac{(g_1 \delta_1/kT^2)e^{-\delta_1/kT}}{g_0 + g_1 e^{-\delta_1/kT}}.$$

Therefore, $$U = -Ng\mu_B \mathscr{H} JB_J(a) + \frac{N\delta_1}{1 + (g_0/g_1)e^{\delta_1/kT}} + \mathscr{H}M. \tag{14-21}$$

According to Eq. (14-16), the first term on the right is $-\mathscr{H}M$, which cancels the third term, so that

$$\boxed{U = \frac{N\delta_1}{1 + (g_0/g_1)e^{\delta_1/kT}}.} \tag{14-22}$$

Since $$T \, dS = dU - \mathscr{H} \, dM,$$

$$T \frac{dS}{dT} = \frac{dU}{dT} - \mathscr{H} \frac{dM}{dT}. \tag{14-23}$$

At constant M, the left-hand member becomes C_M, and since U is a function of T only, dU/dT is also a function of T only. Therefore,

$$C_M = \frac{dU}{dT}, \qquad (14\text{-}24)$$

and from the expression for U in Eq. (14-22)

$$C_M = \frac{-N\delta_1(g_0/g_1)(-\delta_1/kT^2)e^{\delta_1/kT}}{[1+(g_0/g_1)e^{\delta_1/kT}]^2}.$$

If $N = N_A$, then, since $N_A k = R$, we have the heat capacity per gram-ion c_M given by

$$\boxed{\frac{c_M}{R} = \frac{\delta_1^2}{k^2T^2}\frac{(g_0/g_1)e^{\delta_1/kT}}{[1+(g_0/g_1)e^{\delta_1/kT}]^2}.} \qquad (14\text{-}25)$$

This is known as *Schottky's equation* and is plotted in Fig. 14-4 for three different values of the ratio g_1/g_0.

To appreciate the numerical aspects of Schottky's equation, consider a magnetic-ion subsystem in which $\delta_1/k = 0.1°K$ and $g_0/g_1 = 1$. From the middle curve of Fig. 14-4 we see that, at $T = \delta_1/k = 0.1°K$, $c_M/R = 0.2$. Since $R = 8.3$ J/g · ion · deg, $c_M \approx 1700$ mJ/g · ion · deg. If the rest of the

Fig. 14-4   *Schottky heat capacity of a magnetic-ion subsystem whose lowest energy level, in the absence of an external magnetic field, is split into two states with degeneracies g_0 and g_1, for several values of g_1/g_0.*

crystal had a Debye Θ of about $250°K$ and, say, 100 times as many particles, the heat capacity would be, from Eq. (11-47),

$$c \approx 100 \left(\frac{125}{\Theta} \right)^3 T^3 \approx 100 \times \tfrac{1}{8} \times (0.1)^3 \approx 0.013 \text{ mJ/mole} \cdot \text{deg}.$$

The heat capacity of the magnetic-ion subsystem is therefore over 100,000 times as large as the rest of the crystal!

Many subsystems have values of δ_1/k less than $0.1°K$ but are of interest and of use at temperatures above this value. When $T \gg \delta_1/k$, Eq. (14-25) reduces to

$$\frac{c_M}{R} = \frac{g_0/g_1}{(1 + g_0/g_1)^2} \frac{(\delta_1/k)^2}{T^2} = \frac{\text{const.}}{T^2}.$$

The "tail" of the Schottky curve is therefore an inverse square curve. It is an interesting and important fact that this inverse-square behavior is true at *higher temperatures* not only when Stark-effect splitting gives rise to two degenerate levels but also when there are *any number* of closely spaced levels. Also, other causes of splitting when $\mathcal{H} = 0$, such as magnetic interactions among the ions, are found to give rise to a $1/T^2$ curve. It is therefore the custom to represent the heat capacity per gram-ion of a paramagnetic salt at temperatures above the Schottky maximum by the equation

$$\boxed{\frac{c_M}{R} = \frac{A/R}{T^2}.} \tag{14-26}$$

Values of A/R are listed in the last column of Table 14-2 for four paramagnetic salts, and the $1/T^2$ law is verified in Fig. 14-5 for copper potassium sulfate.

The last salt, cerium magnesium nitrate (abbreviated CMN), plays an important role in low-temperature physics. It is a complicated crystal with a structure that is highly anisotropic. Parallel to the axis of symmetry (the so-called trigonal axis), the Landé splitting factor g is so small that the Curie constant is almost zero. Perpendicular to this axis, however, the Curie constant has an appreciable value. If a single crystal is placed with its trigonal axis parallel to an external field, its magnetization is very small. A simple rotation through 90 deg is all that is needed to magnetize the crystal. Moreover, the heat capacity constant A/R is remarkably small, indicating a very small value for the various factors that split the lowest energy level of the cerium ion in the absence of an external magnetic field. It is believed that this splitting is due to ionic interaction rather than the Stark effect.

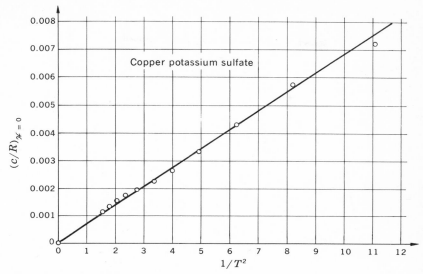

Fig. 14-5   *Test of the relation $c/R \propto 1/T^2$. (Ashmead.)*

The most important thermal property of a magnetic-ion subsystem is the entropy. According to Eq. (14-7),

$$S = NkT\left(\frac{\partial \ln Z}{\partial T}\right)_{\mathscr{H}} + Nk \ln Z;$$

and from Eq. (14-14),

$$\ln Z = \ln \sinh (J + \tfrac{1}{2})a - \ln \sinh \frac{a}{2} + \ln (g_0 + g_1 e^{-\delta_1/kT}).$$

When $\ln Z$ is introduced into the expression for S, the resulting equation looks rather formidable but has simple properties when the temperature range is divided into two parts:

(1) $\qquad T \gg \delta_1/k \qquad$ and $\qquad S = S_1(\mathscr{H}/T).$ (14-27)

(2) $\qquad T \le \delta_1/k \qquad$ and $\qquad S = S_2(T,\mathscr{H}).$

If S is plotted as a function of T, at various values of $\mathscr{H}$, the resulting curves resemble those of Fig. 14-6. The ST curve for $\mathscr{H} = 0$ is particularly significant. Within the range indicated by vertical dashed lines, $S_{\mathscr{H}=0}$ is constant because the temperature is too low to provide an appreciable heat capacity of the nonmagnetic particles, but too high to allow crystalline field splitting

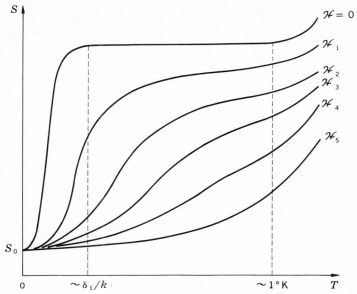

Fig. 14-6   *Entropy of a magnetic-ion subsystem as a function of temperature for various values of the magnetic field. In the region between the two dashed lines, $S_{\mathcal{H}=0}$ is constant, $U = constant$, and $C_M = 0$.*

or ionic magnetic interaction to show an appreciable effect. Since the only term involving the dependence of *internal* energy on temperature [Eq. (14-22)] is provided by the interaction of the ions with either the crystalline field or with one another, the internal energy is also constant in this temperature region. Finally, since $C_M = T\, dS/dT = dU/dT$, it follows that $C_M = 0$ in this range.

14-5   Production of Millidegree Temperatures by Ionic Demagnetization

Almost every property of matter shows interesting changes or variations in the temperature range below about 20°K. Temperatures down to about 1°K are easily obtained by causing He^4 to evaporate rapidly. With He^3 it is possible to reach about 0.3°K. In 1926 it was suggested independently by Giauque and by Debye that much lower temperatures could be achieved with the aid of paramagnetic salts. The principle of the method is presented graphically in Fig. 14-7, where the entropy of a magnetic-ion subsystem is plotted against the temperature for two values of the external magnetic field, 0 and $\mathscr{H}_i$. At a temperature in the neighborhood of 1°K, where the lattice heat capacity of the nonmagnetic particles is negligibly small, the salt is magnetized isothermally in the process $k \rightarrow i$. For this process the second $T\,dS$ equation gives

$$T\,dS = 0 + T\left(\frac{\partial M}{\partial T}\right)_{\mathscr{H}}d\mathscr{H}.$$

The derivative $(\partial M/\partial T)_{\mathscr{H}}$ is a measure of the change of alignment of a system of magnets accompanying a rise of temperature (disordering effect) when the external field (ordering effect) is kept constant. The derivative is therefore *negative* for all substances of the type dealt with in this chapter. (In the next chapter we shall learn about a superconductor for which an increase of magnetic field is a disordering effect!) Since $(\partial M/\partial T)_{\mathscr{H}}$ is negative, heat goes *out* during an isothermal magnetization.

The second step, $i \rightarrow f$, is a reversible adiabatic reduction of $\mathscr{H}$ in which

$$0 = C_{\mathscr{H}}\,dT + T\left(\frac{\partial M}{\partial T}\right)_{\mathscr{H}}d\mathscr{H}.$$

Since $(\partial M/\partial T)_{\mathscr{H}}$ and $d\mathscr{H}$ are both negative, it follows that dT is negative. This change in temperature is called the *magnetocaloric effect*. Experiments of this sort were first performed by Giauque in America and were then taken up by Kurti and Simon in England and by de Haas and Wiersma in Holland. In these experiments a paramagnetic salt is cooled to as low a temperature as possible with the aid of liquid helium. A strong magnetic field is then

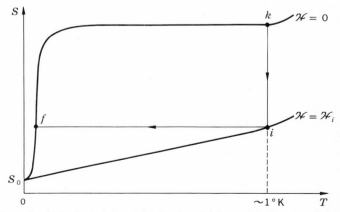

Fig. 14-7   *In the isothermal magnetization $k \rightarrow i$, the entropy decreases. In the adiabatic demagnetization $i \rightarrow f$ (to zero field), the temperature decreases.*

applied, producing a rise of temperature in the substance and a consequent flow of heat to the surrounding helium, some of which is thereby evaporated. After a while, the substance is both strongly magnetized and as cold as possible. At this moment, the space surrounding the substance is evacuated. The magnetic field is now reduced to zero, and the temperature of the paramagnetic salt drops to a low value.

The paramagnetic salt is either a single crystal, a pressed powder, or a mixture of small crystals in the form of either a sphere, a cylinder, or a spheroid. It is placed in a space that may be connected at one time to a pump or, at another time, to a gas supply. This space is surrounded by liquid helium whose pressure (and therefore temperature) may be controlled. Surrounding the liquid helium is liquid nitrogen, and the intervening space is evacuated. Helium gas is admitted into the space containing the para-magnetic salt before the magnet is switched on. The rise of temperature produced by switching on the magnet causes a flow of heat through this helium gas into the liquid helium. In other words, the helium gas is used as a conductor of heat to enable the paramagnetic salt to come to tempera-ture equilibrium rapidly. It is therefore called the *exchange gas*. As soon as temperature equilibrium is attained, the exchange gas is pumped out, leaving the paramagnetic salt thermally insulated. In many past experiments, the adiabatic demagnetization was accomplished by swinging the entire cryostat out of the magnetic field produced by a huge electromagnet such as that depicted in Fig. 14-8. In recent years, solenoids have been made of many thousands of turns of fine superconducting wire, through which from 10 to 100 A may be sent. There is no power dissipation in the coil so long as it is maintained at a temperature below which the wire is superconducting. The physical principles involved in the construction and operation of supercon-ducting magnets will be explained in the next chapter. The conventional experimental apparatus is compared roughly with the more modern one in Fig. 14-9. With a superconducting magnet, (1) the sample space may be made larger; (2) the magnetic field may be made stronger; (3) the cost of the magnet may be one-quarter that of a conventional magnet; and (4) the power requirement is negligible.

The next step is to estimate the temperature. For this purpose, separate coils of wire surrounding the paramagnetic salt are used. The paramagnetic susceptibility $M/\mathscr{H}$, which is a function of the temperature, is measured by means of a special bridge circuit. A new temperature scale is now defined with the aid of Curie's equation. The new temperature T^*, called the *magnetic temperature*, is defined as

$$T^* = \frac{\text{Curie constant}}{\text{susceptibility}} = \frac{C_C \mathscr{H}}{M}.$$

Fig. 14-8   *The famous electromagnet of the Laboratoire Aimé Cotton at Bellevue, near Paris, used by Simon and Kurti in some of their pioneer experiments. (Courtesy of N. Kurti.)*

Fig. 14-9   *Adiabatic demagnetization experiments are carried out more readily with a super-conducting magnet.*

It is seen that, in the region where Curie's law holds, T^* is the real Kelvin temperature, whereas in the region around absolute zero T^* is expected to differ somewhat from the Kelvin temperature.

The early results of the great pioneers in this field are listed in Table 14-3 (compiled by Burton, Grayson-Smith, and Wilhelm).

There is a set of conditions, easily achieved in the laboratory, under which it is possible to calculate the final temperature achieved after an adiabatic demagnetization:

1   The initial temperature is low enough to make the contributions of the nonmagnetic particles negligible.

2   The temperature never gets lower than the tail of the Schottky curve where $C_M = A/T^2$.

3   Values of $\mathcal{H}/T$ are always small enough that Curie's law is obeyed, $M/\mathcal{H} = C_C/T$.

4   The external magnetic field is reduced to a low value at which the magnetization is M_f. Both $\mathcal{H}_f$ and M_f may be made equal to zero.

Under these conditions we may use the first $T\,dS$ equation as follows:

$$T\,dS = C_M\,dT - T\left(\frac{\partial \mathcal{H}}{\partial T}\right)_M dM.$$

From Curie's equation, we get

$$\left(\frac{\partial \mathcal{H}}{\partial T}\right)_M = \frac{M}{C_C},$$

and we also have

$$C_M = \frac{A}{T^2}.$$

Table 14-3   Pioneer Results in the Magnetic Production of Low Temperatures

Experimenters	Date	Paramagnetic salt	Initial field, Oe	Initial temp., °K	Final magnetic temp., T^*
Giauque and MacDougall	1933	Gadolinium sulfate	8,000	1.5	0.25
De Haas, Wiersma, and Kramers	1933	Cerium fluoride	27,600	1.35	0.13
		Dysprosium ethyl sulfate	19,500	1.35	0.12
		Cerium ethyl sulfate	27,600	1.35	0.085
De Haas and Wiersma	1934	Chromium potassium alum	24,600	1.16	0.031
	1935	Iron ammonium alum	24,075	1.20	0.018
		Alum mixture	24,075	1.29	0.0044
		Cesium titanium alum	24,075	1.31	0.0055
Kurti and Simon	1935	Gadolinium sulfate	5,400	1.15	0.35
		Manganese ammonium sulfate	8,000	1.23	0.09
		Iron ammonium alum	14,100	1.23	0.038
		Iron ammonium alum	8,300	1.23	0.072
		Iron ammonium alum	4,950	1.23	0.114

Substituting these values into the first $T \, dS$ equation and setting $dS = 0$ for an adiabatic demagnetization, we get

$$0 = \frac{A}{T^2} dT - T \frac{M}{C_C} dM$$

or

$$A \int_{T_i}^{T_f} \frac{dT}{T^3} = \frac{1}{C_C} \int_{M_i}^{M_f} M \, dM,$$

where the substance is demagnetized to magnetization M_f. Upon performing the integrations,

$$\frac{A}{2} \left(\frac{1}{T_f^2} - \frac{1}{T_i^2} \right) = \frac{1}{2C_C} (M_i^2 - M_f^2),$$

and using Curie's equation,

$$\frac{1}{T_f^2} - \frac{1}{T_i^2} = \frac{C_C}{A} \left(\frac{\mathscr{H}_i^2}{T_i^2} - \frac{\mathscr{H}_f^2}{T_f^2} \right),$$

or

$$\frac{T_f}{T_i} = \sqrt{\frac{(C_C/A)\mathscr{H}_f^2 + 1}{(C_C/A)\mathscr{H}_i^2 + 1}}. \tag{14-28}$$

When $\mathscr{H}_f = 0$,

$$\left(\frac{T_i}{T_f} \right)^2 = 1 + \frac{C_C}{A} \mathscr{H}_i^2, \tag{14-29}$$

which shows that the lowest temperatures are reached by salts in which A is small and C_C is large. From the values of A/R and C_C in Table 14-2, it may be seen that cerium magnesium nitrate is the most favorable salt by a factor of over 100. The graph in Fig. 14-10 shows that the conditions under which Eq. (14-29) was derived hold well for CMN down to 0.01°K. The remainder of the graph (down to 0.002°K) is the result of experiments by Daniels and Robinson; Hudson, Kaeser, and Radford; and de Klerk, combined with experiments and theoretical calculations of Frankel, Shirley, and Stone. The entire graph enables CMN to be used as a thermometer down to 0.002°K.

Most experiments on adiabatic demagnetization are performed in order to achieve the lowest possible temperature, in which case demagnetization proceeds until $\mathscr{H}_f = 0$. If, instead of demagnetizing to zero field, we stay within the region of field and temperature designated by the space between the vertical dashed lines of Fig. 14-6 (e.g., $\mathscr{H}_5 \rightarrow \mathscr{H}_2$, or $\mathscr{H}_3 \rightarrow \mathscr{H}_1$), then curious results are obtained. First of all, the entropy is a function of $\mathscr{H}/T$ *only*, therefore, during an isentropic reduction of $\mathscr{H}$ (*not to zero*), since S is

Fig. 14-10   *Adiabatic demagnetization to zero field of cerium magnesium nitrate.* (*R. B. Frankel, D. A. Shirley, and N. J. Stone, 1965.*)

constant, *the ratio* $\mathscr{H}/T$ *must remain constant.* That this is true under the conditions specified is demonstrated by the experimental results of Hill and Milner, shown in Fig. 14-11. Second, if $\mathscr{H}/T$ is constant, since M is a function of $\mathscr{H}/T$ only, M *is constant!* If, therefore, the magnetization does not change, the term adiabatic "demagnetization" is a misnomer. As a result, the word

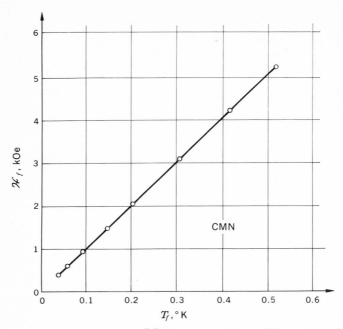

Fig. 14-11   *Constancy of the ratio $\mathcal{H}_f/T_f$ during adiabatic "degaussing" of CMN from $\mathcal{H}_i$, T_i (always the same) to $\mathcal{H}_f$, T_f. (J. S. Hill and J. H. Milner, 1957.)*

"degaussing" has been suggested. If M does not change (and this has been experimentally verified by de Haas, Wiersma, and Casimir, 1936 and 1940), then *the work* $-\int\mathcal{H}\,dM$ *is zero.* But in an adiabatic process, the work done is equal to the change of internal energy, so that ΔU is zero. Since the heat capacity at constant magnetization C_M is equal to $(\partial U/\partial T)_M$, then C_M is zero. If the first $T\,dS$ equation is applied to this process,

$$T\,dS = C_M\,dT - T\left(\frac{\partial\mathcal{H}}{\partial T}\right)_M dM,$$

we have dS, C_M, and dM all equal to zero. Of course, it must be understood that these results apply only when temperatures are not too low and the field is not reduced to zero. These conditions will be found to be important in certain experiments on nuclear magnetic subsystems.

Let ϵ_i be the energy of an ion with total quantum number m_i in a field $\mathcal{H}$. When the field changes a small amount $d\mathcal{H}$, the energy change $d\epsilon_i$ is

$$d\epsilon_i = -g\mu_\mathrm{B}m_i\,d\mathcal{H};$$

and if N_i is the population of the m_ith state,

$$\Sigma N_i \, d\epsilon_i = -(\Sigma N_i g \mu_\text{B} m_i) \, d\mathcal{H},$$

or $$\Sigma N_i \, d\epsilon_i = -M \, d\mathcal{H}. \tag{14-30}$$

Now $\Sigma N_i \epsilon_i$ is the *total* energy of the ions, that is, the sum of the internal energy U and the magnetic potential energy $-\mathcal{H}M$. Thus,

$$\Sigma N_i \epsilon_i = U - \mathcal{H}M,$$

and $$\Sigma \epsilon_i \, dN_i + \Sigma N_i \, d\epsilon_i = dU - \mathcal{H} \, dM - M \, d\mathcal{H}.$$

Since $\Sigma N_i \, d\epsilon_i = -M \, d\mathcal{H}$, this reduces to

$$\Sigma \epsilon_i \, dN_i = dU - \mathcal{H} \, dM,$$

or $$\boxed{\Sigma \epsilon_i \, dN_i = T \, dS.} \tag{14-31}$$

It follows that an isothermal decrease of entropy, which takes place in the first step of any experiment for producing low temperatures, must involve changes in N_i, that is, population changes. During the second step, however, in which an adiabatic demagnetization takes place, dS is zero, and therefore the dN_i's are zero—that is, the populations remain unchanged.

In Fig. 14-12k, the magnetic-ion subsystem is in zero field, and therefore the magnetic energy states are extremely close together, with some of the

Fig. 14-12   *Changes in energy states and ionic populations during isothermal magnetization $k \to i$ and adiabatic demagnetization $i \to f$.*

degeneracy being removed by internal electric and magnetic effects. Since the states are so close together, they are equally populated. From $k \rightarrow i$ the populations change so that the low-energy states become highly populated, as shown in Fig. 14-12i. In the last step, $i \rightarrow f$, the populations remain constant in order to keep the entropy constant.

14-6   Low-temperature Thermometry

When a gas is liquefied, the normal boiling point (or, in the case of carbon dioxide, the normal sublimation point) and the triple-point temperatures and pressures must be determined with great accuracy. Temperatures are usually measured with a helium-gas thermometer according to the principles developed in Chap. 1. The bulb of the gas thermometer is often incorporated within the liquefaction apparatus. Pressures are usually measured with a mercury manometer, sighted through the telescope of a cathetometer. Once these temperatures and pressures are measured, they may be used as fixed points for the calibration of gas thermometers of simpler design. Some of the most important fixed points of low-temperature physics are listed in Table 14-4.

Table 14-4   Useful Fixed Points in Low-temperature Physics

Gas	Critical point	Normal boiling point	Triple point	Normal sublimation point
Carbon dioxide	304°K 73 atm		216.6°K 5.11 atm	194.7°K 760 mm
Nitrogen	126.26°K 33.54 atm	77.35°K 760 mm	63.14°K 94 mm	
Hydrogen	33°K 12.8 atm	20.26°K 760 mm	13.96°K 54.1 mm	
Helium IV	5.20°K 1718 mm	4.215°K 760 mm	2.172°K 37.86 mm	
Helium III	3.32°K 890 mm	3.195°K 760 mm	? ?	

The lowest temperature that can be reached easily with liquid helium is about 1°K. This is achieved by pumping the vapor away as fast as possible through as wide a tube as possible. With special high-speed pumps, temperatures as low as 0.7°K have been reached, but this is rare. Temperatures lower than 0.7°K cannot be reached by pumping liquid helium because a film of liquid helium II creeps up the walls of the pumping tube, vaporizes, and then recondenses. This phenomenon will be discussed in the next chapter.

In studying the properties of matter at low temperatures, the experimental apparatus is usually surrounded by a bath of liquid He^4, and a measurement of the pressure of the vapor in equilibrium either with the liquid bath itself or of some liquid helium in a separate bulb, in conjunction with a vapor-pressure-temperature table, serves to determine the temperature of the apparatus and of any secondary thermometer mounted on the apparatus. Everything depends on how accurately the relation between helium vapor pressure and temperature is known.

Up to 1955, various approximate thermodynamic PT relations, similar to the sublimation equation given in Art. 12-5, were used and provided values of temperature adequate for many of the research projects. In the early 1950s, however, the development of secondary thermometers such as carbon resistors and paramagnetic salts gave rise to a host of temperature measurements that could be compared with the results obtained from PT tables. Small anomalies began to show up, and these could be explained only as discontinuities and inconsistencies in the vapor-pressure–temperature relationship. In the spring of 1955, Clement and his coworkers at the U.S. Naval Research Laboratory developed an empirical PT relation that resolved practically all the existing discrepancies within a few millidegrees. Not long after, H. van Dijk and M. Durieux derived the following thermodynamic equation between P and T, in which departure from ideality of the He^4 vapor was taken into account as well as the pressure dependence of the enthalpy of the liquid:

$$\ln P = - \frac{l_0}{RT} + \frac{5}{2} \ln T - \frac{1}{RT} \int_0^T s'' \, dT + \frac{1}{RT} \int_0^P v'' \, dP$$
$$- \frac{2B}{v'''} + \ln \frac{Pv'''}{RT} + i_0,$$

where P is in millimeters of mercury, $l_0 = 59.50$ J/mole, and $i_0 = 12.2440$. Using the latest values for the various properties of liquid and gaseous helium, van Dijk published a table of P and T values which was just as successful as Clement's in resolving the existing difficulties and which had the further advantage of a thermodynamic background. In 1958, the table of van Dijk and Durieux was accepted by the Advisory Committee on Thermometry of the International Committee on Weights and Measures and designated as the "He^4 Scale of 1958," abbreviated T_{58}.

Measurement of the vapor pressure of the much more expensive light isotope He^3 enables one to measure temperature from the critical temperature

3.32°K down to 0.2°K. The very tedious measurements and calculations leading to a table of temperatures and He³ vapor pressures were made by Roberts, Sherman, Sydoriak, and Brickwedde. The table, known as the "T_{62} scale," was accepted by the Advisory Committee in 1962 and was recognized as equivalent to the T_{58} scale in the region of overlap.

The gas thermometer and the vapor-pressure thermometer are elaborate, exacting, and sluggish devices. To measure heat capacities, thermal conductivities, and several other physical quantities of interest at low temperatures, many measurements of small temperature changes must be made quickly and accurately. For these purposes, secondary thermometers must be used.

One of the first to be employed was a resistance thermometer made of carbon. Pieces of paper with carbon deposited on them or strips of carbon prepared by painting with colloidal suspensions have two advantages. They have extremely small heat capacities and can therefore follow temperature changes quickly, and their electric resistance, which increases rapidly as the temperature is reduced, is insensitive to the presence of a magnetic field. The main disadvantage of such thermometers is their lack of reproducibility. They must be calibrated anew each time they are used.

In 1951, Clement and Quinell discovered that carbon composition radio resistors, made by Allen-Bradley and rated from $\frac{1}{2}$ to 1 W, had all the properties most desired in a low-temperature secondary thermometer—namely, high sensitivity, reproducibility, and insensitivity to magnetic fields. The reasons for these desirable properties are not understood, but to such thermometers are attributed the accuracy of much of the work done in low-temperature physics since 1951. In using small radio resistors as thermometers, the plastic coating is first removed and replaced by a thin coat of lacquer. The thermometer is then attached to the experimental apparatus or placed in a hole drilled for that purpose. The resistance is measured at a number of temperatures that are known from measurements of the helium vapor pressure. The greatest number of such measurements has been made by J. R. Clement, who tried several empiric equations to represent the relation between the resistance R' and T. One of the most satisfactory equations is

$$\sqrt{\log R'/T} = a + b \log R', \tag{14-32}$$

which fits the experimental results within a few millidegrees. If a carbon resistance thermometer is calibrated in the liquid helium range and *then kept below* 20°K, it will retain its calibration indefinitely. After warming to room temperature, however, it will have to be recalibrated when brought back to helium temperatures.

Higher reproducibility is attainable with the aid of germanium resistance thermometers developed by Kunzler, Geballe, and Hull at the Bell Telephone

Laboratories. The germanium is "doped" with excess arsenic atoms and then sealed in helium-filled capsules. In an analysis of several of these semiconductor thermometers along with radio resistor thermometers, Lindenfeld gives as an upper limit to the variability of the temperature corresponding to a given resistance the value ± 0.4 mdeg. This is better than that possible with carbon resistors. The main advantage of germanium thermometers is their reproducibility. They retain their calibration after any number of cycles between helium and room temperatures. Two germanium thermometers A and B are compared with an encapsulated carbon thermometer C (0.1 W, 68 Ω at room temperature) in Fig. 14-13.

Some paramagnetic salts obey Curie's law very closely down to 1°K and even lower. If the Curie constant is determined by measurements at known temperatures, then the magnetic salt may be used as a thermometer. In the liquid helium range, the change of magnetization of all paramagnetic salts is rather small. To measure temperature to 1 mdeg, the magnetization must be measured with tremendous accuracy with the aid of a specially constructed ac mutual-inductance bridge. The magnetic thermometer is of most importance in the temperature range below 1°K, where its magnetization changes by a larger amount for a small temperature change.

At temperatures below the region in which Curie's law holds and which have been represented by the so-called magnetic temperature $T^* = C_c \mathscr{H}/M$, the corresponding Kelvin temperatures must be determined. To understand how this is done, consider the ST curves of Fig. 14-14 showing a number of isothermal magnetizations ($1 \rightarrow 2$, $1 \rightarrow 4$, or $1 \rightarrow 6$, etc.) and a number of adiabatic demagnetizations ($2 \rightarrow 3$, $4 \rightarrow 5$, or $6 \rightarrow 7$, etc.). By measuring the magnetic susceptibility at each of the points numbered 3, 5, 7, etc., and by using the known value of the Curie constant, the T^* values may be obtained at these points. Taking the process $1 \rightarrow 2$ as a typical isothermal magnetization, we may calculate the entropy change $S_2 - S_1$ by applying the second $T\,dS$ equation,

$$T\,dS = C_{\mathscr{H}}\,dT + T\left(\frac{\partial M}{\partial T}\right)_{\mathscr{H}} d\mathscr{H}.$$

Integrating from 1 to 2, we get

$$S_1 - S_2 = -\int_0^{\mathscr{H}_{\max}} \left(\frac{\partial M}{\partial T}\right)_{\mathscr{H}} d\mathscr{H}. \tag{14-33}$$

Since the paramagnetic salt in question obeys Brillouin's equation accurately, the right-hand integral may be evaluated, and therefore after a series of such calculations we may obtain $S_4 - S_2$, $S_6 - S_2$, $S_8 - S_2$, etc. But these entropy

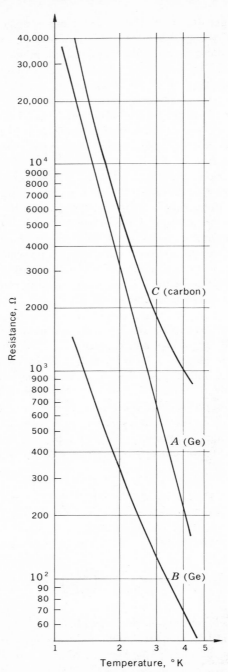

Fig. 14-13   *Comparison of carbon and germanium thermometers. (P. Lindenfeld, 1964.)*

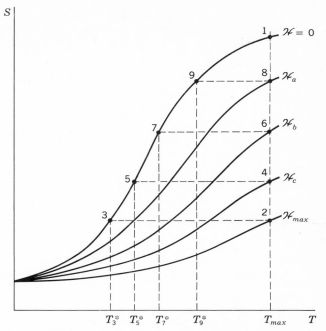

Fig. 14-14   *Isothermal magnetizations and adiabatic demagnetizations on an entropy temperature diagram. Above T_{max} are Kelvin temperatures; below T_{max} are magnetic temperatures.*

changes are equal to $S_5 - S_3$, $S_7 - S_3$, $S_9 - S_3$, etc. Since the T^* values are known at the points 3, 5, 7, etc., a graph of $S - S_3$ can be plotted against T^*, as shown in Fig. 14-15a.

Now let us imagine that we have performed the adiabatic demagnetization $2 \rightarrow 3$ and are at the minimum temperature, characterized by the magnetic

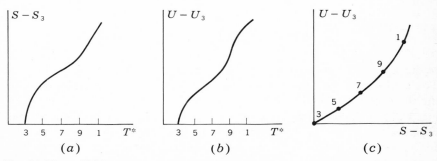

Fig. 14-15   *Kelvin temperatures at the points 3, 5, 7, etc., are obtained by measuring the slope of the curve in (c) at the designated points.*

temperature T_3^*. With the aid of some suitable heating device (such as a gold heating coil used by Giauque, the absorption of gamma rays used by Kurti and Simon, or magnetic hysteresis used by de Klerk), let us measure the heat absorbed at zero magnetic field in going from 3 to 5, from 3 to 7, from 3 to 9, and from 3 to 1. Since these values of heat are measured in zero magnetic field, no work is done, and hence the heat is equal to the internal-energy change $U - U_3$. These internal-energy changes are plotted against T^* in Fig. 14-15b.

Combining graphs (a) and (b), we get the graph of Fig. 14-15c, in which $U - U_3$ is plotted against $S - S_3$. Since the point 3 is always the same, U_3 and S_3 are constants, and therefore the *slope* of the curve at any point is $(\partial U/\partial S)_{\mathscr{H}=0}$. Since $T\,dS = dU - \mathscr{H}\,dM$ and $\mathscr{H} = 0$,

$$(\partial U/\partial S)_{\mathscr{H}=0} = T.$$

Once this procedure has been followed and a table of values of T^* and T, such as Table 14-5, has been obtained, other thermometers such as radio

Table 14-5   Calibration Data for a Sphere of CMN
(*Compiled by R. B. Frankel, D. A. Shirley, and N. J. Stone, 1965.*)

$\mathscr{H}_i/T_i$, kOe/deg	S/R (calculated)	$1/T^*$	$1/T$, deg^{-1}	$\mathscr{H}_i/T_i$, kOe/deg	S/R (calculated)	$1/T^*$	$1/T$, deg^{-1}
1.0	0.691	20	20	7.8	0.590	180	181
1.9	0.686	40	40	8.75	0.567	200	210
2.9	0.678	60	60	10.2	0.529	230	249
3.8	0.667	80	80	12.1	0.477	260	305
4.6	0.654	100	100	14.2	0.420	290	383
5.4	0.640	120	120	15.5	0.384	300	430
6.2	0.625	140	140	18.0	0.321	310	500
6.9	0.610	160	160				

resisters, germanium crystals, or other paramagnetic salts, can be calibrated. The most widely used thermometric salt is a single crystal of CMN cut into the shape of a sphere. The calibration curve between T^* and T, shown in Fig. 14-16, is the combined effort of many physicists, but the final corrections were made by Frankel, Shirley, and Stone, who used radioactive, oriented cerium ions whose temperature was measured by noting the asymmetry of γ-ray emission.

Fig. 14-16   *Relation between T* and T for a sphere of CMN. (Frankel, Shirley, and Stone, 1965.)*

14-7   Magnetic Refrigerator

At the conclusion of an adiabatic demagnetization, the temperature immediately starts to rise because of the unavoidable heat leak that is present in every cryostat, no matter how well designed. If the experiment under consideration can be performed quickly and does not itself involve too large a dissipation of energy into the system, adequate results may be obtained. When, however, the experiment itself requires a dissipation of about 50 ergs/s, a continuous refrigeration is needed. For this purpose, Daunt and Heer designed a magnetic refrigerator, operating in a cycle, in which iron ammonium alum could be magnetized while in contact with one helium bath (hot reservoir) and demagnetized when in contact with another helium bath (cold reservoir).

A schematic diagram of the apparatus is shown in Fig. 14-17. Notice that there are two thin metal rods marked "thermal valve." These rods are made of lead and connect the paramagnetic salt contained in the "working cell" with the upper helium bath and with the lower "reservoir cell," respectively. At any temperature below 7.22°K, lead becomes superconducting and, at the same time, becomes a very poor heat conductor. If, however, the superconductivity is removed with the aid of a magnetic field of only a few hundred

Fig. 14-17   *Magnetic refrigerator of Daunt and Heer.*

oersteds (provided by the two "valve magnets"), the lead immediately becomes a good heat conductor.

During magnetization of the salt in the working cell, the upper thermal valve is magnetized and the lower is not. During demagnetization, the reverse is the case. Each cycle takes about 2 min, and at the end of about 30 min the lower reservoir reached a temperature of about 0.20°K, with a heat extraction rate of about 70 ergs/s. The design features of Daunt and

Heer have been incorporated into a magnetic refrigerator (constructed by A. D. Little Co. of Cambridge, Mass.) composed of all necessary parts that perform automatically.

14-8 Polarization of Magnetic Nuclei

The magnetic moments of the chromium, iron, and gadolinium ions are due to uncompensated spins of the electrons that surround the respective nuclei. When a paramagnetic salt containing, for example, the chromium ion with $J = \frac{3}{2}$ is placed in a magnetic field of the order of 10^4 Oe and the temperature is lowered to about $1°K$ (so that the ratio $\mathscr{H}/T$ is of the order of 10^4 Oe/deg), the ionic magnets become partially oriented in the direction of the field. A convenient measure of this partial orientation is provided by the ratio of the magnetic moment M to the maximum value or saturation value M_{sat}. When this ratio is expressed in percent, it is often called the *magnetic polarization*. From Eq. (14-16),

$$\frac{M}{M_{sat}} = B_J \left(\frac{g\mu_B \mathscr{H}}{kT} \right),$$

and under the conditions specified,

$$\frac{g\mu_B \mathscr{H}}{kT} \approx \frac{2 \times 0.9 \times 10^{-20} \times 10^4}{1.4 \times 10^{-16} \times 1} \approx 1.3.$$

In Fig. 14-2, $B_{\frac{3}{2}}(1.3) = 0.76$; that is, the ionic magnets are 76 percent polarized.

The particles inside the nucleus of an atom also have spins that give rise to *nuclear magnetism*. The resultant nuclear spin is characterized by a quantum number I that plays the same role as the atomic quantum number J. A nuclear magnetic moment is much smaller than that of an atom, by a factor of almost 2000. In the expression for a Bohr magneton $\mu_B = eh/4\pi mc$, if we substitute the mass of a proton, we get a *nuclear magneton* where

$$\mu_N = \frac{\mu_B}{m_p/m_e} = \frac{0.9 \times 10^{-20}}{1840}$$

$$\approx 5 \times 10^{-24} \text{ erg/Oe.}$$

When nuclear magnets are subjected to an external magnetic field, the lowest energy level of the nucleus splits into a number of separate states, each of which is characterized by a nuclear magnetic quantum number that may take on discrete values corresponding to discrete orientations of the nuclear magnetic moment with respect to the external magnetic field. These values range from $-I$ to $+I$ in integral steps—an exact replica of the atomic situation, where m took on values from $-J$ to $+J$ in integral steps.

The calculation of the nuclear magnetic moment M_N parallels perfectly that for the atomic moment, so that

$$M_N = N\mu_N g_N I B_I \left(\frac{g_N \mu_N \mathcal{H}}{T} \right), \tag{14-34}$$

where g_N is the nuclear splitting factor, which we shall take as equal to 2. Suppose that we have a nucleus with $I = \frac{3}{2}$ and want to produce a nuclear polarization of 76 percent. Then,

$$B_I(g_N \mu_N \mathcal{H}/kT) = 0.76$$

and
$$\frac{g_N \mu_N \mathcal{H}}{kT} = 1.3$$

or
$$\frac{\mathcal{H}}{T} = \frac{1.3 \times 1.4 \times 10^{-16}}{2 \times 5 \times 10^{-24}} \approx 2 \times 10^7 \text{ Oe/deg.}$$

If, therefore, we used a field of 2×10^4 Oe, the nuclear-spin system would have to be at a temperature of 10^{-3} °K in order to provide a nuclear magnetic polarization of 76 percent. If we could settle for a smaller polarization, we could start at, say, 10^{-2} °K. Lining up nuclei in the same direction is a very valuable procedure for the physicist. If the nucleus is radioactive and emits alpha particles or beta particles or gamma rays, it is important to know whether these emanations are emitted as abundantly in one direction relative to the magnetic moment as in another. If they are emitted equally in all directions, one refers to their *symmetry* or *isotropy*. A preferred direction indicating *asymmetry* or *anisotropy* enables the nuclear physicist to accomplish the following:

1   Test various *conservation laws* that are supposed to hold during nuclear disintegrations.
2   Obtain information about the *shape* of the nucleus.
3   Obtain numerical values of certain constants needed in the theory of nuclear processes.

Nuclear polarization has been achieved by using a very low temperature and a very large field; but this procedure, known as the *brute-force method*, has not been available in many laboratories.

The method of nuclear polarization that has been most fruitful was suggested first by Gorter and Rose and involves the behavior of a nucleus in the very strong *local* magnetic field (over 100 kOe) produced by *its own* electronic structure. To understand this, let us consider the implications of the theoretically derived and experimentally verified result that the magnetization of an isolated spin system (whether atomic or nuclear, provided that neither $\mathscr{H}$ nor T is close to zero) is a function of $\mathscr{H}/T$ only. If, for example, 50 percent magnetic saturation is achieved with a particular paramagnetic salt at a temperature of 1°K with a field of 10,000 Oe, then at a temperature of 0.01°K a field of only 100 Oe would be needed to produce the same magnetic polarization. In other words, if the proper material were used, starting at 1°K and demagnetizing (or "degaussing") from a field of 10,000 Oe to a field of 100 Oe, the temperature would drop ($\mathscr{H}/T = $ const.) to about 0.01°K, but *the magnetic polarization would still be the same.* One could also demagnetize to zero field, thereby reaching a somewhat lower temperature, and then raise the field to 100 Oe and still have available about 50 percent polarization. Gorter and Rose realized that these polarized ionic magnets would give rise to a unidirectional local field at the nucleus of each ion which would be much larger than any field then achievable in the laboratory (before the advent of superconducting magnets)—of the order of 100,000 Oe or more.

This experiment was carried out several times by Roberts and his coworkers at Oak Ridge Laboratories. They polarized Mn and Sm nuclei and detected their polarization by measuring their ability to scatter polarized slow neutrons from the Oak Ridge reactor.

When radioactive cobalt nuclei Co^{60} are polarized, γ rays are emitted with different intensities in different directions. By comparing the intensity in one direction with that at right angles to this direction, a quantity called the *anisotropy* is defined. Experiment shows that the anisotropy is a sensitive function of the temperature, so that, if this function has been determined from previous experiments, a measurement of γ-ray anisotropy enables one to obtain the temperature.

One of the most spectacular experiments in nuclear cryogenics was performed by Ambler, Hudson, and Wu at the National Bureau of Standards in Washington, D.C., in 1957. Lee and Yang, who were later awarded the Nobel prize, suggested that the nuclei of Co^{60}, in undergoing radioactive decay, might emit beta particles (electrons) more abundantly toward one magnetic pole than toward the other. To test this hypothesis, polarization of the cobalt nuclei was necessary. Beta-ray counters were then used to show whether there was a different reading in the direction of the north poles than in the reverse direction. The apparatus is shown in Fig. 14-18. The Co^{60}, obtained by neutron bombardment of nonradioactive Co^{59}, was introduced

Fig. 14-18   *Apparatus of Ambler, Hudson, and Wu to measure β-particle emission from polarized Co⁶⁰ nuclei. (Liquid He and N₂ dewars and β-ray counters not shown.)*

into the crystal lattice of cerium magnesium nitrate in the form of a thin layer lying in the bottom of a cup-shaped housing of this material. The beta particles emitted by Co^{60} (in decaying to Ni^{60}) produced scintillations in a small crystal of anthracene. The light flashes traveled up a *light pipe*, consisting of a 4-ft lucite rod whose upper end communicated with a photomultiplier tube and counter.

The strong magnetic axis of the CMN crystals was horizontal, so that isothermal magnetization and adiabatic demagnetization to zero field could be accomplished with a horizontal magnetic field. By this means, the CMN housing and Co^{60} layer were cooled below 0.01°K. A solenoid was then slipped over the outer dewar, and a vertical field of about 100 Oe was used to polarize the Co^{60} ions without appreciable warming of the CMN. The strong local fields at the nuclei of the ions polarized the Co^{60} nuclei, the direction of polarization depending upon the direction of the current in the solenoid. The north poles could therefore be made to face either toward the anthracene crystal or away from it.

The beta-particle ejection from Co^{60} is accompanied by gamma-ray emission. Although they are not shown in Fig. 14-18, there were two gamma-ray counters to detect and to measure any gamma-ray anisotropy. Since gamma-ray anisotropy had already been measured as a function of temperature, it served as a convenient thermometer. The curve in Fig. 14-19 shows that *there are many more beta particles emitted in a direction opposite to the solenoid field,* that is, the south poles of the Co^{60} nuclei emit beta particles more abundantly than the north poles. This result is in direct contradiction to a nuclear principle, known as the *principle of the conservation of parity,* which had assumed that certain nuclear processes should behave the same way for one configuration of the nucleus as for its mirror image. The experimental proof that parity is not conserved in beta decay has had a profound effect on theoretical and experimental physics.

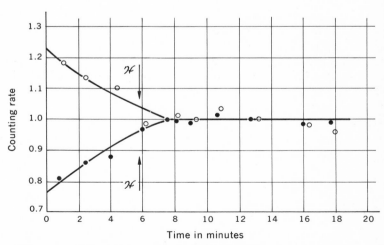

Fig. 14-19   *Asymmetry in beta-particle emission from polarized nuclei. Increasing time denotes increasing temperature. Maximum polarization is at the lowest temperature.*

14-9   Production of Microdegree Temperatures by Nuclear Demagnetization

Since nuclear magnets are only about one one-thousandth as strong as ionic magnets, their polarization requires temperatures around 0.01°K and fields from 50 to 100 kOe. We have seen how local fields of this magnitude may be provided by the uncompensated spins of the electrons circulating outside each nucleus itself. If these polarized nuclei could then be made to undergo a reversible adiabatic demagnetization, they would cool off to a temperature in the neighborhood of 10^{-5} °K. Since these nuclei occupy a thin layer on a large crystal at 0.01°K, however, any loss of polarization would be much more isothermal than adiabatic. You cannot expect a few nuclei to cool off a big crystal.

The only method that has been used so far to achieve temperatures below 10^{-3} °K involves a double process, consisting of an ionic demagnetization followed by a nuclear demagnetization. Two separate magnetic fields supplied by two separate magnets are used, as shown schematically in Fig. 14-20, a diagram prepared by Kurti of Oxford, in whose laboratory such experiments have been carried out. In each of the four parts of this figure, the electronic stage represents a mass of chromium potassium alum in which are embedded 1500 enameled copper wires, each with a diameter of 0.0003 in. The copper wires continue for a distance of about 8 in. and are then bent over and bound together to form the nuclear stage itself. The first part of the cooling is done with the aid of chromium ions, and the second part by *copper nuclei*. The fine, insulated copper wires serve three purposes:

1   Provide a heat-conducting medium between the nuclear and the electronic stages.
2   Minimize eddy currents induced by demagnetization.
3   Produce a low temperature by nuclear demagnetization.

The four steps in Fig. 14-20 are as follows:

(*a*)   Isothermal magnetization of the electronic stage.
(*b*)   Adiabatic demagnetization of the electronic stage and cooling of nuclear stage to 10^{-2} °K.
(*c*)   Isothermal magnetization of the nuclear stage.
(*d*)   Adiabatic demagnetization of the nuclear stage, with an accompanying temperature drop to about 10^{-5} °K.

The experiment is not as simple as it sounds. To quote Kurti, "The stringency of the conditions to be satisfied can be illustrated by remarking

Fig. 14-20   *The four steps in nuclear cooling.* (*N. Kurti.*)

that even a minute amount of heating such as results from a small pin dropping through a height of one-eighth of an inch would warm a bulky specimen of several ounces from one-millionth of a degree to the starting temperature of one one-hundredth of a degree and thereby spoil the experiment." Even the eddy currents induced in the copper wires by virtue of slight variations of current (ripples) in the magnet coils must be prevented with the aid of the metal ripple shield shown in Fig. 14-21. The magnetic fields were supplied by solenoids in which currents of thousands of amperes were maintained.

The lowest temperature ever obtained anywhere (1968) *is* 1.2×10^{-6} °K!

One of the biggest experimental difficulties to overcome in a double demagnetization process is the heat transfer between the nuclear and electronic stages. During the isothermal magnetization of the nuclear stage, this transfer must be good. During the following demagnetization, it must be poor. In the experiments of Kurti's group, the fine copper wires represent a compromise that served both purposes only moderately well. Another difficulty is to separate the electronic from the nuclear stage by a distance great enough to confine each magnetic field to its own paramagnetic particles. Both of these problems can be partially solved by a clever method conceived by Blaisse. Suppose the nuclear stage constitutes a *core* completely surrounded

Liquid N_2

Vacuum space

He^4 at $0.9°K$

He^3 at $0.35°K$

KCr alum at $10^{-2}°K$

Ripple shield

Copper nuclei at $10^{-6}°K$

Fig. 14-21   *Cryostat for nuclear cooling (symbolic).*

by a crystal (or a group of crystals identically oriented) of cerium magnesium nitrate with its strong magnetic axis pointing toward, let us say, the *x* axis. Suppose that we perform the following operations:

1   Magnetize isothermally at 1°K *in the x direction.*
2   Insulate thermally.
3   *Rotate the field to the y direction.* Since CMN is practically nonmagnetic in this direction, it therefore undergoes an adiabatic demagnetization and its temperature drops, *even though the field is still there.*
4   Wait until the cold CMN has cooled the nuclear core, and then reduce the magnetic field to zero, thereby cooling the core by its own adiabatic demagnetization.

Another method, suggested by Kittel, is to polarize the nuclear magnets by microwaves at a temperature of 1°K and in a steady magnetic field of, say, 10^4 Oe. Removal of the high-frequency field adiabatically should result in cooling to about 10^{-3} °K. Then demagnetization from 10^4 Oe to zero should give about 10^{-7} °K. This method would have the advantage that there would be no heat-transfer problems, since all the operations are made on the nuclear magnetic subsystem.

14-10 Negative Kelvin Temperatures

Let us recall the original definition of the Kelvin scale of temperature: Two Kelvin temperatures are to each other as the heats transferred during isothermal processes at these temperatures, provided that these isothermal processes terminate on the *same* adiabatic surfaces. If Q and Q_s are the absolute values of the heats transferred at temperatures T and T_s, respectively, the original Kelvin definition provides the relation

$$T = T_s \frac{Q}{Q_s}.$$

If T_s refers to an arbitrary standard, the choice of a number for T_s is also arbitrary. If it is chosen to be negative, then all temperatures would be expressed by negative numbers. Whether T_s is chosen positive or negative, as Q is made smaller and smaller in any unordered way, the limiting value of Q is zero (i.e., the least amount of heat that can be transferred is no heat at all), and therefore *the lowest value of T is zero*. In other words, the lowest temperature is absolute zero, and if negative temperatures have any meaning at all, *they cannot mean temperatures colder than absolute zero!* But what is meant when the Kelvin scale is defined in the usual way with $T_s = +273.16°K$?

A clue as to the meaning of negative Kelvin temperatures is provided by the expression for temperature used in statistical thermodynamics,

$$T = \left(\frac{\partial U}{\partial S}\right)_V.$$

The most familiar thermodynamic systems, such as a mole of ideal gas or a mole of crystal, *have an infinite number of energy levels*. As the temperature is raised, more and more atoms are raised to higher levels. This requires more and more energy, and results in greater and greater disorder as the atoms are distributed over more and more states. As the energy goes up (positive dU), the entropy also goes up (positive dS); hence the ratio dU/dS is positive. For T to be negative, *an increase of energy would have to be accompanied by a decrease of entropy!* This obviously cannot take place when a system has an infinite number of energy levels.

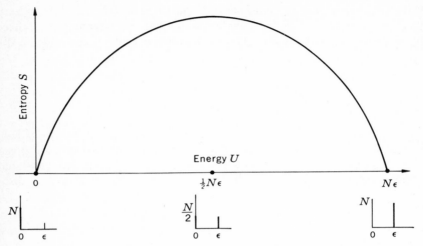

Fig. 14-22   *Relation between entropy and energy of a system of particles that can exist in only two energy levels.*

Another way of looking at the matter is with the aid of the Boltzmann equation,

$$\frac{N_2}{N_1} = e^{-(\epsilon_2 - \epsilon_1)/kT}.$$

If the system has an infinite number of energy levels, an increase of temperature produces increased populations of higher and higher energy levels, but no energy level ever gets populated more than the one below it, so that the ratio N_2/N_1 is always less than 1 and T is positive. At $T = \infty$, N_2 would be equal to N_1, but this would require an infinite amount of energy because of the infinite number of energy levels! Evidently, for T to be negative, N_2 would have to be *larger* than N_1; that is, the upper energy levels would have to be populated *more* than the lower ones. This would require even more than infinite energy—which is even more than nonsensical. We conclude, therefore, that *in the case of an ordinary system which has an infinite number of energy levels, negative temperatures are an absurdity.*

But what about a system which has only a finite number of energy levels? Suppose, for the sake of argument, that a system were capable of existing in only two energy levels. Let the system consist of N particles and the levels have energies 0 and ϵ, where ϵ is an atomic constant, independent of any external field. The curve showing the relation between entropy S and internal energy U is shown in Fig. 14-22. At zero energy, all N atoms are in the lower energy level, which is a state of minimum disorder, or zero entropy. When the two energy levels are equally populated, the internal energy of the system is $N\epsilon/2$ and there is maximum disorder and, hence, maximum entropy. If and when all N atoms are in the upper energy level, $U = N\epsilon$, and again we have minimum disorder, or zero entropy. The left half of the curve has a positive slope, and therefore $(\partial U/\partial S)$ is positive. *The right half, with negative slope, is the region of negative temperatures.*

As we start at the origin in Fig. 14-22 and go to the right, we proceed in the direction of increasing energy, increasing hotness, and therefore increasing temperature. At the position of maximum entropy, where both energy levels are equally populated, the temperature is infinite. Beyond the maximum the temperature must be hotter than infinity. Hence, *negative temperatures are hotter than infinity!* If we object to this conclusion, we are really objecting to the original definition of the Kelvin scale. Everything would be much neater if we defined a new quantity, the *negciptemp*, equal to the negative reciprocal of the Kelvin temperature; thus,

$$n = -\frac{1}{T}.$$

When S is plotted against the negciptemp, the resulting curve is shown in Fig. 14-23. Here absolute zero is at an infinite distance to the left; the origin is at $T = \infty$, and negative temperatures are to the right of the origin, with

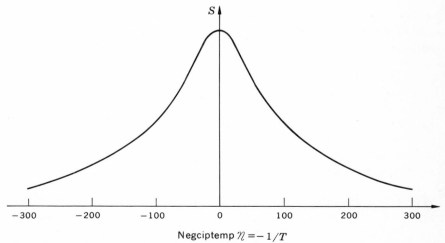

Negciptemp $n = -1/T$

Fig. 14-23   *Graph of entropy vs. n, the negciptemp (negative reciprocal of Kelvin temperature).*

"minus zero" an infinite distance to the right. It is psychologically more appealing to have the coldest possible temperature represented by $-\infty$ and the hottest conceivable temperature by $+\infty$, instead of by 0 and -0, respectively, with both $+\infty$ and $-\infty$ between.

Therefore, to achieve negative Kelvin temperatures, we must find a system with a finite number of energy levels and, somehow or other, succeed in producing a *population inversion*—that is, an equilibrium (or near-equilibrium) state in which there are more particles in upper states than in lower ones.

To reduce the temperature of a substance far below 1°K, the magnetic and thermal properties of a magnetic subsystem (ionic or nuclear) were used. The purpose of such experiments was to cool the *entire substance*, not just the subsystem. To accomplish this, it was necessary to satisfy the following conditions:

1   The magnetic ions must interact among themselves with sufficient strength and speed that (like the molecules of a gas) statistical equilibrium can be assumed and a definite temperature can be attributed to the ionic subsystem.

2   The nonmagnetic particles (called, for simplicity, the *lattice*) must have practically no heat capacity in the low-temperature region under consideration.

3   Equilibrium between the magnetic-ion subsystem and the lattice must be attained fairly rapidly.

To achieve negative temperatures, we must make use of the magnetic and thermal properties of a *nuclear* magnetic subsystem under the following conditions (one of which is the same as, while two are entirely different from, those just listed):

1   The nuclear magnetic subsystem comes to equilibrium with itself very rapidly.

2   The lattice is at room temperature, with a large heat capacity.

3   Equilibrium between the nuclear magnetic subsystem and the lattice is attained slowly enough (from, say, 2 min to several hours) that experiments can be performed on the nuclear subsystem in this time interval, as though the subsystem were isolated.

The system found by Pound, Purcell, and Ramsey in 1951 to satisfy the conditions for the production of negative temperatures is the subsystem consisting of the nuclei of the lithium ions in a LiF crystal. These were found to come to equilibrium among themselves in 10^{-5} sec, to require about 2 min or more to come to equilibrium with the lattice, and each to have a lowest energy level that is split into only four nuclear magnetic states ($I = \frac{3}{2}$) by an external magnetic field. The weak interactions among these magnetic nuclei involved emission and absorption of photons produced by transitions between some of the four states. That is, one nucleus would go from an upper to a lower state in emitting a photon, and the nucleus absorbing this photon would go from a lower to an upper state. These interactions play the same role in the achievement and maintenance of equilibrium as the collisions between gas molecules.

Experiments on the nuclear magnetic subsystem of LiF take place in a region of temperature and field similar to that enclosed within the vertical dashed lines of Fig. 14-6. In this region both S and M are functions of $\mathcal{H}/T$ only; therefore, in an adiabatic demagnetization, since S is constant, both $\mathcal{H}/T$ and M are constant. The internal energy is a function of T only and has an appreciable value and variation with T only at temperatures very much lower than those at which the experiments were made. During an adiabatic change of field, dU and dS are both zero, and therefore the expression for the temperature dU/dS becomes indeterminate. The previous analysis of negative temperatures presupposed that the energy-level spacing was an atomic constant. With a nuclear (or ionic) magnetic subsystem, however, the level spacing $\Delta\epsilon$ depends upon $\mathcal{H}$, and the magnetic energy $g\mu\mathcal{H}$ is not internal but external potential energy. To obtain a useful and appropriate expression for T, we use the *magnetic enthalpy H^**, where

$$H^* = U - \mathcal{H}M. \tag{14-35}$$

Since

$$dH^* = dU - \mathcal{H}\,dM - M\,d\mathcal{H}$$

$$= T\,dS - M\,d\mathcal{H},$$

we get

$$T = \left(\frac{\partial H^*}{\partial S}\right)_{\mathcal{H}}. \tag{14-36}$$

Choosing U to have the value zero, $H^* = -\mathcal{H}M$. Since both M and S are functions of $\mathcal{H}/T$, then M is a function of S, and $-\mathcal{H}M$ is a function of both S and $\mathcal{H}$. In Fig. 14-24, the lower half of the graph is a plot of $-\mathcal{H}M$ vs. S at five different values of $\mathcal{H}$, with the lowest curve (at $\mathcal{H}_1$) referring to the largest field. Notice that $(\partial H^*/\partial S)_{\mathcal{H}}$, the slope of any constant-field curve, is the temperature T and that the vertical line $a \rightarrow b$, at constant S, represents an adiabatic demagnetization from a large field $\mathcal{H}_1$ to a small one $\mathcal{H}_5$ during which M and $\mathcal{H}/T$ remain constant. In the upper half of Fig. 14-24, $+\mathcal{H}M$ is plotted against S for reversed fields, that is, for negative values of $\mathcal{H}$. The slope of every upper curve at every point is negative, and the process $c \rightarrow d$ represents an adiabatic magnetization during which the nuclear subsystem *cools* from -10 to $-400°$K.

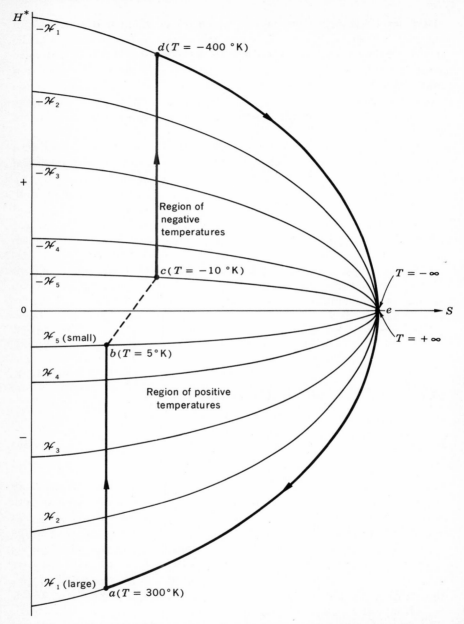

Fig. 14-24   *Magnetic enthalpy H* vs. entropy S of nuclear magnetic subsystem at five different magnetic fields and for the same fields reversed. a → b, adiabatic demagnetization; b → c, rapid magnetic field reversal; c → d, adiabatic magnetization; d → e → a, cooling through infinity at constant large magnetic field.*

14-11   The Experiment of Pound, Purcell, and Ramsey

In the experiment of Pound, Purcell, and Ramsey, the crystal was placed in a magnetic field of about 6300 Oe and allowed to come to thermal equilibrium at room temperature, 300°K. Under these circumstances,

$$a = \frac{g_N \mu_N \mathcal{H}}{kT} = \frac{2 \times 5 \times 10^{-24} \times 6300}{1.4 \times 10^{-16} \times 300}$$
$$= 1.5 \times 10^{-6}.$$

At such values of a, the Brillouin function reduces to

$$B_I(a) = \frac{I + 1}{3} a,$$

and the fractional polarization is

$$\frac{M}{M_{\text{sat}}} = \frac{\frac{3}{2} + 1}{3} \times 1.5 \times 10^{-6}$$
$$= 1.3 \times 10^{-6}.$$

Although this is a very small value, the methods of nuclear magnetic resonance (nmr) are still effective in showing the difference between the number of nuclei whose magnetic moments are in the direction of the field and those whose moments are opposite. The crystal is placed inside a small coil that is connected in series with a variable capacitor. The coil and capacitor form the resonant circuit in a radio-frequency oscillator, the frequency of which may be varied by adjusting the variable capacitor. The output of the oscillator is observed with an ordinary AM receiver. If the frequency of the oscillator is adjusted to a value $\nu_{\mathcal{H}}$, where

$$h\nu_{\mathcal{H}} = \Delta\epsilon = g_N \mu_N \mathcal{H},$$

and $$\nu(\mathcal{H} = 6300 \text{ Oe}) \approx \frac{2 \times 5 \times 10^{-24} \times 6300}{6.6 \times 10^{-27}} \approx 10^7 \text{ Hz},$$

then some of the Li nuclei with their spins parallel to the field will be flipped so that their spins become antiparallel, with an *absorption* of energy, and some of the Li nuclei with their spins antiparallel to the field will be flipped to the parallel position, with an *emission* of energy. But since these two processes occur with equal probability, and since there are slightly more nuclei with their spins parallel than antiparallel, there is a *net absorption* of energy, which is observed as a drop in the amplitude of the oscillator output, and hence as a drop in the output of the AM receiver. This drop in output corresponded to a positive temperature for the nuclear subsystem at 300°K.

Fig. 14-25   *Relation between nuclear magnetic polarization and the magnetic field for slow passage compared with that for fast passage.*

The next step, $a \rightarrow b$ in Fig. 14-24, was to remove the crystal from the magnetic field of 6300 Oe to a coil in a field of about 100 Oe, reversibly (slowly) and adiabatically, during which the polarization (parallel to the field) remained constant and the temperature presumably fell to about 5°K, although no attempt was made to measure this nuclear-spin temperature. In a field of 100 Oe, a lithium nuclear "magetic top" undergoes precession with a period of about 1 µs. By discharging a capacitor through the coil containing the LiF crystal, *the magnetic field was reversed to a value of about* -100 Oe *in a time of 0.2 μs, during which time the nuclear magnets could not follow the field.* (Such a field reversal is *highly irreversible*.) In this process, $b \rightarrow c$ in Fig. 14-24, the slight polarization parallel to the field at b (due to more nuclear magnets in lower states than in upper ones) became a polarization *opposite* the field (more nuclei in upper states than in lower ones), with a temperature about $-10°$K. The next process, $c \rightarrow d$, represents the adiabatic magnetization accomplished by putting the crystal back into the reversed field of 6300 Oe, during which the temperature cooled from -10 to $-400°$K. The last step, $d \rightarrow e \rightarrow a$, was the inevitable cooling due to interaction with the lattice, in which the temperature decreased from $-400°$K to $-\infty$ (which is the same as $+\infty$) and then went back to $+300°$K.

The success of the experiment depended on performing the field reversal in a time less than the Larmor precession period and bringing the crystal back to its place in a time less than the relaxation time for equilibrium between nuclear subsystem and lattice. A symbolic field-vs.-time graph is shown in Fig. 14-25, with a comparison between the *fast-passage* (negative temperature) result and a *slow-passage* one. The small arrows indicate the magnetic polarization of the Li nuclear subsystem.

In the 2-min period in which the nuclear subsystem was at negative temperatures, the AM receiver of the nmr apparatus showed an increase in signal at $\nu_\mathcal{H}$, indicating a net emission of energy from the Li nuclei and thereby proving the existence of negative temperatures.

Figure 14-26 shows the changes in the spacing and the populations of the energy levels during the experiment of Pound, Purcell, and Ramsey, which

Fig. 14-26   *Steps in the experiment of Pound, Purcell, and Ramsey.*

in the opinion of this author ranks among the most significant experiments of modern times.

14-12   Thermodynamics at Negative Temperatures

Classical thermodynamics takes some peculiar twists at negative temperatures, but much remains the same as at positive temperatures. Take, for example, the entropy principle, which states that the sum of all the entropy changes accompanying a natural irreversible process is positive. Suppose that Q units of heat leave a hot reservoir at a temperature, say, of $-40°K$ and enter a colder reservoir at, say, $-100°K$, as shown in Fig. 14-27a. (Recall that the hottest negative temperature is -0 and the coldest is $-\infty$.) Since heat leaves the hotter reservoir, the entropy change is $-Q/-50$; whereas the entropy change of the colder reservoir is $+Q/-100$. The total entropy change is

$$\frac{-Q}{-50} + \frac{Q}{-100} = \frac{Q}{100},$$

which is positive, just as it is with positive temperatures.

In Fig. 14-27b is shown an attempt to imitate the way a heat engine

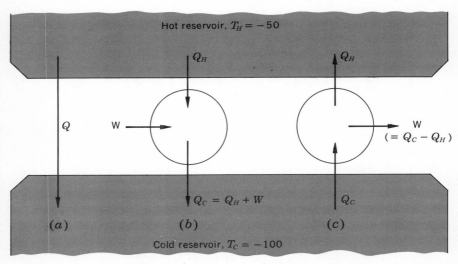

Fig. 14-27   (a) *Spontaneous flow of heat in the direction of decreasing temperature.* (b) *A costly device for doing something that requires no device.* (c) *A heat engine that could be used to convert heat $Q_C - Q_H$ from the cold reservoir completely into work.*

behaves, but at negative temperatures. Since, by definition of the Kelvin scale,

$$\frac{Q_H}{Q_C} = \frac{T_H}{T_C} = \frac{-50}{-100} = \frac{1}{2},$$

when Q_H units of heat leave the hotter reservoir, *twice as much* heat must enter the colder one. Therefore, instead of work W being done *by* the engine, work would have to be done *on* the engine in order not to violate the principle of the conservation of energy. But the device depicted in Fig. 14-27*b* is an expensive gadget for doing a job that requires no device at all. If all you want is to push heat into a cold reservoir, it is sufficient merely to allow Q_H to flow *naturally* from the hot to the cold reservoir.

To get W units of work *out* of a heat engine operating between reservoirs at negative temperatures, you would have to make use of the device shown in Fig. 14-27*c*, where Q_C units of heat are taken *from* the cold reservoir (as though it were a refrigerator). Then a *smaller* quantity Q_H would go into the hotter reservoir, and the rest would be available for work. But the hot reservoir could be dispensed with, for the Q_H units of heat would naturally flow back to the colder reservoir. The net result would be that $Q_C - Q_H$ units of heat were extracted from the *colder* reservoir and converted completely into work, in violation of the Kelvin-Planck statement of the second law. This is the only principle of classical physics that is violated by systems at negative temperatures—but it is an important and interesting one.

Up to the present time, the only real use for systems at negative temperatures has been in the rapidly expanding field of masers and lasers. Perhaps, in the future, experiments on heat engines and refrigerators will be performed at negative temperatures. Then it will truly be fun to be an engineer.

14-13   Third Law of Thermodynamics

We have seen how the Joule-Kelvin effect is employed to produce liquid helium at a temperature below 5°K. The rapid adiabatic vaporization of liquid helium then results in a further lowering of the temperature to about 1°K with He^4 and to about 0.3°K with He^3. The magnetocaloric effect is then used to lower the temperature of a paramagnetic compound (magnetic-ion subsystem *plus* lattice) to about 0.001°K. In principle, it is possible to achieve still lower temperatures of matter by repeated applications of the magnetocaloric effect. Thus, after the original isothermal magnetization, the first adiabatic demagnetization might be used to provide a large amount of material at temperature T_{f1} to serve as a heat reservoir for the next isothermal magnetization of a smaller amount of material. A second adiabatic demagnetization might then give rise to a lower temperature T_{f2}, and so on. The question which naturally arises at this point is whether the magneto-caloric effect may be used to cool a substance to absolute zero.

Experiment shows that the fundamental feature of all cooling processes is that the lower the temperature achieved, the more difficult it is to go lower. For example, the colder a liquid is, the lower the vapor pressure, and the harder it is to produce further cooling by pumping away the vapor. The same is true for the magnetocaloric effect: if one demagnetization produces a temperature T_{f1}, say, one-tenth the original T_i, then a second demagnetization from the same original field will produce a temperature T_{f2} which is also approximately one-tenth of T_{f1}. Under these circumstances, an infinite number of adiabatic demagnetizations would be required to attain absolute zero. Generalizing from experience, we may state the following:

By no finite series of processes is the absolute zero attainable.

This is known as either *the principle of the unattainability of absolute zero* or *the unattainability statement of the third law of thermodynamics*. Just as in the case of the second law of thermodynamics, the third law has a number of alternative or equivalent statements. Another statement of the third law is the result of experiments leading to calculations of the way the entropy change of a condensed system during a *reversible, isothermal* process ΔS_T behaves as T approaches zero. For example, the entropy change of a solid during a reversible isothermal compression may either be measured at different T's or be calculated from the second $T\,dS$ equation, leading to

$$\Delta S_T = S(T,P_1) - S(T,0) = -\int_0^{P_1} \left(\frac{\partial V}{\partial T}\right)_P dP.$$

Since β decreases as T decreases, this example of ΔS_T decreases as T decreases. The entropy change of a paramagnetic salt during a reversible isothermal magnetization also decreases as T decreases, because

$$\Delta S_T = S(T,\mathscr{H}_1) - S(T,0) = \int_0^{\mathscr{H}_1} \left(\frac{\partial M}{\partial T}\right)_{\mathscr{H}} d\mathscr{H},$$

and $(\partial M/\partial T)_{\mathscr{H}}$ decreases with T. Experimental evidence is very strong to support the view that, as T decreases, ΔS_T decreases provided that the system is a solid or a liquid—that is, a condensed system. The following principle is therefore accepted:

The entropy change associated with any isothermal reversible process of a condensed system approaches zero as the temperature approaches zero.

Let us call this theorem the *Nernst-Simon statement of the third law of thermodynamics*. Both this statement and the unattainability statement have had a long and checkered career since the original paper by Nernst in 1907. It took 30 years of experimental and theoretical research, during which time there were periods of great confusion, before all differences of opinion were resolved and the statement was agreed upon. Nernst originally stated, as the third law, that the temperature derivative of the change of Helmholtz function during an isothermal process approaches zero as the temperature approaches zero. He did not think in terms of entropy and, moreover, was of the opinion that this statement and also the unattainability statement could be derived from the second law with the additional assumption that the heat capacities of all materials approached zero as the temperature approached zero. Nernst also maintained that both statements were true for all kinds of processes, both reversible and irreversible. It was mainly the experiments and arguments of Simon in the period from 1927 to 1937 that made precise the region of validity of the third law.

In order to show that the Nernst-Simon statement and the unattainability statement are equivalent, it is necessary to derive an equation for the limiting value of the entropy change accompanying an isothermal reversible process. Let us return to a paramagnetic salt and consider any isentropic demagnetization, $i \rightarrow f$ of Fig. 14-28. The entropy change between

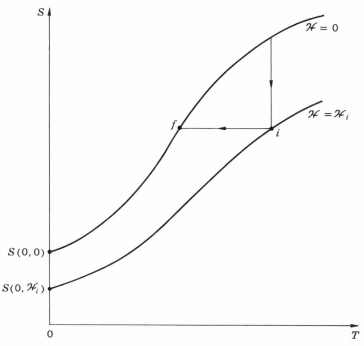

Fig. 14-28   *Diagram to derive Eq. (14-37).*

the point $(T = 0, \mathcal{H} = \mathcal{H}_i)$ and the state i is

$$S_i - S(0,\mathcal{H}_i) = \int_0^{T_i} \frac{C_{\mathcal{H}=\mathcal{H}_i}}{T} \, dT,$$

where $C_{\mathcal{H}}$ is the heat capacity at constant field, a positive quantity for all values of $\mathcal{H}$. The change in entropy between the point $(T = 0, \mathcal{H} = 0)$ and f is

$$S_f - S(0,0) = \int_0^{T_f} \frac{C_{\mathcal{H}=0}}{T} \, dT.$$

Since $S_i = S_f$ and $S(0,\mathcal{H}_i) - S(0,0) = \lim [S(T,\mathcal{H}_i) - S(T,0)]$, we have

$$\lim_{T \to 0} [S(T,\mathcal{H}_i) - S(T,0)] = \int_0^{T_f} \frac{C_{\mathcal{H}=0}}{T} \, dT - \int_0^{T_i} \frac{C_{\mathcal{H}=\mathcal{H}_i}}{T} \, dT. \quad (14\text{-}37)$$

To prove the equivalence of the unattainability and Nernst-Simon statements of the third law, we proceed in the same manner as in the case of the Kelvin-Planck and Clausius statements of the second law.

Let $U =$ truth of the unattainability statement;
$-U =$ falsity of the unattainability statement;
$N =$ truth of the Nernst-Simon statement;
$-N =$ falsity of the Nernst-Simon statement.

As before, $U \equiv N$

when $-U \supset -N$ and $-N \supset -U.$

1   To prove that $-U \supset -N$, suppose that it is possible to find a value of T_i which makes $T_f = 0$, thereby violating the unattainability statement. Then, from Eq. (14-37), the left-hand member would be negative, thereby violating the Nernst statement.

2   To prove that $-N \supset -U$, suppose that the left-hand member of Eq. (14-37) had any negative value, thereby violating the Nernst-Simon statement. Then it would be possible to find a value of T_i in Eq. (14-37) that would make the second integral equal to this negative number. As a result, the first integral would vanish and T_f would be zero, thereby violating the unattainability statement.

The fact that $-N \supset -U$ may also be readily seen from Fig. 14-29a. If the point $(0,\mathcal{H}_i)$ lies below the point $(0,0)$, then the adiabatic demagnetization $6 \to 7$ could be used to lower the system to absolute zero.

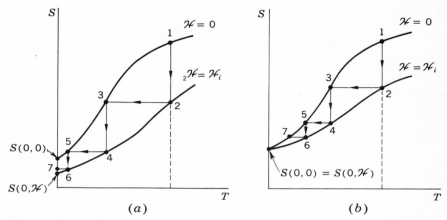

Fig. 14-29   (*a*) *If the Nernst-Simon statement of the third law were not true, the processes* 5 → 6 *and* 6 → 7 *could be used to attain absolute zero.* (*b*) *Diagram to show the equivalence of the three statements of the third law.*

To complete the proof of the equivalence of the unattainability and the Nernst-Simon statements of the third law, one ought to consider a type of system that undergoes a decrease of entropy during an isothermal demagnetization and a decrease of temperature during an adiabatic magnetization, such as a *superconductor in the intermediate state*. Since the proof proceeds in exactly the same way as before, however, nothing would be gained by repeating the details.

A paramagnetic substance was invoked in the proof of the equivalence of U and N only for convenience and concreteness. By means of a slight change in symbols, the same proof may be applied to any system whatever, since all systems are capable of undergoing an isothermal reversible decrease of entropy followed by a reversible adiabatic decrease of temperature. Furthermore, the Nernst-Simon statement also applies to materials in frozen metastable equilibrium, provided that the isothermal process in question does not disturb this frozen equilibrium.

Referring to Fig. 14-29*b*, we see that, in the isothermal process 1 → 2, there is a decrease of entropy and that in 3 → 4 there is another decrease, and so on. If the entropy of the system at absolute zero is called the *zero-point entropy*, we see that a third equivalent statement of the third law is as follows:

By no finite series of processes can the entropy of a system be reduced to its zero-point value.

The equivalence of all three statements of the third law is clearly displayed in Fig. 14-29*b*.

There are many physical and chemical facts which substantiate the third law. For example, using Clapeyron's equation,

$$\frac{dP}{dT} = \frac{s^{(f)} - s^{(i)}}{v^{(f)} - v^{(i)}}$$

in conjunction with a phase change that takes place at low temperature, the statement that

$$\lim_{T \to 0} (s^{(f)} - s^{(i)}) = 0,$$

implies that

$$\lim_{T \to 0} \frac{dP}{dT} = 0,$$

since $v^{(f)} - v^{(i)}$ is not zero for a first-order phase transition. This is substantiated by the melting curve of solid helium shown in Figs. 12-30 to 12-32. As a matter of fact dP/dT of solid He^4 approaches zero very rapidly, as shown by the experimental result of Simon and Swenson, that

$$\frac{dP}{dT} = 0.425 T^7.$$

There are many other applications of the third law in the fields of physical chemistry and statistical mechanics. For further study, the writings of Simon and of Guggenheim are recommended.

The fact that absolute zero cannot be attained is no cause for misgiving. A temperature of 3×10^{-6} °K represents a fraction of room temperature (300°K) equal to

$$\frac{3 \times 10^{-6}}{3 \times 10^2} = 10^{-8}.$$

Cryogenics has therefore enabled us to get to one one-hundred-millionth of room temperature. The temperature of the sun, 6,000°K, is only 200 times room temperature, and the temperature in the interior of the hottest star, about 3×10^9 °K, is 10 million times room temperature. Cryogenics is still ahead by a factor of 10.

A chronological account of the progress toward lower temperatures is given in Table 14-6 (reproduced with the kind permission of *International Science and Technology*).

Table 14-6   The 100-year Journey toward Absolute Zero

Date	Investigator	Country	Development	Temp., °K
1860	Kirk	Scotland	*First step toward deep refrigeration:* reached temperatures below freezing point of Hg.	234.0
1877	Cailletet	France	*First liquefied oxygen:* used throttling process from pressure vessel, obtaining fine mist only.	90.2
1884	Wroblewski & Olzewski	Poland	*First property measurements at low temperatures:* used small quantities of liquid N_2 and O_2.	77.3
1898	Dewar	England	*First liquefied hydrogen:* used Joule-Kelvin effect and counterflow heat exchanger.	20.4
1908	Kamerlingh-Onnes	Netherlands	*First liquefied helium:* used same method as Dewar; shortly thereafter, lowered pressure over liquid to get 1°K.	4.2
1927	Simon	Germany & England	*Developed helium liquefier:* used adiabatic expansion from pressure vessel with liquid H_2 precooling.	4.2
1933	Giauque & MacDougall	U.S.	*First adiabatic demagnetization:* Principle first proposed by Giauque and Debye in 1926.	0.25
1934	Kapitza	England & U.S.S.R.	*Developed helium liquefier using expansion engine:* Made possible liquefaction of helium without liquid H_2 precooling.	4.2
1946	Collins	U.S.	*Developed commercial helium liquefier:* used expansion engines and counterflow heat exchangers.	2.0
1956	Simon & Kurti	England	*First nuclear experiments:* used adiabatic demagnetization of nuclear stage of a paramagnetic salt.	10^{-5}
1960	Kurti	England	*Reached lowest temperature so far:* Nuclear cooling methods.	10^{-6}

PROBLEMS

14-1   In a magnetic field $\mathcal{H}$, where the total energy of an ion is

$$\epsilon_i = -g\mu_B \mathcal{H} m_i + \delta_i,$$

the number of ions N_i with magnetic quantum number m_i is given by the Boltzmann equation. The total magnetization M is

$$M = \Sigma N_i g\mu_B m_i.$$

Show that

$$M = NkT\left(\frac{\partial \ln Z}{\partial \mathcal{H}}\right)_T.$$

14.2   (a) Derive Eq. (14-22) directly from the relation $U = \Sigma N_i \delta_i$ and Boltzmann's equation. (b) Prove that, when $J = \frac{1}{2}$,

$$B_J(a) = \tanh \frac{a}{2}.$$

14-3   Prove that, when splitting of the lowest energy level by the crystalline field is neglected,

(a) $$\frac{S}{R} = \ln \frac{e^{(J+\frac{1}{2})a} - e^{-(J+\frac{1}{2})a}}{e^{\frac{1}{2}a} - e^{-\frac{1}{2}a}} - JaB_J(a).$$

(b)   When $a \ll 1$,

$$\frac{S}{R} = \ln(2J+1) - \frac{J(J+1)a^2}{3}$$

$$= \ln(2J+1) - \frac{C_C}{R}\frac{\mathcal{H}^2}{T^2},$$

where C_C is the Curie constant.

14-4   Convert the second energy equation (Chap. 11) into a form appropriate to the coordinates $\mathcal{H}$, M, and T. Prove that, since $M = f(\mathcal{H}/T)$, U of a magnetic-ion subsystem must be a function of T only.

14-5   For a paramagnetic salt obeying Brillouin's equation, prove that:

(a) $$C_\mathcal{H} - C_M = -\mathcal{H}\left(\frac{\partial M}{\partial T}\right)_\mathcal{H}.$$

(b)   As $T \to 0$ at constant $\mathcal{H}$, $C_{\mathcal{H}} \to C_M$.

(c)
$$\left(\frac{\partial H^*}{\partial \mathcal{H}}\right)_T = T\left(\frac{\partial M}{\partial T}\right)_{\mathcal{H}} - M.$$

14-6   Between absolute zero and the Curie point T_C, an *antiferromagnetic* oxide has a magnetic susceptibility that is roughly proportional to the temperature; thus,

$$\frac{M}{\mathcal{H}} = C_C' T.$$

Show that (a) the magnetic enthalpy is a function of temperature only and that (b) the heat capacity at constant field is a function of temperature only.

14-7

(a)   Prove that, for a paramagnetic gas,

$$T \, dS = C_{V,M} \, dT + T\left(\frac{\partial P}{\partial T}\right)_{V,M} + T\left(\frac{\partial \mathcal{H}}{\partial T}\right)_{V,M} dM.$$

(b)   If the gas is ideal and obeys Curie's law, show that

$$T \, dS = C_{V,M} \, dT + nRT \frac{dV}{V} - \frac{T}{C_C} M \, dM.$$

(c)   Sketch a reversible adiabatic surface on a TVM diagram, assuming $C_{V,M}$ to be constant.

14-8   A paramagnetic salt obeys Curie's law and also $C_M = A/T^2$. Show that:

(a)
$$S = -\frac{1}{2}\frac{A}{T^2} - \frac{M^2}{2C_C} + \text{const.}$$

(b)
$$C_{\mathcal{H}} - c_M = C_C \frac{\mathcal{H}^2}{T^2}.$$

(c)   The equation of an adiabat is $M = \text{const.} \dfrac{\mathcal{H}}{\sqrt{1 + (C_C/A)\mathcal{H}^2}}$

14-9   Make a graph of the heat capacity of gadolinium sulfate as a function of T from 1.5 to 5.0°K and for values of $\mathcal{H}$ equal to 0, 2, 5, and 10 kOe.

14-10   Take a paramagnetic solid obeying Curie's law through a Carnot cycle, and verify that

$$\frac{Q_H}{Q_C} = \frac{T_H}{T_C}.$$

14-11   From the microscopic point of view, the disorder of a paramagnetic solid may be increased in two ways: by increasing the temperature and by decreasing the field. From this point of view, explain why a reversible adiabatic demagnetization should be accompanied by a decrease in temperature.

14-12   Using Schottky's equation, Eq. (14-25), and setting $\delta_1/kT = x$,
(a)   Show that the heat capacity is a maximum when

$$\frac{\dfrac{x}{2} - 1}{\dfrac{x}{2} + 1} = \frac{g_1}{g_0} e^{-x}$$

and find the maximizing value of x when $g_1/g_0 = \frac{3}{2}$.
(b)   What is the maximum value of c_M/R when $g_1/g_0 = \frac{3}{2}$?

14-13   Two gram-ions of gadolinium sulfate obeying Curie's law are in a magnetic field of 20 kOe and at a temperature of 15°K. The field is reduced reversibly and isothermally to zero.
(a)   How much heat is transferred?
(b)   How much work is done?
(c)   What is the internal energy change?
(d)   What would be the final temperature if the process were performed reversibly and adiabatically?

14-14   At what initial temperature should iron ammonium alum be in order that an adiabatic demagnetization from an initial field of 10 kOe to zero final field yield a final temperature of 0.2°K?

14-15   CMN originally at 1.5°K is magnetized isothermally from zero field to 5 kOe.
(a)   What is the heat of magnetization per gram-ion?
(b)   After it is demagnetized adiabatically to a field of 1 kOe, what is the final temperature?

14-16   What initial field is required in order that an adiabatic demagnetization to zero field should lower the temperature from 1 to 10^{-2} °K, using the following:
(a)   Chromium potassium alum?
(b)   CMN?

14-17   A solid at temperature T is placed in an external magnetic field of 30 kOe.
(a)   If the solid contains weakly interacting magnetic ions with $J = \frac{1}{2}$ and $g = 1$, to what temperature must one cool the solid so that 75 percent of the atoms are polarized with their magnetic moments parallel to the external magnetic field?
(b)   If, on the other hand, the solid were paraffin with many protons (but no magnetic ions), with $I = \frac{1}{2}$, $g_N = 2$, and a magnetic moment equal to 1.41×10^{-23} erg/Oe, to what temperature must the paraffin be lowered to achieve a nuclear polarization of 75 percent?

14-18   A sample of mineral oil is placed in an external magnetic field $\mathscr{H}$. Each proton has $I = \frac{1}{2}$ and a magnetic moment μ. An applied radio-frequency field can induce transitions between the two energy states if its frequency ν is equal to $2\mu\mathscr{H}$. The power absorbed from this radiation field is proportional to the *difference* in the number of nuclei in the two energy levels. Assuming that $kT \gg 2\mu\mathscr{H}$, how does the absorbed power depend on T?

14-19

(a)   One gram-ion of chromium potassium alum is at 1°K and at 10 kOe. After undergoing an adiabatic demagnetization to zero field, it is immersed in 36 moles of liquid He^4 at 4.2°K whose specific heat capacity equals 2.5 J/g · deg. What is the final temperature of the combination?

(b)   If, at the conclusion of the demagnetization in part (a), the alum is immersed in 36 moles of liquid He^4 at 2°K, whose specific heat capacity equals $0.104 T^{6.2}$ J/g · deg, what is the final temperature of the combination?

14-20   Sketch a Carnot engine cycle on a $\mathscr{H}M$ diagram:

(a)   At positive temperatures.

(b)   At negative temperatures.

(c)   Why is it impossible to operate a Carnot engine between a reservoir at a negative temperature and one at a positive temperature?

14-21   Suppose the magnetization of a paramagnetic solid is given by

$$M = M_{\text{sat}} f(a),$$

where $a = g\mu\mathscr{H}/kT$ and $f(a) = 0$ when $a = 0$, and $f(a) \to 1$ when $a \to \infty$. The change of entropy during an isothermal reversible increase of field from 0 to $\mathscr{H}_i$ is given by

$$
\begin{aligned}
\Delta S_T &= \int_0^{\mathscr{H}_i} \left(\frac{\partial M}{\partial T}\right)_{\mathscr{H}} d\mathscr{H} \\
&= \int_0^{\mathscr{H}_i} M_{\text{sat}} f'(a) \left(\frac{-g\mu\mathscr{H}}{kT^2}\right) \frac{kT}{g\mu} da \\
&= -\frac{M_{\text{sat}} k}{g\mu} \int_0^{a_i} a f'(a) \, da.
\end{aligned}
$$

Determine whether the Nernst-Simon statement of the third law is true in the following cases:

(a)   Curie's equation: $f(a) = a$.

(b)   Langevin's equation: $f(a) = \coth a - \dfrac{1}{a}$.

(c)   Brillouin's equation, with $J = \frac{1}{2}$: $f(a) = \tanh \dfrac{a}{2}$.

(d)   Brillouin's equation, with any J: $f(a) = B_J(a)$.

14-22   Using the Nernst-Simon statement of the third law, prove that:

(a)   For a reversible cell or a thermocouple,

$$\lim_{T \to 0} \left(\frac{d\mathcal{E}}{dT} \right) = 0.$$

(b)   For a surface film of liquid He^4 or He^3,

$$\lim_{T \to 0} \left(\frac{d\mathcal{J}}{dT} \right) = 0.$$

14-23

(a)   At $T = 0$, $(\partial S/\partial V)_{T=0} = 0$, and also

$$\frac{\partial}{\partial V} \left[\left(\frac{\partial S}{\partial V} \right)_T \right]_{T=0} = 0.$$

From this fact, prove that

$$\lim_{T \to 0} \left[\frac{\partial (1/\kappa)}{\partial T} \right]_V = 0$$

where κ is the isothermal compressibility.

(b)   In the case of a solid whose equation of state is

$$Pv + G(v) = \Gamma u,$$

where $G(v)$ is a function of volume only and Γ is a constant, prove that c_V approaches zero as T approaches zero.

15.

SUPERFLUIDITY AND SUPERCONDUCTIVITY

15-1   Superfluidity of Liquid Helium II

Helium gas at a pressure of 1 atm liquefies at 4.215°K. If the temperature of a system consisting of liquid helium in equilibrium with its own vapor is lowered to the λ point (2.172°K), liquid helium II is formed. As the temperature is further reduced, the density of liquid helium II decreases, indicating that the volume expansivity is negative. The violent bubbling that takes place by virtue of the unavoidable heat leak into a very cold liquid at its boiling point ceases when helium passes through its λ point. This provides a simple visual method of observing the attainment of the λ point and indicates an anomalously high thermal conductivity for liquid helium II.

One of the most significant properties of liquid helium II is its abnormally low viscosity. According to Poiseuille's law, the rate of flow of a liquid through a tube or an annular space is inversely proportional to the viscosity, other factors remaining constant. If the rate of flow of liquid helium through a fine annulus is measured as a function of temperature, the solid curve of Fig. 15-1 is obtained. At the λ point, the rate of flow increases abruptly and provides experimental evidence of a very low viscosity. The result of a similar experiment on the light isotope of helium of mass number 3 is shown as a dashed curve. No such phenomenon has been observed for liquid helium III.

A theory of liquid helium II was advanced by Landau in 1941 to account for its peculiar behavior. Landau assumed that the energy levels of liquid helium II (not of separate helium atoms) consisted of two sets of overlapping continuous energy states: one representing the levels for sound quanta, or *phonons*, and the other for quanta of vortex motion, or *rotons*. The lowest phonon level was assumed to be below the lowest roton level by an energy gap. On the basis of other assumptions, Landau was able to construct a quantum hydrodynamics that accounted quite well for many of the properties of liquid helium II.

Fig. 15-1   *Rate of flow of liquid helium III and of liquid helium IV through a* 7 × 10^{-5}-*cm annulus. (D. W. Osborne, B. Weinstock, B. M. Abraham, 1949.)*

An equally plausible point of view was developed from quantum statistical mechanics by F. London, who envisaged the formation of liquid helium II from liquid helium I at the λ point as a peculiar type of quantum condensation, known as *Bose-Einstein condensation*. This is a phenomenon which takes place not in ordinary space like the familiar condensation but in momentum space, where the condensed particles have zero-point energy and momentum.

Many of the statements of both Landau's and London's theories rest on plausibility arguments rather than on derivation from quantum theory. This situation has been considerably improved by the researches of Feynman, who has succeeded in deriving, on the basis of quantum statistics, the energy-level and energy-gap picture of Landau while at the same time retaining the Bose-Einstein condensation idea of London.

Both Landau's and London's points of view were redescribed by Tisza in picturesque language by a phenomenological theory of liquid helium II—known as the *two-fluid model*—which, although not meant to be taken literally, has the virtue of simplicity and has proved very helpful to experimentalists. According to this picture, liquid helium II is to be imagined as a mixture of two liquids composed of (1) normal atoms with normal viscosity and (2) superfluid atoms with zero-point energy and entropy, capable of moving through the normal atoms without friction.

If ρ is the density of liquid helium II, ρ_n the density of the normal part, and ρ_s the density of the superfluid part,

$$\rho = \rho_n + \rho_s. \tag{15-1}$$

At the λ point, all the atoms are normal and $\rho_n/\rho = 1$, whereas at absolute zero all the atoms are superfluid and $\rho_n/\rho = 0$.

If a disk or a set of concentric disks is set in oscillation in liquid helium II, the amplitude of oscillation will decrease with the time because of the viscosity of the liquid. If the disks are extremely close together, many of the normal atoms are dragged by the disks through the superfluid atoms; as a result, the moment of inertia of the disk system will depend on the density of normal atoms at the particular temperature chosen. By combining the results of these two experiments and by applying plausible equations, Andronikash-villi was able to measure the ratio ρ_n/ρ as a function of the temperature. At lower temperatures, de Klerk, Hudson, and Pellam were able to infer values of ρ_n/ρ from their measurements of the speed of "second sound," a phenomenon in liquid helium II to be described later. The combined results of all these measurements are shown in Fig. 15-2, where it may be seen that ρ_n/ρ

Fig. 15-2   *Variation of normal fluid concentration with the temperature. (Measurements of Andronikashvilli, de Klerk, Hudson, and Pellam.)*

varies as the fourth power of T up to about 0.6°K, and from there on the variation is more complicated. It is an interesting fact that the heat capacity and the thermal conductivity of liquid helium II also abruptly change their temperature dependence at 0.6°K. These facts lead us to believe that, at temperatures below 0.6°K, only phonons play a significant role.

Since ρ_n/ρ increases so markedly as the temperature rises, a temporary scarcity of superfluid atoms may be produced locally—i.e., in a small region of a vessel containing liquid helium II—if the temperature of that region is raised, either by heat leaking in from the outside or by heat supplied by an electric heater. As a result, superfluid atoms diffuse into the region. This motion of superfluid atoms relative to normal atoms accounts for the abnormally high heat conductivity of liquid helium II. It is more a transport of mass than a transport of heat.

In a mixture of liquid helium 4 and liquid helium 3, a temperature increase at one place causes a flow of superfluid He^4 atoms to that place but not of atoms of He^3 since liquid He^3 shows no superfluidity. This has been used to increase the concentration of He^3 in a mixture to a value far above normal.

15-2   Fountain Effect

One of the most peculiar phenomena of liquid helium II is the *fountain effect*, discovered by Allen and Jones in 1938. They observed that the level of liquid in a vessel communicating through a narrow capillary to a surrounding bath of liquid rose above that of the surrounding bath when heat was supplied electrically to the liquid in the vessel, as shown in Fig. 15-3a. A more striking manifestation of this effect can be demonstrated with the apparatus shown in Fig. 15-3b. The helium between the grains of finely ground emery was warmed by the radiation from a flashlight, and the consequent increase of pressure gave rise to a fountain of liquid helium, which has been observed to be as high as 30 cm.

The fountain effect may be epitomized as follows: If two chambers or two parts of a vessel communicate with each other through a very narrow capillary, a thin slit, a small hole, or the spaces between a closely packed powder, etc., and if the liquid helium II in one chamber is maintained at temperature T_1 and pressure P_1, then, if the temperature of the helium in the other chamber is maintained at T_2, the pressure will automatically become P_2, a positive temperature gradient giving rise to a positive pressure gradient. The numerical measure of the fountain effect is taken to be

$$f = \frac{P_2 - P_1}{T_2 - T_1},$$

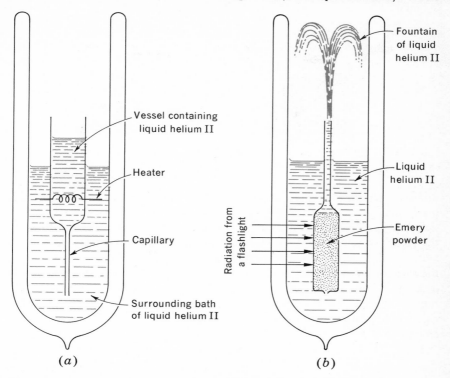

Fig. 15-3 *(a) Apparatus of Allen and Jones with which the fountain effect was first observed. (b) Apparatus of Allen and Misener for showing the fountain effect.*

or, as it will be shown later,

$$f = \left(\frac{\partial P}{\partial T}\right)_g,$$

where g is the Gibbs function.

When liquid helium II is transferred through a very small hole, slit, or capillary, it is generally accepted that only superfluid atoms are transported, carrying with them their zero-point energy and entropy. If we choose as a standard state for the calculation of entropy of liquid helium the state at absolute zero and arbitrarily assign zero entropy to this state, then, since liquid helium at absolute zero consists exclusively of superfluid atoms, we may ascribe zero entropy to superfluid atoms. Therefore, when liquid helium escapes through a narrow space, *no entropy is lost.*

Suppose two vessels, each containing liquid helium II, are connected by a narrow capillary, as shown in Fig. 15-4. If the vessels are maintained at

Fig. 15-4   *Reversible transfer of mass dm of superfluid atoms.*

different temperatures T_0 and T, respectively, with the aid of suitable reservoirs, then for a given pressure on one mass of helium there will exist a definite equilibrium pressure on the other. Suppose both pistons are moved to the right very slowly so that P_0 and T_0 are maintained constant on the left and P and T constant on the right, these being equilibrium values. Let m, the mass of liquid helium II on the right, increase by dm. Assuming that (1) only superfluid atoms, carrying no entropy, move through the capillary and that (2) there is no friction in and no heat conduction through the capillary, then each portion of helium undergoes an isothermal, isobaric reversible change of mass.

It should be remarked that the behavior of a quantity of liquid helium II which loses superfluid atoms only, and thus loses no entropy *by virtue of this flow*, is entirely different from the behavior of the usual "open system" of classical thermodynamics, where entropy *is* transferred by virtue of the flow of matter.

When the pistons move, only superfluid atoms flow through the capillary. Since these atoms carry no entropy, the entropy in the left-hand vessel is therefore distributed over a smaller mass and the temperature tends to rise. This is prevented, however, by the reservoir at constant temperature. Therefore, a flow of heat must take place to the reservoir. That is, when liquid helium II in the left-hand chamber loses superfluid atoms (loses mass), it loses no entropy through the capillary but loses entropy to the reservoir of an amount

$$s_0(m_0 - dm) - s_0 m_0 = -s_0 \, dm,$$

where s_0 is the specific entropy of liquid helium II at the constant temperature T_0 and constant pressure P_0. Since s_0 is a function of T_0 and P_0, it remains constant during the process.

The entropy change of the reservoir is dQ_0/T_0, where dQ_0 is the heat transferred from the liquid helium to the reservoir. Since the process is reversible, the sum of all the entropy changes is zero. Remembering once again that there is no entropy change accompanying the flow of matter, we have

$$\frac{dQ_0}{T_0} - s_0 \, dm = 0,$$

or

$$dQ_0 = T_0 s_0 \, dm.$$

Similarly, for the right-hand portion, which gains dm grams of superfluid atoms, thereby gaining no entropy from the incoming atoms but gaining it instead from the reservoir, we have

$$dQ = Ts \, dm.$$

Considering the system as a whole,

$$\text{Net heat transferred} = Ts \, dm - T_0 s_0 \, dm,$$

$$\text{Net energy change} = (u - u_0) \, dm,$$

$$\text{Net work done} = (Pv - P_0 v_0) \, dm,$$

where u and v represent the specific energy and volume, respectively, at constant T and P; while u_0 and v_0 refer to constant T_0 and P_0. Obviously, u, u_0, v, v_0 all remain constant during the process.

Applying the first law of thermodynamics, we get

$$Ts \, dm - T_0 s_0 \, dm = (u - u_0) \, dm + (Pv - P_0 v_0) \, dm,$$

or

$$g_0 = g. \tag{15-2}$$

Considering P_0 and T_0 on the left to remain constant and varying P and T on the right, we have

$$dg = 0,$$

or

$$-s \, dT + v \, dP = 0,$$

and finally,

$$\boxed{\left(\frac{\partial P}{\partial T}\right)_g = \frac{s}{v},} \tag{15-3}$$

which is the *fountain-effect equation*. P is expressed in dynes per square centimeter, s in ergs per gram-degree, and v in cubic centimeters per gram. If the pressure is measured in centimeters of helium, then letting y be the height of the helium column, a_g the acceleration of gravity, and ρ the density of

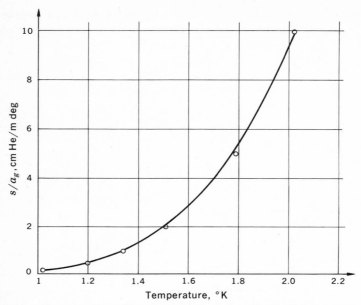

Fig. 15-5   *Fountain effect. (Experimental points from D. V. Osborne, "Experimental Cryophysics," p. 324, 1961.) Solid curve represents s/a_g. (Kramers, Wasscher, Bots, and Gorter, 1960.)*

helium, $P = y\rho a_g$, and the fountain-effect equation may be written as

$$\left(\frac{\partial y}{\partial T}\right)_{a!} = \frac{s}{v\rho a_g} = \frac{s}{a_g}. \tag{15-4}$$

Values of the entropy may be calculated from data on the specific heat. Thus,

$$s = \int_0^T \frac{c\,dT}{T}.$$

The measurement of the fountain-effect pressure must be corrected to allow for the increased vapor pressure in the warmer vessel. When this correction (which may amount to as much as 10 percent) is made, there is excellent agreement between the experimental results and the calculated entropy values, as shown in Fig. 15-5.

15-3   Second Sound

According to the two-fluid theory of liquid helium II, the ratio of the number of normal to superfluid atoms depends strongly on temperature. A rapid, local temperature fluctuation gives rise to a rapid, local variation in the ratio ρ_n/ρ_s without altering the sum $\rho_n + \rho_s = \rho$. An ordinary longitudinal wave (*first sound*) is the propagation of fluctuations in ρ throughout a medium. Fluctuations in the ratio ρ_n/ρ_s, *without change of* ρ, propagated through liquid helium II were predicted independently by Tisza and Landau; these are called *second sound*. Second sound may be compared with first sound in another way: in first sound, vibrations of normal and superfluid atoms *together* are propagated through a medium; whereas in second sound, vibrations of normal and superfluid atoms *relative to each other* are propagated.

First sound may be produced in liquid helium by a vibrating piston and, when so produced, is propagated with a speed w_1 in agreement with the laws of classical physics, except that $\gamma = 1$ and there are no temperature differences between compressions and rarefactions. The temperature variation of w_1 is shown in Fig. 15-6, where it may be seen that a striking discontinuity of slope occurs at the λ point.

Second sound may be produced by a temperature pulse or by periodic temperature fluctuations produced in a flat, disk-shaped heater by an appropriate electric current. This method is very simple but has the disadvantage of providing a continual supply of heat, which boils away the liquid helium. To avoid this, it has been found possible to generate second sound by variations in temperature of a paramagnetic salt produced by

Fig. 15-6   *Speed of first sound in liquid helium. (Van Itterbeck and Forrez, 1954.)*

superposing an alternating magnetic field on a steady field. Under these conditions, the temperature fluctuations are alternately above and below the ambient temperature, and there is no net input of heat.

The speed of second sound was first measured by Peshkov, and the most recent measurements are those of de Klerk, Hudson, and Pellam. In some of the measurements, stationary second-sound waves were set up in a cylindrical column of liquid helium II between two flat disks wound with resistance wire. An alternating electric current was used to produce the necessary temperature fluctuations in one disk, and the fluctuations in resistance produced by the temperature changes at the other disk served to detect the nodes or antinodes. In other measurements, a pulse of current in one disk caused a temperature pulse to be propagated along a cylindrical column, and the velocity of this pulse was measured with electronic techniques.

The mathematical expression for the speed of second sound may be derived in a simple manner from the laws of thermodynamics, by making use of the two-fluid model. Consider a column of liquid helium II indefinitely long, of cross-sectional area A, and at temperature T. Suppose that heat Q is supplied at one end by a source at temperature $T + \Delta T$ for a time τ. Both ΔT and τ may be chosen arbitrarily small. The temperature rise ΔT will be propagated along the column with a speed w_2, the speed of second sound. It is assumed that the propagation takes place without dispersion and without attenuation. In time τ, a column of length $w_2\tau$ and of volume $w_2\tau A$ will be affected. This volume of fluid, which we shall call the *system*, is shown as the shaded region in Fig. 15-7.

The system differs from the rest of the liquid helium not only in temperature but also in the motions of the normal and superfluid atoms. The normal atoms have a velocity v_n in the direction of propagation, and the superfluid atoms have a velocity v_s in the opposite direction. The total momentum per unit volume is $\rho_n v_n + \rho_s v_s$, where ρ_n and ρ_s are the densities of normal and superfluid atoms, respectively, the total density ρ being equal to $\rho_n + \rho_s$. In the propagation of second sound, the total momentum per unit volume is zero, in contrast with that of first sound.

Fig. 15-7   *Propagation of a second-sound pulse in liquid helium II.*

If H is the heat necessary to increase the temperature of the system by ΔT, then

$$H = \rho c w_2 \tau A \, \Delta T, \qquad (15\text{-}5)$$

where c is the specific heat capacity of the system. If, after the time interval τ, the heat source is turned off, the region of elevated temperature and relative motion of normal and superfluid atoms appears successively at neighboring points in the fluid, and thus is propagated with a speed w_2. The energy H disappears at one place and appears at another. We may therefore speak of a *heat current*, but this should not be confused with a convection or conduction current. The heat H produces a slight increase in the number of normal atoms and a consequent slight decrease in the number of superfluid atoms. The expression might therefore with more reason be called an *excitation-energy current*.

The contribution to the entropy change of the system due to the increase of temperature is

$$
\begin{aligned}
\Delta S &= \rho c w_2 \tau A \int_T^{T+\Delta T} \frac{dT}{T}, \\
&= \rho c w_2 \tau A \ln\left(1 + \frac{\Delta T}{T}\right) = \rho c w_2 \tau A \left[\frac{\Delta T}{T} - \frac{1}{2}\left(\frac{\Delta T}{T}\right)^2\right] \\
&= \frac{H}{T}\left(1 - \frac{1}{2}\frac{\Delta T}{T}\right).
\end{aligned}
\qquad (15\text{-}6)
$$

Since this amount of entropy crosses area A in time τ, the *entropy current density* is $H/T\tau A$, correct to the first order in $\Delta T/T$. According to the two-fluid model, this entropy is carried by the normal atoms only, the superfluid atoms being assumed to possess zero entropy, referred to a standard state at absolute zero. Since the normal atoms, of density ρ_n, move with speed v_n and possess entropy per unit mass s_n, the entropy current density is given by $\rho_n s_n v_n$. But $\rho s = \rho_n s_n$, since $s_s = 0$, and hence the entropy current density is equal to $\rho s v_n$, or

$$H = \rho s v_n \tau A T. \qquad (15\text{-}7)$$

From Eqs. (15-5) and (15-7), it follows that

$$\frac{\Delta T}{T} = \frac{s v_n}{c w_2},$$

and

$$\boxed{H \frac{\Delta T}{T} = \frac{\rho s^2 v_n^2 \tau A T}{c w_2}.} \qquad (15\text{-}8)$$

The kinetic energy K of the system may be calculated as follows:

$$\frac{K}{w_2 \tau A} = \tfrac{1}{2}\rho v_n^2 + \tfrac{1}{2}\rho_s v_s^2.$$

But

$$\rho_n v_n + \rho_s v_s = 0,$$

or

$$v_s = -\frac{\rho_n}{\rho_s} v_n;$$

whence

$$\frac{K}{w_2 \tau A} = \tfrac{1}{2}\rho_n \left(1 + \frac{\rho_n}{\rho_s}\right) v_n^2 = \tfrac{1}{2}\rho \frac{\rho_n}{\rho_s} v_n^2,$$

and

$$\boxed{K = \tfrac{1}{2}\rho \frac{\rho_n}{\rho_s} v_n^2 w_2 \tau A.} \tag{15-9}$$

If the source is turned off after time τ, this kinetic energy travels through the liquid without dissipation. Thus, at any moment, there exists a quantity of liquid of volume $w_2 \tau A$ with excitation energy per unit volume $H/w_2 \tau A = \rho c \, \Delta T$, and with kinetic energy per unit volume $K/w_2 \tau A = \tfrac{1}{2}\rho\rho_n v_n^2 / \rho_s$. *Neither energy is transformed into the other; both coexist and remain constant in time as they proceed through the liquid.*

To derive an expression for the speed of second sound, it is merely necessary to find a relation between $H \, \Delta T/T$ and K. Let Q be the heat leaving the source at $T + \Delta T$; H be the heat necessary to raise the system in temperature by ΔT; and K be the kinetic energy of the system. Then, from the first law of thermodynamics,

$$Q = H + K.$$

The entropy change of the source is

$$-\frac{Q}{T + \Delta T}.$$

The entropy change of the system due to the temperature rise has already been shown to be

$$\frac{H}{T}\left(1 - \frac{1}{2}\frac{\Delta T}{T}\right).$$

Assuming, as usual, that the process is reversible, the total entropy change of the universe is zero; whence

$$-\frac{Q}{T + \Delta T} + \frac{H}{T}\left(1 - \frac{1}{2}\frac{\Delta T}{T}\right) = 0.$$

Substituting for Q its value given by the first law, we get

$$-\frac{H}{T+\Delta T} - \frac{K}{T+\Delta T} + \frac{H}{T}\left(1 - \frac{1}{2}\frac{\Delta T}{T}\right) = 0.$$

This gives

$$\frac{1}{2}\frac{H\,\Delta T}{T^2} - \frac{K}{T} = 0,$$

or

$$H\frac{\Delta T}{T} = 2K. \tag{15-10}$$

Substituting the results of Eqs. (15-8) and (15-9) into Eq. (15-10), we get

$$\frac{\rho s^2 v_n^2 \tau AT}{cw_2} = \rho\,\frac{\rho_n}{\rho_s}\,v_n^2 w_2 \tau A,$$

or

$$\boxed{w_2 = \sqrt{\frac{\rho_s}{\rho_n}\frac{s^2 T}{c}}\,,} \tag{15-11}$$

which is the equation for the speed of second sound.

The temperature variation of the speed of second sound is shown in Fig. 15-8. Above 1°K, the speed remains fairly constant at a value of about 18 m/s until almost 2°K. It then decreases to zero at the λ point. As the tem-

Fig. 15-8 *Temperature dependence of the speed of second sound in liquid helium II. (De Klerk, Hudson, and Pellam, 1954.)*

perature goes below 0.6°K, it is seen that the speed of second sound, like other properties of liquid helium II, undergoes a change of slope.

Using the equation for the speed of second sound in conjunction with experimental measurements of w_2, c, and s, de Klerk, Hudson, and Pellam calculated the temperature variation of ρ_n/ρ, and it is these values which are plotted in Fig. 15-2.

15-4   Fourth Sound

In first sound, normal and superfluid atoms vibrate together, and the propagation of these vibrations involves pressure and density variations but no temperature variations. In second sound, the normal and superfluid atoms vibrate with respect to each other, and in the propagation of such vibrations there occur variations of temperature but not of pressure or of density. In 1948, J. R. Pellam suggested that liquid helium II might support a wave in which only the superfluid atoms undergo vibrations, the normal atoms being immobilized in the narrow spaces of a porous material. In 1959, Atkins came to the same conclusion and called this type of wave motion *fourth sound*. (Third sound will be discussed in the next section.) When the normal atoms are free to move, both first and second sound exist. When the normal atoms are damped, first sound degenerates into fourth sound, whereas second sound fails to propagate.

In the experiments of I. Rudnick and K. A. Shapiro, a resonator was filled with densely packed porous material having channels of less than 0.03 mm in diameter for frequencies less than 10 kHz. For this purpose, Polypore filter paper and Cr_2O_3 ("green rouge") were used. The results are shown in Fig. 15-9, where the speed of fourth sound is seen to lie within the limits of first and second sound. The speed of fourth sound is given with sufficient accuracy by the equation

$$w_4 = \left(\frac{\rho_s}{\rho} w_1^2 + \frac{\rho_n}{\rho} w_2^2 \right)^{\frac{1}{2}}. \tag{15-12}$$

15-5   Creeping Film; Third Sound

It was observed by Kamerlingh-Onnes, in 1922, that the levels of liquid helium II in two concentric vessels placed one within the other soon became equalized without there being any opening or communicating tube between the two vessels. Rollin, in 1936, showed that this phenomenon was due to a thin film which formed on any solid surface placed in liquid helium II.

Fig. 15-9   *Speed of first, second, and fourth sound in liquid helium II.* (*I. Rudnick and K. A. Shapiro, 1964.*)

The film creeps with a definite critical velocity, without friction, from the higher to the lower level, as shown in Fig. 15-10a to c. Starting with the pioneer experiments of Daunt and Mendelssohn in England and of Kikoin and Lasarew in Russia, a tremendous amount of ingenuity, skill, and energy has been displayed by many physicists in devising and carrying out experi-

$$(a) \qquad\qquad (b) \qquad\qquad (c)$$

Fig. 15-10   *Filling and emptying of a vessel by a creeping film of liquid helium II.*

ments on helium films. Unlike the fountain effect and second sound, where a combination of the two-fluid picture of liquid helium II and thermodynamics enables one to calculate simple equations that are found to agree with experiment, there is no theoretical derivation of an equation for the rate of flow of liquid by film transport, and *no two experiments agree* concerning the dependence of flow rate on, for example, (1) difference of level, (2) depth of the source level from the top of the beaker over which the film is creeping, (3) temperature, (4) material and smoothness of the creep surface, (5) existence of possible temperature differences, (6) method of filling or emptying one of the vessels, and (7) effect of radiation.

The most recent series of experiments on rate of film creep, conducted under carefully controlled conditions in which purity and uniformity of temperature were emphasized, was carried out in 1965 by R. W. Selden, J. H. Werntz, P. J. Fleming, and J. R. Dillinger in Wisconsin. They used five slightly different experimental systems, all variations of the system shown symbolically in Fig. 15-11. All glass surfaces over which the film could creep constituted one side of a thin wall, the other side of which was in contact with liquid helium in which temperature differences could be kept down to about 10^{-6} deg. Measurements were made of the rate of flow R of volume per unit length of periphery, as a function of the level difference ΔH for different temperatures and different values of H, both when filling and while emptying. A few of the results are shown in Fig. 15-12, where it may be seen that filling rates are different from emptying rates and that both are dependent on ΔH, but not in a simple linear manner. The only agreement among different experimenters is that the rate of film transfer is zero at the lambda point and increases as T decreases, assuming values somewhere between about 6×10^{-5} and 15×10^{-5} cm³/s · cm. Everyone is also in agreement with the excellent measurements of L. C. Jackson, establishing that the thickness of a helium film is of the order of 10^{-6} cm, or about 100 atoms thick, and decreases the farther the film is from the liquid level.

In 1959, Atkins predicted the existence of a surface wave on a liquid helium film and called such a wave *third sound*. He assumed that the superfluid

Fig. 15-11   *Symbolic sketch of apparatus of Selden, Werntz, Fleming, and Dillinger (1965) to study film transfer rates.*

Fig. 15-12   *A few of the experimental results of Selden, Werntz, Fleming, and Dillinger on film flow. (Solid curves 1, 2, and 3 refer to filling at temperatures 1.479, 1.441, and 1.481°K, respectively. Dashed curves 1, 2, and 3 refer to emptying.)*

component oscillates, while the normal component remains locked to the wall. The result is an oscillation in the thickness of the film with secondary variations in pressure and temperature. The phenomenon is somewhat similar to classical shallow-water waves. Third sound was produced and detected by C. W. F. Everitt, K. R. Atkins, and A. Denenstein in 1962 and was studied again in 1964. It was excited in a horizontal film of liquid helium II by pulses of infrared radiation and was detected by measuring the variations in film thickness by the same optical method that had been employed by Jackson to measure the thickness of static films. The speed of third sound was found to be in the range of 20 to 500 cm/s, depending mostly on the height y of the film above the bulk liquid. The experimental results seemed to be in fair agreement with a simplified theoretical equation

$$w_3^2 = 3(\rho_s/\rho)a_g y, \tag{15-13}$$

where a_g is the acceleration of gravity.

15-6   Other Effects of Superfluidity

The fountain effect and the propagation of second sound are outstanding *thermal* effects of superfluidity. Film creep, on the other hand, is concerned more with the hydrodynamics of the superfluid component in liquid helium and is therefore not of primary interest in a text devoted to the subject of heat. Since a small amount of space had been devoted to film creep, however, the other hydrodynamic effects should at least be mentioned for perhaps two reasons: (1) they provide examples of quantum effects on a macroscopic level, and (2) they have exact analogs in some of the properties of superconductors to be studied in the remainder of this chapter.

1. *Persistent flow*   Suppose that a thin-walled glass container, packed with a fine powder whose particles are of the order of 10^{-3} mm in size, is filled with liquid helium II and is then raised in temperature above the lambda point. If at this temperature the container (1) is given an angular momentum and (2) is then cooled below the lambda point—say, to about $1°K$, where the ratio of superfluid density ρ_s to the total density ρ is almost unity—and if, finally, (3) the rotation is stopped, experiment shows that superfluid flow persists. Increasing the temperature to within a millidegree of the lambda point causes a corresponding decrease in angular momentum, which comes back reversibly to its former value, however, when the original ratio of ρ_s/ρ is restored. Experiments of this sort, or similar in principle, go back as far as 1950 and are associated with some of the great pioneers in low-temperature physics: D. V. Osborne, C. T. Lane, and E. L. Andronikashvilli. The results shown in Fig. 15-13 were obtained in 1965 by J. B. Mehl and

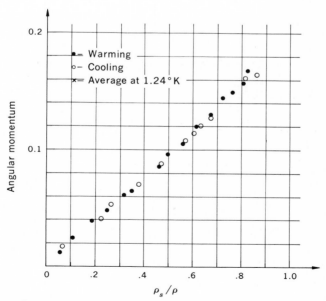

Fig. 15-13   *Proportionality between angular momentum of persisting flow and superfluid density. (J. B. Mehl and W. Zimmerman, 1965.)*

W. Zimmerman, who found that the helium current persisted for 5 hr without any measurable reduction in angular momentum. An undiminished circulation of superfluid helium in a container is like a large atom with its circulating electrons. A better parallel, however, is the persistent electric current in a superconductor.

2. *Quantized vortex lines and rings*   When a solid cylinder rotates about its axis of symmetry, the linear speed of a point v is directly proportional to the distance r from the point to the axis, according to the elementary relation $v = \omega r$. When water is draining out of a sink through a hole in the center, the water rotates in a manner which is quite different and which is known as *irrotational*, where

$$v = \frac{K}{r},$$

where K is constant. Since v cannot be infinite, r must have a minimum size, say, a. A cylinder, such as that shown in Fig. 15-14a, of outer radius R and inner radius a, whose particles move in circles with speeds such that

$$v = \frac{K}{r} \qquad \text{(for } a < r < R)$$

and
$$v = 0 \qquad \text{(for } r < a),$$
(15-14)

constitutes a *vortex line*. If the vortex line is bent so as to form a complete

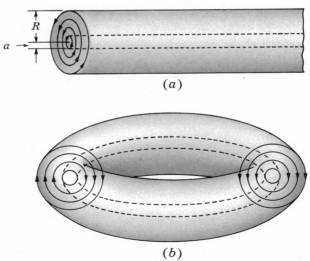

(a)

(b)

Fig. 15-14   (a) *Vortex line.* (b) *Vortex ring.*

circle (a torus or doughnut), the system is known as a *vortex ring*, as shown in Fig. 15-14*b*.

It was first suggested by Onsager, and later substantiated by Feynman, that vortices should exist in superfluid helium, satisfying the Bohr-Sommerfeld quantum condition

$$\oint p_s \, ds = nh, \tag{15-15}$$

where p_s is the tangential momentum of a helium atom of magnitude mv, ds is an element of its circular path, and n is a quantum number that may take on integer values. This becomes

$$mv \oint ds = nh,$$

or
$$v = \frac{nh}{2\pi m} \frac{1}{r}, \tag{15-16}$$

satisfying Eq. (15-14), with $K = nh/2\pi m$. If $n = 1$, $2\pi K$ has its smallest value:

$$2\pi K \ (n = 1) = \frac{h}{m} = \frac{6.63 \times 10^{-27} \text{ erg} \cdot \text{s}}{6.67 \times 10^{-24} \text{ g}},$$
$$= 0.997 \times 10^{-3} \text{ cm}^2/\text{sec}. \tag{15-17}$$

The first attempt to look for such vortices in superfluid helium was made in 1961 by W. F. Vinen, who used a fine wire stretched along the axis of a cylindrical vessel containing liquid helium II. He reasoned that, when the system is set in rotation, a vortex line should be set up around the wire which should affect its frequency of transverse vibration. Vinen's experiment was reasonably successful and was followed by a number of researches involving different methods of measurement. The beautiful experiments of G. W. Rayfield and F. Reif in California and of G. Careri, S. Cunsolo, P. Mazzoldi, and M. Santini in Rome involved the motion of positive and negative helium ions through superfluid helium.

Rayfield and Reif were able to show that a positive or negative helium ion is quickly surrounded by many helium atoms in the form of a vortex ring and that such rings move through superfluid helium with almost frictionless motion at a temperature of 0.28°K. The quantity R in Fig. 15-14 was taken to be the radius of the ring itself, in which case the value of v at $r = R$ is the velocity of the vortex ring perpendicular to its plane. Classical hydrodynamics provides the following equations for the energy E and velocity v of a vortex ring, whose radius R is much greater than a, moving through a medium of

Fig. 15-15   *Relation between velocity v and energy E of a vortex ring. The points are experimental data for positive and negative charge carriers. The curve is the theoretical relation predicted by Eqs. (15-18) and (15-19). (G. W. Rayfield and F. Reif, 1963.)*

density ρ:

$$E = \tfrac{1}{2}\rho(2\pi K)^2 R \left(\ln \frac{8R}{a} - \frac{7}{4} \right), \qquad (15\text{-}18)$$

and
$$v = \frac{K}{2R} \left(\ln \frac{8R}{a} - \frac{1}{4} \right). \qquad (15\text{-}19)$$

Rayfield and Reif measured v as a function of E for both positive and negative ions and obtained the experimental points shown in Fig. 15-15. The curve is the theoretical relation obtained by combining Eqs. (15-18) and (15-19), and the agreement is remarkable. The experiments gave the values

$$2\pi K = 1.00 \times 10^{-3} \ \text{cm}^2/\text{s},$$

corresponding to $n = 1$, and

$$a = 1.28 \ \overset{\circ}{\text{A}},$$

which is of the order of atomic dimensions.

15-7   Motion of He³ through Superfluid He⁴

The phase diagram of He³ (Fig. 12-31) shows that there is only one liquid phase. Many attempts have been made to discover a new phase at very low temperatures and to detect superfluidity in this or any other liquid phase. Up to 1968, all such attempts have met with failure at all temperatures down to about 1 mdeg. Liquid He³, however, may be dissolved in liquid He⁴, and the study of such solutions has led to some very interesting and useful effects, as seen in the following examples: (1) When He³ is dissolved in He⁴, heat is absorbed; and when the process takes place adiabatically, the system cools. (2) If heat is applied to the solution at a temperature (say, 0.6°K) at which the vapor pressure of He⁴ is less than 0.001 mm, the dissolved He³ will vaporize out of the solution, because the He³ vapor pressure is 0.6 mm. (3) *If a solution of He³ is lowered in temperature below* 0.87°K, *the solution will separate into two phases* with a distinct boundary—one phase a concentrated solution (of He³ in He⁴) and a *denser* phase, a dilute solution (G. K. Walters and

Fig. 15-16   *"Harwell" He³-He⁴ dilution refrigerator.*

W. M. Fairbank, 1956). (4) He^3 atoms diffuse through superfluid He^4 from one place to another where the concentration of He^3 is smaller.

An ingenious refrigeration cycle was developed by Hall, Ford, and Thompson and independently by Neganov, Borisov, and Liburg in 1965; this is now used in an actual refrigerator, built by the Oxford Instrument Company in England. The refrigerator is capable of maintaining the temperature of an experimental space at about $0.1°K$, with a refrigerating capacity of about 20 ergs/s, by circulating 2×10^{-5} moles of He^3 per second. A symbolic diagram of the apparatus is shown in Fig. 15-16. Let us assume that the apparatus has been running for sufficient time to establish a steady state, with the He^4 bath at $1.3°K$, the evaporator at $0.6°K$, and the dilution chamber at about $0.1°K$. The pump delivers pure He^3 (point a), which on its way to point b is cooled to almost $0.1°K$. It enters the concentrated solution at point c, and then some of it crosses the phase boundary into the dilute solution at d. Both the solution $b \rightarrow c$ and the phase separation $c \rightarrow d$ involve the absorption of heat from the materials in the space surrounding the dilution chamber. The He^3 then moves through He^4 from d to e, where heat is supplied to vaporize the He^3 at a pressure of about 0.02 mm. A pump finally brings the He^3 back to its original pressure at a.

15-8   Superconducting Transition Temperature

As the temperature is reduced, the electrical resistance of many metals decreases until a residual value is reached. Further reduction of temperature, even to the millidegree range, often shows no further change of resistance. About half the metals, however, exhibit a most extraordinary behavior known as *superconductivity:* that is, after the residual value of the resistance has been reached and the temperature is further reduced, the resistance suddenly drops to zero. Superconductivity has been found in 26 metallic elements (in bulk, at atmospheric pressure or lower) and in well over a thousand alloys and compounds. The transition from normal resistance to zero resistance in the case of pure, strain-free metals (often single crystals) takes place in a very narrow temperature interval, about 10 mdeg or less; hence the *transition temperature* T_C can be measured with accuracy. If the resistance-vs.-temperature curve shows a more gradual decrease from normal to zero resistance, the transition temperature is taken to be the temperature of the midpoint of the curve.

Values of T_C are printed below the chemical symbol for each superconducting element in the periodic table shown in Fig. 15-17. It is an interesting fact that, until the present time, superconductivity has never been observed in the alkali metals, the alkaline earth metals, or the noble metals. It is seen

3 Li	4 Be					Simple metals				5 B	6 C	7 N	8 O	9 F	10 Ne
11 Na	12 Mg		Transition metals			Noble metals				13 Al 1.18	14 Si	15 P	16 S	17 Cl	18 A
19 K	20 Ca	21 Sc	22 Ti 0.39	23 V 5.30	24 Cr	25 Mn	26 Fe	27 Co	28 Ni	29 Cu	30 Zn 0.88	31 Ga 1.09	32 Ge	33 As	34 Se	35 Br	36 Kr
37 Rb	38 Sr	39 Y	40 Zr 0.49	41 Nb 9.20	42 Mo 0.95	43 Tc 8.22	44 Ru 0.47	45 Rh	46 Pd	47 Ag	48 Cd 0.56	49 In 3.40	50 Sn 3.72	51 Sb	52 Te	53 I	54 Xe
55 Cs	56 Ba	57 La 4.87 6.00	72 Hf 0.17	73 Ta 4.48	74 W 0.012	75 Re 1.70	76 Os 0.67	77 Ir 0.14	78 Pt	79 Au	80 Hg 4.15 3.95	81 Tl 2.39	82 Pb 7.19	83 Bi	84 Po	85 At	86 Rn
87 Fr	88 Ra	89 Ac	90 Th 1.37	91 Pa 1.4	92 U 1.8	93 Np	94 Pu	95 Am	96 Cm	97 Bk	98 Cf	99 Es	100 Fm	101 Md	102 No	

Fig. 15-17 *Positions of superconducting elements in periodic table; transition temperatures*

in Fig. 15-17 that superconductivity is confined to the simple metals and the transition metals. There are no superconductors with only one valence electron, and there is also none with six valence electrons.

When alloys of superconducting elements are formed, the values of T_C often lie between those of the separate components, as with Mo and Nb on the left of Fig. 15-18. The reverse may also occur, however, as shown on the right side of Fig. 15-18, where an alloy of 70 percent Mo and 30 percent Re has a T_C of 11°K, although neither constituent has a T_C above 2°K. The largest values of T_C have been obtained by forming compounds of Nb with other metals: for example, 20.1°K for a compound of Nb, Al, and Ge; 18.07°K for Nb_3Sn; 18.0°K for Nb_3Al; 17.91°K for NbSn. Some of the most peculiar superconductors are compounds in which *none* of the elements is a superconductor, including Bi_3Sr (5.62°K), Ge_2Sc (1.30°K), PtSb (2.1°K), $RhTe_2$ (1.51°K), and many others. Many of the superconducting alloys and compounds have been planned, caused to be made, and studied by B. Matthias at the Bell Telephone Laboratories. It is his contention that, someday, every metal will be found to be superconducting, provided that it is sufficiently pure and the temperature is low enough.

One of the first attempts to apply modern quantum theory to the problem of superconductivity was made in 1950 by H. Fröhlich, who for the first time took into account the interaction between the free electrons and the lattice,

Fig. 15-18 *Superconducting transition temperatures of alloys of Nb and Mo and of Re and Mo. (B. T. Matthias, 1963.)*

instead of limiting himself to the electrons only. Although a complete theory could not be formulated at that time, one result that was obtained created great interest: namely, that the transition temperatures of the various isotopes of an element should vary inversely as the square root of the isotopic mass $\mathscr{M}$; thus,

$$T_C \propto \mathscr{M}^\alpha, \qquad\qquad (15\text{-}20)$$

Fig. 15-19 *Log-log plots showing (a) that $\alpha = -\frac{1}{2}$ for Sn isotopes; (b) that $\alpha = -\frac{1}{3}$ for Mo isotopes. (T. H. Geballe and B. T. Matthias, 1963.)*

with $\alpha = -\frac{1}{2}$. The measurements made in the 1950s on Sn, Hg, Tl, and Pb agreed quite well with Fröhlich's equation, but recent measurements on Mo, Re, and Os give α values much less than $-\frac{1}{2}$, and Zr and Ru show no isotope effect at all. Experimental results for Sn and Mo are shown in Fig. 15-19, and other results are listed in Table 15-1. Recently, it was shown that α for the uranium isotopes is $+2$.

Table 15-1   Isotope Effect and Pressure Effect of Superconducting Elements

Element	Isotope effect α	$\partial T_C/\partial P$, μdeg/atm	Element	Isotope effect α	$\partial T_C/\partial P$ μdeg/atm
13 Al		-29	73 Ta		$-\ 2.6$
30 Zn	-0.5	-16	75 Re	-0.38	0
31 Ga		-18	76 Os	-0.21	$-\ 1.8$
40 Zr	0	$+15$	80 Hg(α)	-0.5	$-\ 37$
42 Mo	-0.34	$-\ 1$	81 Tl	-0.5	$+\ 23$
44 Ru	0	$-\ 3$	82 Pb	-0.5	$-\ 38$
48 Cd	-0.40	-20	90 Th		$-\ 17$
49 In		-43	92 U	$+2$	$+130$
50 Sn	-0.5	-46			

The superconducting transition temperature depends also on pressure, as shown for three superconducting compounds in Fig. 15-20a. In most cases, an increase of pressure causes a decrease in T_C; but with Tl and U the reverse is true, as is shown in Table 15-1. In this table it may also be seen that there is a large pressure effect when the isotope exponent is $\frac{1}{2}$, but in four cases where α is much less than $\frac{1}{2}$ (Mo, Ru, Re, and Os) the pressure effect is either small or zero. It is not certain whether this is a real correlation or not.

The superconducting transition temperature of a thin film is different from that of the bulk metal, as shown in Fig. 15-20b, where the T_C of a Pb film is seen to decrease as the film thickness decreases. So profound are the effects of film thickness and of pressure that some non-superconductors become superconducting when formed into a film (Be, 7°K; Ge, 8.4°K; Bi, 6°K), and others when the pressure is raised to thousands of atmospheres (Se, 6.8°K; Te, 3.3°K; Bi, 6°K).

Besides strains and impurities, there is one more condition that affects the superconducting transition temperature, namely, the electrostatic charge on the metal. This effect has not been studied extensively, but it has been found to be reversible. If the addition of a charge has raised the temperature by ΔT_C, then the removal of this charge will bring T_C back to its original value.

Fig. 15-20   (a) *Decrease of transition temperature with hydrostatic pressure. (C. B. Muller and E. J. Saur, 1964.)* (b) *Transition temperatures of lead films superimposed on thick copper films. (P. Hilsch, R. Hilsch, and G. v. Minnigerode, 1963.)*

15-9   Magnetic Properties of Type I Superconductors

Of the 26 elements shown in the periodic table of Fig. 15-17, which become superconducting without being subjected to a high pressure or deposited as a thin film, the 9 simple metals on the right side of the table are of particular interest. Because these have low melting points and are physically soft, they are labeled *soft superconductors*. Suppose that a soft superconductor is made in the form of a cylinder about ten times as long as its diameter, is placed in a magnetic field longitudinally, and is kept at a constant temperature less than T_C. If the field starts at zero intensity and is then increased, the metal will remain superconducting until a *critical field* $\mathcal{H}_C$ is reached, at which point it will become normal. The transition from the superconducting state to the normal state covers a very narrow range of $\mathcal{H}$ and may be said to occur *at* the value $\mathcal{H}_C$. Furthermore, if $\mathcal{H}$ is now reduced, the transition to superconductivity takes place at the same value $\mathcal{H}_C$.

The magnitude of the critical field required to destroy superconductivity depends only on the temperature. Thus $\mathcal{H}_C$ is a function of T only and is shown in Fig. 15-21. It should be noticed that each $\mathcal{H}_C$-vs.-T curve divides the $\mathcal{H}T$ plane into two regions, superconducting and normal, like a phase-transition curve on a PT diagram. All curves show the following properties: (1) the slope is always negative; (2) the slope at the point $T = T_C$ ($\mathcal{H}_C = 0$)

is *finite;* (3) the slope at $T = 0$, by extrapolation, is zero. The relation between critical field and temperature for the soft superconductors is almost parabolic. That is, to a first approximation,

$$\mathscr{H}_C = \mathscr{H}_0 \left(1 - \frac{T^2}{T_C^2} \right), \tag{15-21}$$

where $\mathscr{H}_0$ is the critical field at absolute zero. Only when great accuracy is desired is it necessary to take into account departures from this simple parabolic relation. Values of T_C, $\mathscr{H}_0$, and the slope $d\mathscr{H}_C/dT$ at $T = T_C$ are given in Table 15-2, along with some of the thermal properties of soft superconductors.

A simple relation between $\mathscr{H}_0$ and T_C was discovered by H. W. Lewis in 1956 not only for the soft superconductors but also for some compounds that, like the soft superconductors, do not have a partly filled d or f shell. The line plotted in Fig. 15-22 shows that, for these superconductors, $\mathscr{H}_0 \propto T_C^{1.3}$.

Fig. 15-21   *Threshold field vs. temperature for eight soft superconductors and for three superconducting transition metals.*

Table 15-2   Properties of the Soft Superconductors

Metal	T_c, °K	$\mathcal{H}_0$, Oe	$\left(\dfrac{d\mathcal{H}_c}{dT}\right)_{T=T_c}$, Oe/deg	Θ, °K	γ', mJ/mole · deg²	v, cm³/mole
13 Al	1.175	105	−158	428	1.35	9.93
30 Zn	0.88	53	−121	310	0.65	9.20
31 Ga	1.09	51	− 93	320	0.60	11.8
48 Cd	0.56	30	− 86	209	0.69	13.0
49 In	3.41	283	−156	108	1.66	15.4
50 Sn	3.72	306	−147	199	1.78	16.1
80 Hg	$\begin{cases} 4.15(\alpha) \\ 3.95(\beta) \end{cases}$	411 / 339	−194	72	1.81	13.8
81 Tl	2.39	171	−126	79	1.5	17.3
82 Pb	7.19	803	−226	105	3.0	18.3

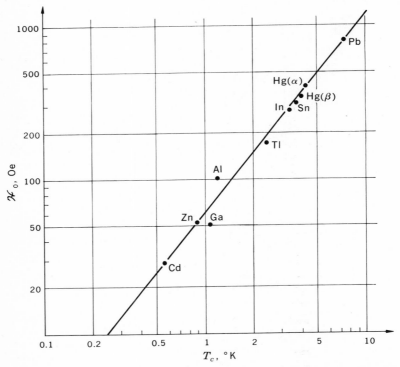

Fig. 15-22 $\mathcal{H}_0 \propto T_c^{1.3}$ for soft superconductors that do not have a partly filled d or f shell. (H. W. Lewis, 1956.)

The remaining seventeen superconducting transition metals, if made very pure and free of strain and preferably in the form of single crystals, also show properties similar to those of the soft superconductors, although their values of $\mathcal{H}_0$ and T_C do not satisfy the simple relation that $\mathcal{H}_0 \propto T_C^{1.3}$. There are other properties that will be described later, such as coherence length and penetration depth, which these two sets of superconductors have in common, so that it is now the practice to refer to all such metals as *type I superconductors*. Magnetic and thermal properties of the superconducting transition metals are given in Table 15-3.

Table 15-3   **Properties of the Superconducting Transition Metals**

Metal	T_C, °K	$\mathcal{H}_0$, Oe	$\left(\dfrac{d\mathcal{H}_C}{dT}\right)_{T=T_C}$, Oe/deg	Θ, °K	γ', mJ/mole · deg²	v, cm³/mole
22 Ti	0.39	56	−300	420	3.5	10.6
23 V	5.30	1310	−482	380	9.8	8.39
40 Zr	0.49	47	−170	291	2.80	14.1
41 Nb	9.20	1985	−453	275	7.80	10.8
42 Mo	0.95	97	–	450	2.0	9.40
43 Tc	8.22	–	−350	–	–	8.6
44 Ru	0.47	66	−196	600	3.3	8.40
57 La	$\begin{cases}(\alpha)4.87\\(\beta)6.00\end{cases}$	789 1095	– –	152 140	9.4 11.5	22.4
72 Hf	0.165	–	–	252	2.16	13.5
73 Ta	4.48	830	−334	240	5.9	10.9
74 W	0.012	1.07	–	400	1.21	9.54
75 Re	1.70	201	−235	430	2.3	9.07
76 Os	0.67	80	−183	500	2.4	8.45
77 Ir	0.14	19	–	420	3.1	8.54
90 Th	1.37	162	–	170	4.7	19.8
91 Pa	1.4	–	–	–	–	15.0
92 U(γ)	1.8	∼2000	–	182	10.3	12.5

By forming alloys of type I superconductors, by forming compounds, by depositing as thin films, by introducing strains through cold-working, and by introducing impurities, superconductors with entirely different properties may be fabricated. Known as *type II superconductors*, these will be found to have great practical importance.

The zero electrical resistance of type I superconductors was discovered by Kamerlingh-Onnes in 1911. Applying Maxwell's electromagnetic equations to a material of infinite conductivity, it was concluded that a superconducting

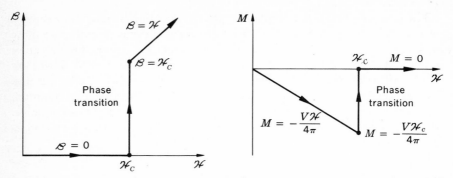

Fig. 15-23   *Behavior of magnetic induction $\mathcal{B}$ and magnetization M of a superconductor when the field is increased isothermally.*

metal, if placed in a weak magnetic field at room temperature and then cooled down below T_C *while still in the field,* would retain its magnetic flux as long as it was maintained at its low temperature. The argument based on classical electromagnetic theory was so convincing that no one checked the conclusion experimentally for twenty years. In 1931, Meissner cooled a superconductor in a weak magnetic field to a temperature below its T_C and discovered that, at the moment the metal became superconducting, all magnetic lines of force were expelled and *the magnetic induction $\mathcal{B}$ became zero.* This result is now known as the *Meissner effect,* and the property $\mathcal{B} = 0$ is considered to be just as fundamental as the property $R' = 0$. In fact, the most commonly used method of determining whether a material is superconducting and, if so, the value of T_C employs the change in self-inductance of a solenoid when the sample under investigation is located inside the coil. The solenoid is made part of a parallel resonant circuit that controls the frequency of an oscillator, and changes in frequency corresponding to changes in inductance create an "unbalance" in a bridge circuit, which then causes a signal to appear at the input to a detector. The detector amplifies this signal, and its output is plotted as a function of temperature to show the superconducting transition of the sample.

Suppose that a type I superconductor is made in the shape of a long thin cylinder and placed longitudinally in a magnetic field. The behavior of the magnetic induction $\mathcal{B}$ and the magnetization M, as the field is increased isothermally, is shown in Fig. 15-23. $\mathcal{H}_C$ is the critical field appropriate to the particular temperature chosen. It may be seen that, while the metal is superconducting, $\mathcal{B} = 0$; and since

$$\mathcal{B} = \mathcal{H} + 4\pi \frac{M}{V},$$

it follows that

$$M = -\frac{V\mathcal{H}}{4\pi}. \tag{15-22}$$

Beyond the critical field, however,

$$\mathcal{B} = \mathcal{H} \quad \text{and} \quad M = 0.$$

The fact that $\mathcal{B} = 0$ or $M = -V\mathcal{H}/4\pi$ means that a superconductor is a *perfect diamagnetic.*

The transition from superconductivity to normal conductivity at constant temperature T and at constant critical field $\mathcal{H}_c$, performed under the ideal circumstances just described, is a *phase transition*. Since experiment shows a latent heat, the transition is of the first order. If the magnetic Gibbs function is defined in the usual way, that is,

$$G^* = U - TS - \mathcal{H}M,$$

we get

$$dG^* = dU - T\,dS - \mathcal{H}\,dM - S\,dT - M\,d\mathcal{H}.$$

Since $T\,dS = dU - \mathcal{H}\,dM$, this reduces to

$$dG^* = -S\,dT - M\,d\mathcal{H}.$$

At constant T and $\mathcal{H}$, $dG^* = 0$ and

$$G^{*(s)} = G^{*(n)}$$

where the superscripts (s) and (n) stand for superconducting and normal phases, respectively. At a temperature $T + dT$ and a field $\mathcal{H}_c + d\mathcal{H}_c$,

$$G^{*(s)} + dG^{*(s)} = G^{*(n)} + dG^{*(n)}.$$

Therefore,

$$dG^{*(s)} = dG^{*(n)},$$

$$-S^{(s)}\,dT - M^{(s)}\,d\mathcal{H}_c = -S^{(n)}\,dT - M^{(n)}\,d\mathcal{H}_c,$$

and

$$-\frac{d\mathcal{H}_c}{dT} = \frac{S^{(n)} - S^{(s)}}{M^{(n)} - M^{(s)}}.$$

Since

$$M^{(n)} - M^{(s)} = 0 + \frac{V\mathcal{H}_c}{4\pi},$$

we get

$$-\frac{d\mathcal{H}_c}{dT} = 4\pi \frac{S^{(n)} - S^{(s)}}{V\mathcal{H}_c}. \tag{15-23}$$

The third law of thermodynamics requires that the entropy difference

$S^{(n)} - S^{(s)}$ vanish at absolute zero; therefore the slope $d\mathscr{H}_C/dT$ must be zero at $T = 0$.

Since $S^{(n)} - S^{(s)} = L/T$, where L is the latent heat, we get

$$L = - \frac{TV\mathscr{H}_C}{4\pi} \cdot \frac{d\mathscr{H}_C}{dT}. \tag{15-24}$$

This derivation is in all respects equivalent to the derivation of Clapeyron's equation. The value of $d\mathscr{H}_C/dT$ may be obtained from the $\mathscr{H}_C T$ curve, and hence L may be calculated. Values of L calculated in this way agree very well with those obtained calorimetrically. It is interesting that L vanishes at two extremes of temperature: namely, at $T = 0$, where $d\mathscr{H}_C/dT = 0$, and at $T = T_C$, where $\mathscr{H}_C = 0$.

Since the phase transition in zero field takes place with no latent heat, it is therefore a higher-order phase transition—one of three types depicted in Fig. 12-25. Heat-capacity measurements, to be treated in detail later, show that the transition is of the second order and may possibly be the *only* example of a transition of this type.

15-10   Heat Capacities of Type I Superconductors

The apparatus for measurement of the heat capacity of a superconducting substance differs from that for an ordinary substance only in the provision for a magnetic field to destroy superconductivity at temperatures below T_C. As a rule, the heat capacity is measured in the absence of a field at temperatures above and below T_C in order to show the transition at T_C as well as the temperature dependence below T_C. Then a field larger than $\mathscr{H}_0$ is applied, and the complete temperature dependence of the normal heat capacity is measured. Temperature is measured usually with a carbon or germanium resistance thermometer that is inserted into the sample, and heat is supplied by a momentary current in a heating coil wound around the sample. Resistance-vs.-time curves are plotted automatically on a recording instrument, and the data read from the records are fed into a computer.

A typical set of experimental results is shown in Fig. 15-24, where the measurements done for tin by Keesom and van Laer in 1938 are compared with those of Corak, Goodman, Satterthwaite, and Wexler in 1955. As is usual at low temperatures, $c_P = c_V = c$, and c/T is plotted against T^2 since, in the normal state, c in mJ/mole $\cdot$ deg^2 is given by Eq. (11-53),

$$c = \left(\frac{125}{\Theta}\right)^3 T^3 + \gamma' T.$$

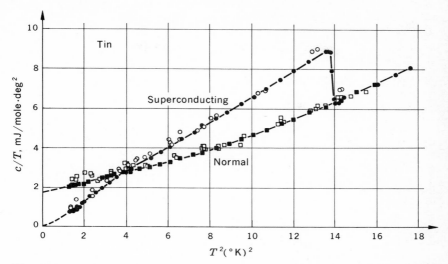

Fig. 15-24   *Measurements of heat capacity of tin by Keesom and van Laer, 1938 (open circles, super; open squares, normal), and by Corak, Goodman, Satterthwaite, and Wexler, 1956 (solid circles, super; solid squares, normal).*

Experimental curves of the same character are obtained for transition metals of great purity and freedom from strain, as shown by the results of H. A. Leupold and H. A. Boorse (1964) on a single crystal of Nb in Fig. 15-25. Values of the electronic constant γ' and the Debye Θ are listed in Tables 15-2 and 15-3.

The behavior of the heat capacity in the superconducting phase is entirely different from that in the normal phase as shown in Figs. 15-24 and 15-25. From these experimental graphs, it is possible to read values of $c^{(s)} - c^{(n)}$ that may be used in conjunction with simple thermodynamic equations, as follows.

It has been shown with the aid of the magnetic Gibbs function that, for a reversible transition from superconductivity to normal conductivity at temperature T and field $\mathscr{H} = \mathscr{H}_c$, an equation similar to Clapeyron's equation holds. Thus, from Eq. (15-23),

$$S^{(n)} - S^{(s)} = -\frac{V}{4\pi} \mathscr{H}_c \frac{d\mathscr{H}_c}{dT}.$$

Differentiating both sides with respect to T and multiplying by T, we get

$$T \frac{dS^{(n)}}{dT} - T \frac{dS^{(s)}}{dT} = -\frac{VT}{4\pi} \frac{d}{dT}\left(\mathscr{H}_c \frac{d\mathscr{H}_c}{dT}\right).$$

Fig. 15-25   *Normal and superconducting heat capacities of a single crystal of Nb. (H. A. Leupold and H. A. Boorse, 1964.)*

The terms on the left-hand side are heat capacities, so that for 1 mole of material

$$c^{(s)} - c^{(n)} = \frac{vT}{4\pi} \frac{d}{dT}\left(\mathcal{H}_c \frac{d\mathcal{H}_c}{dT}\right). \tag{15-25}$$

This is a very valuable equation, but it must be used with care. If calorimetric measurements are particularly difficult, as they are with mercury, it is necessary to use Eq. (15-25) in conjunction with magnetic measurements ($\mathcal{H}_c$ as a function of T) in order to find γ'. If the material is very pure and quite free from strain, the phase transition from superconductivity to normal conductivity may take place reversibly, and the equation may be used with confidence. It is difficult, however, to get some of the hard superconductors pure and strain-free. When this is the case and the measured values of $\mathcal{H}_c$ are introduced into Eq. (15-25), the calorimetric data so derived may be in error by a large factor.

Equation (15-25) may be used with more confidence to infer the magnetic properties of superconductors from calorimetric data. Thus, performing the differentiation indicated, we get

$$c^{(s)} - c^{(n)} = \frac{vT}{4\pi}\left(\frac{d\mathcal{H}_C}{dT}\right)^2 + \frac{vT}{4\pi}\mathcal{H}_C\frac{d^2\mathcal{H}_C}{dT^2}.$$

At $T = T_C$, $\mathcal{H}_C = 0$ and the second member on the right is zero. Thus,

$$\left(\frac{d\mathcal{H}_C}{dT}\right)_{T=T_C} = \sqrt{\frac{4\pi}{vT_C}(c^{(s)} - c^{(n)})_{T=T_C}}; \qquad (15\text{-}26)$$

and from this equation, known as the *Rutgers equation*, the slope of the $\mathcal{H}_C$-vs.-T curve at the transition temperature T_C may be found from calorimetric measurements.

Integrating Eq. (15-25) from $T = 0$ to $T = T_C$, we get

$$\int_0^{T_C}(c^{(s)} - c^{(n)})\,dT = \frac{v}{4\pi}\int_{\mathcal{H}_0}^0 T\,d\left(\mathcal{H}_C\frac{d\mathcal{H}_C}{dT}\right).$$

The right-hand member may be integrated by parts, with the result that

$$\int_0^{T_C}(c^{(s)} - c^{(n)})\,dT = \frac{v}{4\pi}T\mathcal{H}_C\frac{d\mathcal{H}_C}{dT}\Big]_0^{T_C} - \frac{v}{4\pi}\int_{\mathcal{H}_C}^0 \mathcal{H}_C\frac{d\mathcal{H}_C}{dT}\,dT.$$

The first term on the right vanishes at both the upper and lower limits, and the second term reduces to a simple integral; thus,

$$\int_0^{T_C}(c^{(s)} - c^{(n)})\,dT = \frac{v\mathcal{H}_0^2}{8\pi},$$

and
$$\mathcal{H}_0 = \sqrt{\frac{8\pi}{v}\int_0^{T_C}(c^{(s)} - c^{(n)})\,dT}. \qquad (15\text{-}27)$$

With tin and vanadium the values of $\mathcal{H}_0$, and indeed the entire $\mathcal{H}_C$-vs.-T curve calculated from calorimetric data, agree very well with purely magnetic measurements.

X-ray diffraction studies of the crystal lattice of a metal before and after the superconducting transition indicate no change in any property of the crystal lattice. It is therefore assumed that a superconducting metal has the same Debye Θ as in the normal phase. If we subtract the lattice heat capacity $(125/\Theta)^3 T^3$ from the superconducting heat capacity, therefore, we ought to

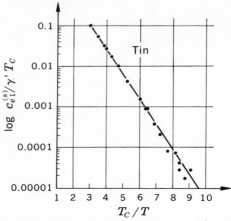

Fig. 15-26   *Superconducting electronic heat capacity of tin. (H. R. O'Neal and N. E. Phillips, 1965.)*

get a heat capacity associated with the superconducting electrons, $c_{el}^{(s)}$. Thus,

$$c_{el}^{(s)} = c^{(s)} - \left(\frac{125}{\Theta}\right)^3 T^3. \tag{15-28}$$

In Figs. 15-26 and 15-27, the logarithm of the ratio $c_{el}^{(s)}/\gamma' T_C$ is plotted against T_C/T. Many of the experimental points lie on a straight line, indicating that the electronic contribution to the superconducting heat capacity obeys the

Fig. 15-27   *Superconducting electronic heat capacity of niobium. (H. A. Leupold and H. A. Boorse, 1964.)*

equation

$$\frac{c_{el}^{(s)}}{\gamma' T_C} = ae^{-bT_c/T},\tag{15-29}$$

approximately. This behavior has been observed for many type I superconductors and has an important theoretical significance in terms of an *energy gap*, as we shall see in the next section.

15-11   Energy Gap

Many of the properties of superfluid helium were adequately described by the two-fluid model, in which He^4 below the λ point was imagined to consist of a mixture of normal atoms and superfluid atoms with densities ρ_n and ρ_s, respectively. As the temperature was reduced, normal atoms underwent a type of "condensation" and became superfluid. Conversely, the absorption of heat provided the energy to raise superfluid atoms to the normal state, as well as to raise the temperature. These picturesque ideas are legitimate interpretations of the rigorous statements and equations of quantum statistical mechanics. A similar situation exists with regard to superconductivity. The free electrons in a superconducting metal below T_C were imagined by Gorter and Casimir, in 1934, to be a mixture of normal electrons and superconducting electrons. As the temperature was reduced, normal electrons underwent a type of condensation and became superconducting. Absorption of heat was needed to raise the energy of the superconducting electrons to the normal state as well as to raise the temperature. To account for persisting electric currents in superconductors, F. London and H. London in 1935 made additions to Maxwell's equations, which in conjunction with the two-fluid model of Gorter and Casimir enabled the description of existing phenomena of superconductivity and suggested further experiments leading to other phenomena.

Valuable as they have been and are, two-fluid models of superfluidity and of superconductivity cannot, however, be regarded as physical theories. No adequate *microscopic* theory of superconductivity based on quantum ideas was developed until 1957, forty-six years after the discovery of superconductivity, when J. Bardeen, L. N. Cooper, and J. R. Schrieffer succeeded in applying quantum mechanics to the behavior of free electrons in a crystal lattice. If the free electrons are regarded as an ideal gas obeying the Fermi-Dirac statistics, only repulsive forces are taken into account, and the behavior and properties of the lattice are ignored. Under these circumstances, it would be quite impossible to account for the isotope effect or the heat-capacity results.

It was pointed out by Cooper, however, that the presence of an electron in a lattice of positive ions gives rise to a slight distortion of the lattice, which may be described as a slight crowding of positive ions. This clump of positive ions then serves to attract another electron, so that attractive forces among electrons may be deduced. The attractive force produced by lattice interaction can take place over a distance of as much as 10^{-4} cm, in agreement with an idea previously postulated by A. B. Pippard, namely, that the phenomenon of superconductivity pointed to the existence of a long-range influence which must exist over a *coherence length* of the order of 10^{-4} cm. Cooper was able to show theoretically that the effect of electron attraction in a crystal lattice is to produce pairs of electrons (now known as *Cooper pairs*) which move as a unit without exchanging energy with the vibrating lattice ions.

According to the theory of Bardeen, Cooper, and Schrieffer (hereafter abbreviated BCS), when energy is supplied to the superconductor, some of the Cooper pairs may be broken apart into separate electrons. There is therefore an *energy gap* of 2ϵ between the Cooper pair and the two separated electrons. It was found, in the last section, that the superconducting heat capacity could be regarded as the sum of a lattice portion $(125/\Theta)^3 T^3$ and an electronic portion $c_{el}^{(s)}$, which roughly obeyed the equation

$$\frac{c_{el}^{(s)}}{\gamma' T_C} = a e^{-bT_c/T}.$$

This equation has the form needed to describe a process involving an energy gap ϵ, where

$$\frac{\epsilon}{kT} = \frac{bT_C}{T},$$

and therefore

$$\frac{2\epsilon}{kT_C} = 2b. \tag{15-30}$$

If the various portions of the curves in Figs. 15-26 and 15-27 are used to provide values of b, this quantity—and therefore also ϵ—is found to have a temperature variation. Heat-capacity measurements, as a rule, provide this temperature variation at the lower temperatures, but fortunately there are other methods that provide the complete temperature dependence of ϵ. Points obtained by several different methods are shown in Fig. 15-28, where it is seen that the experimental results are in good agreement with the curve derived from the BCS theory. The quantity ϵ_0 is the value of ϵ at absolute zero.

Values of $2\epsilon_0/kT_C$ for 12 superconductors are given in Table 15-4 and are

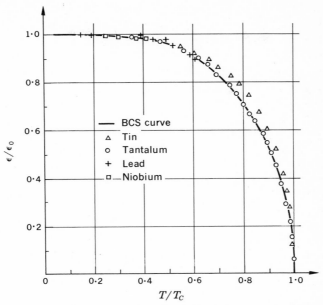

Fig. 15-28   *Variation of energy gap with temperature. Solid curve is derived from BCS theory (J. Sutton and P. Townsend, 1963.)*

Table 15-4   **Energy Gap at** $T = 0$; **Values of** $2\epsilon_0/kT_C$

Element	$\dfrac{2\epsilon_0}{kT_C}$	$\dfrac{T_C}{\Theta}$	$2\dfrac{T_C}{\mathcal{H}_0}\left(-\dfrac{d\mathcal{H}_C}{dT}\right)_{T_c}$
13 Al	3.3	0.0027	3.5
23 V	3.5	0.014	3.9
30 Zn	3.1	0.0028	4.0
31 Ga	3.4	0.0034	4.0
41 Nb	3.7	0.033	4.0
48 Cd	3.1	0.0027	3.2
49 In	3.6	0.032	3.6
50 Sn	3.5	0.019	3.5
73 Ta	3.6	0.019	3.6
80 Hg(α)	4.6	0.058	4.1
81 Tl	3.6	0.030	3.6
82 Pb	4.2	0.069	4.2

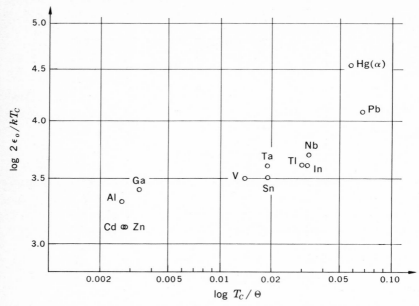

Fig. 15-29   *Relation between energy gap $2\epsilon_0$ and T_C/Θ for type I superconductors.*

plotted logarithmically against T_C/Θ in Fig. 15-29. The rough relation shown on the graph has some theoretical significance in terms of the BCS theory. It was pointed out by A. M. Toxen in 1965 that there was a good correlation between values of $2\epsilon_0/kT_C$ and the quantity in the last column of Table 15-4.

15-12   Type II Superconductors

When a superconductor is placed in a magnetic field of intensity $\mathcal{H}$, no magnetic lines of force penetrate so long as $\mathcal{H} < \mathcal{H}_C$. The transition from the finite outside value $\mathcal{H}$ to the inside zero value cannot, however, be discontinuous. The inclusion by the Londons of an additional term with the classical electromagnetic equations enabled them to derive the result that the field $\mathcal{H}_i$ *inside* a superconductor drops from its outside value $\mathcal{H}$ to a value of zero very abruptly according to the equation

$$\mathcal{H}_i = \mathcal{H}e^{-x/\lambda}, \tag{15-31}$$

where x is the distance perpendicular to the boundary and λ is the distance for $\mathcal{H}_i$ to be reduced to $1/e$ of the value $\mathcal{H}$ outside. The quantity λ, called the *penetration depth*, was first measured by D. Shoenberg in mercury, by sub-dividing the mercury into minute droplets. As was to be expected, λ was found to be very small, of the order of 5×10^{-6} cm. It was also found to vary with T according to the equation

$$\lambda = \frac{\lambda_0}{\sqrt{1 - T^4/T_C^4}},\tag{15-32}$$

where λ_0 is the penetration depth at absolute zero.

It was mentioned in the previous section that the electron-electron attrac-tion which is produced among the free electrons in a superconductor by interaction with the lattice and which is responsible for the formation of Cooper pairs is active over a distance—the *coherence length* ξ—of about 10^{-4} cm. One of the characteristic features of a type I superconductor is that $\lambda \ll \xi$, as shown schematically in Fig. 15-30a. Another feature of a type I superconductor is provided by the behavior already studied, depicted in Fig. 15-30b, in which the isothermal transition from the superconducting phase to the normal one takes place at constant $\mathcal{H}_c$ (when the sample is a long cylinder parallel to the field), so that the $\mathcal{H}_c T$ curve divides the $\mathcal{H} T$ plane into *only two* regions, superconducting and normal.

The coherence length ξ of a superconductor is a measure of the mean free path of the electrons, that is, the average distance between two consecutive processes which result in the scattering of the electron. Electrons can collide with or be scattered by impurities, crystal defects, or boundaries, and *such impediments can be deliberately created in a crystal*. The greater the frequency of scattering, the smaller the coherence length. Experiment shows that the same factors which increase scattering also increase the magnetic field penetration, so that it is possible by injecting impurities, by creating crystal defects through cold-working, by alloying, or by depositing the substance as a very thin film to effect *both* a reduction of the coherence length ξ *and* an increase of penetration depth λ.

A superconductor in which $\lambda \gg \xi$ is called a *type II superconductor* and is depicted schematically in Fig. 15-31a. It has most unusual properties and important practical applications. Instead of starting the isothermal $s \rightarrow n$ transition at $\mathcal{H}_c$, it starts at a lower field $\mathcal{H}_{c1}$; then, instead of a sudden phase transition at constant critical field, the isothermal phase transition is smeared over a range of values of $\mathcal{H}$, from $\mathcal{H}_{c1}$ to a value $\mathcal{H}_{c2}$ that is larger than $\mathcal{H}_c$, as shown in Fig. 15-31b. As a result, the $\mathcal{H} T$ plane is subdivided into *three* regions: (a) below $\mathcal{H}_{c1}$, superconducting; (b) above $\mathcal{H}_{c2}$, normal; and (c) between $\mathcal{H}_{c1}$ and $\mathcal{H}_{c2}$, where the material is said to be in the *mixed phase*, in which it contains superconducting as well as normal regions and can there-fore carry an electric current without resistance. This is usually a large

Fig. 15-30   *Fundamental properties of a type I superconductor. (a) Magnetic field penetration depth* λ *and coherence length* ξ *are such that* λ ≪ ξ. *(b) There is an abrupt isothermal phase transition at* $\mathcal{H}_C$, *and only two phases exist: superconducting and normal.*

region, and $\mathcal{H}_{c2}$ may be as much as 10 times as large as $\mathcal{H}_c$. As a result, at the proper temperature, a type II superconductor can remain superconducting in a large field (up to about 200,000 Oe!) or can carry a huge current without becoming normal. Because of this property, superconducting solenoids may be wound and, once a current of about 20 to 30 A is set up, will provide a field of, say, 60,000 to 100,000 Oe *without any power consumption.*

The most striking aspect of type II superconductors is the mechanism of magnetic flux penetration in the mixed state, and its analog with quantized vortices in liquid helium II. If a current is induced in a superconducting ring, the current persists undiminished for as long a time as the ring is maintained at the appropriate temperature. Careful measurements of the magnetic field of this *persistent current* show that the current would last over 100,000 years. It is generally believed that such a persistent current is an example of a quantum process on a macroscopic scale, like the motions of the extranuclear electrons of a giant atom. If the ring of current is made smaller, it encloses a smaller magnetic flux and, when very small, may be considered a vortex ring of current. F. London first realized that the magnetic flux produced by a current vortex should exist in discrete quanta, and he calculated a quantum of flux to be hc/e. A large current vortex would contain so many flux quanta

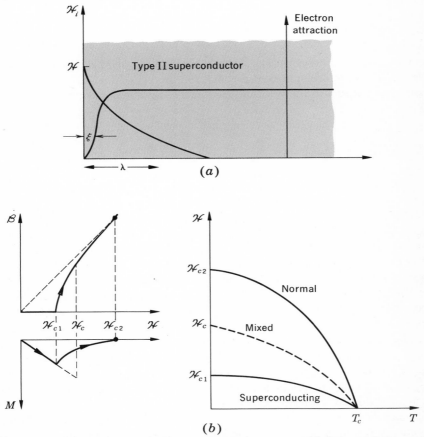

Fig. 15-31   *Fundamental properties of a type II superconductor. (a) Magnetic field penetration depth λ and coherence length ξ are such that $\lambda \gg \xi$. (b) The isothermal phase transition starts at a field $\mathcal{H}_{c1}$ smaller than $\mathcal{H}_c$ and ends at a field $\mathcal{H}_{c2}$ larger than $\mathcal{H}_c$, and three phases exist: superconducting, mixed, and normal.*

that any change in current or flux would appear continuous. If the vortices are made extremely small, however, such as in a vanishingly thin superconducting cylinder, and if such a cylinder is placed in a weak field, as the field is increased the flux should increase in discrete steps. Difficult as this experiment sounds, it was performed by two experimental groups independently— B. S. Deaver and W. M. Fairbank in America and R. Doll and M. Näbauer in Germany in 1961. The results of these notable experiments confirmed London's prediction, but the size of the flux quantum (or *fluxoid*) was found to be only one-half as large as expected. This is regarded as a direct experimental verification of the existence of Cooper pairs. Since the current is carried by pairs of electrons, each with a charge of $2e$, the flux quantum should be $hc/2e$. Flux quantization was also shown to exist very close to the transition temperature T_C of a superconductor by R. D. Parks and W. A. Little in 1964.

The penetration of the magnetic field through a type II superconductor is considered to be accomplished through minute cylindrical current vortices, with axes parallel to the field and each enclosing one quantum of magnetic flux.

PROBLEMS

15-1   A thermally insulated vessel contains liquid helium at 4.2°K and atmospheric pressure. Helium vapor is pumped away isentropically until the remaining liquid and vapor achieve a temperature of 1°K. What fraction of the initial amount of liquid helium evaporates during the process? (In the temperature range from 1 to 2.2°K, the specific heat of liquid helium equals $0.104 T^{6.2}$ J/g · deg, and from 2.2 to 4.2°K it remains approximately constant at about 2.5 J/g · deg. The heat of vaporization at 1°K is 20.1 J/g.)

15-2   Liquid helium is contained in a vessel designed to show the fountain effect. If the fountain is found to be 30 cm when the temperature increase is 5 mdeg, what is the entropy in J/g · deg?

15-3   A column of liquid helium II is at a temperature of 1.5°K.

(a)   Find ρ_n/ρ, ρ_s/ρ, and ρ_s/ρ_n.

(b)   If $c = 1.13$ J/g · deg, calculate the speed of second sound.

(c)   A small region at one end of the column undergoes an increase of temperature of 10 mdeg. Calculate v_n and v_s.

(d)   The density at 1.5°K is 0.146 g/cm³. Calculate the excitation energy per unit volume and the kinetic energy per unit volume.

(e)   Verify that $H \Delta T/T = 2K$.

15-4

(a)   Calculate the speed of fourth sound at 1.5°K.

(b)   Calculate the speed of third sound at 1.5°K and 10 cm above the level of the bulk liquid.

15-5   A vortex ring in liquid He^4 has a quantum number $n = 1$, a radius $R = 1.28 \times 10^{-3}$ cm, and a hollow core of radius $a = 1.28$ Å. (a) Calculate the velocity of the ring and (b) the energy, if the density of He is 0.146 g/cm^3.

15-6   Using the curves in Fig. 15-21, calculate the work done and the heat absorbed by 100 cm^3 of material during the transition from the superconducting to the normal phase at 3°K when the material is (a) tin, (b) mercury, and (c) lead.

15-7   Show that, if G^* denotes the magnetic Gibbs function,

$$G^{*(s)} \text{ (at } T, \mathcal{H}c) = G^{*(s)} \text{ (at } T, 0) + \frac{V \mathcal{H}_c^2}{8\pi}.$$

15-8   In the transition of a type I superconductor from the superconducting to the normal phase at a constant temperature T, show that:

(a)
$$S^{(s)} - S^{(s)} = \frac{V}{8\pi} \frac{d}{dT} (\mathcal{H}_c^2).$$

(b)
$$C^{(s)} - C^{(n)} = \frac{VT}{8\pi} \frac{d^2}{dT^2} (\mathcal{H}_c^2).$$

15-9   Assuming that, for a type I superconductor,

$$c^{(s)} = c_{el}^{(s)} + \left(\frac{125}{\Theta}\right)^3 T^3$$

and

$$c^{(n)} = \gamma' T + \left(\frac{125}{\Theta}\right)^3 T^3,$$

show that, when T is near absolute zero, the entropy change from the superconducting to the normal phase is expressed as:

(a)
$$s^{(n)} - s^{(s)} = \gamma' T.$$

(b)
$$\mathcal{H}_c^2 = \mathcal{H}_0^2 - \frac{4\pi\gamma'}{v} T^2.$$

(c)   Explain how it is possible to measure γ' of a superconducting metal noncalorimetrically and magnetically.

15-10   Prove that:

(a)
$$\int_0^{T_c} \frac{c^{(s)}}{T}\, dT = \int_0^{T_c} \frac{c^{(n)}}{T}\, dT.$$

(b)
$$\int_0^1 \frac{c_{el}^{(s)}}{\gamma' T}\, d\left(\frac{T}{T_c}\right) = 1.$$

(c)
$$\int_0^1 \frac{c_{el}^{(s)}}{\gamma' T_c}\, d\left(\frac{T}{T_c}\right) = \frac{1}{2} + \frac{v\mathcal{H}_0^2}{8\pi\gamma' T_c^2}.$$

15-11   Figure P15-1a and b displays the difference between a paramagnetic crystal and a type I superconductor.

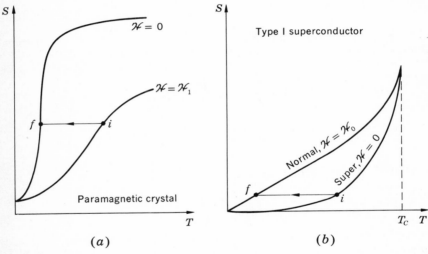

Fig. P15-1

(a)   Discuss the isentropic process $i \to f$ in each figure from the standpoint of order and disorder.

(b)   Assuming the lattice contribution to the heat capacity to be negligible, so that

$$c^{(n)} = \gamma' T$$

and

$$c^{(s)} = \gamma' T_c a e^{-bT_c/T},$$

derive an expression for the temperature T_f achieved by an adiabatic *magnetization*.

16.

CHEMICAL EQUILIBRIUM

16-1 Dalton's Law

Imagine a homogeneous mixture of inert ideal gases at a temperature T, a pressure P, and a volume V. Suppose there are n_1 moles of gas A_1, n_2 moles of gas A_2, etc., up to n_c moles of gas A_c. Since there is no chemical reaction, the mixture is in a state of equilibrium with the equation of state

$$PV = (n_1 + n_2 + \cdots + n_c)RT,$$

or
$$P = \frac{n_1}{V} RT + \frac{n_2}{V} RT + \cdots + \frac{n_c}{V} RT.$$

It is clear that the expression

$$\frac{n_k}{V} RT$$

represents the pressure that the kth gas would exert if it occupied the volume V alone. This is called the *partial pressure* of the kth gas and is denoted by p_k. Thus,

$$p_1 = \frac{n_1}{V} RT, \qquad p_2 = \frac{n_2}{V} RT, \qquad \ldots, \qquad p_c = \frac{n_c}{V} RT,$$

and
$$P = p_1 + p_2 + \cdots + p_c. \tag{16-1}$$

The above equation expresses the fact that the total pressure of a mixture of ideal gases is equal to the sum of the partial pressures. This is *Dalton's law*.

Now,
$$V = (n_1 + n_2 + \cdots + n_c) \frac{RT}{P}$$
$$= \sum n_k \frac{RT}{P},$$

and the partial pressure of the kth gas is

$$p_k = \frac{n_k}{V} RT.$$

Substituting the value for V, we get

$$p_k = \frac{n_k}{\Sigma n_k} P.$$

The ratio $n_k/\Sigma n_k$ is called the *mole fraction* of the kth gas and is denoted by x_k. Thus,

$$x_1 = \frac{n_1}{\Sigma n_k}, \qquad x_2 = \frac{n_2}{\Sigma n_c}, \qquad \cdots, \qquad x_c = \frac{n_c}{\Sigma n_k},$$

and

$$p_1 = x_1 P, \qquad p_2 = x_2 P, \qquad \cdots, \qquad p_c = x_c P.$$

The mole fractions are convenient dimensionless quantities with which to express the composition of a mixture. It is clear that

$$x_1 + x_2 + \cdots + x_c = \frac{n_1}{\Sigma n_k} + \frac{n_2}{\Sigma n_k} + \cdots + \frac{n_c}{\Sigma n_k}$$

$$= 1.$$

Hence, if all but one mole fraction is determined, the last can be calculated from the above equation.

16-2   Semipermeable Membrane

If a narrow tube of palladium is closed at one end and the open end is sealed into a glass tube, as shown in Fig. 16-1, the system may be pumped to a very high vacuum. If the palladium remains at room temperature, the vacuum can be maintained indefinitely. If, however, an ordinary bunsen burner is placed so that the blue cone surrounds part of the tube, with the rest of the flame causing the palladium tube to become red-hot, hydrogen present in the blue cone will pass through the tube, but other gases will not. Red-hot palladium is said to be a *semipermeable membrane*, permeable to hydrogen only. This is the simplest laboratory method of obtaining pure dry hydrogen.

Experiment shows that hydrogen continues to flow through the red-hot palladium until the pressure of hydrogen in the vessel reaches a value equal to the partial pressure of the hydrogen in the flame. When the flow stops,

Fig. 16-1   *Palladium tube permeable to hydrogen.*

membrane equilibrium is said to exist. Membrane equilibrium is achieved when the partial pressure of the gas to which the membrane is permeable is the same on both sides of the membrane. We shall suppose that there exists a special membrane permeable to each gas with which we have to deal. Whether this is actually so is not important. We shall make use of the principle of the semipermeable membrane as an ideal device for theoretical purposes.

16-3   Gibbs' Theorem

With the aid of a device equipped with two semipermeable membranes, it is possible to conceive of separating in a reversible manner a mixture of two inert ideal gases. The vessel depicted in Fig. 16-2 is divided into two equal compartments by a rigid wall, which is a membrane permeable only to the gas A_1. Two pistons coupled so that they move together at a constant distance apart are constructed of materials such that one is impermeable to all gases, and the other is permeable only to the gas A_2. The initial state is depicted in Fig. 16-2*i*. A mixture of A_1 and A_2 is in the left-hand chamber, and the right-hand chamber is evacuated.

Now imagine pushing the coupled pistons to the right in such a manner that the following conditions are satisfied:

1   The motion is infinitely slow, so that membrane equilibrium exists at all times.

2   There is no friction.

3   The whole system is kept at constant temperature.

These conditions define a *reversible isothermal process*. Consider the system at any intermediate state such as that depicted in Fig. 16-2k. If p_1 and p_2 are the partial pressures, respectively, of A_1 and A_2 in the mixture, P_1 is the pressure of A_1 alone, and P_2 the pressure of A_2 alone, then the forces acting on the coupled pistons are:

$$\text{Force to the left} = (p_1 + p_2) \times \text{area},$$

and $$\text{Sum of the forces to the right} = (P_1 + P_2) \times \text{area}.$$

Since membrane equilibrium exists, $p_1 = P_1$ and $p_2 = P_2$; whence the resultant force acting on the coupled pistons is zero. After the pistons have moved all the way to the right, the gases are completely separated as shown in Fig. 16-2f.

Since the resultant force was infinitesimal in the beginning and zero throughout the remainder of the process, $W = 0$. Also, since the process was isothermal and the internal energy of an ideal gas is a function of T only,

(i) Initial equilibrium state

(k) Intermediate equilibrium state

(f) Final equilibrium state

Fig. 16-2   *Reversible isothermal separation of two inert ideal gases.*

$U_f = U_i$. Finally, since the process was both reversible and isothermal, the heat transferred Q is equal to $T(S_f - S_i)$. We have, therefore, the result that

$$T(S_f - S_i) = 0,$$

and since T is not zero,

$$S_i = S_f.$$

Now S_i is the entropy of the mixture at the temperature T and the volume V, while S_f is the sum of the entropies of the two gases, each at the same temperature and each occupying the volume V alone. If we define the *partial entropy* of one of the gases of a mixture as the entropy that the gas would have if it occupied the whole volume alone at the same temperature, then we obtain the result that the *entropy of a mixture of ideal gases is the sum of the partial entropies*. This is known as *Gibbs' theorem*. The generalization for any number of gases is obvious.

16-4   Entropy of a Mixture of Inert Ideal Gases

Imagine a number of inert ideal gases separated from one another by suitable partitions, all the gases being at the same temperature T and pressure P. Suppose there are n_1 moles of gas A_1, n_2 moles of A_2, etc., up to n_c moles of A_c. Before the partitions are removed, the entropy of the whole system S_i is the sum of the separate entropies. The entropy of 1 mole of the kth gas at temperature T and pressure P is

$$s_k = \int c_{Pk} \frac{dT}{T} + s_{0k} - R \ln P;$$

therefore,

$$S_i = \sum n_k \left(\int c_{Pk} \frac{dT}{T} + s_{0k} - R \ln P \right)$$

$$= R \sum n_k \left(\frac{1}{R} \int c_{Pk} \frac{dT}{T} + \frac{s_{0k}}{R} - \ln P \right).$$

It is convenient to represent the first two terms within the parentheses by σ, thus:

$$\sigma_k = \frac{1}{R} \int c_{Pk} \frac{dT}{T} + \frac{s_{0k}}{R}. \tag{16-2}$$

Then

$$S_i = R\Sigma n_k(\sigma_k - \ln P). \tag{16-3}$$

After the partitions are removed, the temperature and pressure remain the same because there is no chemical reaction, but the gases diffuse and, by

Gibbs' theorem, the entropy of the mixture is the sum of the partial entropies. The partial entropy of the kth gas is the entropy that the kth gas would have if it occupied the whole volume alone at the same temperature, in which case it would exert a pressure equal to the partial pressure p_k. Therefore, the total entropy of the mixture is

$$S_f = R\Sigma n_k(\sigma_k - \ln p_k).$$

Since $p_k = x_k P$,

$$S_f = R\Sigma n_k(\sigma_k - \ln P - \ln x_k). \tag{16-4}$$

The change of entropy due to the diffusion of any number of inert gases is therefore equal to

$$S_f - S_i = -R\Sigma n_k \ln x_k. \tag{16-5}$$

Each of the mole fractions is a number less than unity with a negative logarithm. The whole expression is therefore positive, as it should be. Since

$$x_k = \frac{n_k}{\Sigma n} = \frac{n_k RT}{\Sigma n RT} = \frac{n_k Pv}{PV} = \frac{n_k v}{V},$$

we may write

$$S_f - S_i = n_1 R \ln \frac{V}{n_1 v} + n_2 R \ln \frac{V}{n_2 v} + \cdots.$$

The above result shows that the entropy change due to the diffusion of any number of ideal gases is the same as that which would take place if each gas were caused to undergo a free expansion from the volume that it occupies alone at T and P to the volume of the mixture at the same T and P. The validity of this result was assumed in Chap. 9 in order to calculate the entropy change of the universe when two ideal gases diffuse. The assumption is therefore seen to be justified.

As an example, consider the diffusion of 1 mole of helium and 1 mole of neon. Then,

$$S_f - S_i = -R(1 \ln \tfrac{1}{2} + 1 \ln \tfrac{1}{2})$$

$$= 2R \ln 2.$$

In this expression there are no quantities such as heat capacities or entropy constants that distinguish one gas from another. The result is the same for the diffusion of any two inert ideal gases, no matter how similar or dissimilar they are. If the two gases are identical, however, the concept of diffusion has no meaning, and there is no entropy change. From the microscopic point of view, this means that the diffusion of any two dissimilar gases brings about the same degree of disorder, whereas the diffusion of two identical gases introduces no element of disorder.

The application of mathematics to the macroscopic processes of nature usually gives rise to continuous results. Our experience suggests that, as the two diffusing gases become more and more alike, the entropy change due to diffusion should get smaller and smaller, approaching zero as the gases become identical. The fact that this is not the case is known as *Gibbs' paradox*. The paradox has been resolved by Bridgman in the following way: To recognize that two gases are dissimilar requires a set of experimental operations. These operations become more and more difficult as the gases become more and more alike; but, at least in principle, the operations are possible. In the limit, when the gases become identical, there is a discontinuity in the instrumental operations inasmuch as no instrumental operation exists by which the gases may be distinguished. Hence a discontinuity in a function, such as that of an entropy change, is to be expected.

16-5   Gibbs Function of a Mixture of Inert Ideal Gases

The enthalpy and the entropy of 1 mole of an ideal gas at temperature T and pressure P are, respectively,

$$h = h_0 + \int c_P \, dT$$

and

$$s = \int c_P \frac{dT}{T} + s_0 - R \ln P;$$

therefore the molar Gibbs function $g = h - Ts$ is equal to

$$g = h_0 + \int c_P \, dT - T \int c_P \frac{dT}{T} - Ts_0 + RT \ln P.$$

Applying the formula for integration by parts,

$$\int c_P \, dT - T \int c_P \frac{dT}{T} = -T \int \frac{\int c_P \, dT}{T^2} \, dT,$$

we get

$$g = h_0 - T \int \frac{\int c_P \, dT}{T^2} \, dT - Ts_0 + RT \ln P$$

$$= RT \left(\frac{h_0}{RT} - \frac{1}{R} \int \frac{\int c_P \, dT}{T^2} \, dT - \frac{s_0}{R} + \ln P \right).$$

It is convenient to denote the first three terms within the parentheses by ϕ, thus:

$$\phi = \frac{h_0}{RT} - \frac{1}{R} \int \frac{\int c_P \, dT}{T^2} \, dT - \frac{s_0}{R}. \tag{16-6}$$

The molar Gibbs function of an ideal gas may therefore be written as

$$\boxed{g = RT(\phi + \ln P),} \tag{16-7}$$

where ϕ is a function of T only.

Consider a number of inert ideal gases separated from one another, all at the same T and P. Suppose there are n_1 moles of gas A_1, n_2 moles of A_2, etc., up to n_c moles of A_c. Before the gases are mixed, the Gibbs function of the system G is the sum of the separate Gibbs functions, or

$$G_i = \Sigma n_k g_k$$

$$= RT\Sigma n_k(\phi_k + \ln P),$$

where the summation extends from $k = 1$ to $k = c$. To express the Gibbs function after mixing G_f, it is necessary merely to replace the total pressure P by the partial pressure p_k. (Why?) Thus,

$$G_f = RT\Sigma n_k(\phi_k + \ln p_k)$$

$$= RT\Sigma n_k(\phi_k + \ln P + \ln x_k).$$

Therefore, $G_f - G_i = RT\Sigma n_k \ln x_k,$

where the expression on the right is a negative quantity. It is seen therefore that the Gibbs function after diffusion is less than the Gibbs function before diffusion. This will be shown later to be an expression of a general law that holds for all irreversible processes which take place at constant T and P.

We have shown that the Gibbs function of a mixture of inert ideal gases at temperature T and pressure P is

$$\boxed{G = RT\Sigma n_k(\phi_k + \ln P + \ln x_k),} \tag{16-8}$$

where ϕ is given by Eq. (16-6).

16-6   Chemical Equilibrium

Consider a homogeneous mixture of 1 mole of hydrogen and 1 mole of oxygen at room temperature and at atmospheric pressure. It is a well-known fact that this mixture will remain indefinitely at the same temperature, pressure, and composition. The most careful measurements over a long period of time will disclose no appreciable spontaneous change of state. One might be inclined to deduce from this that such a mixture represents a system in a state of thermodynamic equilibrium. However, this is not the case. If a small piece of platinized asbestos is introduced or if an electric spark is created across two electrodes, an explosion takes place involving a sudden change in the temperature, the pressure, and the composition. If at the end of the explosion the system is brought back to the same temperature and pressure, it will be found that the composition is now $\frac{1}{2}$ mole of oxygen, no measurable amount of hydrogen, and 1 mole of water vapor.

The piece of material such as platinized asbestos by whose agency a chemical reaction is started is known as a *catalyst*. If chemical combination is started in a mixture of 1 mole of hydrogen and 1 mole of oxygen with different amounts and different kinds of catalysts and if the final composition of the mixture is measured in each case, it is found that: (1) the final composition does not depend on the amount of catalyst used; (2) the final composition does not depend on the kind of catalyst used; (3) the catalyst itself is the same at the end of the reaction as at the beginning. These results lead us to the following conclusions:

1   The initial state of the mixture is a state of mechanical and thermal equilibrium but not of chemical equilibrium.
2   The final state is a state of thermodynamic equilibrium.
3   The transition from the initial nonequilibrium state to the final equilibrium state is accompanied by a chemical reaction that is too slow to be measured when it takes place spontaneously. Through the agency of the catalyst, the reaction is caused to take place more rapidly.

Imagine a vessel divided into two compartments by a removable partition as shown in Fig. 16-3a. Suppose that one compartment contains a dilute solution of sodium chloride and water maintained at a pressure of 1 atm and at a temperature of 20°C—the mole fraction of the salt being, say, 0.01. Under these conditions the solution is in thermodynamic equilibrium. Suppose that the other compartment contains solid salt in equilibrium also at a pressure of 1 atm and a temperature of 20°C. Now imagine that the partition is removed (Fig. 16-3b) and that the pressure and temperature of the whole

Fig. 16-3 *Transport of matter across the boundary between two phases.*

system are kept constant at the original values. Experiment shows that some solid salt dissolves; i.e., the mole fraction of the salt in the solution increases spontaneously at constant pressure and temperature. After a while, the change ceases and the mole fraction is found to be about 0.1.

Focusing our attention on the solution from the moment it was put in contact with the solid salt, we are led to the following conclusions:

1 The initial state of the solution (at the moment it was put in contact with the solid salt) is one of mechanical and thermal equilibrium but not of chemical equilibrium.

2 The final state of the solution is a state of thermodynamic equilibrium.

3 The transition from the initial nonequilibrium state to the final equilibrium state is accompanied by a transport of a chemical constituent into the solution.

16-7   Thermodynamic Description of Nonequilibrium States

A *phase* is defined as a system or a portion of a system composed of any number of chemical constituents satisfying the requirements (1) that it is homogeneous and (2) that it has a definite boundary. The hydrogen-oxygen mixture described in Art. 16-6 is a gaseous phase of two chemical constituents and of constant mass. The salt solution is a liquid phase of two chemical constituents whose mass, when in contact with the solid-salt phase, is variable. Although the initial states of both these phases are nonequilibrium states, it is possible to describe them in terms of thermodynamic coordinates. Since each phase is in mechanical and thermal equilibrium, a definite P and T may be ascribed to each; since each has a definite boundary, each has a definite volume; and since each is homogeneous, the composition of each phase may be described by specifying the number of moles of each constituent. In general, a phase consisting of c chemical constituents in mechanical and thermal equilibrium may be described with the aid of the coordinates P, V, T, n_1, n_2, . . . , n_c.

Under a given set of conditions, a phase may undergo a change of state in which some or all of these coordinates change. While this is going on, the phase passes through states not of thermodynamic equilibrium but of mechanical and thermal equilibrium only. These states are connected by an equation of state that is a relation among P, V, T, and the n's. Whether a phase is in chemical equilibrium or not, it has a definite internal energy and enthalpy. Both U and H may be regarded as functions of P, V, T, and the n's; and upon eliminating one of the coordinates by means of the equation of state, U and H may be expressed as a function of any two of P, V, and T and all the n's. Since entropy is a measure of the molecular disorder of the system, the entropy of a phase that is not in chemical equilibrium must have a meaning. We shall assume that the entropy of a phase, and therefore the Helmholtz and Gibbs functions also, can be expressed as functions of any two of P, V, and T and all the n's.

During a change of state the n's, which determine the composition of the phase, change either by virtue of a chemical reaction or by virtue of a transport of matter across the boundaries between phases, or both. In general, under given conditions, there is a set of values of the n's for which the phase is in chemical and therefore in thermodynamic equilibrium. The functions that express the properties of a phase when it is not in chemical equilibrium must obviously reduce to those for thermodynamic equilibrium when the equilibrium values of the n's are substituted. We are therefore led to assume that *any property of a phase in mechanical and thermal equilibrium can be represented by a function of any two of P, V, T, and the n's of the same form as that used to denote the same property when the phase is in thermodynamic equilibrium.*

Consider, for example, a phase consisting of a mixture of ideal gases. When the gases are inert, the equation of state is

$$PV = \Sigma n_k RT;$$

the entropy is

$$S = R\Sigma n_k(\sigma_k - \ln P - \ln x_k);$$

and the Gibbs function is

$$G = RT\Sigma n_k(\phi_k + \ln P + \ln x_k).$$

According to the assumption just made, these same equations may be used in connection with an ideal-gas phase in mechanical and thermal equilibrium when the gases are chemically active, when the phase is in contact with other phases, or under both conditions, whether chemical equilibrium exists or not. Under these conditions the n's and x's are variables. Whether they are all independent variables or not is a question that cannot be answered until the conditions under which a change of state takes place are specified. It is clear that, if the mass of the phase remains constant and the gases are inert, the n's and x's are constants. If the mass of the phase remains constant and the gases are chemically active, then it will be shown that each n (and therefore each x) is a function of only one independent variable, the degree of reaction. If the mass of the phase is variable, the number of n's that are independent depends on the number of other phases in contact with the original phase and on the chemical constituents of these other phases.

A system composed of two or more phases is called a *heterogeneous system*. Any extensive property such as V, U, S, H, F, or G of any one of the phases may be expressed as a function of, say, T, P, and the n's of that phase. Thus, for the Gibbs function of the first phase,

$$G^{(1)} = \text{function of } (T,P,n_1^{(1)},n_2^{(1)}, \ldots);$$

for the second phase,

$$G^{(2)} = \text{function of } (T,P,n_1^{(2)},n_2^{(2)}, \ldots);$$

etc. The Gibbs function of the whole heterogeneous system is therefore

$$G = G^{(1)} + G^{(2)} + \cdots.$$

This result holds for any extensive property of a heterogeneous system.

16-8   Conditions for Chemical Equilibrium

Consider any hydrostatic system of constant mass, either homogeneous or heterogeneous, in mechanical and thermal equilibrium but not in chemical equilibrium. Suppose that the system is in contact with a reservoir at temperature T and undergoes an infinitesimal irreversible process involving an exchange of heat dQ with the reservoir. The process may involve a chemical reaction or a transport of matter between phases or both. Let dS denote the entropy change of the system and dS_0 the entropy change of the reservoir. The total entropy change of the universe is therefore $dS_0 + dS$; and since the performance of an irreversible process is attended by an increase in the entropy of the universe, we may write

$$dS_0 + dS > 0.$$

Since
$$dS_0 = -\frac{dQ}{T},$$

we have
$$-\frac{dQ}{T} + dS > 0,$$

or
$$dQ - T\,dS < 0.$$

During the infinitesimal irreversible process, the internal energy of the system changes by an amount dU, and an amount of work $P\,dV$ is performed. The first law can therefore be written in its usual form,

$$dQ = dU + P\,dV,$$

and the inequality becomes

$$\boxed{dU + P\,dV - T\,dS < 0.} \tag{16-9}$$

This inequality holds during any infinitesimal portion and, therefore, during all infinitesimal portions of the irreversible process. According to the assumption made in the preceding article, U, V, and S may all be regarded as functions of thermodynamic coordinates.

During the irreversible process for which the above inequality holds, some or all of the coordinates may change. If we restrict the irreversible process by imposing the condition that two of the thermodynamic coordinates remain constant, then the inequality can be reduced to a simpler form. Suppose, for example, that the internal energy and the volume remain constant. Then the inequality reduces to $dS > 0$, which means that the entropy of a system at constant U and V increases during an irreversible process, approaching a maximum at the final state of equilibrium. This result, however, is obvious from the entropy principle, since a system at constant U and V is isolated and is therefore, so to speak, its own universe. The two most important sets of conditions are the following:

1   *If T and V are constant,* the inequality reduces to

$$d(U - TS) < 0,$$

or
$$dF < 0, \tag{16-10}$$

expressing the result that *the Helmholtz function of a system at constant T and V decreases during an irreversible process* and becomes a minimum at the final equilibrium state.

2   *If T and P are constant,* the inequality reduces to

$$d(U + PV - TS) < 0,$$

or
$$dG < 0, \tag{16-11}$$

expressing the result that *the Gibbs function of a system at constant T and P decreases during an irreversible process* and becomes a minimum at the final equilibrium state.

The student will recall that the condition for equilibrium of a conservative mechanical system is that the potential energy shall be a minimum. The Helmholtz and Gibbs functions are therefore seen to play a similar role in thermodynamics. For this reason, Gibbs called the function F the *thermodynamic potential at constant volume* and the function G the *thermodynamic potential at constant pressure*.

16-9   Condition for Mechanical Stability

In discussing the important equation

$$C_P - C_V = -T \left(\frac{\partial V}{\partial T}\right)_P^2 \left(\frac{\partial P}{\partial V}\right)_T$$

in Art. 11-7, the remark was made that $(\partial P/\partial V)_T$ is always negative. This will now be proved for any system of constant mass. Consider the system depicted symbolically in Fig. 16-4. At first, each half of the system is in equilibrium as well as the entire system. Suppose, now, that the left half is compressed by an amount δv and the right half is expanded by the same amount, with each half remaining at constant temperature and the *total* volume remaining constant.

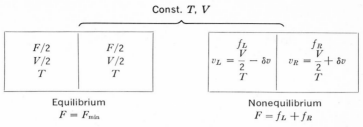

Fig. 16-4   *Transition from a state of thermodynamic equilibrium to a state characterized by a lack of mechanical equilibrium.*

The Helmholtz function f_L of the left half may now be expanded in a Taylor series about its equilibrium value $F_{min}/2$ as follows:

$$f_L = \frac{F_{min}}{2} - \left(\frac{\partial f}{\partial v}\right)_T \delta v + \frac{1}{2}\left(\frac{\partial^2 f}{\partial v^2}\right)_T (\delta v)^2 - \cdots,$$

which may be terminated after the squared term if δv is small enough. But there is no difference between the behavior of half the system and that of the whole system, or

$$\left(\frac{\partial f}{\partial v}\right)_T = \left(\frac{\partial F}{\partial V}\right)_T.$$

Hence

$$f_L = \frac{F_{min}}{2} - \left(\frac{\partial F}{\partial V}\right)_T \delta v + \frac{1}{2}\left(\frac{\partial^2 F}{\partial V^2}\right)_T (\delta v)^2.$$

Similarly, for the right half,

$$f_R = \frac{F_{min}}{2} + \left(\frac{\partial F}{\partial V}\right)_T \delta v + \frac{1}{2}\left(\frac{\partial^2 F}{\partial V^2}\right)_T (\delta v)^2.$$

Adding these two equations, the total Helmholtz function of the system *in the nonequilibrium state* is

$$f_L + f_R = F_{min} + \left(\frac{\partial^2 F}{\partial V^2}\right)_T (\delta v)^2,$$

or

$$f_L + f_R - F_{min} = \delta F_{T,V} = \left(\frac{\partial^2 F}{\partial V^2}\right)_T (\delta v)^2.$$

The relation between F and the volume v of either half of the system at

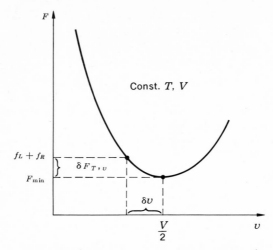

Fig. 16-5   *Dependence of Helmholtz function of the entire system on the volume of half of it, when the total volume and the temperature are constant.*

constant T and V is shown in Fig. 16-5. Since $\delta F_{T,V}$ is positive, it follows that

$$\left(\frac{\partial^2 F}{\partial V^2}\right)_T > 0.$$

But

$$\left(\frac{\partial F}{\partial V}\right)_T = -P,$$

and hence, finally,

$$\left(\frac{\partial P}{\partial V}\right)_T < 0.$$

This is *the condition for mechanical stability.*

16-10   Thermodynamic Equations for a Phase

Consider a phase composed of c chemical constituents, of which there are n_1 moles of substance A_1, n_2 moles of A_2, etc., n_c moles of A_c; the phase is in thermal equilibrium at temperature T and in mechanical equilibrium at pressure P. The Gibbs function of the phase can be written as follows:

$$G = \text{function of } (T, P, n_1, n_2, \ldots, n_c).$$

If the constituents are inert, the phase is in chem
thermodynamic equilibrium. Imagine the performanc
reversible process in which the temperature and pressure
and dP, respectively, and the numbers of moles of the v.
are altered by the amounts dn_1, dn_2, . . . , dn_c. Since we h
the constituents are inert, the changes in the n's are to be reg
plished by the reversible addition or withdrawal of the const. ...s with the
aid of suitable semipermeable membranes. The resulting change in the Gibbs
function of the phase is given by

$$dG = \frac{\partial G}{\partial T} dT + \frac{\partial G}{\partial P} dP + \frac{\partial G}{\partial n_1} dn_1 + \frac{\partial G}{\partial n_2} dn_2 + \cdots + \frac{\partial G}{\partial n_c} dn_c,$$

where it is understood that G is a function of T, P, and the n's and that each
partial derivative implies that all variables other than the one indicated are
to be kept constant.

As a special case, consider an infinitesimal reversible process in which all
the dn's are zero. Under these conditions, the composition and the mass of
the phase remain constant, and the equation becomes

$$dG = \frac{\partial G}{\partial T} dT + \frac{\partial G}{\partial P} dP \qquad \text{(for constant composition and mass)}.$$

But, for this case, it has already been shown that

$$dG = -S\,dT + V\,dP.$$

It follows, therefore, that

$$\frac{\partial G}{\partial T} = \left(\frac{\partial G}{\partial T}\right)_{P,n_1,n_2,\ldots,n_c} = -S, \tag{16-12}$$

$$\frac{\partial G}{\partial P} = \left(\frac{\partial G}{\partial P}\right)_{T,n_1,n_2,\ldots,n_c} = V, \tag{16-13}$$

and $\quad dG = -S\,dT + V\,dP + \dfrac{\partial G}{\partial n_1} dn_1 + \dfrac{\partial G}{\partial n_2} dn_2 + \cdots + \dfrac{\partial G}{\partial n_c} dn_c.$

Now consider the effect upon the Gibbs function when a small amount of
one of the constituents (say, the kth constituent, A_k) is introduced into the
phase, T, P, and the other n's remaining constant. If dn_k moles of A_k are intro-

uced, the effect on the Gibbs function is expressed by the partial derivative

$$\mu_k = \frac{\partial G}{\partial n_k},\tag{16-14}$$

where μ_k is called the *chemical potential* of the kth constituent of the phase in question. A chemical potential of one constituent is a function of T, P, and *all* the n's. If a substance is not present in a phase, it does not follow that its chemical potential is zero. The chemical potential is a measure of the effect on the Gibbs function when a substance *is* introduced. Even though the substance is not present in the phase, there is always the possibility of introducing it, in which case the Gibbs function would be altered and the value of μ would be finite. We may now write

$$dG = -S\,dT + V\,dP + \mu_1\,dn_1 + \mu_2\,dn_2 + \cdots + \mu_c\,dn_c$$

for an infinitesimal change in the Gibbs function of any phase consisting of inert constituents.

Suppose, now, that the constituents are chemically active. Changes in the n's may then take place because of a chemical reaction. Although the phase is always considered to be in thermal and mechanical equilibrium, an infinitesimal process involving a change in T, P, and the n's will, in general, be irreversible, since chemical equilibrium may not exist. In accordance with our previous assumption as to the form of the expressions denoting properties of a phase in thermal and mechanical equilibrium but not in chemical equilibrium, *we shall assume that the equation*

$$\boxed{\begin{aligned} dG &= -S\,dT + V\,dP + \mu_1\,dn_1 + \mu_2\,dn_2 + \cdots + \mu_c\,dn_c \\ &= -S\,dT + V\,dP + \Sigma\mu_k\,dn_k \end{aligned}}\tag{16-15}$$

correctly expresses the change in the Gibbs function for any *infinitesimal process in which the n's may be caused to change either by the transfer of constituents to or from the phase or by the agency of a chemical reaction, or both.*

Imagine a phase at constant T and P in which all constituents are increased in the same proportion. Since the Gibbs function is an extensive quantity, it also will be increased in the same proportion. Infinitesimal changes in the mole numbers in the same proportion are represented by

$$dn_1 = n_1\,d\lambda, \qquad dn_2 = n_2\,d\lambda, \qquad \ldots, \qquad dn_c = n_c\,d\lambda,$$

and the corresponding change in G is

$$dG = G\,d\lambda,$$

where $d\lambda$ is the proportionality factor. Since

$$dG_{T,P} = \mu_1\, dn_1 + \mu_2\, dn_2 + \cdots + \mu_c\, dn_c,$$

we have

$$G\, d\lambda = \mu_1 n_1\, d\lambda + \mu_2 n_2\, d\lambda + \cdots + \mu_c n_c\, d\lambda,$$

or

$$\boxed{\begin{aligned} G &= \mu_1 n_1 + \mu_2 n_2 + \cdots + \mu_c n_c \\ &= \Sigma \mu_k n_k. \end{aligned}}$$

(16-16)

Equation (16-16) shows that *the chemical potentials are intensive quantities*, for if all the n's are increased in the same proportion at constant T and P, the μ's must remain constant in order that G increase in the same proportion.

16-11   Chemical Potentials

The chemical potentials play a fundamental role in chemical thermodynamics. The chemical potential of the kth constituent of a phase is defined as

$$\mu_k = \frac{\partial G}{\partial n_k}$$

and is a function of T, P, and all the n's. In order that μ_k may be an intensive quantity, it is clear that the n's must be combined in such a way that, when all of them are multiplied by the same factor, the value of μ_k remains the same. The mole fraction of the kth constituent,

$$x_k = \frac{n_k}{\Sigma n},$$

satisfies that requirement; hence it is to be expected that μ_k is a function of T, P, and x_k. The actual form of the function depends, of course, on the nature of the phase. Consider the following phases:

1   *Phase consisting of only one constituent.*   In this simple but not trivial case,

$$G = \mu n$$

and

$$\mu = \frac{G}{n} = g;$$

(16-17)

i.e., the chemical potential is the molar Gibbs function and is a function of T and P only.

2   *Phase consisting of a mixture of ideal gases.*   In this case we have, from Art. 16-5,

$$G = RT\Sigma n_k(\phi_k + \ln P + \ln x_k),$$

which, when compared with the general equation

$$G = \Sigma n_k \mu_k,$$

shows that the chemical potential of one ideal gas in a mixture of ideal gases is

$$\mu = RT(\phi + \ln P + \ln x), \tag{16-18}$$

which may be written in the two alternate forms

$$\mu = RT(\phi + \ln p)$$

and $$\mu = g + RT \ln x. \tag{16-19}$$

3   *Phase consisting of an ideal solution.*   An ideal solution is defined as one in which the chemical potential of each constituent is of the form

$$\mu_k = g_k + RT \ln x_k, \tag{16-20}$$

where g_k is the Gibbs function of 1 mole of the kth constituent in the pure state, expressed as a function of T and P.

4   *Phase consisting of a dilute solution.*   In the case of a dilute solution in which the mole fraction of the solvent x_0 is very much larger than each of the mole fractions of the solutes $x_1, x_2, \ldots$, it can be shown that, for the solvent,

$$\mu_0 = g_0 + RT \ln x_0, \tag{16-21}$$

where g_0 is the molar Gibbs function of the solvent in the pure state, expressed as a function of T and P. For any one of the solutes,

$$\mu_k = g_{0k} + RT \ln x_k, \tag{16-22}$$

where g_{0k} is a function of T and P only but depends upon the nature of the solvent as well as upon the solute.

5   *Other phases.*   By defining functions known as *fugacity* and *activity coefficients*, it is possible to express the chemical potentials of con-

stituents of a mixture of real gases and also of concentrated solutions. This is beyond the scope of this book.

We shall assume that it is always possible to express the chemical potential of any constituent of any phase as a function of T, P, and the x of that constituent. It will be a surprise to the student to discover how much valuable information can be obtained with the aid of this assumption, without knowing the exact expressions for the chemical potentials of the constituents of a phase.

16-12 Degree of Reaction

If we introduce into a vessel a mixture of any arbitrary number of moles of water vapor, hydrogen, and oxygen, the chemical reaction capable of taking place is indicated by the notation

$$H_2O \rightleftharpoons H_2 + \tfrac{1}{2}O_2,$$

where the quantity on the left is called an *initial constituent* and those on the right *final constituents*. The numbers which precede the chemical symbols and which "balance" the equation (it is understood that both H_2O and H_2 are preceded by unity) are called the *stoichiometric coefficients* and are proportional to the number of moles of the constituents that *change* during the reaction. Thus, if 1 mole of water vapor dissociates, then 1 mole of hydrogen and $\tfrac{1}{2}$ mole of oxygen are formed; or if 0.1 mole of water vapor dissociates, then 0.1 mole of hydrogen and 0.05 mole of oxygen are formed; or if n_0 moles of water vapor dissociate (n_0 being any number whatever), then n_0 moles of hydrogen and $n_0/2$ moles of oxygen are formed. Similarly, if the reaction proceeds to the left to the extent that n_0' moles of hydrogen combine with $n_0'/2$ moles of oxygen, then n_0' moles of water vapor are formed.

In general, suppose that we have a mixture of four substances whose chemical symbols are A_1, A_2, A_3, and A_4. Let A_1 and A_2 be the initial constituents and A_3 and A_4 the final constituents, with the reaction being represented by

$$\nu_1 A_1 + \nu_2 A_2 \rightleftharpoons \nu_3 A_3 + \nu_4 A_4.$$

We have chosen four substances only for convenience. The equations to be developed are of such a character that they can easily be applied to reactions in which any number of substances participate. The ν's are the stoichiometric coefficients, which are always positive integers or fractions.

Let us start with arbitrary amounts of *both* initial and final constituents. If we imagine the reaction to proceed completely to the right, at least one of the initial constituents (say, A_1) will completely disappear. Then it is possible to find a positive number n_0 such that the original number of moles of each of the initial constituents is expressed in the form

$$n_1 \text{ (original)} = n_0 \nu_1$$

and
$$n_2 \text{ (original)} = n_0 \nu_2 + N_2,$$

where N_2 is a constant representing the number of moles of A_2 that cannot combine. If we imagine the reaction to proceed completely to the left, at least one of the final constituents (say, A_3) will completely disappear. In this event, another positive number n_0' may be found such that the original number of moles of each final constituent is expressed in the form

$$n_3 \text{ (original)} = n_0' \nu_3$$

and
$$n_4 \text{ (original)} = n_0' \nu_4 + N_4.$$

If the reaction is imagined to proceed completely to the left, there is the maximum amount possible of each initial constituent and the minimum amount of each final constituent:

$$n_1(\text{max}) = (n_0 + n_0')\nu_1, \qquad n_3(\text{min}) = 0,$$
$$n_2(\text{max}) = (n_0 + n_0')\nu_2 + N_2, \qquad n_4(\text{min}) = N_4.$$

If the reaction is imagined to proceed completely to the right, there is the minimum amount possible of each initial constituent and the maximum amount of each final constituent:

$$n_1(\text{min}) = 0, \qquad n_3(\text{max}) = (n_0 + n_0')\nu_3,$$
$$n_2(\text{min}) = N_2, \qquad n_4(\text{max}) = (n_0 + n_0')\nu_4 + N_4.$$

Suppose that the reaction proceeds partially either to the right or to the left to such an extent that there are n_1 moles of A_1, n_2 moles of A_2, n_3 moles of A_3, and n_4 moles of A_4 present at a given moment. We define the *degree of reaction* ϵ in terms of any one of the initial constituents (say, A_1) as the fraction

$$\epsilon = \frac{n_1(\text{max}) - n_1}{n_1(\text{max}) - n_1(\text{min})}. \tag{16-23}$$

It follows from this definition that $\epsilon = 0$ when the reaction is completely to the left and $\epsilon = 1$ when the reaction is completely to the right. When the reaction consists in the dissociation of one initial constituent, ϵ is called the *degree of dissociation;* when it consists in the ionization of one initial constituent, ϵ is called the *degree of ionization.* Expressing $n_1(\max)$ and $n_1(\min)$ in terms of the constants that express the original amounts of the constituents, we get

$$\epsilon = \frac{(n_0 + n_0')\nu_1 - n_1}{(n_0 + n_0')\nu_1};$$

and, solving for n_1,

$$n_1 = (n_0 + n_0')\nu_1(1 - \epsilon).$$

The number of moles of each of the constituents is therefore given by the following expressions:

$$
\begin{aligned}
n_1 &= (n_0 + n_0')\nu_1(1 - \epsilon), & n_3 &= (n_0 + n_0')\nu_3\epsilon, \\
n_2 &= (n_0 + n_0')\nu_2(1 - \epsilon) + N_2, & n_4 &= (n_0 + n_0')\nu_4\epsilon + N_4.
\end{aligned}
\tag{16-24}
$$

When a chemical reaction takes place, all the n's change, but not independently. The restrictions imposed on the n's are given by the above relations. These equations therefore are examples of *equations of constraint.*

The equations of constraint are equally valid whether the system is heterogeneous or homogeneous. If each constituent is present in, say, φ different phases, with $n_1^{(1)}$ moles of constituent A_1 in phase 1 and $n_1^{(2)}$ moles of the same constituent in phase 2, etc., then the total number of moles of constituent A_1 is

$$n_1 = n_1^{(1)} + n_1^{(2)} + \cdots + n_1^{(\varphi)} = (n_0 + n_0')\nu_1(1 - \epsilon),$$

etc., for the other constituents. For the present, however, we shall limit ourselves to homogeneous systems, reserving heterogeneous systems for Chap. 18.

Since all the n's are functions of ϵ only, it follows that in a homogeneous system all the mole fractions are functions of ϵ only. An example will show how simple these expressions are when the starting conditions are simple. Consider a vessel containing n_0 moles of water vapor only, with no hydrogen or oxygen present. If dissociation occurs until the degree of dissociation is ϵ, then the n's and x's are shown as functions of ϵ in Table 16-1. Since the chemical potential of each gas in the mixture is a function of T, P, and x, it follows that every chemical potential is a function of T, P, and ϵ.

If the reaction is imagined to proceed to an infinitesimal extent, the degree of reaction changing from ϵ to $\epsilon + d\epsilon$, the various n's will change by the following amounts:

$$
\begin{aligned}
dn_1 &= -(n_0 + n_0')\nu_1\, d\epsilon, & dn_3 &= (n_0 + n_0')\nu_3\, d\epsilon, \\
dn_2 &= -(n_0 + n_0')\nu_2\, d\epsilon, & dn_4 &= (n_0 + n_0')\nu_4\, d\epsilon.
\end{aligned}
$$

Table 16-1 $H_2O \rightleftharpoons H_2 + \frac{1}{2}O_2$

A	ν	n	x
$A_1 = H_2O$	$\nu_1 = 1$	$n_1 = n_0(1 - \epsilon)$	$x_1 = \dfrac{1 - \epsilon}{1 + \epsilon/2}$
$A_3 = H_2$	$\nu_3 = 1$	$n_3 = n_0\epsilon$	$x_3 = \dfrac{\epsilon}{1 + \epsilon/2}$
$A_4 = O_2$	$\nu_4 = \frac{1}{2}$	$n_4 = \dfrac{n_0\epsilon}{2}$	$x_4 = \dfrac{\epsilon/2}{1 + \epsilon/2}$
		$\Sigma n = n_0(1 + \epsilon/2)$	

These equations show that the changes in the n's are proportional to the ν's, with the factor of proportionality being, for the initial constituents, $-(n_0 + n_0') \, d\epsilon$ and, for the final constituents, $+(n_0 + n_0') \, d\epsilon$. Another way of writing these is as follows:

$$\frac{dn_1}{-\nu_1} = \frac{dn_2}{-\nu_2} = \frac{dn_3}{\nu_3} = \frac{dn_4}{\nu_4} = (n_0 + n_0') \, d\epsilon, \qquad (16\text{-}25)$$

which shows perhaps more clearly that the dn's are proportional to the ν's.

16-13   Equation of Reaction Equilibrium

Consider a homogeneous phase consisting of arbitrary amounts of the four constituents A_1, A_2, A_3, and A_4, capable of undergoing the reaction

$$\nu_1 A_1 + \nu_2 A_2 \rightleftharpoons \nu_3 A_3 + \nu_4 A_4.$$

Suppose that the phase is at a uniform temperature T and pressure P. If n_1, n_2, n_3, and n_4 denote the numbers of moles of each constituent that are present at any moment and μ_1, μ_2, μ_3, and μ_4 are the respective chemical potentials, then the Gibbs function of the mixture is

$$G = \mu_1 n_1 + \mu_2 n_2 + \mu_3 n_3 + \mu_4 n_4.$$

The n's are given by the equations of constraint:

$$n_1 = (n_0 + n_0')\nu_1(1 - \epsilon), \qquad\qquad n_3 = (n_0 + n_0')\nu_3\epsilon,$$
$$n_2 = (n_0 + n_0')\nu_2(1 - \epsilon) + N_2, \qquad n_4 = (n_0 + n_0')\nu_4\epsilon + N_4.$$

The μ's are functions of T, P, and ϵ. It therefore follows that G is a function of T, P, and ϵ.

Let us imagine that the reaction is allowed to take place at constant T and P. Under these conditions, the Gibbs function decreases; i.e., during an infinitesimal change in ϵ from ϵ to $\epsilon + d\epsilon$,

$$dG_{T,P} < 0.$$

We have shown that, for any infinitesimal change to which a phase in thermal and mechanical equilibrium is subjected,

$$dG = -S\,dT + V\,dP + \mu_1\,dn_1 + \mu_2\,dn_2 + \cdots.$$

Therefore, for this mixture of four constituents,

$$dG_{T,P} = \mu_1\,dn_1 + \mu_2\,dn_2 + \mu_3\,dn_3 + \mu_4\,dn_4,$$

with the equations of constraint in differential form:

$$dn_1 = -(n_0 + n_0')\nu_1\,d\epsilon, \qquad dn_3 = (n_0 + n_0')\nu_3\,d\epsilon,$$
$$dn_2 = -(n_0 + n_0')\nu_2\,d\epsilon, \qquad dn_4 = (n_0 + n_0')\nu_4\,d\epsilon.$$

Substituting, we obtain a general expression for an infinitesimal change of the Gibbs function at constant T and P. Thus,

$$dG_{T,P} = (n_0 + n_0')(-\nu_1\mu_1 - \nu_2\mu_2 + \nu_3\mu_3 + \nu_4\mu_4)\,d\epsilon. \qquad (16\text{-}26)$$

It follows from this equation that when the reaction proceeds spontaneously to the right, so that $d\epsilon$ is positive, then, in order that $dG_{T,P} < 0$,

$$\nu_1\mu_1 + \nu_2\mu_2 > \nu_3\mu_3 + \nu_4\mu_4 \qquad \text{(reaction to right)}.$$

Conversely, if the reaction proceeds spontaneously to the left,

$$\nu_1\mu_1 + \nu_2\mu_2 < \nu_3\mu_3 + \nu_4\mu_4 \qquad \text{(reaction to left)}.$$

The mixture will be in equilibrium at the given T and P when the Gibbs function is a minimum at which an infinitesimal change in ϵ will produce no change in the Gibbs function. Therefore, for $dG_{T,P} = 0$ at equilibrium, we have

$$\boxed{\nu_1\mu_1 + \nu_2\mu_2 = \nu_3\mu_3 + \nu_4\mu_4} \qquad \text{(at equilibrium)} \qquad (16\text{-}27)$$

which is called the *equation of reaction equilibrium*. It should be noted that this equation contains only intensive variables. Evidently, to determine the composition of a homogeneous mixture after the reaction has come to equilibrium, it is necessary merely to substitute the appropriate expressions for the chemical potentials into the equation of reaction equilibrium. This will be done in the case of ideal gases in the next chapter.

PROBLEMS

16-1   Prove Gibbs' theorem by using the apparatus depicted in Fig. 16-2 in such a way that the gases are separated reversibly and adiabatically.

16-2   What is the minimum amount of work required to separate 1 mole of air at 27°C and 1 atm pressure (assumed to be composed of $\frac{1}{5}O_2$ and $\frac{4}{5}N_2$) into O_2 and N_2, each at 27°C and 1 atm pressure?

16-3   Calculate the entropy change of the universe due to the diffusion of two ideal gases (1 mole of each) at the same temperature and pressure, by calculating $\int dQ/T$ over a series of reversible processes involving the use of the apparatus depicted in Fig. 16-2.

16-4 n_1 moles of an ideal monatomic gas at temperature T_1 and pressure P are in one compartment of an insulated container. In an adjoining compartment separated by an insulating partition are n_2 moles of another ideal monatomic gas at temperature T_2 and pressure P. When the partition is removed:

(*a*)   Show that the final pressure of the mixture is P.

(*b*)   Calculate the entropy change when the gases are identical.

(*c*)   Calculate the entropy change when the gases are different.

16-5 n_1 moles of an ideal gas at pressure P_1 and temperature T are in one compartment of an insulated container. In an adjoining compartment, separated by a partition, are n_2 moles of an ideal gas at pressure P_2 and temperature T. When the partition is removed:

(*a*)   Calculate the final pressure of the mixture.

(*b*)   Calculate the entropy change when the gases are identical.

(*c*)   Calculate the entropy change when the gases are different.

(*d*)   Prove that the entropy change in part (*c*) is the same as that which would be produced by two independent free expansions.

16-6   Suppose that we have 1 mole of a monatomic gas A whose nuclei are in their lowest energy state and 1 mole of a monatomic gas B consisting of exactly the same atoms as A, except that the nuclei are in an excited state whose energy ϵ is much larger than kT and whose lifetime is much larger than the time for diffusion to take place. Both gases are at the same pressure and are maintained at the same temperature T by a heat reservoir.

(a)   Immediately after the nuclei of gas B have been excited, diffusion takes place. Calculate the entropy change of the universe.

(b)   After the nuclei of gas B have been excited, a time much larger than the lifetime of the excited state is allowed to elapse, and then diffusion takes place. Calculate the entropy change of the universe.

(c)   Show that the answer to part (b) is larger than that to (a). (This problem is due to M. J. Klein.)

16-7   Consider the system depicted in Fig. P16-1, where the whole system and also each half are in equilibrium. Consider a process to take place

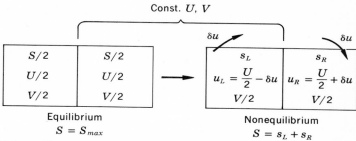

Fig. P16-1   *Transition from a state of thermodynamic equilibrium to a state characterized by a lack of thermal equilibrium.*

in which each half of the system remains at the constant volume $V/2$, but a small amount of heat δu (at constant volume $dQ = dU$) is extracted from the left half and transferred to the right half, as shown in Fig. P16-1. Realizing that

$$\left(\frac{\partial s}{\partial u}\right)_v = \left(\frac{\partial S}{\partial U}\right)_V,$$

(a)   Expand the entropy s_L of the left half by means of a Taylor series about the equilibrium value $S_{max}/2$, terminating the series after the squared term. Do the same for s_R.

(b)   Show that

$$\delta S_{U,V} = s_L + s_R - S_{max} = \left(\frac{\partial^2 S}{\partial U^2}\right)_V (\delta u)^2.$$

(c)   Show that $C_V > 0$, which is the *condition for thermal stability*.

16-8   (a)   Show that the molar Helmholtz function of an ideal gas is

$$f = u_0 - T \int \frac{\int c_V \, dT}{T^2} \, dT - T s_0 - RT \ln v.$$

(b)   Show that the Helmholtz function of a mixture of inert ideal gases is

$$F = \Sigma n_k (f_k + RT \ln x_k).$$

(c)   Show that the change in the Helmholtz function due to diffusion is

$$F_f - F_i = RT\Sigma n_k \ln x_k.$$

16-9   Consider a hydrostatic system of constant mass maintained in thermal and mechanical equilibrium. It is not in chemical equilibrium, however, because of chemical reactions and transport of matter between phases. Under these circumstances, the system undergoes an irreversible cycle. Prove that

$$\oint_I \frac{dQ}{T} < 0.$$

16-10   By means of the equations $dG = -S\,dT + V\,dP + \Sigma\mu_k\,dn_k$ and $G = \Sigma\mu_k n_k$, prove that:

(a) $-S\,dT + V\,dP = \Sigma n_k\,d\mu_k.$

(b) $-s\,dT + v\,dP = \Sigma x_k\,d\mu_k.$

16-11   Show that, if the internal energy of a phase is expressed as a function of S, V, n_1, n_2, . . . , n_c, then:

(a) $dU = T\,dS - P\,dV + \Sigma\mu_k\,dn_k$ where $\mu_k = (\partial U/\partial n_k)_{S,V,\text{ other } n\text{'s}}.$

(b) $U = TS - PV + \Sigma\mu_k n_k.$

(c) $-S\,dT + V\,dP = \Sigma n_k\,d\mu_k.$

16-12   Show that, if the Helmholtz function of a phase is expressed as a function of T, V, n_1, n_2, . . . , n_c, then:

(a) $dF = -S\,dT - P\,dV + \Sigma\mu_k\,dn_k$ where $\mu_k = (\partial F/\partial n_k)_{T,V,\text{other } n\text{'s}}.$

(b) $F = -PV + \Sigma\mu_k n_k.$

(c) $-S\,dT + V\,dP = \Sigma n_k\,d\mu_k.$

16-13   Prove that:

(a) $$Td\left(\frac{F}{T}\right) = -\frac{U}{T}\,dT - P\,dV + \Sigma\mu_k\,dn_k.$$

(b) $$d(PV) = S\,dT + P\,dV + \Sigma n_k\,d\mu_k.$$

16-14   Show that, for an ideal gas in a mixture of ideal gases,

$$d\mu_k = \frac{\mu_k - h_k}{T} \, dT + v_k \, dP + RT \, d \ln x_k.$$

16-15   Consider a uniform substance of variable mass. Suppose that at any moment there are n moles of substance and that the system undergoes an infinitesimal reversible process in which n changes by dn. For any *1 mole* of substance,

$$dq = T \, ds = du + P \, dv,$$

and the total heat transfer $dQ = n \, dq = nT \, ds$.

(a)   Prove that

$$dQ = dU + P \, dV - h \, dn,$$

where U and V refer to the entire system, but h is the molar enthalpy.

(b)   From Prob. 16-11a, show that

$$T \, dS = dU + P \, dV - g \, dn.$$

(c)   How does $T \, dS$ differ from dQ?

(d)   Show that, if T and P remain constant, $dQ = 0$ but $T \, dS$ does not.

16-16   Starting with n_0 moles of CO and n_0 moles of H_2O capable of undergoing the reaction

$$CO + H_2O \rightleftharpoons CO_2 + H_2$$

in the gaseous phase, set up a table of values of A, v, n, and x, similar to that of Table 16-1.

16-17   Starting with n_0 moles of H_2S and $2n_0$ moles of H_2O, capable of undergoing the reaction

$$H_2S + 2H_2O \rightleftharpoons 3H_2 + SO_2$$

in the gaseous phase, set up a table of values of A, v, n, and x, similar to that of Table 16-1.

17.

IDEAL-GAS REACTIONS

17-1   Law of Mass Action

It has been shown that when four substances which are capable of undergoing the reaction

$$\nu_1 A_1 + \nu_2 A_2 \rightleftharpoons \nu_3 A_3 + \nu_4 A_4,$$

and which constitute a homogeneous phase at constant temperature and pressure, come to equilibrium, the equation of reaction equilibrium

$$\nu_1 \mu_1 + \nu_2 \mu_2 = \nu_3 \mu_3 + \nu_4 \mu_4$$

must be satisfied. If the constituents are ideal gases, then the chemical potentials are given by expressions of the type

$$\mu_k = RT(\phi_k + \ln P + \ln x_k),$$

where the ϕ's are functions of the temperature only. Substituting in the equation of reaction equilibrium, we get

$$\nu_1(\phi_1 + \ln P + \ln x_1) + \nu_2(\phi_2 + \ln P + \ln x_2)$$
$$= \nu_3(\phi_3 + \ln P + \ln x_3) + \nu_4(\phi_4 + \ln P + \ln x_4).$$

Rearranging terms,

$$\nu_3 \ln x_3 + \nu_4 \ln x_4 - \nu_1 \ln x_1 - \nu_2 \ln x_2$$
$$+ (\nu_3 + \nu_4 - \nu_1 - \nu_2) \ln P = -(\nu_3\phi_3 + \nu_4\phi_4 - \nu_1\phi_1 - \nu_2\phi_2),$$

or

$$\ln \frac{x_3^{\nu_3} x_4^{\nu_4}}{x_1^{\nu_1} x_2^{\nu_2}} P^{\nu_3 + \nu_4 - \nu_1 - \nu_2} = -(\nu_3\phi_3 + \nu_4\phi_4 - \nu_1\phi_1 - \nu_2\phi_2).$$

The right-hand member is a quantity whose value depends only on the temperature. Denoting it by $\ln K$, where K is known as the *equilibrium constant*,

$$\ln K = -(\nu_3\phi_3 + \nu_4\phi_4 - \nu_1\phi_1 - \nu_2\phi_2),$$ (17-1)

we get finally

$$\boxed{\left(\frac{x_3^{\nu_3}x_4^{\nu_4}}{x_1^{\nu_1}x_2^{\nu_2}}\right)_{\epsilon=\epsilon_e} P^{\nu_3+\nu_4-\nu_1-\nu_2} = K,}$$ (17-2)

which is called the *law of mass action*. K has the dimensions of pressure raised to the $(\nu_3 + \nu_4 - \nu_1 - \nu_2)$th power. The fraction involving the equilibrium values of the x's is a function of the equilibrium value of ϵ—that is, of ϵ_e—and hence the law of mass action is seen to be a relation among ϵ_e, P, and T.

It is obvious that, if there are more than two initial constituents and two final constituents, the law of mass action becomes

$$\left(\frac{x_3^{\nu_3}x_4^{\nu_4}\cdots}{x_1^{\nu_1}x_2^{\nu_2}\cdots}\right)_{\epsilon=\epsilon_e} P^{\nu_3+\nu_4+\cdots-\nu_1-\nu_2-\cdots} = K,$$

where K is given by

$$\ln K = -(\nu_3\phi_3 + \nu_4\phi_4 + \cdots - \nu_1\phi_1 - \nu_2\phi_2 - \cdots).$$

17-2   Experimental Determination of Equilibrium Constants

It has been pointed out that a mixture of hydrogen and oxygen will remain indefinitely without reacting at atmospheric pressure and at room temperature. If the temperature is raised considerably, however, water vapor forms and equilibrium takes place quickly. If the mixture is then cooled very suddenly so as not to disturb the equilibrium, an analysis of the composition of the mixture yields the values of the mole fractions corresponding to equilibrium at the high temperature. The equilibrium has, so to speak, been "frozen." Sometimes a flow method is used. The reacting gases are mixed in known proportions at a low temperature, and the mixture is caused to flow slowly through a long reacting tube at a desired temperature. The gases remain at this temperature a sufficient time for equilibrium to take place. The mixture is then allowed to flow through a capillary, where it is suddenly cooled. The equilibrium values of the mole fractions are then measured by the methods of chemical analysis.

It is a consequence of the law of mass action that the equilibrium constant corresponding to a given temperature is independent of the amounts of products which are originally mixed. For example, in the case of the "water-gas" reaction,

$$CO_2 + H_2 \rightleftharpoons CO + H_2O,$$

the law of mass action requires that, at equilibrium,

$$\frac{x_{CO} x_{H_2O}}{x_{CO_2} x_{H_2}} P^{1+1-1-1} = K,$$

or

$$\frac{x_{CO} x_{H_2O}}{x_{CO_2} x_{H_2}} = \text{const.}$$

at a constant temperature, independent of the starting conditions. For conditions that involve starting with arbitrary amounts of CO_2 and H_2 and maintaining the temperature constant at 1259°K, the equilibrium values of the mole fractions are given in Table 17-1, where it may be seen that K is quite constant.

Table 17-1   Equilibrium data for the Water-gas Reaction
$CO_2 + H_2 \rightleftharpoons CO + H_2O$ at 1259°K

Original mixture		Equilibrium mixture			$K = \dfrac{x_{CO} x_{H_2O}}{x_{CO_2} x_{H_2}}$
x_{CO_2}	x_{H_2}	x_{CO_2}	$x_{CO} = x_{H_2O}$	x_{H_2}	
0.101	0.899	0.0069	0.094	0.805	1.60
0.310	0.699	0.0715	0.2296	0.4693	1.58
0.491	0.509	0.2122	0.2790	0.2295	1.60
0.609	0.391	0.3443	0.2645	0.1267	1.60
0.703	0.297	0.4750	0.2282	0.0685	1.60

The water-gas reaction is an example of a reaction that does not involve a change in the total number of moles. If such a reaction were to take place at constant temperature and pressure, there would be no change in volume. There are, however, many reactions in which the total number of moles varies. In such cases, it is possible to measure the value of the degree of reaction at equilibrium by merely measuring the volume (or the density) of the mixture at equilibrium. If ϵ_e is known, the equilibrium constant can then be calculated. As an example of this procedure, consider the dissociation of nitrogen tetroxide according to the equation

$$N_2O_4 \rightleftharpoons 2NO_2.$$

If we start with n_0 moles of N_2O_4 at temperature T and pressure P, the initial volume is expressed as

$$V_0 = n_0 \frac{RT}{P}.$$

If V_e denotes the volume at equilibrium, with the temperature and pressure remaining the same, then

$$V_e = [n_0(1 - \epsilon_e) + 2n_0\epsilon_e] \frac{RT}{P},$$

where ϵ_e is the value of the degree of dissociation at equilibrium. This can be written as

$$V_e = (1 + \epsilon_e)V_0,$$

or

$$\epsilon_e = \frac{V_e}{V_0} - 1.$$

Since the density ρ is inversely proportional to the volume, we get finally

$$\epsilon_e = \frac{\rho_0}{\rho_e} - 1.$$

Now, at equilibrium,

$$x_{N_2O_4} = \frac{n_0(1 - \epsilon_e)}{n_0(1 + \epsilon_e)} \quad \text{and} \quad x_{NO_2} = \frac{2n_0\epsilon_e}{n_0(1 + \epsilon_e)};$$

therefore the law of mass action becomes

$$\frac{[2\epsilon_e/(1 + \epsilon_e)]^2}{(1 - \epsilon_e)/(1 + \epsilon_e)} P = K,$$

or

$$\frac{4\epsilon_e^2}{1 - \epsilon_e^2} P = K.$$

The pressure is always measured in atmospheres. Numerical data for this reaction are given in Table 17-2, where it is seen that at the constant temperature of 323°K the equilibrium constant remains fairly constant for three different values of the pressure.

There are many other methods of measuring equilibrium constants. For a complete account of this important branch of physical chemistry, the student is referred to an advanced treatise.

Table 17-2 $N_2O_4 \rightleftharpoons 2NO_2$

Temp., °K	P, atm	ρ_0 (air = 1)	ρ_e (air = 1)	$\epsilon_e = \dfrac{\rho_0}{\rho_e} - 1$	$K = \dfrac{4\epsilon_e^2}{1 - \epsilon_e^2} P$, atm
	0.124	3.179	1.788	0.777	0.752
323	0.241	3.179	1.894	0.678	0.818
	0.655	3.179	2.144	0.483	0.797

17-3   Heat of Reaction

The equilibrium constant is defined by the equation

$$\ln K = -(\nu_3\phi_3 + \nu_4\phi_4 - \nu_1\phi_1 - \nu_2\phi_2).$$

Differentiating $\ln K$ with respect to T, we get

$$\frac{d}{dT}\ln K = -\left(\nu_3\frac{d\phi_3}{dT} + \nu_4\frac{d\phi_4}{dT} - \nu_1\frac{d\phi_1}{dT} - \nu_2\frac{d\phi_2}{dT}\right).$$

Since

$$\phi = \frac{h_0}{RT} - \frac{1}{R}\int\frac{\int c_P\,dT}{T^2}\,dT - \frac{s_0}{R},$$

we have

$$\frac{d\phi}{dT} = -\frac{h_0}{RT^2} - \frac{\int c_P\,dT}{RT^2}$$

$$= -\frac{1}{RT^2}\left(h_0 + \int c_P\,dT\right),$$

and

$$\frac{d\phi}{dt} = -\frac{h}{RT^2}. \qquad (17\text{-}3)$$

Therefore,

$$\frac{d}{dT}\ln K = \frac{1}{RT^2}(\nu_3 h_3 + \nu_4 h_4 - \nu_1 h_1 - \nu_2 h_2),$$

where all the h's refer to the same temperature T and the same pressure P. The right-hand term has a simple interpretation. If ν_1 moles of A_1 and ν_2 moles of A_2 are converted at constant temperature and pressure into ν_3 moles of A_3 and ν_4 moles of A_4, the heat transferred will be equal to the final enthalpy $\nu_3 h_3 + \nu_4 h_4$ minus the initial enthalpy $\nu_1 h_1 + \nu_2 h_2$. Calling this heat the *heat of reaction* and denoting it by ΔH, we have

$$\Delta H = \nu_3 h_3 + \nu_4 h_4 - \nu_1 h_1 - \nu_2 h_2, \qquad (17\text{-}4)$$

and

$$\frac{d}{dT} \ln K = \frac{\Delta H}{RT^2}.$$

(17-5)

The preceding equation, called the *van't Hoff isobar*, is one of the most important equations in chemical thermodynamics.

Rewriting the equation as

$$\frac{d \ln K}{dT/T^2} = \frac{\Delta H}{R},$$

or

$$\frac{d \ln K}{d(1/T)} = -\frac{\Delta H}{R},$$

we get

$$\Delta H = -2.30R \frac{d \log K}{d(1/T)}.$$

(17-6)

The van't Hoff isobar enables one to calculate the heat of reaction at any desired temperature or within any desired temperature range, once the temperature variation of the equilibrium constant is known. The slope of the curve obtained by plotting $\log K$ against $1/T$, multiplied by $2.30R$, is the heat of reaction at the temperature corresponding to the point chosen. As a rule, $\log K$ can be measured only within a small temperature range, in which case the curve is usually a straight line.

As an example of this procedure, consider the dissociation of water vapor according to the reaction

$$H_2O \rightleftharpoons H_2 + \tfrac{1}{2}O_2.$$

Starting with n_0 moles of water vapor and no hydrogen or oxygen, the mole fractions corresponding to any value ϵ of the degree of dissociation are shown in Table 16-1. At equilibrium,

$$\left(\frac{x_3^{\nu_3} x_4^{\nu_4}}{x_1^{\nu_1}}\right)_{\epsilon=\epsilon_e} P^{\nu_3+\nu_4-\nu_1} = K,$$

or

$$\frac{\dfrac{\epsilon_e}{1+\epsilon_e/2}\left(\dfrac{\epsilon_e/2}{1+\epsilon_e/2}\right)^{\frac{1}{2}}}{\dfrac{1-\epsilon_e}{1+\epsilon_e/2}} P^{\frac{1}{2}} = K,$$

or

$$\frac{\epsilon_e^{\frac{3}{2}}}{(2+\epsilon_e)^{\frac{1}{2}}(1-\epsilon_e)} P^{\frac{1}{2}} = K.$$

When ϵ_e is very much smaller than unity, this equation reduces to

$$K = \sqrt{\frac{\epsilon_e^3 P}{2}}.$$

In Table 17-3 experimental value of ϵ_e are given at a number of tempera-

Table 17-3 $H_2O \rightleftharpoons H_2 + \frac{1}{2}O_2$ $(P = 1 \text{ atm})$

Temp., °K	ϵ_e (measured)	$K = \dfrac{\epsilon_e^{\frac{3}{2}} P^{\frac{1}{2}}}{(2 + \epsilon_e)^{\frac{1}{2}} (1 - \epsilon_e)},$ $(\text{atm})^{\frac{1}{2}}$	log K	$\dfrac{1}{T}$
1500	1.97×10^{-4}	1.95×10^{-6}	-5.71	6.67×10^{-4}
1561	$3.4 \ \times 10^{-4}$	4.48×10^{-5}	-5.36	6.41×10^{-4}
1705	$1.2 \ \times 10^{-3}$	2.95×10^{-5}	-4.53	5.87×10^{-4}
2155	$1.2 \ \times 10^{-2}$	$9.0 \ \times 10^{-4}$	-3.05	4.64×10^{-4}
2257	1.77×10^{-2}	1.67×10^{-3}	-2.78	4.43×10^{-4}
2300	$2.6 \ \times 10^{-2}$	2.95×10^{-3}	-2.53	4.35×10^{-4}

tures and at constant atmospheric pressure, along with the corresponding values of K, log K, and $1/T$. The graph of log K against $1/T$ is shown in Fig. 17-1, where it is seen that the points lie on a straight line with a slope equal to $-13,100$. It follows, therefore, that the heat of dissociation at the average temperature of about 1900°K is equal to

$$\Delta H = -2.30 \, R \times -13,100$$

$$= 250 \text{ kJ/mole.}$$

It is rather difficult to measure the heat of reaction accurately by a direct calorimetric method. Most heats of reaction are obtained either with the aid of the van't Hoff isobar or by means of a reversible cell. In a few cases in which it is possible to measure the equilibrium constant over a very wide temperature range, the graph of log K against $1/T$ is found to have a variable slope, indicating that the heat of reaction depends on the temperature. Such a graph is impossible to obtain in most cases, however, since at low temperatures a reaction either does not proceed or, if it does, the equilibrium value of the degree of reaction is too small to measure. Thus, in the case of the dissociation of water vapor, the degree of dissociation at room temperature and atmospheric pressure is about 10^{-27}, which means that under these conditions not even one molecule of H_2O dissociates.

To obtain the heat of reaction at any desired temperature, it is necessary

Fig. 17-1   *Graph of log K against $1/T$ for dissociation of water vapor.*

to know the temperature dependence of the heat capacities of all the reacting gases. Since

$$\Delta H = \nu_3 h_3 + \nu_4 h_4 - \nu_1 h_1 - \nu_2 h_2$$

and

$$h = h_0 + \int c_P \, dT,$$

then

$$\Delta H = \nu_3 h_{03} + \nu_4 h_{04} - \nu_1 h_{01} - \nu_2 h_{02} + \int (\nu_3 c_{P3} + \nu_4 c_{P4} - \nu_1 c_{P1} - \nu_2 c_{P2}) \, dT.$$

Denoting the constant part by ΔH_0 thus:

and defining

$$\Delta H_0 = \nu_3 h_{03} + \nu_4 h_{04} - \nu_1 h_{01} - \nu_2 h_{02} \tag{17-7}$$

$$\Delta C_P = \nu_3 c_{P3} + \nu_4 c_{P4} - \nu_1 c_{P1} - \nu_2 c_{P2}, \tag{17-8}$$

we get

$$\boxed{\Delta H = \Delta H_0 + \int \Delta C_P \, dT.} \tag{17-9}$$

The integral can be determined by substituting for the c_P's the empiric equations expressing their temperature dependence. If ΔH is known at one temperature, therefore, ΔH_0 can be calculated and the equation may be used to provide ΔH at any temperature.

17-4   Nernst's Equation

The equilibrium constant is defined by the equation

$$\ln K = -(\nu_3\phi_3 + \nu_4\phi_4 - \nu_1\phi_1 - \nu_2\phi_2),$$

where

$$\phi = \frac{h_0}{RT} - \frac{1}{R}\int\frac{\int c_P\,dT}{T^2}\,dT - \frac{s_0}{R}.$$

We have, therefore,

$$\ln K = -\frac{1}{RT}(\nu_3 h_{03} + \nu_4 h_{04} - \nu_1 h_{01} - \nu_2 h_{02})$$
$$+ \frac{1}{R}\int\frac{\int(\nu_3 c_{P3} + \nu_4 c_{P4} - \nu_1 c_{P1} - \nu_2 c_{P2})\,dT}{T^2}\,dT$$
$$+ \frac{1}{R}(\nu_3 s_{03} + \nu_4 s_{04} - \nu_1 s_{01} - \nu_2 s_{02}).$$

Defining

$$\Delta S_0 = \nu_3 s_{03} + \nu_4 s_{04} - \nu_1 s_{01} - \nu_2 s_{02},$$

the equation becomes

$$\boxed{\ln K = -\frac{\Delta H_0}{RT} + \frac{1}{R}\int\frac{\int \Delta C_P\,dT}{T^2}\,dT + \frac{\Delta S_0}{R},} \qquad (17\text{-}10)$$

which is known as *Nernst's equation*.

An interesting application of Nernst's equation was made by **Megh Nad Saha** to the thermal ionization of a monatomic gas. If a monatomic gas is heated to a high enough temperature, some ionization occurs and the atoms,

Table 17-4 $A \rightleftharpoons A^+ + e$

A	ν	n	x
$A_1 = A$	$\nu_1 = 1$	$n_1 = n_0(1 - \epsilon_e)$	$x_1 = \dfrac{1 - \epsilon_e}{1 + \epsilon_e}$
$A_3 = A^+$	$\nu_3 = 1$	$n_3 = n_0\epsilon_e$	$x_3 = \dfrac{\epsilon_e}{1 + \epsilon_e}$
$A_4 = e$	$\nu_4 = 1$	$n_4 = n_0\epsilon_e$	$x_4 = \dfrac{\epsilon_e}{1 + \epsilon_e}$
	$\nu_3 + \nu_4 - \nu_1 = 1$	$\Sigma n = n_0(1 + \epsilon_e)$	

ions, and electrons may be regarded as a mixture of three ideal monatomic gases undergoing the reaction

$$A \rightleftharpoons A^+ + e.$$

Starting with n_0 moles of atoms alone, the state of affairs at equilibrium is shown in Table 17-4. For this reaction,

$$\ln K = \ln \frac{x_3^{\nu_3} x_4^{\nu_4}}{x_1^{\nu_1}} P^{\nu_3 + \nu_4 - \nu_1}$$

$$= \ln \frac{[\epsilon_e/(1 + \epsilon_e)][\epsilon_e/(1 + \epsilon_e)]}{(1 - \epsilon_e)/(1 + \epsilon_e)} P,$$

or
$$\ln K = \ln \frac{\epsilon_e^2}{1 - \epsilon_e^2} P.$$

ΔH_0 is the amount of energy necessary to ionize 1 mole of atoms. If we denote the ionization potential of the atom in volts by E, then $\Delta H_0 = N_F E$, where N_F is Faraday's constant. Since the three gases are monatomic, each c_P is equal to $\frac{5}{2}R$. Therefore $\Delta C_P = \frac{5}{2}R$, and

$$\frac{1}{R} \int \frac{\int \Delta C_P \, dT}{T^2} \, dT = \tfrac{5}{2} \ln T.$$

Let us put

$$\frac{\Delta S_0}{R} = \ln B.$$

Introducing these results into Nernst's equation, we get

$$\ln \frac{\epsilon_e^2}{1 - \epsilon_e^2} P = -\frac{N_F E}{RT} + \frac{5}{2} \ln T + \ln B.$$

Expressing P in atmospheres, changing to common logarithms, and introducing the value of B from statistical mechanics, Saha finally obtained the formula

$$\log \frac{\epsilon_e^2}{1 - \epsilon_e^2} P(\text{atm}) = -(5050 \text{ deg/V}) \frac{E}{T} + \frac{5}{2} \log T + \log \frac{\omega_i \omega_e}{\omega_a} - 6.491,$$

$$(17\text{-}11)$$

where ω_i, ω_e, and ω_a are constants that refer, respectively, to the ion, the electron, and the atom.

In order to apply Saha's equation to a specific problem, it is necessary to know the ionization potential and the ω's. A complete discussion of these quantities is beyond the scope of this book. Values of these constants for a few elements are listed in Table 17-5. The constant ω for an electron is 2.

Table 17-5   Values of E and ω

Element	E, V	ω_a	ω_i
Na	5.12	2	1
Cs	3.87	2	1
Ca	6.09	1	2
Cd	8.96	1	2
Zn	9.36	1	2
Tl	6.07	2	1

Saha applied his equation to the determination of the temperature of a stellar atmosphere. The spectrum of a star contains lines which originate from atoms (*arc lines*) and also those which originate from ions (*spark lines*). A comparison of the intensity of a spark line with that of an arc line, both referring to the same element, gives rise to a value of the degree of ionization ϵ_e. Treating a star as a sphere of ideal gas, it is possible to obtain an estimate of the pressure of a stellar atmosphere. Since all the other quantities are known, the temperature can be calculated.

17-5   Affinity

It was shown in Art. 16-5 that the molar Gibbs function of an ideal gas at temperature T and pressure P is equal to

$$g = RT(\phi + \ln P).$$

If we have four gases that can engage in the reaction

$$\nu_1 A_1 + \nu_2 A_2 \rightleftharpoons \nu_3 A_3 + \nu_4 A_4,$$

we define the Gibbs function change of the reaction by the expression

$$\Delta G = \nu_3 g_3 + \nu_4 g_4 - \nu_1 g_1 - \nu_2 g_2, \tag{17-12}$$

where the g's refer to the gases completely separated at T, P. It should be emphasized that ΔG is defined in terms of the separate Gibbs functions of the gases, not in terms of the mixture. Among American chemists, ΔG is known as the *free-energy change*. The connection between ΔG and the behavior of the gases when mixed is shown by introducing the values of the g's. Thus,

$$\Delta G = RT(\nu_3\phi_3 + \nu_4\phi_4 - \nu_1\phi_1 - \nu_2\phi_2) + RT \ln P^{\nu_3 + \nu_4 - \nu_1 - \nu_2}.$$

But
$$\ln K = -(\nu_3\phi_3 + \nu_4\phi_4 - \nu_1\phi_1 - \nu_2\phi_2);$$

therefore,
$$\Delta G = -RT \ln K + RT \ln P^{\nu_3 + \nu_4 - \nu_1 - \nu_2}. \tag{17-13}$$

The student will recall that K also contains the factor P raised to the $(\nu_3 + \nu_4 - \nu_1 - \nu_2)$th power. It follows, therefore, that the above equation will be satisfied when both P's are measured in the same units, whatever the units are. If we express P in atmospheres as usual and calculate ΔG when each gas is at a pressure of 1 atm, the second term on the right drops out. Under these conditions, ΔG is known as the *standard Gibbs function change* and is denoted by ΔG°. Therefore,

$$\boxed{\Delta G^0 = -RT \ln K.} \tag{17-14}$$

Let us imagine that ν_1 moles of A_1 and ν_2 moles of A_2 are mixed at uniform temperature T and pressure P and that chemical reaction takes place, thereby forming constituents A_3 and A_4. At any moment when the degree of reaction is ϵ, the Gibbs function of the mixture is

$$G = \mu_1 n_1 + \mu_2 n_2 + \mu_3 n_3 + \mu_4 n_4,$$

where
$$n_1 = \nu_1(1 - \epsilon), \qquad n_3 = \nu_3\epsilon,$$
$$n_2 = \nu_2(1 - \epsilon), \qquad n_4 = \nu_4\epsilon,$$

and each chemical potential is a function of T, P, and ϵ. It follows that G is a function of T, P, and ϵ; therefore, at constant T and P, G is a function of ϵ only. The graph of G against ϵ has somewhat the form shown in Fig. 17-2.

At the equilibrium point where $\epsilon = \epsilon_e$, the curve has a minimum at which

$$\left(\frac{\partial G}{\partial \epsilon}\right)_{T,P} = 0 \qquad \text{(at } \epsilon = \epsilon_e).$$

The slopes of the curve at the points $\epsilon = 0$ and $\epsilon = 1$ may be calculated from the equation derived in Art. 16-13, namely,

$$dG_{T,P} = (n_0 + n_0')(\nu_3\mu_3 + \nu_4\mu_4 - \nu_1\mu_1 - \nu_2\mu_2)\, d\epsilon,$$

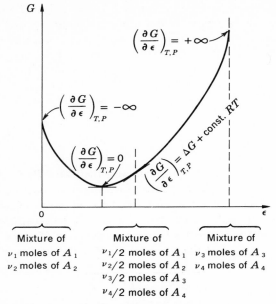

Fig. 17-2   *Graph of G against ϵ at constant T and P.*

which in this case becomes

$$\left(\frac{\partial G}{\partial \epsilon}\right)_{T,P} = \nu_3\mu_3 + \nu_4\mu_4 - \nu_1\mu_1 - \nu_2\mu_2. \qquad (17\text{-}15)$$

Since $\mu_k = RT(\phi_k + \ln P + \ln x_k)$

and $g_k = RT(\phi_k + \ln P),$

the chemical potential may be written in convenient form

$$\mu_k = g_k + RT \ln x_k.$$

Therefore,

$$\left(\frac{\partial G}{\partial \epsilon}\right)_{T,P} = \nu_3 g_3 + \nu_4 g_4 - \nu_1 g_1 - \nu_2 g_2$$
$$+ RT(\nu_3 \ln x_3 + \nu_4 \ln x_4 - \nu_1 \ln x_1 - \nu_2 \ln x_2),$$

or $$\left(\frac{\partial G}{\partial \epsilon}\right)_{T,P} = \Delta G + RT \ln \frac{x_3^{\nu_3} x_4^{\nu_4}}{x_1^{\nu_1} x_2^{\nu_2}}. \qquad (17\text{-}16)$$

It should be borne in mind that the x's in this equation are not equilibrium values but correspond to *any* value of ϵ. Now, when $\epsilon = 0$, there are no final constituents, and therefore both x_3 and x_4 are zero. Hence,

$$\left(\frac{\partial G}{\partial \epsilon}\right)_{T,P} = -\infty \qquad \text{(at } \epsilon = 0\text{).}$$

On the other hand, when $\epsilon = 1$, there are no initial constituents and therefore x_1 and x_2 are zero. Hence,

$$\left(\frac{\partial G}{\partial \epsilon}\right)_{T,P} = +\infty \qquad \text{(at } \epsilon = 1\text{).}$$

The graph in Fig. 17-2 has these properties.

Consider the point $\epsilon = \frac{1}{2}$ at which there are $\nu_1/2$ moles of A_1; $\nu_2/2$ moles of A_2; $\nu_3/2$ moles of A_3; and $\nu_4/2$ moles of A_4. At this point the constituents are present in proportion to their stoichiometric coefficients, and the mole fractions are

$$x_1 = \frac{\nu_1}{\Sigma \nu}, \qquad x_3 = \frac{\nu_3}{\Sigma \nu},$$

$$x_2 = \frac{\nu_2}{\Sigma \nu}, \qquad x_4 = \frac{\nu_4}{\Sigma \nu}.$$

The slope of the curve at this point indicates whether such a mixture is in equilibrium or not. If this slope is positive, the equilibrium point is to the left; i.e., when both the initial and final constituents are mixed, there will be a tendency for the reaction to proceed to the left, causing initial constituents to be formed. Conversely, if the slope of the curve at $\epsilon = \frac{1}{2}$ is negative, the equilibrium point is to the right; or when both initial and final constituents are mixed, there will be a tendency for the reaction to proceed to the right, causing final constituents to be formed. Finally, if this slope is zero, a mixture of both initial and final constituents is in equilibrium, and there is no tendency for the reaction to proceed at all.

It is seen, therefore, that the *sign* of the slope of the $G\epsilon$ curve at $\epsilon = \frac{1}{2}$ is an indication of the behavior of a system composed of initial and final constituents mixed in proportion to their stoichiometric coefficients. Furthermore, it is obvious from the curve that the *magnitude* of this slope is a measure of the departure from or nearness to equilibrium of such a mixture. We shall call the slope of the $G\epsilon$ curve at the point $\epsilon = \frac{1}{2}$ the *affinity* of the reaction, which is equal to

$$\left(\frac{\partial G}{\partial \epsilon}\right)_{T,P} (\epsilon = \tfrac{1}{2}) = \Delta G + RT \ln \frac{(\nu_3/\Sigma \nu)^{\nu_3}(\nu_4/\Sigma \nu)^{\nu_4}}{(\nu_1/\Sigma \nu)^{\nu_1}(\nu_2/\Sigma \nu)^{\nu_2}}. \qquad (17\text{-}17)$$

This equation is true at all temperatures and pressures. Let us choose $T = 298°K$ and $P = 1$ atm. The last term on the right is a constant for each reaction. When all the ν's are unity, this term is zero. In general, its value is much less than ΔG°_{298}. Consequently, ΔG°_{298} has much more effect on the quantity $\partial G / \partial \epsilon$ than the other term. We may therefore write:

$$\frac{\partial G}{\partial \epsilon}\left[\begin{array}{l} \epsilon = \frac{1}{2} \\ T = 298°K \\ P = 1 \text{ atm} \end{array}\right] \sim \Delta G^{\circ}_{298}. \qquad (17\text{-}18)$$

Therefore, *the standard Gibbs function change at 298°K is an indication of the direction and amount to which a reaction will proceed at this temperature.* For example, ΔG°_{298} for the water-vapor reaction is a large positive number, meaning that the equilibrium point is far to the left of $\epsilon = \frac{1}{2}$, and therefore ϵ_e is very small. Again, ΔG°_{298} is a large negative number for the reaction $NO \rightleftharpoons \frac{1}{2}N_2 + \frac{1}{2}O_2$; therefore the equilibrium point is far to the right of $\epsilon = \frac{1}{2}$, and ϵ_e is almost unity.

17-6   Displacement of Equilibrium

The equilibrium value of the degree of reaction was obtained by setting $(\partial G / \partial \epsilon)_{T,P}$ equal to zero. This, however, is the condition that G be a maximum as well as a minimum. In order to verify that G is a minimum, it is necessary to show that $(\partial^2 G / \partial \epsilon^2)_{T,P}$ is positive at the equilibrium point. For a mixture of arbitrary amounts of four chemically active ideal gases, we have

$$\left(\frac{\partial G}{\partial \epsilon}\right)_{T,P} = (n_0 + n'_0)\left(\Delta G + RT \ln \frac{x_3^{\nu_3}x_4^{\nu_4}}{x_1^{\nu_1}x_2^{\nu_2}}\right)$$

for all values of ϵ. Therefore, since ΔG is a function of T and P only,

$$\left(\frac{\partial^2 G}{\partial \epsilon^2}\right)_{T,P} = (n_0 + n'_0)RT\frac{d}{d\epsilon} \ln \frac{x_3^{\nu_3}x_4^{\nu_4}}{x_1^{\nu_1}x_2^{\nu_2}}. \qquad (17\text{-}19)$$

The right-hand member of this equation can be easily evaluated for any value of ϵ (the details of this calculation constitute Prob. 17-14a), and is found to be

$$\frac{d}{d\epsilon} \ln \frac{x_3^{\nu_3}x_4^{\nu_4}}{x_1^{\nu_1}x_2^{\nu_2}} = \frac{n_0 + n'_0}{\Sigma n_k}\left[\frac{\nu_1^2}{x_1} + \frac{\nu_2^2}{x_2} + \frac{\nu_3^2}{x_3} + \frac{\nu_4^2}{x_4} - (\Delta\nu)^2\right], \qquad (17\text{-}20)$$

where $\Delta\nu = \nu_3 + \nu_4 - \nu_1 - \nu_2$. It may be proved rigorously that the expression in brackets is positive for all values of the ν's and x's. The proof, however, is rather lengthy. If we do not insist on complete generality but choose as starting conditions $n_0\nu_1$ moles of A_1 and $n_0\nu_2$ moles of A_2, with no amount of A_3 and A_4, then the preceding equation reduces to the following simple form (this calculation constitutes Prob. 17-14c):

$$\frac{d}{d\epsilon} \ln \frac{x_3^{\nu_3}x_4^{\nu_4}}{x_1^{\nu_1}x_2^{\nu_2}} = \frac{n_0}{\Sigma n_k} \frac{(\nu_1 + \nu_2)(\nu_3 + \nu_4)}{\epsilon(1 - \epsilon)}. \tag{17-21}$$

Since the right-hand member of this equation is always positive for all ν's and all values of ϵ, it follows that $(\partial G^2/\partial\epsilon^2)_{T,P}$ is always positive; hence, when $\epsilon = \epsilon_e$, G is a minimum and not a maximum. It will be seen that this plays an important role in determining the displacement of equilibrium when the temperature or the pressure is changed.

Let us consider first the effect on the equilibrium value of the degree of reaction of a change of temperature at constant pressure. We know that at equilibrium the law of mass action provides us with a relation among T, ϵ_e, and P, which may be written in the form

$$\ln K = \ln \left(\frac{x_3^{\nu_3}x_4^{\nu_4}}{x_1^{\nu_1}x_2^{\nu_2}}\right)_{\epsilon=\epsilon_0} + (\nu_3 + \nu_4 - \nu_1 - \nu_2) \ln P,$$

where $\ln K$ is a function of T only, and the first term on the right is a function of ϵ_e only. Now,

$$\left(\frac{\partial\epsilon_e}{\partial T}\right)_P = \left(\frac{\partial\epsilon_e}{\partial \ln K}\right)_P \left(\frac{\partial \ln K}{\partial T}\right)_P$$

$$= \frac{(d \ln K)/dT}{(\partial \ln K/\partial\epsilon_e)_P}.$$

Using the van't Hoff isobar to evaluate the numerator and the law of mass action to evaluate the denominator, we get

$$\left(\frac{\partial\epsilon_e}{\partial T}\right)_P = \frac{\Delta H}{RT^2 \, d[\ln (x_3^{\nu_3}x_4^{\nu_4}/x_1^{\nu_1}x_2^{\nu_2})]/d\epsilon_e}. \tag{17-22}$$

Since we have already mentioned that the denominator on the right is positive, it follows that the sign of $(\partial\epsilon_e/\partial T)_P$ is determined by the sign of ΔH.

Therefore, *an increase of temperature at constant pressure causes a shift in the equilibrium value of the degree of reaction in the direction in which the heat of reaction is absorbed.*

To determine the effect of a change of pressure at constant temperature, we write

$$\left(\frac{\partial \epsilon_e}{\partial P}\right)_T = -\left(\frac{\partial \epsilon_e}{\partial \ln K}\right)_P \left(\frac{\partial \ln K}{\partial P}\right)_{\epsilon_e}$$

$$= -\frac{(\partial \ln K/\partial P)_{\epsilon_e}}{(\partial \ln K/\partial \epsilon_e)_P}.$$

Using the law of mass action to evaluate both numerator and denominator, we get

$$\left(\frac{\partial \epsilon_e}{\partial P}\right)_T = -\frac{\nu_3 + \nu_4 - \nu_1 - \nu_2}{P \, d[\ln \, (x_3^{\nu_3} x_4^{\nu_4}/x_1^{\nu_1} x_2^{\nu_2})]/d\epsilon_e}. \qquad (17\text{-}23)$$

The numerator on the right is proportional to the change in the number of moles of the constituents as the reaction proceeds to the right. If it is positive, this means that the volume increases at constant T and P. Therefore, *an increase of pressure at constant temperature causes a shift in the equilibrium value of the degree of reaction in the direction in which a decrease of volume takes place.*

17-7   Heat Capacity of Reacting Gases in Equilibrium

Let us consider, as usual, a mixture of arbitrary amounts of four ideal gases capable of undergoing the reaction

$$\nu_1 A_1 + \nu_2 A_2 \rightleftharpoons \nu_3 A_3 + \nu_4 A_4.$$

At equilibrium, the enthalpy of the mixture is

$$H = \Sigma n_k h_k$$

where

$$n_1 = (n_0 + n_0')\nu_1(1 - \epsilon_e), \qquad n_3 = (n_0 + n_0')\nu_3\epsilon_e,$$

$$n_2 = (n_0 + n_0')\nu_2(1 - \epsilon_e) + N_2, \qquad n_4 = (n_0 + n_0')\nu_4\epsilon_e + N_4,$$

and ϵ_e is the equilibrium value of the degree of reaction. Suppose that an infinitesimal change of temperature takes place *at constant pressure* in such a way that equilibrium is maintained. Then ϵ_e will change to the value $\epsilon_e + d\epsilon_e$, and the enthalpy will change by the amount

$$dH_P = \Sigma n_k \, dh_k + \Sigma h_k \, dn_k.$$

Since $dh_k = c_{Pk} \, dT$ and $dn_k = \pm (n_0 + n_0') \nu_k \, d\epsilon_e,$

$$dH_P = \Sigma n_k c_{Pk} \, dT + (n_0 + n_0')(\nu_3 h_3 + \nu_4 h_4 - \nu_1 h_1 - \nu_2 h_2) \, d\epsilon_e,$$

and the heat capacity of the reacting gas mixture is

$$C_P = \left(\frac{\partial H}{\partial T}\right)_P = \sum n_k c_{Pk} + (n_0 + n_0') \, \Delta H \left(\frac{\partial \epsilon_e}{\partial T}\right)_P.$$

From the preceding article,

$$\left(\frac{\partial \epsilon_e}{\partial T}\right)_P = \frac{\Delta H}{RT^2 \, d[\ln \, (x_3^{\nu_3} x_4^{\nu_4}/x_1^{\nu_1} x_2^{\nu_2})]/d\epsilon_e};$$

consequently,

$$C_P = \sum n_k c_{Pk} + (n_0 + n_0') \frac{(\Delta H)^2}{RT^2 \, d[\ln \, (x_3^{\nu_3} x_4^{\nu_4}/x_1^{\nu_1} x_2^{\nu_2})]/d\epsilon_e}. \qquad (17\text{-}24)$$

As an example, consider the equilibrium mixture of H_2O vapor, H_2, and O_2 caused by the dissociation of 1 mole of H_2O at 1 atm and 1900°K. We have $n_0 = 1$, $n_0' = 0$, $\Delta H = 250$ kJ/mole, $R = 8.31$ J/mole $\cdot$ deg, $\epsilon_e = 3.2 \times 10^{-3}$, $\Sigma n_k = n_0(1 + \epsilon_e/2)$, $\nu_1 = 1$, $\nu_2 = 0$, $\nu_3 = 1$, $\nu_4 = \frac{1}{2}$, and

$$\frac{d}{d\epsilon_e} \ln \frac{x_3^{\nu_3} x_4^{\nu_4}}{x_1^{\nu_1} x_2^{\nu_2}} = \frac{n_0}{\Sigma n_k} \frac{(\nu_1 + \nu_2)(\nu_3 + \nu_4)}{\epsilon_e(1 - \epsilon_e)}.$$

Hence
$$C_P - \sum n_k c_{Pk} = \frac{(\Delta H)^2 (1 + \epsilon_e/2)\epsilon_e(1 - \epsilon_e)}{RT^2(\nu_1 + \nu_2)(\nu_3 + \nu_4)}$$
$$= \frac{(250{,}000)^2 \times 3.2 \times 10^{-3}}{8.31 \times (1900)^2 \times \frac{3}{2}}$$
$$= 4.32 \text{ J/deg.}$$

PROBLEMS

17-1   Show that the law of mass action may be written

$$\frac{p_3^{\nu_3} p_4^{\nu_4}}{p_1^{\nu_1} p_2^{\nu_2}} = K,$$

where the p's are the equilibrium values of the partial pressures.

17-2   Starting with n_0 moles of NH_3, which dissociates according to the equation $NH_3 \rightleftharpoons \frac{1}{2}N_2 + \frac{3}{2}H_2$, show that at equilibrium

$$K = \frac{\sqrt{27}}{4} \frac{\epsilon_e^2}{1 - \epsilon_e^2} P.$$

17-3   Starting with n_0 moles of CO and $3n_0$ moles of H_2, which react according to the equation $CO + 3H_2 \rightleftharpoons CH_4 + H_2O$, show that at equilibrium

$$K = \frac{4\epsilon_e^2 (2 - \epsilon_e)^2}{27(1 - \epsilon_e)^4 P^2}.$$

17-4   A mixture of $n_0\nu_1$ moles of A_1 and $n_0\nu_2$ moles of A_2 at temperature T and pressure P occupies a volume V_0. When the reaction

$$\nu_1 A_1 + \nu_2 A_2 \rightleftharpoons \nu_3 A_3 + \nu_4 A_4$$

has come to equilibrium at the same T and P, the volume is V_e. Show that

$$\epsilon_e = \frac{V_e - V_0}{V_0} \frac{\nu_1 + \nu_2}{\nu_3 + \nu_4 - \nu_1 - \nu_2}.$$

17-5   At 35°C and 1 atm, the degree of dissociation of N_2O_4 at equilibrium is 0.27.

(a)   Calculate K.

(b)   Calculate ϵ_e at the same temperature when the pressure is 100 mm.

(c)   The equilibrium constant for the dissociation of N_2O_4 has the values 0.664 and 0.141 at the temperatures 318 and 298°K, respectively. Calculate the average heat of reaction within this temperature range.

17-6   The equilibrium constant of the reaction $SO_3 \rightleftharpoons SO_2 + \frac{1}{2}O_2$ has the following values:

Kelvin temperature	800	900	1000	1105
Equilibrium constant	0.0319	0.153	0.540	1.59

Determine the average heat of dissociation graphically.

17-7   Calculate the degree of ionization of cesium vapor at 10^{-6} atm at the two temperatures 2260 and 2520°K.

17-8   Calculate the degree of ionization of calcium vapor in the sun's chromosphere. The temperature and pressure of the sun's chromosphere are approximately 6000°K and 10^{-10} atm, respectively.

17-9   (a)   Show that

$$\Delta G = \Delta H + T\left(\frac{\partial \Delta G}{\partial T}\right)_P.$$

(b)   Show that

$$\Delta G = -RT \ln \frac{x_3^{\nu_3} x_4^{\nu_4}}{x_1^{\nu_1} x_2^{\nu_2}}$$

where the x's are equilibrium values.

17-10   Calculate the heat capacity of the equilibrium mixture of Prob. 17-7 at the temperature of 2260°K.

17-11   When 1 mole of HI dissociates according to the reaction

$$HI \rightleftharpoons \tfrac{1}{2}H_2 + \tfrac{1}{2}I_2$$

at $T = 675°K$, $K = 0.132$ and $\Delta H = 2950$ J/mole. Calculate $(\partial\epsilon_e/\partial T)_P$ at this temperature.

17-12   Starting with ν_1 moles of A_1 and ν_2 moles of A_2, show that:

(a)   At any value of ϵ,

$$G = \epsilon(\nu_3\mu_3 + \nu_4\mu_4 - \nu_1\mu_1 - \nu_2\mu_2) + \nu_1\mu_1 + \nu_2\mu_2.$$

(b)   At equilibrium,

$$G(\text{min}) = \nu_1\mu_{1e} + \nu_2\mu_{2e},$$

where the subscript e denotes an equilibrium value.

(c) $\dfrac{G - G(\text{min})}{RT} = \epsilon\left(\ln \dfrac{x_3^{\nu_3}x_4^{\nu_4}}{x_1^{\nu_1}x_2^{\nu_2}} - \ln \dfrac{x_{3e}^{\nu_3}x_{4e}^{\nu_4}}{x_{1e}^{\nu_1}x_{2e}^{\nu_2}}\right) + \ln x_1^{\nu_1}x_2^{\nu_2} - \ln x_{1e}^{\nu_1}x_{2e}^{\nu_2}.$

(d)   At $\epsilon = 0$,

$$\frac{G_0 - G(\text{min})}{RT} = \ln \left(\frac{\nu_1}{\nu_1 + \nu_2}\right)^{\nu_1}\left(\frac{\nu_2}{\nu_1 + \nu_2}\right)^{\nu_2} - \ln x_{1e}^{\nu_1}x_{2e}^{\nu_2}.$$

(e)   At $\epsilon = 1$,

$$\frac{G_1 - G(\text{min})}{RT} = \ln \left(\frac{\nu_3}{\nu_3 + \nu_4}\right)^{\nu_3}\left(\frac{\nu_4}{\nu_3 + \nu_4}\right)^{\nu_4} - \ln x_{3e}^{\nu_3}x_{4e}^{\nu_4}.$$

17-13   In the case of the ionization of a monatomic gas, show that:

(a) $$\frac{G - G(\text{min})}{RT} = \epsilon\left(\ln\frac{\epsilon^2}{1 - \epsilon^2} - \ln\frac{\epsilon_e^2}{1 - \epsilon_e^2}\right) + \ln\frac{1 - \epsilon}{1 + \epsilon} - \ln\frac{1 - \epsilon_e}{1 + \epsilon_e}.$$

(b)   At $\epsilon = 0$,

$$\frac{G_0 - G(\text{min})}{RT} = -\ln\frac{1 - \epsilon_e}{1 + \epsilon_e}.$$

(c)   At $\epsilon = 1$,

$$\frac{G_1 - G(\text{min})}{RT} = \ln\frac{1}{4} - \ln\frac{\epsilon_e^2}{(1 + \epsilon_e)^2}.$$

(d)   Plot $[G - G(\text{min})]/2.30RT$ against ϵ for the ionization of cesium vapor at 2260°K and 10^{-6} atm, using the result of Prob. 17-7.

17-14   (a)   Prove that, for a mixture of reacting ideal gases,

$$\frac{d}{d\epsilon}\ln\frac{x_3^{\nu_3}x_4^{\nu_4}}{x_1^{\nu_1}x_2^{\nu_2}} = \frac{n_0 + n_0'}{\Sigma n_k}\frac{1}{\psi},$$

where $$\frac{1}{\psi} = \frac{\nu_1^2}{x_1} + \frac{\nu_2^2}{x_2} + \frac{\nu_3^2}{x_3} + \frac{\nu_4^2}{x_4} - (\Delta\nu)^2$$

and $$\Delta\nu = \nu_3 + \nu_4 - \nu_1 - \nu_2.$$

(b)   If we start with $n_0\nu_1$ moles of A_1, $n_0\nu_2$ moles of A_2, and no A_3 or A_4, show that

$$\psi = \frac{\epsilon(1 - \epsilon)}{(\nu_1 + \nu_2)(\nu_3 + \nu_4)}.$$

17-15   Prove that, for a mixture of reacting ideal gases *in equilibrium*,

(a) $$\left(\frac{\partial V}{\partial P}\right)_T = -\frac{V}{P} - \frac{(n_0 + n_0')RT(\Delta\nu)^2}{P^2(d/d\epsilon_e)\ln(x_3^{\nu_3}x_4^{\nu_4}/x_1^{\nu_1}x_2^{\nu_2})}.$$

(b) $$\left(\frac{\partial V}{\partial T}\right)_P = \frac{V}{T} + \frac{(n_0 + n_0')\Delta\nu\,\Delta H}{PT(d/d\epsilon_e)\ln(x_3^{\nu_3}x_4^{\nu_4}/x_1^{\nu_1}x_2^{\nu_2})}.$$

(c) $$\left(\frac{\partial P}{\partial T}\right)_{\epsilon_e} = -\frac{P\,\Delta H}{RT^2\,\Delta\nu}.$$

17-16   Prove that, for a mixture of reacting ideal gases *in equilibrium*,

$$dS = \sum n_k\left[\sum x_k c_{Pk} + \frac{\psi(\Delta H)^2}{RT^2}\right]\frac{dT}{T} - R\sum n_k\left[1 + \frac{\psi\,\Delta H\,\Delta\nu}{RT}\right]\frac{dP}{P}.$$

18.

HETEROGENEOUS SYSTEMS

18-1   Thermodynamic Equations for a Heterogeneous System

It was shown in Art. 16-10 that the Gibbs function of any homogeneous phase, consisting of c constituents and in thermal and mechanical equilibrium at temperature T and pressure P, is equal to

$$G = \Sigma \mu_k n_k,$$

where each chemical potential is a function of T, P, and the mole fraction of the respective constituent, and the summation is taken over all the constituents. Furthermore, if the phase undergoes an infinitesimal process involving a change of temperature dT, a change of pressure dP, and changes in each of the n's, the accompanying change in the Gibbs function is equal to

$$dG = -S\,dT + V\,dP + \Sigma \mu_k \, dn_k.$$

Suppose we have a heterogeneous system of φ phases, all homogeneous and all at the uniform temperature T and pressure P. Let us denote constituents, as usual, by subscripts and phases by superscripts. The total Gibbs function of the heterogeneous system G is the sum of the Gibbs functions of all the phases; i.e.,

$$
\begin{aligned}
G = \ & \Sigma \mu_k^{(1)} n_k^{(1)} \text{ over all the constituents of the 1st phase} \\
& + \Sigma \mu_k^{(2)} n_k^{(2)} \text{ over all the constituents of the 2d phase} \\
& \cdots\cdots\cdots\cdots\cdots\cdots\cdots\cdots\cdots\cdots\cdots\cdots\cdots\cdots \\
& + \Sigma \mu_k^{(\varphi)} n_k^{(\varphi)} \text{ over all the constituents of the } \varphi\text{th phase.}
\end{aligned}
\tag{18-1}
$$

If an infinitesimal process takes place in which *all* the phases undergo a change in temperature dT and a change in pressure dP, then the change in the Gibbs function is

$$
\begin{aligned}
dG = \ & -S^{(1)}\, dT + V^{(1)}\, dP + \Sigma\mu_k^{(1)}\, dn_k^{(1)} && \text{(for 1st phase)} \\
& -S^{(2)}\, dT + V^{(2)}\, dP + \Sigma\mu_k^{(2)}\, dn_k^{(2)} && \text{(for 2d phase)} \\
& \,\cdot\ \cdot\ \cdot\ \cdot\ \cdot\ \cdot\ \cdot\ \cdot\ \cdot\ \cdot\ \cdot\ \cdot\ \cdot\ \cdot && \cdot\ \cdot\ \cdot\ \cdot\ \cdot\ \cdot\ \cdot \\
& -S^{(\varphi)}\, dT + V^{(\varphi)}\, dP + \Sigma\mu_k^{(\varphi)}\, dn_k^{(\varphi)} && \text{(for φth phase).}
\end{aligned}
$$

This equation evidently reduces to

$$
dG = -S\, dT + V\, dP + \Sigma\mu_k^{(1)}\, dn_k^{(1)} + \Sigma\mu_k^{(2)}\, dn_k^{(2)} + \cdots + \Sigma\mu_k^{(\varphi)}\, dn_k^{(\varphi)},
\tag{18-2}
$$

where S and V are the entropy and volume, respectively, of the whole heterogeneous system.

The problem of the equilibrium of a heterogeneous system is to obtain an equation or a set of equations among the μ's that hold when all the phases are in chemical equilibrium. If the system is assumed to approach equilibrium at constant T and P, then G is a minimum at equilibrium, and the problem can be stated thus: *To render G a minimum at constant T and P, subject to whatever conditions are imposed on the n's by virtue of the constraints of the system.* The mathematical condition that G be a minimum at constant T and P is that

$$
dG_{T,P} = 0.
$$

Hence, the equation that must be satisfied at equilibrium is

$$
dG_{T,P} = \Sigma\mu_k^{(1)}\, dn_k^{(1)} + \Sigma\mu_k^{(2)}\, dn_k^{(2)} + \cdots + \Sigma\mu_k^{(\varphi)}\, dn_k^{(\varphi)} = 0, \quad (18\text{-}3)
$$

where the dn's are not all independent but are connected by equations of constraint.

To return for a moment to the system treated in Chap. 16—namely, one phase consisting of a mixture of chemically active substances—we found that the equations of constraint were of such a simple form that, by direct substitution, G could be expressed as a function of T, P, and only one other independent variable ϵ and that $dG_{T,P}$ could be expressed in terms of only one differential $d\epsilon$, thus:

$$
dG_{T,P} = (n_0 + n_0')(\nu_3\mu_3 + \nu_4\mu_4 - \nu_1\mu_1 - \nu_2\mu_2)\, d\epsilon.
$$

At equilibrium, when $dG_{T,P} = 0$, only one equation, the equation of reaction equilibrium, was obtained.

In the case of a heterogeneous system, however, the situation is more complicated. In the first place there is, as a rule, more than one independent variable besides T and P. In the second place, the equations of constraint are usually of such a nature that it is either impossible or exceedingly cumbersome to attempt by direct substitution to express G in terms of the independent variables only and dG in terms of differentials of these independent variables. Finally, instead of only one equation of equilibrium, there may be several, depending on the type of heterogeneous system.

We are therefore confronted with a type of problem that requires the use of Lagrange's method of undetermined multipliers.

18-2   Phase Rule without Chemical Reaction

Consider a heterogeneous system of c chemical constituents that do not combine chemically with one another. Suppose that there are φ phases, each of which is in contact with every other phase in such a way that there are no impediments to the transport of any constituent from one phase to another. Let us assume temporarily that every constituent is present in every phase. As usual, constituents will be denoted by subscripts and phases by superscripts. As we have shown previously, the Gibbs function of the whole heterogeneous system is

$$G = \sum_{1}^{c} n_k^{(1)} \mu_k^{(1)} + \sum_{1}^{c} n_k^{(2)} \mu_k^{(2)} + \cdot \cdot \cdot + \sum_{1}^{c} n_k^{(\varphi)} \mu_k^{(\varphi)},$$

where all the summations extend from $k = 1$ to $k = c$, since all the constituents are present in all the phases. G is a function of T, P, and the n's, of which there are $c\varphi$ in number. Not all these n's, however, are independent. Since there are no chemical reactions, the only way in which the n's may change is by the transport of constituents from one phase to another, in which case the total number of moles of each constituent remains constant. We have as our equations of constraint, therefore,

$$n_1^{(1)} + n_1^{(2)} + \cdot \cdot \cdot + n_1^{(\varphi)} = \text{const.}$$
$$n_2^{(1)} + n_2^{(2)} + \cdot \cdot \cdot + n_2^{(\varphi)} = \text{const.}$$
$$\cdot \ \cdot \ \cdot \ \cdot \ \cdot \ \cdot \ \cdot \ \cdot \ \cdot \ \cdot \ \cdot \ \cdot \ \cdot \ \cdot \ \cdot \ \cdot \ \cdot$$
$$n_c^{(1)} + n_c^{(2)} + \cdot \cdot \cdot + n_c^{(\varphi)} = \text{const.}$$

In order to find the equations of chemical equilibrium, it is necessary to render G a minimum at constant T and P, subject to these equations of constraint. Applying Lagrange's method, we have

$$dG = \mu_1^{(1)} \, dn_1^{(1)} + \cdots + \mu_c^{(1)} \, dn_c^{(1)} + \cdots + \mu_1^{(\varphi)} \, dn_1^{(\varphi)} + \cdots + \mu_c^{(\varphi)} \, dn_c^{(\varphi)} = 0$$
$$\lambda_1 \; dn_1^{(1)} \qquad\qquad\qquad + \cdots + \lambda_1 \;\; dn_1^{(\varphi)} \qquad\qquad\qquad = 0$$

$$\lambda_c \, dn_c^{(1)} + \cdots \qquad\qquad\qquad\qquad\qquad + \lambda_c \;\; dn_c^{(\varphi)} = 0,$$

where there are c lagrangian multipliers, one for each equation of constraint. Adding and equating each coefficient of each dn to zero, we get

$$\mu_1^{(1)} = -\lambda_1 \qquad \mu_1^{(2)} = -\lambda_1 \qquad \cdots \qquad \mu_1^{(\varphi)} = -\lambda_1$$

$$\mu_2^{(1)} = -\lambda_2 \qquad \mu_2^{(2)} = -\lambda_2 \qquad \cdots \qquad \mu_2^{(\varphi)} = -\lambda_2$$

$$\cdots\cdots\cdots \qquad \cdots\cdots\cdots \qquad \cdots \qquad \cdots\cdots\cdots$$

$$\mu_c^{(1)} = -\lambda_c \qquad \mu_c^{(2)} = -\lambda_c \qquad \cdots \qquad \mu_c^{(\varphi)} = -\lambda_c$$

or

$$
\boxed{
\begin{aligned}
\mu_1^{(1)} &= \mu_1^{(2)} = \cdots = \mu_1^{(\varphi)} \\
\mu_2^{(1)} &= \mu_2^{(2)} = \cdots = \mu_2^{(\varphi)} \\
\cdots\; &\cdots\cdots\cdots\cdots\cdots \\
\mu_c^{(1)} &= \mu_c^{(2)} = \cdots = \mu_c^{(\varphi)}.
\end{aligned}
}
\qquad (18\text{-}4)
$$

These are the *equations of phase equilibrium*, which express the important fact that at equilibrium the chemical potential of a constituent in one phase must be equal to the chemical potential of the same constituent in every other phase.

As a simple example, suppose that we have only one constituent present in two phases. Then,

$$dG_{T,P} = \mu_1^{(1)} \, dn_1^{(1)} + \mu_1^{(2)} \, dn_1^{(2)};$$

and since $dn_1^{(2)} = -dn_1^{(1)}$,

$$dG_{T,P} = (\mu_1^{(1)} - \mu_1^{(2)}) \, dn_1^{(1)}.$$

Now, before equilibrium is reached, suppose there is a flow of matter from phase 1 to phase 2. Then $dn_1^{(1)}$ is negative; and since this flow is irreversible,

$dG_{T,P}$ must be negative. Therefore, *while the flow is taking place,*

$$\mu_1^{(1)} > \mu_1^{(2)} \qquad \text{(flow of matter from phase 1 to phase 2).}$$

Obviously, the transfer of matter ceases when the two chemical potentials become equal. The chemical potentials of a constituent in two neighboring phases may be compared with the temperatures and pressures of these · phases, thus:

1   If the temperature of phase 1 is greater than that of phase 2, there is a flow of heat that ceases when the temperatures are equal, i.e., when thermal equilibrium is established.

2   If the pressure of phase 1 is greater than that of phase 2, there is a "flow" of work that ceases when the pressures are equal, i.e., when mechanical equilibrium is established.

3   If the chemical potential of a constituent of phase 1 is greater than that of phase 2, there is a flow of that constituent which ceases when the chemical potentials are equal, i.e., when chemical equilibrium is established.

The equations of phase equilibrium expressing the equality of the chemical potentials of any one constituent in all the φ phases are obviously $\varphi - 1$ in number. Therefore, for c constituents, there are altogether $c(\varphi - 1)$ equations among the μ's.

Following out the procedure of Lagrange's method, we should complete our solution of the problem by solving the $c(\varphi - 1)$ equations of phase equilibrium and the c equations of constraint for the φc values of the n's that make G a minimum. These values should, of course, be functions of the parameters T and P. We find, however, that the equations do not contain the n's in such fashion as to determine their values, because of the fact that the equations of equilibrium are equations among the chemical potentials, which are intensive quantities and depend on the x's, which contain the n's in the special form

$$x_k = \frac{n_k}{\Sigma n}.$$

This is another way of saying that the chemical potential for a constituent in a phase depends on the composition of that phase but not on its total mass.

There are many *different* sets of n's that satisfy the equations of phase equilibrium and give rise to the same minimum value of the Gibbs function. This may be seen from the fact that

$$G = \mu_1^{(1)} n_1^{(1)} + \cdots + \mu_c^{(1)} n_c^{(1)} + \cdots + \mu_1^{(\varphi)} n_1^{(\varphi)} + \cdots + \mu_c^{(\varphi)} n_c^{(\varphi)},$$

but at equilibrium the chemical potentials of the same constituent are the same in all phases and hence may be written without any superscripts. Factoring out the μ's, we get

$$G(\text{min}) = \mu_1(n_1^{(1)} + \cdots + n_1^{(\varphi)}) + \cdots + \mu_c(n_c^{(1)} + \cdots + n_c^{(\varphi)}).$$

Therefore, *the minimum value of the Gibbs function is the same for many different distributions of the total mass among the phases.* Since we cannot find the values of the n's at equilibrium, therefore, we may inquire as to whether we can obtain *any* precise information about a heterogeneous system in equilibrium.

As we have seen, the state of the system at equilibrium is determined by the temperature, the pressure, and $c\varphi$ mole fractions. Hence,

$$\text{Total number of variables} = c\varphi + 2.$$

Among these variables there are two types of equations: (1) equations of phase equilibrium, which are $c(\varphi - 1)$ in number; and (2) equations of the type $\Sigma x = 1$, for each phase, and therefore φ such equations altogether. Hence,

$$\text{Total number of equations} = c(\varphi - 1) + \varphi.$$

If there are as many equations as there are variables, then the temperature, pressure, and composition of the whole system at equilibrium are determined. Such a system is called *nonvariant* and is said to have zero variance. If the number of variables exceeds the number of equations by one, then the equilibrium of the system is not determined until one of the variables is arbitrarily chosen. Such a system is called *monovariant* and is said to have a variance of 1. In general, *the excess of variables over equations is called the variance f.* Thus,

$$\text{Variance} = (\text{number of variables}) - (\text{number of equations}),$$

or $$f = \quad (c\varphi + 2) \quad - \quad [c(\varphi - 1) + \varphi];$$

whence $$\boxed{f = c - \varphi + 2.}$$ (18-5)

This is known as the *phase rule*, which was first derived in 1875 by Josiah Willard Gibbs, who was then professor of mathematical physics at Yale University. The phase rule arose from a general theory of the equilibrium of heterogeneous systems that Gibbs developed during the years 1875 to 1878 and published in an obscure journal, *The Transactions of the Connecticut Acad-*

emy. The original paper, entitled "On the Equilibrium of Heterogeneous Substances," was almost 300 pages long. In it, Gibbs considered not only chemical effects but also those produced by gravity, capillarity, and non-homogeneous strains. It stands today as one of the most profound contributions to the world of human thought and, along with Gibbs' researches in vector analysis and statistical mechanics, places him with the greatest of the world's geniuses.

It is a simple matter to remove the restriction that every constituent must be present in every phase. Suppose that constituent A_1 is absent from phase 1. Then the equation of equilibrium that exists when the constituent is present, namely,

$$\mu_1^{(1)} = -\lambda_1,$$

is now lacking. However, to describe the composition of the first phase, we need one mole fraction fewer than before. Therefore, since both the number of equations and the number of variables have been reduced by one, the difference is the same and the phase rule remains unchanged.

To remove the second restriction—that no chemical reaction take place—is more difficult and requires solving the problem *de novo.* Before this is done, however, it is worth while to consider a few simple applications of the phase rule in its present form.

18-3 Simple Applications of the Phase Rule

As simple examples of the use of the phase rule, we shall consider a pure substance, a simple eutectic, and a freezing mixture.

1. *Pure substance*   In the case of a pure substance such as water, the phase rule merely confirms what is already known. If there are two phases in equilibrium (say, solid and vapor), the variance is 1. There is one equation of equilibrium, namely,

$$\mu'(T,P) = \mu'''(T,P),$$

where one prime stands for solid and three primes for vapor. We have already shown that, when a phase consists of only one constituent, the chemical potential is equal to the molar Gibbs function. Hence,

$$g' = g'''$$

is the equation of equilibrium among the two coordinates T and P, which will be recognized as the equation of the sublimation curve. If three phases are in equilibrium, the system is nonvariant, and the two equations of equilibrium

$$g' = g''' \quad \text{and} \quad g'' = g'''$$

serve to determine both T and P. The phase rule shows that the maximum number of phases of a one-constituent system which can exist in equilibrium is three. The various triple points of water confirm this result.

2. *Simple eutectic*   Let us consider a system of two constituents which neither combine to produce a compound nor form a solid solution but which, in the liquid phase, are miscible in all proportions. A mixture of gold and thallium has these properties. Suppose that we have a liquid alloy consisting of 40 percent thallium and 60 percent gold in an evacuated chamber originally at about 1000°C. A mixture of thallium and gold vapors will constitute the vapor phase, and we shall have $c = 2$ and $\varphi = 2$. It follows that the variance is 2; hence, the composition and temperature having been chosen, the vapor pressure is determined. If the temperature is now progressively lowered, a solid phase of pure gold will separate from the liquid at a temperature of about 600°C, and the percentage of thallium in the solution is thus increased. At any given concentration, there will be one and only one temperature at which the three phases—vapor mixture, liquid solution, and solid gold—will be in equilibrium, because now $c = 2$ and $\varphi = 3$; therefore, $f = 1$.

By covering the metals with a piston on which any desired pressure may be exerted, we may exclude the vapor phase and study the variance of the system when only solid and liquid phases are present. In this way, the temperatures and compositions at which equilibrium exists among various phases may be measured and the results plotted on a phase diagram such as that shown in Fig. 18-1.

Point A is the melting point (strictly speaking, the triple point) of pure gold, and B that of pure thallium. When two phases, solution and vapor, are present, the system is divariant; and equilibrium may exist at any temperature and composition represented by a point in the *region* above AEB. When the three phases (solution, vapor, and solid gold) are present, the system is monovariant; and equilibrium may exist only at those temperatures and compositions represented by points on the *curve* AE. Similarly, curve BE represents temperatures and compositions at which the monovariant system consisting of three phases—solution, vapor, and solid thallium—is in equilibrium. The complete curve AEB is known as the *liquidus*.

At E, there are four phases present: solution, vapor, solid gold, and solid

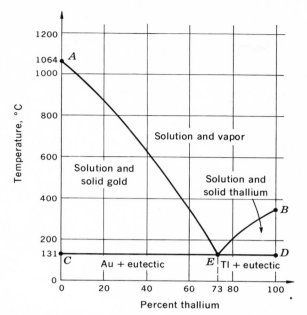

Fig. 18-1   *Phase diagram for eutectic system of gold and thallium.*

thallium. Hence $c = 2$, $\varphi = 4$, and $f = 0$, or the system is nonvariant. This is known as the *eutectic point*, and the composition at this point as the *eutectic composition*.

Solution and solid gold may coexist at all temperatures and compositions represented by points in region *ACE*. Below line *CE*, however, no liquid can exist, and the system consists of a solid with the eutectic mixture plus free gold. Solution and solid thallium coexist in region *BED*, and below *ED* we have eutectic plus free thallium. Line *CED* is known as the *solidus*.

There are many different types of eutectic system, each with phase diagrams of different character. All of them, however, may be understood completely in terms of the phase rule.

3. *Freezing mixture*   A number of years ago, before the commercial use of solid carbon dioxide ("dry ice") as a cooling agent, foods such as ice cream were packed in a container surrounded by a mixture of ice and common salt. If the mixture was thermally insulated and covered, it maintained a constant temperature of about $-21°C$. Another practice that is still current is to melt the ice which forms on the sidewalk by sprinkling salt on it. These phenomena may be clearly understood on the basis of the phase rule.

Fig. 18-2   *Phase diagram for mixture of NaCl and H₂O.*

Consider the phase diagram of NaCl and water shown in Fig. 18-2. A is the triple point of pure water, and B is the transition point where the dihydrate $NaCl \cdot 2H_2O$ changes into NaCl. Except for the upper right-hand portion of the figure, the diagram is in all respects similar to the simple eutectic diagram of Fig. 18-1. At all points on AE, the system is monovariant and consists of three phases: solution, vapor, and ice. Similarly, on EB we have solution, vapor, and dihydrate. Point E is the eutectic point, which, since in this case the system contains water, is called the *cryohydric point*. The mixture of dihydrate and water that forms at the cryohydric point is called a *cryohydrate*.

Only at points below the solidus CED can ice and $NaCl \cdot 2H_2O$ exist as solids together. Consequently, when they are mixed at a temperature above $-21°C$ (as on the sidewalk), they are not in equilibrium, and as a result the ice melts and the salt dissolves. It should be mentioned at this point that, if the system is open to the air at atmospheric pressure, then there is one more constituent (air), which would ordinarily increase the variance by 1. Since the pressure is constant, however, this extra variance is used up, and the system behaves as before.

If ice, salt, water, and vapor at $0°C$ are together in a thermally insulated container, they are not in equilibrium, and some ice will melt and dissolve some salt. But this saturated solution will be too concentrated to be in equilibrium with ice. Ice will therefore melt, lowering the concentration of the solution, which will then dissolve more salt. While this is going on, the temperature of the whole system automatically and spontaneously decreases until the temperature of $-21°C$ is reached. Such a system is known as a *freezing mixture*.

At the transition point B, where NaCl forms, there are three constituents; hence one might expect a maximum of five phases to coexist. This is not the case, however, because a chemical reaction

$$NaCl \cdot 2H_2O \rightleftharpoons NaCl + \text{solution}$$

takes place. We shall see in the next article that the presence of this reaction causes the system to behave as if there were only two constituents, so that only four phases coexist at the point B: solid $NaCl \cdot 2H_2O$, solid NaCl, solution, and vapor.

There are a number of freezing mixtures that are often used for preserving materials at low temperatures. These are listed in Table 18-1.

Table 18-1   Freezing Mixtures

First constituent	Second constituent	Lowest temperature, °C
NH_4Cl	Ice	-15.4
NaCl	Ice	-21
Alcohol	Ice	-30
$CaCl_2 \cdot 6H_2O$	Ice	-55
Alcohol	Solid CO_2	-72
Ether	Solid CO_2	-77

18-4   Phase Rule with Chemical Reaction

Let us consider a heterogeneous system composed of arbitrary amounts of c constituents, assuming for the sake of simplicity that four of the constituents are chemically active, capable of undergoing the reaction

$$\nu_1 A_1 + \nu_2 A_2 \rightleftharpoons \nu_3 A_3 + \nu_4 A_4.$$

Suppose that there are φ phases and, as only a temporary assumption, that all the constituents are present in all the phases. As before, the Gibbs function of the system is

$$G = \sum_1^c \mu_k^{(1)} n_k^{(1)} + \sum_1^c \mu_k^{(2)} n_k^{(2)} + \cdots + \sum_1^c \mu_k^{(3)} n_k^{(\varphi)}.$$

The equations of constraint for those constituents which do not react are of the same type as before; i.e., they express the fact that the total number of moles of each inert constituent is constant. In the case of the chemically active constituents, however, the total number of moles of any one is not constant but is a function of the degree of reaction. Hence, the equations of constraint are:

$$n_1^{(1)} + n_1^{(2)} + \cdots + n_1^{(\varphi)} = (n_0 + n_0')\nu_1(1 - \epsilon)$$

$$n_2^{(1)} + n_2^{(2)} + \cdots + n_2^{(\varphi)} = (n_0 + n_0')\nu_2(1 - \epsilon) + N_2$$

$$n_3^{(1)} + n_3^{(2)} + \cdots + n_3^{(\varphi)} = (n_0 + n_0')\nu_3\epsilon$$

$$n_4^{(1)} + n_4^{(2)} + \cdots + n_4^{(\varphi)} = (n_0 + n_0')\nu_4\epsilon + N_4$$

$$n_5^{(1)} + n_5^{(2)} + \cdots + n_5^{(\varphi)} = \text{const.}$$

$$\cdots \cdots \cdots \cdots \cdots \cdots \cdots \cdots \cdots \cdots \cdots$$

$$n_c^{(1)} + n_c^{(2)} + \cdots + n_c^{(\varphi)} = \text{const.},$$

where n_0, n_0', N_2, and N_4 have their usual meaning. Applying Lagrange's method, we get the equations below (reading across pages 618 and 619).

$$\mu_1^{(1)} dn_1^{(1)} + \cdots + \mu_4^{(1)} dn_4^{(1)} + \cdots + \mu_c^{(1)} dn_c^{(1)} + \cdots +$$

$$\lambda_1 dn_1^{(1)} \qquad\qquad\qquad\qquad\qquad + \cdots +$$

$$\lambda_2 dn_2^{(1)} \qquad\qquad\qquad\qquad + \cdots +$$

$$\lambda_3 dn_3^{(1)} \qquad\qquad\qquad + \cdots +$$

$$\lambda_4 dn_4^{(1)} \qquad\qquad + \cdots +$$

$$\lambda_5 dn_5^{(1)} \qquad\qquad + \cdots +$$

$$\lambda_c dn_c^{(1)} + \cdots +$$

Adding, and equating coefficients of the dn's to zero, we get the usual $c(\varphi - 1)$ equations of phase equilibrium,

$$\mu_1^{(1)} = \mu_1^{(2)} = \cdots = \mu_1^{(\varphi)}$$

$$\mu_2^{(1)} = \mu_2^{(2)} = \cdots = \mu_2^{(\varphi)}$$

$$\cdots\cdots\cdots\cdots\cdots\cdots$$

$$\mu_c^{(1)} = \mu_c^{(2)} = \cdots = \mu_c^{(\varphi)}.$$

Equating the coefficient of $d\epsilon$ to zero, we get an extra equation of equilibrium, namely,

$$\lambda_1 \nu_1 + \lambda_2 \nu_2 - \lambda_3 \nu_3 - \lambda_4 \nu_4 = 0,$$

which, since $\lambda_1 = -\mu_1$ of any phase, $\lambda_2 = -\mu_2$ of any phase, etc., becomes

$$\nu_1 \mu_1 + \nu_2 \mu_2 = \nu_3 \mu_3 + \nu_4 \mu_4.$$

This equation will be recognized as the equation of reaction equilibrium, which in the case of ideal gases was found to lead to the law of mass action.

The rest of the argument follows the same lines as before. There are $c(\varphi - 1)$ equations of phase equilibrium, 1 equation of reaction equilibrium, and φ equations of the type $\Sigma x = 1$. Hence, the total number of equations is

$$c(\varphi - 1) + 1 + \varphi.$$

Since the variables are the same as before, namely, T, P, and the x's, of

---

$$\mu_1^{(\varphi)} dn_1^{(\varphi)} + \cdots + \mu_4^{(\varphi)} dn_4^{(\varphi)} + \cdots + \mu_c^{(\varphi)} dn_c^{(\varphi)} \qquad\qquad\qquad = 0$$

$$\lambda_1 dn_1^{(\varphi)} \qquad\qquad\qquad\qquad\qquad + \lambda_1(n_0 + n_0')\nu_1 d\epsilon = 0$$

$$\lambda_2 dn_2^{(\varphi)} \qquad\qquad\qquad\qquad + \lambda_2(n_0 + n_0')\nu_2 d\epsilon = 0$$

$$\lambda_3 dn_3^{(\varphi)} \qquad\qquad\qquad - \lambda_3(n_0 + n_0')\nu_3 d\epsilon = 0$$

$$\lambda_4 dn_4^{(\varphi)} \qquad\qquad - \lambda_4(n_0 + n_0')\nu_4 d\epsilon = 0$$

$$\lambda_c dn_5^{(\varphi)} \qquad\qquad\qquad\qquad = 0$$

$$\cdot$$

$$\cdot$$

$$\cdot$$

$$\lambda_c dn_c^{(\varphi)} \qquad\qquad\qquad\qquad = 0$$

which there are $c\varphi + 2$ in number, the variance is

$$f = c\varphi + 2 - [c(\varphi - 1) + 1 + \varphi],$$

or $\qquad\qquad f = (c - 1) - \varphi + 2. \qquad\qquad\qquad (18\text{-}6)$

The phase rule in this case is seen to be different, in that $c - 1$ now stands where c formerly stood. For the reason given before, this form of the phase rule remains unchanged when every constituent is not present in every phase. We see therefore that when there are c constituents, present in arbitrary amounts, and only one chemical reaction, there is one extra equation of equilibrium and the variance is reduced by 1. It is obvious that, if there were two independent chemical reactions, there would be two extra equations of equilibrium; whence the phase rule would become $f = (c - 2) - \varphi + 2$. For r independent reactions, we would have

$$f = (c - r) - \varphi + 2. \qquad\qquad\qquad (18\text{-}7)$$

The argument up to now has been based on the fact that only three kinds of equations have existed among the variables T, P, and the x's: equations of phase equilibrium, equations of reaction equilibrium, and equations of the type $\Sigma x = 1$. It often happens, however, that a chemical reaction takes place in such a manner that additional equations expressing further restrictions upon the x's are at hand. Suppose, for example, that we put an arbitrary amount of solid NH_4HS into an evacuated chamber and two new constituents form according to the reaction

$$NH_4HS \rightleftharpoons NH_3 + H_2S.$$

Since gaseous NH_3 and H_2S are in the same phase, the restriction always exists that

$$x_{NH_3} = x_{H_2S}.$$

This constitutes a fourth type of equation, to be added to the three listed at the beginning of this paragraph.

Another example of additional restricting equations among the x's is provided by the phenomenon of dissociation in solution. Suppose that we have a heterogeneous system one of whose phases is a solution of salt 2 in solvent 1. Suppose that the salt dissociates according to the scheme shown in Fig. 18-3a. All the ions, of course, remain in the liquid phase, and no precipitate is formed. Consequently, we have the equation

$$x_3 = x_4,$$

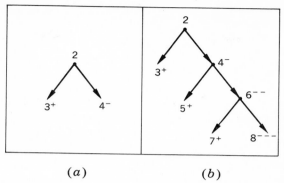

(a) (b)

Fig. 18-3   *Dissociations of a salt that give rise to additional restricting equations among the mole fractions. (a) Single dissociation; (b) multiple dissociation.*

which expresses the fact that the solution is electrically neutral. If multiple dissociation takes place according to the scheme shown in Fig. 18-3b, then there are three independent restricting equations among the x's, namely,

$$x_3 = x_8 + x_6 + x_4,$$

$$x_5 = x_8 + x_6,$$

and $\qquad x_7 = x_8.$

Adding these equations, we get the *dependent* equation

$$x_3 + x_5 + x_7 = 3x_8 + 2x_6 + x_4,$$

expressing the fact of electrical neutrality.

Let us call equations of the preceding type *restricting equations*, and let us suppose that z of them are independent. Then we may list four types of equations among T, P, and the x's, thus:

1   Equations of phase equilibrium [$c(\varphi - 1)$ in number].
2   Equations of reaction equilibrium (r in number).
3   Equations of the type $\Sigma x = 1$ (φ in number).
4   Restricting equations (z in number).

Hence, the total number of equations is

$$c(\varphi - 1) + r + \varphi + z;$$

and, as usual, the total number of variables is $c\varphi + 2$. Therefore,

$$f = c\varphi + 2 - [c(\varphi - 1) + r + \varphi + z],$$

or $$f = (c - r - z) - \varphi + 2.$$

If we define the *number of components c' as the total number of constituents minus the number of independent reactions minus the number of independent restricting equations*, i.e.,

$$\boxed{c' = c - r - z,} \tag{18-8}$$

we may always write the phase rule in the same form, thus:

$$\boxed{f = c' - \varphi + 2.} \tag{18-9}$$

18-5   Determination of the Number of Components

The problem of determining the number of components in a heterogeneous system may be somewhat difficult for the beginner. As a result of experience with the behavior of typical heterogeneous systems, the physical chemist is able to determine the number of components by counting the smallest number of constituents whose specification is sufficient to determine the composition of every phase. The validity of this working rule rests upon a few fundamental facts whose truth we shall demonstrate rigorously in this article.

Example 1

First let us consider a heterogeneous system consisting of a liquid phase composed of a solution of the salt NaH_2PO_4 in water and a vapor phase composed of water vapor. It is important to show that, *so long as no precipitate is formed by virtue of a reaction between the salt and the water, no matter what else we assume to take place in the solution, the number of components is two.*

1   *Neglecting all dissociation.*   There are two constituents, no chemical reactions, and no restricting equations. Hence,

$$c' = 2 - 0 - 0 = 2.$$

$$(a) \qquad\qquad (b)$$

Fig. 18-4   *Multiple dissociation of NaH_2PO_4. (a) Without dissociation of H_2O; (b) with dissociation of H_2O.*

2   *Assuming single dissociation of the salt.*   There are four constituents, NaH_2PO_4, H_2O, Na^+, $H_2PO_4^-$; one chemical reaction,

$$NaH_2PO_4 \rightleftharpoons Na^+ + H_2PO_4^-;$$

and one restricting equation,

$$x_{Na^+} = x_{H_2PO_4^-}.$$

Hence, $c = 4 - 1 - 1 = 2$.

3   *Assuming multiple dissociation of the salt.*   There are seven constituents and three independent chemical reactions, as shown in Fig. 18-4a, and two independent restricting equations,

$$x_{Na^+} = x_{PO_4^{---}} + x_{HPO_4^{--}} + x_{H_2PO_4^-}$$

and

$$x_{H^+} = 2x_{PO_4^{---}} + x_{HPO_4^{--}}.$$

(By adding the two equations, the *dependent* equation expressing electrical neutrality of the solution is obtained.) Hence, $c' = 7 - 3 - 2 = 2$.

4   *Assuming dissociation of the water also.*   There are eight constituents and four independent chemical reactions, as shown in Fig. 18-4b, and two independent restricting equations,

$$x_{Na^+} = x_{PO_4^{---}} + x_{HPO_4^{--}} + x_{H_2PO_4^-}$$

and

$$x_{H^+} = 2x_{PO_4^{---}} + x_{HPO_4^{--}} + x_{OH^-}.$$

Hence, $c' = 8 - 4 - 2 = 2$.

5   *Assuming association of the water.*   A ninth constituent, $(H_2O)_2$, is formed as a result of a fifth independent reaction,

$$H_2O \rightleftharpoons \tfrac{1}{2}(H_2O)_2.$$

There are still the same two independent restricting equations, and hence $c' = 9 - 5 - 2 = 2$.

It is clear, therefore, that it is a matter of indifference as to what chemical changes take place in the solution. The number of components is always two, provided that no precipitate forms.

Example 2

To investigate the effect of precipitate, let us consider a mixture of $AlCl_3$ and water. In this case, the $AlCl_3$ combines with the water to form $Al(OH)_3$, some of which precipitates out of the solution, according to the reaction shown in Fig. 18-5. There are eight constituents and only four independent reactions. At first thought, one might imagine that there are five independent reactions, but if we write the equations of reaction equilibrium corresponding to the four dissociations:

$$3\mu_{H_2O} = 3\mu_{H^+} + 3\mu_{OH^-},$$

$$\mu_{AlCl_3} = \mu_{Al^{+++}} + 3\mu_{Cl^-},$$

$$\mu_{Al(HO)_3} = \mu_{Al^{+++}} + 3\mu_{OH^-},$$

and
$$3\mu_{HCl} = 3\mu_{H^+} + 3\mu_{Cl^-},$$

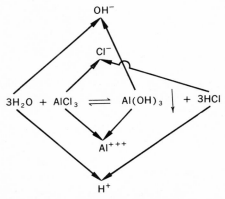

Fig. 18-5   *Dissociation, reaction, and precipitation that occur when $AlCl_3$ is dissolved in water.*

and add the first two and subtract the sum of the last two, we get

$$3\mu_{H_2O} + \mu_{AlCl_3} = \mu_{Al(OH)_3} + 3\mu_{HCl},$$

which is the equation of reaction equilibrium corresponding to the reaction

$$3H_2O + AlCl_3 \rightleftharpoons Al(OH)_3 + 3HCl,$$

which is therefore seen to be a *dependent* reaction.

Since some of the $Al(OH)_3$ has precipitated out, there is only one restricting equation, namely, that expressing the electrical neutrality of the solution,

$$3x_{Al^{+++}} + x_{H^+} = x_{OH^-} + x_{Cl^-}.$$

Consequently, $c' = 8 - 4 - 1 = 3$, and we have an interesting situation in which a heterogeneous system, formed originally by mixing two substances, has three components.

Example 3

As a last example, let us consider a system consisting of water vapor and a solution containing arbitrary amounts of NaCl and KNO_3 in water.

1   *Neglecting all dissociations.* There are five constituents, H_2O, NaCl, KNO_3, $NaNO_3$, KCl; one reaction,

$$NaCl + KNO_3 \rightleftharpoons NaNO_3 + KCl;$$

and one restricting equation,

$$x_{NaNO_3} = x_{KCl}.$$

Hence, $c' = 5 - 1 - 1 = 3$.

2   *Considering all reactions.* There are eleven constituents, which undergo these reactions:

$$H_2O \rightleftharpoons H^+ + OH^-$$

$$NaCl \rightleftharpoons Na^+ + Cl^-$$

$$KNO_3 \rightleftharpoons K^+ + NO_3^-$$

$$NaNO_3 \rightleftharpoons Na^+ + NO_3^-$$

$$KCl \rightleftharpoons K^+ + Cl^-.$$

It should be noticed that the reaction

$$NaCl + KNO_3 \rightleftharpoons NaNO_3 + KCl$$

is not independent of the preceding five but that its equation of reaction equilibrium may be obtained by adding the second and third and subtracting the sum of the fourth and fifth.

There are three restricting equations. The first,

$$x_{Na^+} + x_{NaNO_3} = x_{Cl^-} + x_{KCl},$$

expresses the fact that the amount of sodium lost by the NaCl (to form Na^+ and $NaNO_3$) is equal to the amount of chlorine lost by the NaCl (to form Cl^- and KCl). The second,

$$x_{K^+} + x_{KCl} = x_{NO_3} + x_{NaNO_3},$$

expresses the corresponding fact concerning the loss of potassium and nitrate from KNO_3. The third is

$$x_{H^+} = x_{OH^-}.$$

(The dependent equation of electrical neutrality is obtained by adding these three equations.) Hence, $c' = 11 - 5 - 3 = 3$.

In the event that we start with arbitrary amounts of all five substances (H_2O, NaCl, KNO_3, $NaNO_3$, and KCl), there are still eleven constituents and five independent reactions but only two restricting equations, namely,

$$x_{Na^+} + x_{K^+} + x_{H^+} = x_{Cl^-} + x_{NO_3^-} + x_{OH^-},$$

which expresses electrical neutrality, and

$$x_{H^+} = x_{OH^-}.$$

Hence, $c' = 11 - 5 - 2 = 4$.

18-6   Displacement of Equilibrium

Consider a heterogeneous system of φ phases and c constituents, four of which undergo the reaction

$$\nu_1 A_1 + \nu_2 A_2 \rightleftharpoons \nu_3 A_3 + \nu_4 A_4.$$

Any infinitesimal process involving a change in temperature, pressure, and composition of the phases is accompanied by a change in the Gibbs function equal to

$$dG = -S\,dT + V\,dP + \mu_1^{(1)}\,dn_1^1 + \cdots + \mu_c^{(1)}\,dn_c^{(1)}$$
$$+ \cdots + \mu_1^{(\varphi)}\,dn_1^{(\varphi)} + \cdots + \mu_c^{(\varphi)}\,dn_c^{(\varphi)}.$$

In general, during such an infinitesimal change, there is neither equilibrium among the phases nor equilibrium with regard to the chemical reaction. Complete chemical equilibrium would require both phase equilibrium and reaction equilibrium. *Suppose we assume phase equilibrium only.* Then,

$$\mu_1^{(1)} = \mu_1^{(2)} = \cdots = \mu_1^{(\varphi)}$$

$$\mu_2^{(1)} = \mu_2^{(2)} = \cdots = \mu_2^{(\varphi)}$$

$$\cdot\quad\cdot\quad\cdot\quad\cdot\quad\cdot\quad\cdot\quad\cdot\quad\cdot\quad\cdot\quad\cdot\quad\cdot\quad\cdot\quad\cdot$$

$$\mu_c^{(1)} = \mu_c^{(2)} = \cdots = \mu_c^{(\varphi)},$$

and the change in the Gibbs function becomes

$$dG = -S\,dT + V\,dP + \mu_1(dn_1^{(1)} + \cdots + dn_1^{(\varphi)})$$
$$+ \cdots + \mu_4(dn_4^{(1)} + \cdots + dn_4^{(\varphi)}) + \mu_5(dn_5^{(1)} + \cdots + dn_5^{(\varphi)})$$
$$+ \cdots + \mu_c(dn_c^{(1)} + \cdots + dn_c^{(\varphi)}).$$

But
$$dn_1^{(1)} + \cdots + dn_1^{(\varphi)} = -(n_0 + n_0')\nu_1\,d\epsilon$$
$$dn_2^{(1)} + \cdots + dn_2^{(\varphi)} = -(n_0 + n_0')\nu_2\,d\epsilon$$
$$dn_3^{(1)} + \cdots + dn_3^{(\varphi)} = +(n_0 + n_0')\nu_3\,d\epsilon$$
$$dn_4^{(1)} + \cdots + dn_4^{(\varphi)} = +(n_0 + n_0')\nu_4\,d\epsilon$$
$$dn_5^{(1)} + \cdots + dn_5^{(\varphi)} = 0$$
$$\cdot\quad\cdot\quad\cdot\quad\cdot\quad\cdot\quad\cdot\quad\cdot\quad\cdot\quad\cdot\quad\cdot\quad\cdot\quad\cdot$$
$$dn_c^{(1)} + \cdots + dn_c^{(\varphi)} = 0.$$

Therefore, the change in the Gibbs function during an infinitesimal process in which there is phase equilibrium but not reaction equilibrium is given by

$$dG = -S\,dT + V\,dP + (n_0 + n_0')(\nu_3\mu_3 + \nu_4\mu_4 - \nu_1\mu_1 - \nu_2\mu_2)\,d\epsilon.$$

Since, under these circumstances G is a function of T, P, and ϵ, it follows that

$$\frac{\partial G}{\partial T} = -S,$$

$$\frac{\partial G}{\partial P} = V,$$

and

$$\frac{\partial G}{\partial \epsilon} = (n_0 + n_0')(\nu_3\mu_3 + \nu_4\mu_4 - \nu_1\mu_1 - \nu_2\mu_2).$$

When reaction equilibrium exists at temperature T and pressure P, we must have $\partial G/\partial \epsilon = 0$ at $\epsilon = \epsilon_e$. If we go to a slightly different equilibrium state at temperature $T + dT$ and pressure $P + dP$, then the new degree of reaction will be $\epsilon_e + d\epsilon_e$ and the change in $\partial G/\partial \epsilon$ during this process is zero. Therefore,

$$d\left(\frac{\partial G}{\partial \epsilon}\right) = 0.$$

But

$$d\left(\frac{\partial G}{\partial \epsilon}\right) = \frac{\partial^2 G}{\partial T \, \partial \epsilon} dT + \frac{\partial^2 G}{\partial P \, \partial \epsilon} dP + \frac{\partial^2 G}{\partial \epsilon^2} d\epsilon = 0$$

$$= \frac{\partial}{\partial \epsilon}\left(\frac{\partial G}{\partial T}\right) dT + \frac{\partial}{\partial \epsilon}\left(\frac{\partial G}{\partial P}\right) dP + \frac{\partial^2 G}{\partial \epsilon^2} d\epsilon = 0$$

$$= -\frac{\partial S}{\partial \epsilon} dT + \frac{\partial V}{\partial \epsilon} dP + \frac{\partial^2 G}{\partial \epsilon^2} d\epsilon = 0.$$

Solving for $d\epsilon = d\epsilon_e$, we get

$$d\epsilon_e = \frac{\partial S/\partial \epsilon}{\partial^2 G/\partial \epsilon^2} dT - \frac{\partial V/\partial \epsilon}{\partial^2 G/\partial \epsilon^2} dP. \tag{18-10}$$

Recognizing that, at thermodynamic equilibrium, $dQ = T\,dS$ or

$$\left(\frac{dQ}{d\epsilon}\right)_{T,P} = T\left(\frac{\partial S}{\partial \epsilon}\right)_{T,P}, \tag{18-11}$$

we get

$$\left(\frac{\partial \epsilon_e}{\partial T}\right)_P = \frac{(dQ/d\epsilon)_{T,P}}{T(\partial^2 G/\partial \epsilon^2)_{T,P}} \tag{18-12}$$

$$\left(\frac{\partial \epsilon_e}{\partial P}\right)_T = -\frac{(\partial V/\partial \epsilon)_{T,P}}{(\partial^2 G/\partial \epsilon^2)_{T,P}}. \tag{18-13}$$

Since G is a minimum at thermodynamic equilib.ium, $\partial^2 G/\partial \epsilon^2$ is positive. Equation (18-12) therefore states that an increase of temperature at constant pressure always causes a reaction to proceed in the direction in which heat is absorbed at constant T and P; whereas from Eq. (18-13), we see that an increase of pressure at constant temperature causes a reaction to proceed in the direction in which the volume decreases at constant T and P.

PROBLEMS

18-1   All the lettered points in Fig. P18-1 lie in one plane. The line CD separates the plane into two regions: on the left a wave has the speed v and

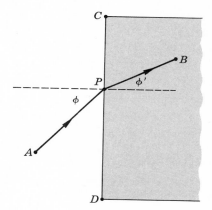

Fig. P18-1

on the right the speed v'. Show by Lagrange's method that the time for the wave to travel the path APB is a minimum when $v/v' = \sin \varphi / \sin \varphi'$.

18-2   A hot metal of mass m, specific heat c_P, and temperature T_i is immersed in a cooler liquid of mass m', specific heat c'_P, and temperature T'_i. The entire system is thermally insulated. If the final temperature of the metal is T_f and that of the liquid is T'_f, show by Lagrange's method that the condition for the entropy change of the universe to be a maximum is that $T_f = T'_f$.

18-3   Consider a homogeneous mixture of four ideal gases capable of undergoing the reaction

$$\nu_1 A_1 + \nu_2 A_2 \rightleftharpoons \nu_3 A_3 + \nu_4 A_4.$$

How many components are there if one starts with:
 (*a*) Arbitrary amounts of A_1 and A_2 only.
 (*b*) Arbitrary amounts of all four gases.
 (*c*) ν_1 moles of A_1 and ν_2 moles of A_2 only.

18-4   Consider a system composed of a solid phase of calcium carbonate ($CaCO_3$), a solid phase of calcium oxide (CaO), and a gaseous phase consisting of a mixture of CO_2, $CaCO_3$ vapor, and CaO vapor, all three constituents being present initially in arbitrary amounts. These are the substances which are present in a limekiln, where the reaction

$$CaCO_3 \rightleftharpoons CaO + CO_2$$

takes place.
  (a)   How many components are there, and what is the variance?
  (b)   Assuming the gaseous phase to be a mixture of ideal gases, show that

$$\frac{p_{CaO}\, p_{CO_2}}{p_{CaCO_3}} = K.$$

  (c)   If solid $CaCO_3$ is introduced into an evacuated chamber, how many components are there, and what is the variance?
18-5   Solid ammonium hydrosulphide (NH_4HS) is mixed with arbitrary amounts of gaseous NH_3 and H_2S, forming a three-constituent system of two phases, undergoing the reaction

$$NH_4HS \rightleftharpoons NH_3 + H_2S.$$

  (a)   How many components are there, and what is the variance?
  (b)   Assuming that the gaseous phase is a mixture of ideal gases, show that

$$\frac{p_{NH_3}\, p_{H_2S}}{p_{NH_4HS}} = K.$$

  (c)   If solid NH_4HS is placed in an evacuated chamber, how many components are there, and what is the variance?
18-6   How many components are there in a system composed of arbitrary amounts of water, sodium chloride, and barium chloride?
18-7   At high temperature the following reactions take place:

$$C + CO_2 \rightleftharpoons 2CO$$

and $CO_2 + H_2 \rightleftharpoons CO + H_2O$. How many components are there if we start with
  (a)   Arbitrary amounts of C, CO_2, and H_2.
  (b)   Arbitrary amounts of C, CO_2, H_2, CO, and H_2O.

18-8   Consider a system consisting of a pure liquid phase in equilibrium with a gaseous phase composed of a mixture of the vapor of the liquid and an inert gas that is insoluble in the liquid. Suppose that the inert gas (sometimes called the *foreign gas*) can flow into or out of the gaseous phase, so that the total pressure can be varied at will.

(*a*)   How many components are there, and what is the variance?

(*b*)   Assuming the gaseous phase to be a mixture of ideal gases, show that

$$g'' = RT(\phi + \ln p),$$

where g'' is the molar Gibbs function of the liquid, and ϕ and p refer to the vapor.

(*c*)   Suppose a little more foreign gas is added, thus increasing the pressure from P to $P + dP$, at constant temperature. Show that

$$v'' \, dP = RT \frac{dp}{p},$$

where v'' is the molar volume of the liquid, which is practically constant.

(*d*)   Integrating at constant temperature from an initial state where there is no foreign gas to a final state where the total pressure is P and the partial vapor pressure is p, show that

$$\ln \frac{p}{P_0} = \frac{v''}{RT} (P - P_0) \qquad \text{(Gibbs equation)},$$

where P_0 is the vapor pressure when no foreign gas is present.

(*e*)   In the case of water at 0°C, at which $P_0 = 4.57$ mm, show that, when there is sufficient air above the water to make the total pressure equal to 10 atm, $p = 4.61$ mm.

18-9   The Gibbs function G of a liquid phase consisting of a solvent and very small amounts of several solutes is

$$G = \mu_0 n_0 + \mu_1 n_1 + \mu_2 n_2 + \cdots,$$

where the subscript zero refers to the solvent, and

$$\mu_k = g_k + RT \ln x_k.$$

(*a*)   Using the relation $V = (\partial G/\partial P)_T$, show that

$$V = \Sigma n_k v_k.$$

(b)   Using the relation $H = G - T(\partial G/\partial T)_P$, show that

$$H = \Sigma n_k h_k,$$

which means that there is no heat of dilution.

18-10   A very small amount of sugar is dissolved in water, and the solution is in equilibrium with pure water vapor.

(a)   Show that the equation of phase equilibrium is

$$g''' = g'' + RT \ln (1 - x),$$

where g''' is the molar Gibbs function of water vapor, g'' the molar Gibbs function of pure liquid water, and x the mole fraction of the sugar in solution.

(b)   For an infinitesimal change in x at constant temperature, show that

$$(v''' - v'') \, dP = RT \, d \ln (1 - x).$$

(c)   Assuming the vapor to behave like an ideal gas and regarding v'' as constant, integrate the preceding equation at constant temperature from an initial state $x = 0$, $P = P_0$, to a final state $x = x$, $P = P_x$, and derive

$$\ln \frac{P_x}{P_0} = \ln (1 - x) + \frac{v''}{RT} (P_x - P_0).$$

P_0 is the vapor pressure of the pure liquid, and P_x the vapor pressure of the dilute solution.

(d)   Justify neglecting the last term on the right, and show that

$$P_x = P_0(1 - x) \qquad \text{(Raoult's law)},$$

or

$$\frac{P_0 - P_x}{P_0} = x.$$

18-11   Consider the system of Prob. 18-10, and let x stand for the mole fraction of the sugar.

(a)   For an infinitesimal change in x at constant pressure, show that

$$-s''' \, dT = -s'' \, dT + R \ln (1 - x) \, dT + RT \, d \ln (1 - x).$$

(b)   Substituting for $R \ln (1 - x)$ the value obtained from the equation of phase equilibrium, show that (a) reduces to

$$0 = \frac{h''' - h''}{T} \, dT + RT \, d \ln (1 - x).$$

(c)   Taking into account that $x \ll 1$ and calling $h''' - h''$ the latent heat of vaporization l_V, show that the elevation of the boiling point is

$$\Delta T = \frac{RT^2}{l_V} x.$$

18-12   A very small amount of sugar is dissolved in water, and the solution is in equilibrium with pure ice. The equation of phase equilibrium is

$$g' = g'' + RT \ln (1 - x),$$

where g' = molar Gibbs function of pure ice,
g'' = molar Gibbs function of pure water,
and x = mole-fraction of sugar in solution.
(a)   For an infinitesimal change in x at constant pressure, show that

$$-s' \, dT = -s'' \, dT + R \ln (1 - x) \, dT + RT \, d \ln (1 - x).$$

(b)   Substituting for $R \ln (1 - x)$ the value obtained from the equation of phase equilibrium, show that (a) reduces to

$$\frac{h'' - h'}{T} \, dT = RT \, d \ln (1 - x).$$

(c)   Taking into account that $x \ll 1$ and calling $h'' - h'$ the heat of fusion l_F, show that the depression of the freezing point is

$$\Delta T = - \frac{RT^2}{l_F} x.$$

APPENDIX A

PHYSICAL CONSTANTS

Constant	Symbol	Rounded value
Electronic charge	e	1.602×10^{-19} C
Electronic rest mass	m	9.109×10^{-28} g
Speed of light in vacuum	c	2.998×10^{10} cm/s
Planck's constant	h	6.626×10^{-27} erg $\cdot$ s
Boltzmann's constant	k	1.381×10^{-16} erg/deg
Avogadro's number	N_A	6.023×10^{23} mole^{-1}
Faraday's constant	N_F	9.649×10^4 C/mole
Bohr magneton	μ_B	9.273×10^{-21} erg/Oe
Nuclear magneton	μ_N	5.051×10^{-24} erg/Oe
Proton rest mass	m_P	1.673×10^{-24} g
Universal gas constant	$R = N_A k$	8.314 J/mole $\cdot$ deg
Stefan-Boltzmann constant	σ	5.670×10^{-5} erg/s $\cdot$ cm^2 $\cdot$ deg^4
One electron volt	1 eV	1.602×10^{-12} erg
One atomic mass unit	1 u	1.660×10^{-24} g
One liter $\cdot$ atmosphere	1 liter $\cdot$ atm	1.013×10^2 J

APPENDIX B

RIEMANN ZETA FUNCTIONS

$$\sum_{n=1}^{\infty} \frac{(-1)^{n-1}}{n^2} = \frac{\pi^2}{12},\tag{1}$$

$$\zeta(2) = \sum_{n=1}^{\infty} \frac{1}{n^2} = \frac{\pi^2}{6},\tag{2}$$

$$\zeta(4) = \sum_{n=1}^{\infty} \frac{1}{n^4} = \frac{\pi^4}{90}.\tag{3}$$

To obtain Eqs. (1) and (2), expand the function

$$f(x) = x^2 \qquad (-\pi \leq x \leq \pi)$$

in a Fourier series:†

$$f(x) = \sum_{n=0}^{\infty} a_n \cos nx,$$

$$a_0 = \frac{1}{\pi} \int_0^{\pi} x^2 \, dx = \frac{\pi^2}{3},$$

$$a_n = \frac{2}{\pi} \int_0^{\pi} x^2 \cos nx \, dx = (-1)^n \frac{4}{n^2}.$$

Hence,

$$x^2 = \frac{\pi^2}{3} + 4 \sum_{n=1}^{\infty} \frac{(-1)^n}{n^2} \cos nx.$$

Setting $x = 0$ gives Eq. (1), and setting $x = \pi$ gives Eq. (2).

† C. R. Wylie, Jr., *Advanced Engineering Mathematics*, 2d ed., McGraw-Hill Book Company, New York, 1960, Chap. 7.

To obtain Eq. (3), expand

$$f(x) = x^4 \qquad (-\pi \le x \le \pi)$$

in a Fourier series:

$$a_0 = \frac{1}{\pi} \int_0^\pi x^4 \, dx = \frac{\pi^4}{5},$$

$$a_n = \frac{2}{\pi} \int_0^\pi x^4 \cos nx \, dx = -(-1)^n \frac{8\pi^2}{n^2} - (-1)^n \frac{48}{n^4}.$$

Hence,

$$x^4 = \frac{\pi^4}{5} + 8\pi^2 \sum_{n=1}^{\infty} \frac{(-1)^n}{n^2} \cos nx - 48 \sum_{n=1}^{\infty} \frac{(-1)^n}{n^4} \cos nx.$$

Setting $x = \pi$ gives

$$\pi^4 = \frac{\pi^4}{5} + 8\pi^2 \sum_{n=1}^{\infty} \frac{1}{n^2} - 48 \sum_{n=1}^{\infty} \frac{1}{n^4}.$$

Substituting Eq. (2) and solving for $\displaystyle\sum_{n=1}^{\infty} \frac{1}{n^4}$ gives Eq. (3).

BIBLIOGRAPHY

TEMPERATURE

Herzfeld, C. M., and F. G. Brickwedde: "Temperature," vol. III, pt. I, Reinhold Publishing Corporation, New York, 1962.

CLASSICAL THERMODYNAMICS

Buchdahl, H. A.: "Concepts of Classical Thermodynamics," Cambridge University Press, New York, 1966.
Callen, H. B.: "Thermodynamics," John Wiley & Sons, Inc., New York, 1960.
Pippard, A. B.: "Classical Thermodynamics," Cambridge University Press, New York, 1957.

STATISTICAL MECHANICS

Guggenheim, E. A.: "Boltzmann's Distribution Law," Interscience Publishers, Inc., New York, 1963.
Lee, J. F., F. W. Sears, and D. L. Turcotte: "Statistical Thermodynamics," Addison-Wesley Publishing Company, Inc., Reading, Mass., 1963.
MacDonald, D. K. C.: "Introductory Statistical Mechanics for Physicists," John Wiley & Sons, Inc., New York, 1963.
Ter Haar, D.: "Elements of Thermostatistics," Holt, Rinehart and Winston, Inc., New York, 1966.

THERMAL PHYSICS

Dugdale, J. S.: "Entropy and Low Temperature Physics," Hutchinson & Co. (Publishers), Ltd., London, 1966.
Fast, J. D.: "Entropy," McGraw-Hill Book Company, New York, 1962.
Fay, J. A.: "Molecular Thermodynamics," Addison-Wesley Publishing Company, Inc., Reading, Mass., 1965.

Landsberg, P. T.: "Thermodynamics," Interscience Publishers, Inc., New York, 1961.

Morse, P. M.: "Thermal Physics," William A. Benjamin, Inc., New York, 1964.

Reif, F.: "Fundamentals of Statistical and Thermal Physics," McGraw-Hill Book Company, New York, 1965.

Wilks, J.: "Third Law of Thermodynamics," Oxford University Press, Fair Lawn, N.J., 1961.

ENGINEERING THERMODYNAMICS

Obert, E. F.: "Concepts of Thermodynamics," McGraw-Hill Book Company, New York, 1960.

Reynolds, W. C.: "Thermodynamics," McGraw-Hill Book Company, New York, 1965.

Schmidt, E.: "Thermodynamics," Dover Publications, Inc., New York, 1949.

Van Wylen, G. J.: "Thermodynamics," John Wiley & Sons, Inc., New York, 1959.

Zemansky, M. W., and H. C. van Ness: "Basic Engineering Thermodynamics," McGraw-Hill Book Company, New York, 1966.

CHEMICAL THERMODYNAMICS

Caldin, E. F.: "Chemical Thermodynamics," Oxford University Press, Fair Lawn, N.J., 1958.

Denbigh, K.: "Principles of Chemical Equilibrium," Cambridge University Press, New York, 1955.

Guggenheim, E. A.: "Thermodynamics," Interscience Publishers, Inc., New York, 1957.

Kirkwood, J. G., and I. Oppenheim: "Chemical Thermodynamics," McGraw-Hill Book Company, New York, 1961.

Reid, C. E.: "Principles of Chemical Thermodynamics," Reinhold Publishing Corporation, New York, 1960.

Wall, F. T.: "Chemical Thermodynamics," W. H. Freeman and Company, San Francisco, 1958.

LOW-TEMPERATURE PHYSICS

Atkins, K. R.: "Liquid Helium," Cambridge University Press, New York, 1959.

Daunt, J. G.: "Helium Three," Ohio State University Press, Columbus, Ohio, 1960.

Din, F., and A. H. Cockett: "Low-temperature Techniques," Interscience Publishers, Inc., New York, 1960.

Garrett, C. G. B.: "Magnetic Cooling," Harvard University Press, Cambridge, Mass., 1954.

Gopal, E. S. R.: "Specific Heats at Low Temperatures," Plenum Press, Inc., New York, 1966.

Hoare, F. E., L. C. Jackson, and N. Kurti: "Experimental Cryophysics," Butterworth Scientific Publications, London, 1961.

Jackson, L. C.: "Low Temperature Physics," John Wiley & Sons, Inc., New York, 1962.

Lane, C. T.: "Superfluid Physics," McGraw-Hill Book Company, New York, 1962.

Lynton, E. A.: "Superconductivity," John Wiley & Sons, Inc., New York, 1962.

McClintock, M.: "Cryogenics," Reinhold Publishing Corporation, New York, 1964.

Mendelssohn, K.: "Cryophysics," Interscience Publishers, Inc., New York, 1960.

Mendelssohn, K.: "Quest for Absolute Zero," McGraw-Hill Book Company, New York, 1966.

Newhouse, V. L.: "Applied Superconductivity," John Wiley & Sons, Inc., New York, 1964.

Scurlock, R. G.: "Low Temperature Behavior of Solids," Dover Publications, Inc., New York, 1966.

Shoenberg, D.: "Superconductivity," Cambridge University Press, New York, 1952.

White, G. K.: "Experimental Techniques in Low-temperature Physics," Oxford University Press, Fair Lawn, N.J., 1959.

ANSWERS TO
SELECTED PROBLEMS

Chapter 1

1-1   (a) $P(V - nb)$; $\dfrac{P'V'}{1 - nB'/V'}$; $P''V''$.

(b) $P(V - nb) = \dfrac{P'V'}{1 - nB'/V'}$.

1-2   (a) $\dfrac{C\mathcal{H}}{M}$; $\Theta + \dfrac{C'\mathcal{H}'}{M'}$; $\dfrac{PV}{nR}$.

(b) $\dfrac{M}{\mathcal{H}} = \dfrac{C}{\theta}$, Curie's equation.

$\dfrac{M'}{\mathcal{H}'} = \dfrac{C'}{\theta - \Theta}$, Weiss' equation.

$PV = nR\theta$, ideal-gas equation.

1-3   419.57°K.

1-4   (a)   4.00°K.

1-5   (a)   4.00°K.

Chapter 2

2-4   (a)   501 atm;   (b)   48.8°C.

2-5   418 atm.

2-11 5.06×10^6 dyn.

2-12   21.3 Hz; 33.8 Hz.

2-13 3.36×10^6 dyn.

Chapter 3

3-3	929 J.
3-6	-0.34 J.
3-7	(*b*) -0.198 J.
3-11	(*a*) -179 J.
	(*b*) -1.13 J at 300°K; -338 J at 1°K.
	(*c*) -180 J at 300°K; -517 J at 1°K.

Chapter 4

4-7	1.23 V.
4-13	3.75×10^{-8} $a\Theta + 1.50 \times 10^{-4}$ $b\Theta^2$.
4-21	2.3 mW/cm · deg.
4-25	0.0046 deg.
4-26	7.16 g.
4-27	1.38 cm².
4-28	1360°K.
4-29	5750°K.
4-30	(*c*) 2.32.
4-31	13 min.

Chapter 5

5-1	(*a*) θ_f same on both sides and equal to θ_0; P_f same on both sides and equal to $5P_0/4$.
	(*b*) V_f on left $= 8 V_0/5$; V_f on right $= 12 V_0/5$.
	(*c*) Non-quasi-static, damped oscillation.
5-2	76 cm.
5-3	125 cm.
5-4	1.7 g.
5-5	Three times the initial value.
5-11	(*b*) 0.221 ft³; 1020 ft·lb.
5-12	(*b*) 500 ft.
5-13	(*b*) 571°K.
5-14	(*a*) 10.2 kJ; (*b*) 614°K; (*c*) 3530°K; (*d*) 107.5 kJ.
5-17	(*c*) -9.5 deg/km.
5-18	1.41.
5-19	(*a*) 1.18 s; (*b*) 69 cm.
5-20	(*a*) 0.966 s; (*b*) 47.1 cm.
5-21	1.27.
5-24	320 m/s.
5-25	1.27.
5-26	80 percent He; 20 percent Ne.

5-27   Diatomic.
5-28   20.25°K.

Chapter 6

6-6   A Kr 86 lamp at 77°K.
6-7   1 V (7730°K); 10^3 V (7.73 × 10^6 °K); 10^6 V (7.73 × 10^9 °K).
6-8   2.41 × 10^{15} atoms/s.
6-9 $k' = A\langle w \rangle / 4V$.
6-10   3.25 s.
6-11   1.85 × 10^{-4} mm of Hg.

Chapter 7

7-5   (a)   362 J;   362 J.
         (b)   362 J;   0.
         (c)   −12.2 J;   −12.2 J;   97 percent.

Chapter 9

9-6   (a) 0; (b) 8.33 J/deg; (c) 5.80 J/deg; (d) 5.80 J/deg.
9-7   (a) 1310 J/deg; −1120 J/deg; 190 J/deg.
         (b) 1310 J/deg; −1210 J/deg; 90 J/deg.
9-9   0.0300R.
9-10   (a) 6.3 J/deg; (b) 1.39 J/deg; (c) 3.80 J/deg.
9-11   (a) 0; (b) 1.83 × 10^{-5} J/deg.
9-12   277 J/deg.
9-13   −16.0 J/deg.
9-14   1.5 atm; 300°K; 0.0570 J/deg.
9-15   (a) $4V_0/9$; (b) $3T_0/2$; (c) $21T_0/4$; (d) $(19/4)nC_vT_0$; (e) $\frac{1}{2}nC_vT_0$;
         (f) 0; (g) $nC_p \ln (21/4) - nR \ln (27/8)$;
         (h) $nC_p \ln (63/8) - 2nR \ln (27/8)$.
9-26   About 400°K.

Chapter 10

10-1   2 × 10^{11}.
10-2   (b) ∼10^{27}; (c) ∼10^{19}; (d) $g'/N = 10^8$.

Chapter 11

11-6   (a) −87.5 J; (b) −50.6 J; (c) −36.9; (d) 0.684 deg.
11-7   (a) 1.11 kJ; (b) −3.96 kJ; (c) 5.07 kJ.
11-8   −0.436 deg; +0.099 deg; +3.63 deg.

Chapter 12

12-3	(a) 37°K; (b) $P = 34.9$ atm; $T = 20.6$°K.
12-4	70 percent.
12-6	63.6 kJ/mole; 69.5 kJ/mole; 65.4 kJ/mole.
12-7	(a) 132 kJ/mole; (b) 1.21.
12-8	(a) 195°K; (b) $l_{SU} = 31.2$ kJ/mole; $l_{FU} = 5.80$ kJ/mole; $l_{VA} = 25.4$ kJ/mole.
12-9	(a) $l_{SU}/R = 137$ deg; $l_{FU}/R = 19.2$ deg; $l_{VA}/R = 118$ deg. (b) 0.0463 atm/deg.
12-11	7.2.
12-16	600.8°K.
12-17	(c) 6.7 percent.
12-18	(b) 428 atm/deg; (c) -2.29°C, 306 atm.
12-19	(d) 0.77 percent.
12-20	(c) 8.26 μ/s.

Chapter 13

13-1	(a) 3.6 J; (b) -3.18 J; (c) 6.78 J; (d) -1.21 deg.
13-4	(b) -0.900, -0.336, $+1.40$, $+1.37$ deg/m.
13-7	-214 kJ.
13-8	-188 kJ.
13-12	0.25, 1.00, 25.0, 100 mdeg.
13-14	(a) -6.67 mV. (b) -33.8 mV; -101 J; out. (c) $+0.152$ mV/deg.
13-23	(a) 6000°K; (b) 9.84 erg/cm^3; (c) 3.28 dyn/cm^2.
13-24	(a) 160 erg; (b) 120 erg; (c) 40 erg; (d) 431°K.

Chapter 14

14-12	(a) 2.538 (b) 0.6102
14-13	(a) 10.4 J; (b) 10.4 J; (c) 0; (d) 1.44°K.
14-14	4.04°K.
14-15	(a) -0.264 J; (b) 0.3°K.
14-16	(a) 89 kOe; (b) 4 kOe.
14-17	(a) 1.03°K; (b) 0.00315°K.
14-19	(a) 2.00°K; (b) 0.14°K.

Chapter 15

15-1	19 percent.
15-2	0.588 J/g · deg.

15-3   (*a*)   0.1, 0.9, 9;   (*b*)   21.9 m/s.
15-4   (*a*)   223 m/s;   (*b*)   1.62 m/s.
15-5   (*a*)   0.826 cm/s;   (*b*)   1.10 $\times$ 10^{-9} erg.
15-6   (*a*) -0.00796 J;   0.0313 J.
           (*b*) -0.0318 J;   0.0685 J.
           (*c*) -0.0363 J;   0.140 J.

Chapter 16

16-2   1250 J.

Chapter 17

17-5   (*a*)   0.315 atm;   (*b*)   0.613;   (*c*)   61,200 J/mole.
17-6   94,600 J/mole.
17-7   39 percent;   81 percent.
17-8   100 percent.
17-10   709 J/deg.
17-11   0.00129 deg^{-1}.

INDEX

INDEX